Linear
Systems

Linear Systems

Naresh K. Sinha

McMaster University

WILEY

John Wiley & Sons, Inc.

New York • Chichester • Brisbane • Toronto • Singapore

Recognizing the importance of preserving what has been written, it is a policy of John Wiley & Sons, Inc. to have books of enduring value published in the United States printed on acid-free paper, and we exert our best efforts to that end.

Acquisitions Editor / Charity Robey
Production Manager / Katharine Rubin
Designer / Laura Nicholls
Production Supervisor / Linda Muriello
Manufacturing Manager / Denis Clarke

Library of Congress Cataloging-in-Publication Data

Sinha, N. K. (Naresh Kumar), 1927–
    Linear systems/Naresh K. Sinha.
    p. cm.
    Includes bibliographical references and indexes.

    1. System analysis.   I. Title.
QA402.S539 1991
003'.74—dc20   90-28484
                                           CIP

Printed in Singapore   ica

10 9 8 7 6 5 4 3 2 1

To: Meena, Raka, Alka, and Anand

About the Author

Naresh K. Sinha obtained the B.Sc. (Engineering) degree from Banaras Hindu University in 1948 and the Ph.D. degree in Electrical Engineering from the University of Manchester in 1955.

Dr. Sinha taught at Bihar Institute of Technology in India and the University of Tennessee at Knoxville before joining the Faculty of Engineering of McMaster University in 1965, where he is currently Professor in the Department of Electrical and Computer Engineering. He served as the Chairman of that Department from July 1982 to June 1988 and has also been Visiting Professor at Stanford University, the Institute of Control Sciences at Moscow, Tianjin University, and the Beijing University of Science and Technology.

In addition to *Linear Systems*, Professor Sinha is the author or coauthor of about 400 technical papers and one graduate level book, *Modeling and Identification of Dynamic Systems* (Van Nostrand Reinhold, 1983). He is also the author of a senior undergraduate level book, *Control Systems* (Holt, Rinehart & Winston, 1986), the editor of *Microprocessor-based Control Systems* (D. Reidel Publishing Company, 1986), and the coauthor of *Microcomputer-based Numerical Methods for Science and Engineering* (Holt, Rinehart & Winston, 1986).

Included in Dr. Sinha's research interests are the areas of adaptive control, system modeling and identification, robotics, and industrial applications of modern control theory.

Preface

This book is intended for a one-semester junior level course on linear systems for students in electrical and computer engineering. The theory is presented in a way that will prepare the student for specializing in diverse areas like communication systems, control systems, power systems, and computer systems within the disciplines of electrical and computer engineering. The basis for this approach is that it is pedagogically more effective to develop the theories of continuous-time and discrete-time systems in a unified manner and to take advantage of the fact that some concepts are understood more easily for one type of system than the other.

In fact, the book contains a little more material than can be taught comfortably in one semester. Currently, the first six chapters are taught in a one-semester course in McMaster University (two lecture hours per week), although frequency response (Chapter 7) and state equations (Chapter 8) had been included in the past when this course had three lecture hours per week. For schools that have the quarter system, the entire book can be covered in two quarters at the junior level at a leisurely pace.

We start in the first chapter with a brief classification of systems and their representation by either differential or difference equations, followed by a review of the classical methods for solving these equations. The unified treatment is helpful, since in most schools the students would have studied differential equations but probably might not have been taught about difference equations. The similarities help in a better understanding. Realization of the two types of systems is then studied and the similarities are noted. The chapter concludes by introducing the concepts of stability for both continuous-time and discrete-time systems.

Chapter 2 introduces the student to the various types of signals that appear in the study of systems. This leads to the representation of a continuous-time signal by a continuum of impulses. The response of both continuous-time and discrete-time systems to a unit impulse is studied and is followed by determination of the response to any arbitrary input through convolution. Since the concept of convolution is understood more easily for discrete-time systems, this is followed by extension to continuous-time systems.

Chapters 3 and 4 introduce the reader to the Fourier analysis of continuous-time and discrete-time signals, respectively. Here, it was found pedagogically advantageous to start with the more familiar Fourier series for continuous-time periodic signals and proceed to the Fourier transform of nonperiodic signals by considering the latter as the limiting case when the period becomes infinitely large. The theory of the discrete Fourier series and the discrete-time Fourier transform in Chapter 4 follows easily and leads to a very straightforward presentation of the sampling theorem. In that chapter the students are also introduced to fast Fourier transform algorithms and some applications.

Chapters 5 and 6 develop the theories of Laplace and z-transforms relating these to Fourier transforms. The ideas relating to transfer functions, frequency response, and stability are presented in a unified manner for the two types of systems.

Chapter 7 describes the different types of frequency response plots that are used for understanding the properties of systems that are both continuous-time and discrete-time.

In Chapter 8, the student is returned to the time domain through the study of the state-space representation of systems. Here, again, it is seen that both continuous-time and discrete-time systems have very similar state-space representation.

Finally, in Chapter 9 the reader is introduced to the basic theory of filter design. Both analog and digital filters are studied, including the transformation of analog filters to equivalent digital filters, as well as to the design of finite-impulse response digital filters.

Throughout the book, many interesting problems have been included. To reduce the drudgery of numerical work, a disk containing executable programs has been developed to assist the student in solving these problems on a personal computer. It is not intended, however, that the computer replace the process of thinking and learning. For example, the computer program related to inverse Laplace transformation evaluates the residues at different poles, but the student still has to use this information to obtain the inverse transform. The computer disk and a complete solutions manual are available to instructors adopting the text for classroom use.

ACKNOWLEDGMENTS

It is a pleasure to acknowledge the help that I have received from several individuals in the preparation of this book. I thank particularly Mrs. Christina Kamra, who was the engineering editor at Wiley when the work on the book was started. Other members of the staff of John Wiley & Sons, Inc., who have been very helpful throughout the preparation of the text are Charity Robey, Executive Editor of Engineering, Damarys Camacho, Nancy Prinz, Deborah

Herbert, Laura Nicholls, and Linda Muriello. The following reviewers read earlier versions of the text and made many constructive suggestions for improvement: Professor N. K. Bose, Pennsylvania State University; Professor Ernest Baxa, Clemson University; Professor JoAnne Koskel, Widener University; Professor Gonzalo Arce, University of Delaware; Professor Brian Butz, Temple University; Professor Duane Hanselsman, University of Maine; Dr. Saroj K. Biswas, Temple University; and Dr. Lokesh Datta, Wright State University.

Other friends and colleagues in McMaster University who have helped in several ways are, Dr. T. D. Todd, who has used earlier versions of this text in a junior level course, and Ravi Lingarkar, who went through the final draft of the book and made many valuable suggestions. I am grateful to Professor G. J. Lastman of the University of Waterloo for his help in writing the computer programs that have been included with the book.

I must also add that this book would not have been possible without the patience and encouragement of my wife, Meena.

Naresh K. Sinha

Contents

Chapter 3 / Fourier Analysis of Continuous-time Signals   91

Chapter 4 / Fourier Analysis of Discrete-time Signals   156

Chapter 5 / Laplace Transforms 197

Chapter 6 / z-Transforms 260

Chapter 7 / Frequency Response 309

Chapter 8 / State Space Methods 346

Chapter 9 / Introduction to Filters   392

Answers to Selected Problems   440

Index   459

Systems

1.1 INTRODUCTION

A system may be defined as "a collection of objects arranged in an ordered form, which is, in some sense, purpose or goal directed." This rather broad definition can be applied to many areas. In our daily life we come across a wide variety of systems. Some common technological examples are an automobile, a television receiver, and a hand-held calculator. Additional examples are transportation systems, socioeconomic systems, and political and ecological systems. The human body is an example of a complex biological system.

What constitute a "system" often depends on the viewpoint of the analyst or the designer. For example, an electronic amplifier consisting of many components may be regarded as a system by an electronic engineer. On the other hand, the same amplifier may be one of the many parts of a "control system." Furthermore, this control system may be part of a chemical process (or "system") that contains many such control systems. System theory is the discipline that is devoted to the study of the behavior of systems under different conditions, including the interactions between the components of the system and the effects of external stimuli.

In this book we do not attempt a broad treatment of the subject but, instead, limit ourselves to systems that can be analyzed quantitatively by using the basic physical laws of electricity and mechanics. Thus, any electrical circuit, as well as mechanical or electromechanical devices, will fall into the category of systems that we shall be considering. The essential difference between these systems and the others is that precise laws for quantitative relationships between the variables of the latter have not yet been developed and, in most instances, are still being debated by researchers.

Although a wide variety of systems can be studied, advantage may be taken of certain unifying concepts. For example, it is usually possible to identify a set of variables called *inputs* or *excitations* and another set of variables called *outputs* or *responses*. These may also be considered as the *cause* and the *effect*, respectively. The object of system theory is to develop

1

relationships between these variables so that one may understand and even predict the behavior of the system under different conditions. Systems that are physically very different may often have characteristics that are very similar mathematically. These similarities can be fully exploited through the study of *mathematical models* for both the analysis and design of such systems.

A *model* may be defined as "a representation of the essential aspects of a system so that it presents knowledge of the system in a usable form." To be useful, a model must not be so complicated that it cannot be understood and thereby be unsuitable for predicting the behavior of the system; at the same time, it must not be oversimplified and trivial to the extent that predictions of the behavior of the system based on this model are grossly inaccurate. Engineers often use simplified mathematical models of physical objects. For example, the familiar Ohm's law gives a simple linear model of a resistor. This is often used and has been found to be very convenient, in spite of the fact that actual resistors may be nonlinear. The matter is further complicated by the fact that the flow of current through a resistor causes a rise in temperature which, in turn, affects the resistance. Nevertheless, the linear model provides a close approximation to the behavior of the actual resistor. One important application of mathematical models is that they can be used for simulating complex systems on a computer. These simulations allow engineers not only to study the various interactions within the system but also to design additional components that will improve the performance.

As the general theory of systems requires much more mathematical background, we shall limit ourselves to the theory of linear systems in this book. However, in the next section, we briefly mention the different types of systems that can be studied.

1.2 CLASSIFICATION OF SYSTEMS

Because of their wide variety, systems can be classified in many different ways. In this section, we consider a classification scheme that depends on their basic properties. First, we can divide systems into two basic types: they can be either static or dynamic. These are discussed in the next subsection.

1.2.1 STATIC AND DYNAMIC SYSTEMS

A system is said to be *static* if its outputs (response) at any instant depend only on the present value of the inputs (excitation). A simple example is an electrical circuit that contains only resistors as its circuit elements. A system is said to be *dynamic* if its outputs depend on the present as well as the past values of the inputs. Such a system may be regarded as one with *memory*. An electrical circuit that contains circuit elements that store energy (e.g., inductors and capacitors) can, therefore, be called a dynamic system. Other examples of dynamic systems are mechanical devices that contain springs and inertia.

From a previous study of circuit theory, the reader must be aware that the input–output relations for networks that contain inductors or capacitors (or both) are given by differential equations. This is true for all dynamic systems.

In general, if the output of a linear continuous-time system is represented by $y(t)$ and the input by $u(t)$, the two will be related by a differential equation of the form:

$$a_n \frac{d^n y}{dt^n} + a_{n-1} \frac{d^{n-1} y}{dt^{n-1}} + \cdots + a_1 \frac{dy}{dt} + a_0 y = b_m \frac{d^m u}{dt^m} + \cdots + b_0 u \quad (1.1)$$

Equation 1.1 is called a linear differential equation of order n and for most practical cases $n \geq m$. It is often more convenient to replace d/dt by the operator p, resulting in the equation

$$\left(a_n p^n + a_{n-1} p^{n-1} + \cdots + a_1 p + a_0\right) y(t)$$
$$= \left(b_m p^m + \cdots + b_1 p + b_0\right) u(t)$$

which may be written more compactly as

$$D(p) y(t) = N(p) u(t)$$

where $D(p)$ and $N(p)$ are polynomials in the operator p, as shown here:

$$D(p) = a_n p^n + a_{n-1} p^{n-1} + \cdots + a_1 p + a_0$$
$$N(p) = b_m p^m + b_{m-1} p^{m-1} + \cdots + b_1 p + b_0$$

It is important to note that p is called an operator as it represents the operation of differentiation. It can be considered simply a shorthand notation for the derivative with respect to time, d/dt. It follows that $p^2 y(t)$ is the second derivative of $y(t)$ with respect to time, and so on. As will be seen later, p can often be treated as an algebraic quantity, with the difference that one must be careful of the order. In particular, we must note that $py(t) \neq y(t)p$, that is, it does not satisfy the commutative property.

The reader should also be aware of the fact that a unique solution to the differential equation characterizing the input–output relationship of an electrical circuit can be obtained only if the initial values of the voltage across each capacitor and the current through each inductor are known. This applies, in general, to any dynamic system described by a differential equation of order n, which can be solved uniquely only if n initial (or *boundary*) conditions are known. If all the initial conditions in a system are equal to zero, it is called a *zero-state* system. The concept of state will be introduced in a later section.

If the outputs of a dynamic system depend on the past, present, and future values of the inputs, it is called *anticipatory* or *noncausal*, in contrast to the usual *nonanticipatory* or *causal* system where the outputs depend only on the past and present values of the inputs. Although systems of the noncausal type can be visualized hypothetically, at present they are not

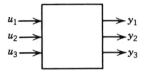

Figure 1.1   A multivariable system.

physically realizable. In this book, we are concerned mainly with causal systems.

In the simplest form, a system may have only one input and one output. An example of such a system is an electrical network driven by a single voltage (or current) source where the output is the voltage across (or the current through) a specified branch of the network. Such systems are often called *single-input single-output* systems. In the more general case, we have systems with several inputs and outputs, as would be true for an electrical network that is driven by several sources and for which the voltages across many branches constitute the output. Such systems are said to be *multivariable* systems. Another example of a multivariable system is the flight control system for an airplane. In this example the outputs are the angular velocities along the three principal axes of the airplane (roll, yaw, and pitch), whereas the inputs are the deflections in the elevator, the aileron, and the rudder. It is customary to represent multivariable systems by a *block diagram* of the type shown in Fig. 1.1. This diagram emphasizes the *cause* and *effect* nature of a system; the inputs can be regarded as the *cause* and the outputs as the *effects*.

In the figure the system is shown to have three inputs and three outputs. For more general multivariable systems there will be m inputs and r outputs, where m and r are integers that are not necessarily equal.

1.2.2   LINEAR AND NONLINEAR SYSTEMS

A system is said to be *linear* if and only if it satisfies the superposition theorem. Note that superposition consists of two basic but quite distinct concepts. One of these is the property of *additivity* and the other is that of *homogeneity*. The first implies that the response of a zero-state system to the sum of two inputs is equal to the sum of the responses to each of the inputs acting alone. Homogeneity requires that the effect of multiplying the input by a constant would be to multiply the output by the same constant. A system is said to be *nonlinear* if its does not satisfy the properties of additivity and homogeneity. These properties can be understood through the following example. Consider a simple single-input single-output system denoted by the block diagram shown in Figure 1.2.

Let the output of a zero-state system for the input $u_1(t)$ be denoted by $y_1(t)$ and the output for the input $u_2(t)$ be denoted by $y_2(t)$. Then the superposition property requires that if the input to the system is described by the expression $[\alpha u_1(t) + \beta u_2(t)]$, where α and β are arbitrary constants, then the corresponding output must be equal to $[\alpha y_1(t) + \beta y_2(t)]$.

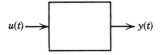

Figure 1.2 A single-input single-output system.

This property of superposition is very useful in calculating the response of a linear system to any arbitrary input that can be expressed as the sum of a number of elementary functions for which the response of the system can be easily calculated. We use the superposition theorem extensively in this book.

For a linear system, the input–output relationship that is represented by equation 1.1, can also be written as

$$y(t) = L(p)u(t) \tag{1.2}$$

where

$$L(p) = \frac{N(p)}{D(p)} \tag{1.3}$$

is called the *system operator*. It plays a very important role in the analysis of linear systems and will be discussed in detail later in this book. It is also called the *operational transfer function* of the system. Note that the system function $L(p)$ is the ratio of the polynomials $N(p)$ and $D(p)$, defined following equation 1.1. In other words, $L(p)$ is a *rational function* of the operator p. For most physical systems, $L(p)$ is a *proper rational function*, that is, the degree of the denominator polynomial $D(p)$ is greater than or equal to that of the numerator $N(p)$.

It is important to note that in the discussions in this section, the initial conditions are assumed to be zero. Not only is this necessary in the application of the superposition theorem but it is also implied in the definition of the system operator.

1.2.3 TIME-VARYING AND TIME-INVARIANT SYSTEMS

A system is said to be *time-invariant* if the system operator does not change with time and *time-varying* if the operator changes with the time. For example, consider an electrical circuit containing a capacitor and a resistor in series, as shown in Fig. 1.3. Here the input is the applied voltage E, and the output is the voltage across the capacitor. Applying Kirchhoff's voltage law, the differential equation for this circuit may be written as

$$RC\frac{dv}{dt} + v = E \tag{1.4}$$

Using the operator notation, this leads to

$$(RCp + 1)v = E$$

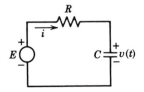

Figure 1.3 An R-C circuit.

The system operator for this case is therefore given by

$$L(p) = \frac{1}{RCp + 1} \tag{1.5}$$

It will be evident that if R and C are constants, then $L(p)$ is a time-invariant operator; but if the value of either R or C varies with time, $L(p)$ will be a time-varying operator. In such cases it is customary to write the system operator as $L_t(p)$, indicating that it varies with time.

1.2.4 DETERMINISTIC AND STOCHASTIC SYSTEMS

A system is said to be *deterministic* if the system operator $L(p)$, as well as the input (or inputs) applied to the system, are known exactly. For such a system, the output (or outputs) for any given input can be determined for all future time if all the initial conditions (states) are known.

There are some systems for which either the parameters of the system operator or the input are not known precisely but can be described only in a statistical sense. Such systems are called *stochastic*.

In real life, there is almost always a certain amount of uncertainty about the model used for a real system. Furthermore, most real systems are subject to random disturbances. It is therefore reasonable to assume that most systems in the real world are stochastic in nature. As a result, a vast amount of literature exists on the subject of stochastic systems. Although this is a very important topic, its study requires a background in probability and statistics that is not assumed in this book. Therefore, we limit ourselves to linear time-invariant deterministic systems.

1.2.5 LUMPED-PARAMETER AND DISTRIBUTED-PARAMETER SYSTEMS

A system is said to be of the *lumped-parameter* type if the effect of an input is felt simultaneously throughout the system, irrespective of its physical dimensions. Such systems are described by ordinary differential equations. For example, an electrical transmission line that is operated at low frequency so that the physical dimensions of the line are small compared with the wavelength can be considered a lumped-parameter system, since the current at each point on the line is identical.

On the other hand, in some systems, the quantities of interest are functions of the spatial dimensions as well as time. These must be described in terms of partial differential equations and are called *distributed-parameter* systems. For example, if we have a transmission line of physical length comparable to the wavelength, the current at different points on the line will not be the same, and it can no longer be modeled as a lumped-parameter system. A chemical reactor, in which the temperature varies with time as well as spatial coordinates, is another common example of such a system. In this book we study only lumped-parameter systems.

1.2.6   CONTINUOUS-TIME AND DISCRETE-TIME SYSTEMS

In the study of lumped-parameter systems, time plays an important role as the only independent variable in the system equations. The system inputs and output are functions of time, which varies continuously and can take any value in the continuous set of real numbers. Most physical systems fall into this category and are called *continuous-time* systems. Some simple and familiar examples are RLC circuits and mechanical systems involving motions of particles.

With the advent of the digital computer, particularly the inexpensive and compact microprocessor, another type of system has assumed considerable importance. In this system, the essential features of the input and output signals are of interest only at specific instants of time, given by

$$t = kT \tag{1.6}$$

where k is an integer and T is called the sampling interval. Such systems are called *discrete-time* systems. This topic has been motivated by (1) the use of a clock pulse generator for timing in digital computers and (2) the sampling theorem, which is discussed in detail in Chapter 4. The latter makes it possible to retain the important properties of a continuous-time signal if it is sampled at a suitable rate.

In many everyday situations the input–output data are available only at discrete instants of time. These can be modeled only as discrete-time systems. A simple example is a savings account that pays compound interest. The interest is calculated either on a daily, monthly, or annual basis and is added to the principal at the end of the designated interval. Hence, changes in the principal amount will take place only at discrete values of time. On the other hand, most physical systems are of the continuous-time nature, but there are situations where it is desirable to model them as discrete-time systems. An interesting example is the digital telephone system. In this case, the continuous-time electrical signals, which are generated by speech, are sampled at the rate of 8000 times per second and are converted into numbers (discrete-time signals) before transmission on the telephone cables. At the receiving end, these numbers are first converted into continuous-time signals and then into sound. An important advantage of this scheme is that by staggering the sampling instants, it is possible to use the same cable for the simultaneous transmission of several messages.

As is true of continuous-time systems, discrete-time systems can also be either *static* or *dynamic*. For the latter, the output at any given sampling instant depends on the present as well as the past values of the input and the output. Such systems are described by *difference equations*. A typical linear difference equation is of the following form:

$$y(k) + a_{n-1}y(k-1) + \cdots + a_1 y(k-n+1) + a_0 y(k-n)$$

$$= b_m u(k) + \cdots + b_0 u(k-m)$$

where $y(i)$ represents $y(iT)$ for any integer i. Systems of this type will be discussed in more detail in Section 1.4, after we have first studied the more familiar continuous-time systems described by linear differential equations with constant coefficients.

Drill Problem 1.1

The input $u(t)$ and the output $y(t)$ of a continuous-time system are related through the equation

$$y(t) = 5u(t) + 8$$

(a) Is this system static or dynamic?

(b) Is this system linear or nonlinear?

Justify your answers.   *Answer:* (a) Static. (b) Nonlinear.

Drill Problem 1.2

The input–output relations of several systems are given below. Are these systems static or dynamic? If a system is dynamic, classify it as to linearity, time-invariance, order, and causality.

(a) $y(t) = u^2(t) + 4$

(b) $y(t) = tu(t)$

(c) $\dfrac{dy}{dt} + ty = u(t)$

(d) $\dfrac{dy}{dt} + y^2 = u(t)$

(e) $\dfrac{d^2 y}{dt^2} + \dfrac{dy}{dt} + 3y = u(t)$

(f) $\dfrac{d^2 y}{dt^2} + \dfrac{dy}{dt} + 3y = u(t) + 2u^2(t)$

(g) $\dfrac{d^2 y}{dt^2} + y\dfrac{dy}{dt} + 3y = u(t)$

(h) $y(k) + 2y(k-1) - 3y(k-2) = 2u(k) + u(k-1)$

(i) $y(k) + 2y(k-1) - 3y(k-2) = 2u(k) + u(k+1)$

(j) $y(k) = ku(k) + k^2u(k-1)$

(k) $y(k) = 2u(k) + 3[u(k-1)]^2$

Answer: (a) Nonlinear, time-invariant, static, and causal.

(b) Linear, time-varying, static, and causal.

(c) Linear, time-varying, first-order, and causal.

(d) Nonlinear, time-invariant, first-order, and causal.

(e) Linear, time-invariant, second-order, and causal.

(f) Nonlinear, time-invariant, second-order, and causal.

(g) Nonlinear, time-invariant, second-order, and causal.

(h) Linear, time-invariant, second-order, and causal.

(i) Linear, time-invariant, second-order, and noncausal.

(j) Linear, time-varying, first-order, and causal.

(k) Nonlinear, time-invariant, first-order, and causal.

1.3 DIFFERENTIAL EQUATION MODELS AND THE p-OPERATOR

The first step in the analysis of any system is obtaining its mathematical model. For a linear lumped-parameter time-invariant continuous-time system, this will be in the form of an ordinary linear differential equation with constant coefficients. Therefore, it can be expressed as a linear operator, as described in Section 1.2.2. This process of determining the linear operator is called *modeling*. The derivation of the model requires knowledge of the physical laws governing the components within the system. For example, for electrical circuits, the differential equations can be obtained by the application of Kirchhoff's laws. Similarly, the laws of mechanics can be used for determining the equations for mechanical systems. In this book, we do not get into the details of how these equations are obtained, although it is assumed that the reader has some familiarity with the derivations of equilibrium equations for electrical networks. Our main emphasis is on the solution of the differential equations obtained for linear-invariant lumped-parameter systems.

For the general case of such systems, with a single input and a single output, the differential equation will be of the same form as is shown in equation 1.1. The degree of the polynomial $N(p)$ is less than or equal to that of $D(p)$, for most physical systems, that is, $L(p)$ is a *proper rational function* of p. In such cases, the degree of the polynomial $D(p)$, denoted by n, is said to be the *order* of the system. In general, $D(p)$ and $N(p)$ may be written as

$$D(p) = p^n + a_1 p^{n-1} + \cdots + a_1 p + a_0 \tag{1.7}$$

and

$$N(p) = b_{n-1} p^{n-1} + \cdots + b_1 p + b_0 \tag{1.8}$$

where the coefficient a_i and b_i are constants. Some of these coefficients may be zero.

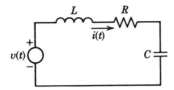

Figure 1.4   An RLC circuit.

Example 1.1

As an example of the use of the p-operator, let us consider the electrical network shown in Figure 1.4. Application of Kirchhoff's voltage law to this circuit gives us the following differential equation:

$$L\frac{di}{dt} + Ri + \int_{-\infty}^{t} \frac{1}{C} i\, dt = \nu(t) \tag{1.9}$$

Differentiating both sides of equation 1.9, we get

$$L\frac{d^2i}{dt^2} + R\frac{di}{dt} + \frac{i}{C} = \frac{d\nu}{dt} \tag{1.10}$$

Alternatively, using the operator notation, equation 1.9 may be written as

$$\left(Lp + R + \frac{1}{pC}\right)i(t) = \nu(t) \tag{1.11}$$

Note that we have replaced integration with the operator p^{-1}. This follows from the fact that integration is the inverse of differentiation. If we now multiply both sides of equation 1.11 by p, we obtain

$$\left(Lp^2 + Rp + \frac{1}{C}\right)i(t) = p\nu(t) \tag{1.12}$$

It is easily seen that the last equation can also be obtained by writing equation 1.10 using the operator notation. Considering the applied voltage $\nu(t)$ as the input and the current $i(t)$ as the output, the system operator for the circuit is obtained from equation 1.12 as

$$L(p) = \frac{p}{Lp^2 + Rp + \dfrac{1}{C}} = \frac{pC}{LCp^2 + RCp + 1} \tag{1.13}$$

■

Example 1.2

Consider the network shown in Figure 1.5. Here the voltage across the capacitor C_2, denoted as $\nu_2(t)$, will be considered the output and the objective is to determine the system function relating it to the input $e(t)$.

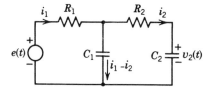

Figure 1.5   Two-loop network.

The loop equations for this network are given below.

$$R_1 i_1 + \frac{1}{C_1} \int_{-\infty}^{t} (i_1 - i_2)\, dt = e(t)$$

$$R_2 i_2 + \frac{1}{C_2} \int_{-\infty}^{t} i_2\, dt + \frac{1}{C_1} \int_{-\infty}^{t} (i_2 - i_1)\, dt = 0 \qquad (1.14)$$

Using the operational notation, equation 1.14 may be written as

$$\left(R_1 + \frac{1}{pC_1} \right) i_1 - \frac{1}{pC_1} i_2 = e(t)$$

$$-\frac{1}{pC_1} i_1 + \left(\frac{1}{pC_1} + R_2 + \frac{1}{pC_2} \right) i_2 = 0 \qquad (1.15)$$

Solving these equations for $i_2(t)$, we obtain

$$i_2(t) = \frac{C_2 p e(t)}{R_1 R_2 C_1 C_2 p^2 + (R_1 C_1 + R_2 C_2) p + 1} \qquad (1.16)$$

Finally, since

$$v_2(t) = \frac{1}{pC_2} i_2(t) \qquad (1.17)$$

the system operator $L(p)$ is given by

$$L(p) = \frac{1}{R_1 R_2 C_1 C_2 p^2 + (R_1 C_1 + R_1 C_2 + R_2 C_2) p + 1} \qquad (1.18)$$

$\blacksquare$

Drill Problem 1.3

Determine the system operator for the network shown in Figure 1.6.

Answer:

$$L(p) = \frac{1}{1 + pC_2 R + p^2 L(C_1 + C_2) + p^3 L C_1 C_2 R}$$

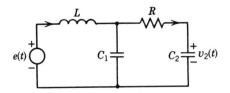

Figure 1.6   Network for drill problem 1.3.

1.4   DIFFERENCE EQUATION MODELS AND THE q-OPERATOR

In the previous section we learned that continuous-time systems are modeled by differential equations. The models for discrete-time systems will be different. To get an understanding of such systems, we recall the simple example of a savings account that pays compound interest. Let the original amount deposited in the account be denoted by p_0 and let the rate of interest by r percent per annum. We also assume that the interest is deposited into the account on a daily basis. Now if we denote the principal in the account after i days as $p(i)$, then we can write the following equation:

$$p(i + 1) = \left(1 + \frac{r}{36500}\right)p(i) \qquad (1.19)$$

Equation 1.19 is a first-order difference equation for this system and can be solved in an iterative manner, starting with $i = 0$, if we know the initial condition $p(0) = p_0$.

In the general case, a linear difference equation of order n will have the following form:

$$y(i) + a_1 y(i - 1) + \cdots + a_n y(i - n)$$
$$= b_0 u(i) + b_1 u(i - 1) + \cdots + b_n u(i - n) \qquad (1.20)$$

Note that the input and output are defined only at discrete values of time. Consequently, these are called *sequences* instead of functions of time. In equation 1.20, $u(i)$, $i = 0, 1, \ldots$, is the input sequence and $y(i)$ is the output sequence corresponding the given input sequence. Observe that we can solve this equation in an iterative manner, for any given input sequence, provided that we know $y(i)$ for $i = 0, 1, \ldots, n - 1$. In other words, we can solve this linear difference equation of order n if we know n initial conditions. It is useful to note the similarity with differential equations.

As seen in the case of differential equations, one may write the difference equation 1.20 in a more compact form by using the operator notation. Let q denote the operator that advances the sequence by one time interval, that is,

$$qx(i) = x(i + 1) \qquad (1.21)$$

Similarly, the inverse of q is the unit delay operator, that is,

$$q^{-1}x(i) = x(i-1) \tag{1.22}$$

Using this operator, we can rewrite equation 1.20 as

$$\left(1 + a_1 q^{-1} + \cdots + a_n q^{-n}\right)y(i)$$
$$= \left(b_0 + b_1 q^{-1} + \cdots + b_n q^{-n}\right)u(i) \tag{1.23}$$

Multiplying both sides of equation 1.23 by q^n, we obtain

$$\left(q^n + a_1 q^{n-1} + \cdots + a_n\right)y(i) = \left(b_0 q^n + b_1 q^{n-1} + \cdots + b_n\right)u(i) \tag{1.24}$$

Finally, we can define the linear discrete-time system function as

$$L(q) = \frac{N(q)}{D(q)} = \frac{b_0 q^n + b_1 q^{n-1} + \cdots + b_n}{q^n + a_1 q^{n-1} + \cdots + a_n} \tag{1.25}$$

It will be seen that the system functions for the two types of systems (continuous-time and discrete-time) are of the form, except that p has been replaced with q. We shall be exploiting this similarity in following sections. In the next two sections, we shall study the main approaches to solving linear differential and difference equations.

Drill Problem 1.4

Determine the system function $L(q)$ for the discrete-time system described by the following difference equation

$$3y(i) + 4y(i-1) + 7y(i-2) = 2u(i) + 5u(i-1)$$

$$Answer: \quad L(q) = \frac{2q^2 + 5q}{3q^2 + 4q + 7}$$

1.5 SOLUTION OF LINEAR DIFFERENTIAL EQUATIONS

In the previous sections, we observed that the models for linear systems are in the form of differential equations for continuous-time systems and in the form of difference equations for discrete-time systems. Consequently, it is normal to expect that the analysis of linear systems often involves the solution of such equations. In fact, a great deal of study has been devoted to the subject, and several sophisticated approaches are possible. Some of these will be studied in later chapters. In this section, we discuss some of the classical methods for solving linear differential equations.

Two basic methods can be used for solving linear differential equations with constant coefficients. One of these is meant primarily for first-order differential equations but can be extended to differential equations of order n by transforming them into a set of n first-order differential equations. The other method is applicable directly to higher order differential equations. We start with the first method.

1.5.1   SOLUTION OF FIRST-ORDER DIFFERENTIAL EQUATIONS

Consider the following linear differential equation

$$\frac{dx}{dt} + ax = f(t) \tag{1.26}$$

where $f(t)$ is a given function of time and $x(0)$ is known.

To solve this equation we first multiply both sides by a function $y(t)$ to obtain

$$y\frac{dx}{dt} + axy = y(t)f(t) \tag{1.27}$$

The objective is to select $y(t)$ so that the left-hand side of equation 1.27 may be a total derivative, that is,

$$y\frac{dx}{dt} + axy = \frac{d}{dt}(xy) = x\frac{dy}{dt} + y\frac{dx}{dt} \tag{1.28}$$

Comparing the left- and right-hand sides of equation 1.28, we find that this condition will be satisfied only if

$$axy = x\frac{dy}{dt} \tag{1.29}$$

which leads us to the following homogeneous differential equation for $y(t)$:

$$\frac{dy}{dt} = ay \tag{1.30}$$

A solution for equation 1.30 is

$$y(t) = e^{at} \tag{1.31}$$

where $y(0)$ has been taken simply as one.

We can now integrate equation 1.27 between the lower limit of 0 and the upper limit of t. This yields

$$x(t)y(t) - x(0)y(0) = \int_0^t y(\tau)f(\tau)\,d\tau \tag{1.32}$$

Substituting for $y(t)$ from equation 1.31 and with some rearrangement, we get

$$x(t) = e^{-at}x(0) + e^{-at}\int_0^t e^{a\tau}f(\tau)\,d\tau \tag{1.33}$$

It should be noted that our solution contains the integral of the product of the functions $e^{a\tau}$ and $f(\tau)$. Evaluation of this integral is fairly straightforward as long as $f(\tau)$ is not a very complicated function. The following example will illustrate the procedure.

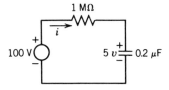

Figure 1.7 R-C network.

Example 1.3

For the RC-circuit shown in Figure 1.7, it is required to determine the voltage across the capacitor if the applied voltage $E = 100$ V and $\nu(0) = 5$ V. Here equation 1.4 takes the following form:

$$0.2\,\frac{d\nu}{dt} + \nu = 100 \tag{1.34}$$

Dividing both sides of equation 1.34 by 0.2, we obtain

$$\frac{d\nu}{dt} + 5\nu = 500 \tag{1.35}$$

A comparison with equation (1.26) leads to the following solution in the form of equation (1.33):

$$\nu(t) = 5e^{-5t} + e^{-5t}\int_0^t 500e^{5\tau}\,d\tau \tag{1.36}$$

Finally, evaluating the integral on the right-hand side, we obtain

$$\nu(t) = 100 - 95e^{-5t} \tag{1.37}$$

This method can be extended to the case when x is an n-dimensional vector instead of a scalar, so that higher order differential equations can be solved after they are written as a set of n first-order differential equations. This approach will be presented in detail in Chapter 8, along with the state-space representation of systems. ∎

Drill Problem 1.5

Solve the following differential equation using the method described in this section, if $\nu(0) = 20$.

$$\frac{d\nu}{dt} + 5\nu = 500e^{-2t} \quad Answer: \quad \nu(t) = \frac{500}{3}e^{-2t} - \frac{440}{3}e^{-5t}$$

1.5.2 SOLUTION OF HIGHER-ORDER DIFFERENTIAL EQUATIONS

A linear differential equation with constant coefficients and order n can be written more compactly using the operator notation, as below

$$D(p)y(t) = N(p)u(t) \tag{1.38}$$

where $D(p)$ is a polynomial of degree n in p, with the coefficient of p^n set equal to 1. In this case it is often called a *monic* polynomial of degree n. We can obtain a unique solution to this equation, if we know n initial conditions, that is, the values of y and its first $n - 1$ derivatives at $t = 0$.

The solution to equation 1.39 consists of two parts. The first, called the *complementary function*, is the solution to the *homogeneous* equation that is obtained by replacing the right-hand side with zero. It is also known as the *natural* or *zero-input* response of the system, since it occurs in the absence of any input. We denote this part by $y_c(t)$. The second part of the solution is called the *particular integral*; it is the component due to the forcing function $u(t)$ and is independent of the initial conditions. It is also called the *zero-state* or *forced* response of the system. This part of the solution is denoted by $y_p(t)$. The complete solution, $y(t)$, is the sum of $y_c(t)$ and $y_p(t)$. This follows from the superposition theorem, which implies that the total response of the system to $u(t)$ must be the sum of the responses to 0 and $u(t)$ taken together. In other words, the complete response is the sum of the zero-input and zero-state responses.

1.5.3 DETERMINING THE COMPLEMENTARY FUNCTION

We start with a simple-minded approach for determining the complementary function. It is easily shown that Ae^{rt} will satisfy the homogeneous equation, where r is a root of the auxiliary equation

$$D(p) = p^n + a_1 p^{n-1} + \cdots + a_0 = 0 \qquad (1.39)$$

formed from the operator equation 1.38. This follows immediately from the fact that differentiation of the exponential with respect to time will result in multiplication by the constant r.

Since the auxiliary polynomial will have n roots, we should expect that the complementary function will be given by

$$y_c(t) = A_1 y_1(t) + A_2 y_2(t) + \cdots + A_n y_n(t) \qquad (1.40)$$

where A_i are constants and $y_i(t)$ are exponential functions corresponding to each of the n roots of the polynomial. Some of these roots may, however, be complex or repeated. Note that complex roots must occur in conjugate pairs, since the coefficients of the auxiliary polynomial are real. Therefore, in this case the pair of complex exponentials can be grouped together to obtain sine and cosine terms multipled by exponentials. For multiple roots, the exponentials are multiplied by powers of t.

In view of the above, we can formulate the following procedure for determining the complementary function.

1. Calculate the n roots of the auxiliary polynomial 1.39. Let these be denoted by r_i, $i = 1, \ldots, n$.
2. For each distinct real root, r_i, the function $y_i(t)$ is $e^{r_i t}$.

3. For each pair of complex conjugate roots $\alpha \pm j\beta$, the functions are of the form $e^{\alpha t} \cos \beta t$ and $e^{\alpha t} \sin \beta t$.

4. For each real root, r, of multiplicity m, the functions are $e^{rt}, te^{rt}, t^2 e^{rt}, \ldots, t^{m-1} e^{rt}$.

5. For each pair of complex conjugate roots $\alpha \pm j\beta$ of multiplicity m, the functions are $e^{\alpha t} \cos \beta t, e^{\alpha t} \sin \beta t, te^{\alpha t} \cos \beta t, te^{\alpha t} \sin \beta t, te^{\alpha t} \cos \beta t, te^{\alpha t} \sin \beta t, \ldots, t^{m-1} e^{\alpha t} \cos \beta t, t^{m-1} e^{\alpha t} \sin \beta t$.

The roots of the auxiliary polynomial are called the *natural modes* of the system, since the corresponding exponential terms will occur in the response of the system to any input. The complementary function, including all these terms is, therefore, the natural response of the system. The actual values of the constants A_i will depend on the initial conditions as well as the particular integral.

Example 1.4

Consider the following homogeneous differential equation:

$$\frac{d^3 y}{dt^3} + 8 \frac{d^2 y}{dt^2} + 37 \frac{dy}{dt} + 50y = 0 \qquad (1.41)$$

The auxiliary equation is obtained as

$$p^3 + 8p^2 + 37p + 50 = 0 \qquad (1.42)$$

The roots of the auxiliary equation are located at -2 and $-3 \pm j4$. The complementary function is therefore given by

$$y_c(t) = A_1 e^{-2t} + A_2 e^{-3t} \cos 4t + A_3 e^{-3t} \sin 4t \qquad (1.43)$$

∎

Example 1.5

Consider the following homogeneous differential equation:

$$\frac{d^3 y}{dt^3} + 7 \frac{d^2 y}{dt^2} + 16 \frac{dy}{dt} + 12y = 0 \qquad (1.44)$$

The auxiliary equation is obtained as

$$p^3 + 7p^2 + 16p + 12 = 0 \qquad (1.45)$$

The roots of the auxiliary equation are located at -2, -2, and -3. Since there are two repeated roots, the complementary function is given by

$$y_c(t) = A_1 e^{-2t} + A_2 te^{-2t} + A_3 e^{-3t} \qquad (1.46)$$

∎

Drill Problem 1.6

Determine the complementary functions for the following differential equations

(a) $\dfrac{d^2y}{dt^2} + 6\dfrac{dy}{dy} + 25y = 0$ *Answer*: $e^{-3t}(A_1 \cos 4t + A_2 \sin 4t)$

(b) $\dfrac{d^2y}{dt^2} + 10\dfrac{dy}{dt} + 25y = 0$ *Answer*: $A_1 e^{-5t} + A_2 t e^{-5t}$

1.5.4 DETERMINING THE PARTICULAR INTEGRAL

We now discuss the evaluation of the particular integral, which is the response resulting from the input (or the forcing function). It is, therefore, often called the *forced response* of the system. Again, we consider a simple-minded approach, which will be applicable to most of the forcing functions that we encounter. First, we write the differential equation using the operator notation, that is,

$$D(p)y_p(t) = N(p)u(t) \tag{1.47}$$

where $y_p(t)$ is the particular integral for a given forcing function, $u(t)$.

The idea behind the method is that, for a given $D(p)$ and $u(t)$, we can obtain the particular integral by performing the inverse of the operation $D(p)$ on both sides of equation 1.47. In other words, we may write

$$y_p(t) = D^{-1}(p)N(p)u(t) \tag{1.48}$$

It follows that the particular integral, $y_p(t)$ is a linear combination of various derivatives of $u(t)$, as determined by the operator

$$L(p) = D^{-1}(p)N(p) \tag{1.49}$$

which can be expanded in a power series in terms of p. This is rather straightforward for the special case when the input is of the form

$$u(t) = Ae^{st} \tag{1.50}$$

Here we utilize the fact that the derivative of this function is obtained by simply multiplying it by s. We can easily generalize this idea to conclude that for any linear operator $L(p)$

$$L(p)u(t) = L(s)Ae^{st} \tag{1.51}$$

Therefore, the particular integral for the linear differential equation given by

$$D(p)y(t) = N(p)Ae^{st} \tag{1.52}$$

will be obtained simply as

$$y_p(t) = \frac{N(s)}{D(s)}Ae^{st} \tag{1.53}$$

It is important to observe that this is valid not only for real s but for also for the more general case when s is complex. In particular, if $u(t)$ is a sinusoid, we may write

$$u(t) = A \cos \omega t = \text{Re}[Ae^{j\omega t}] \tag{1.54}$$

where Re is the short form of "real part of."

In other words, we can replace the cosine function with the exponential Ae^{st}, where $s = j\omega$ and evaluate the particular integral for this input using equation 1.53 for this value of s. The particular integral for the corresponding cosine function input is then simply the real part of this function.

The following examples will illustrate the procedure.

Example 1.6

Consider the differential equation

$$\frac{d^3y}{dt^3} + 8\frac{d^2y}{dt^2} + 37\frac{dy}{dt} + 50y = 4e^{-3t} \tag{1.55}$$

Using the operator notation, equation 1.55 can be written as

$$(p^3 + 8p^2 + 37p + 50)y(t) = 4e^{-3t} \tag{1.56}$$

Since the forcing function is an exponential of the form given by equation 1.50, where the exponent $s = -3$, we replace p by -3, to obtain the particular integral as

$$y_p(t) = \left[\frac{1}{p^3 + 8p^2 + 37p + 50}\right]_{p=-3} 4e^{-3t} = -0.25e^{-3t} \quad (1.57)$$
∎

Example 1.7

We now consider the same problem as in Example 1.6, but this time the forcing function will be given by

$$u(t) = 4\cos 3t \tag{1.58}$$

Using the operator notation, it can be written as

$$(p^3 + 8p^2 + 37p + 50)y(t) = 4\cos 3t = \text{Re}[4e^{st}] \tag{1.59}$$

where $s = j3$ and Re means the "real part of."

Following the procedure described above, we obtain

$$y_p(t) = \text{Re}\left[\frac{4e^{st}}{s^3 + 8s^2 + 37s + 50}\right]_{s=j3}$$

$$= \text{Re}\left[\frac{4(\cos 3t + j\sin 3t)}{-22 + j84}\right]$$

$$= -\frac{22}{1885}\cos 3t + \frac{84}{1885}\sin 3t \tag{1.60}$$
∎

Example 1.8

We now repeat the previous problem with the forcing function:

$$u(t) = 4 \sin 3t \tag{1.61}$$

Here, we start by writing

$$u(t) = \text{Im}[4e^{j3t}] \tag{1.62}$$

where "Im" means "the imaginary part of."

Consequently, the particular integral for this input is obtained as

$$
\begin{aligned}
y_p(t) &= \text{Im}\left[\frac{4e^{st}}{s^3 + 8s^2 + 37s + 50}\right]_{s=j3} \\
&= -\frac{84}{1185} \cos 3t - \frac{22}{1185} \sin 3t
\end{aligned} \tag{1.63}
$$

∎

The same idea can also be applied to the more general case when the input is of the form

$$u(t) = Ae^{\alpha t} \cos \beta t = \text{Re}[Ae^{st}] \tag{1.64}$$

where

$$s = \alpha + j\beta \tag{1.65}$$

Drill Problem 1.7

Determine the particular integral for each of the differential equations given below:

(a) $\dfrac{d^2y}{dt^2} + 6\dfrac{dy}{dt} + 25y = 50$ *Answer:* $y_p(t) = 2$

(b) $\dfrac{d^2y}{dt^2} + 10\dfrac{dy}{dt} + 24y = 50e^{-2t}\cos 3t$

Answer: $y_p(t) = -e^{-2t}\left[\dfrac{2}{13}\cos 3t - \dfrac{36}{13}\sin 3t\right]$

One "special case" must be taken into account. This occurs when the exponent s of the exponential input Ae^{st} corresponds to a root of the auxiliary polynomial $D(p)$. As was seen in the case of the complementary function, the particular integral will now be of the form Bte^{st}. The value of the constant B can be determined by substitution, as before, after removing the corresponding factor from $D(p)$, as shown in the following example.

Example 1.9

Consider the following differential equation:

$$\frac{d^3y}{dt^3} + 8\frac{d^2y}{dt^2} + 37\frac{dy}{dt} + 50y = 4e^{-2t} \tag{1.66}$$

In this instance, the auxiliary equation

$$p^3 + 8p^2 + 37p + 50 = 0 \tag{1.67}$$

has roots at $p = -2$, $-3 + j4$, and $-3 - j4$. Since the exponent of the input function is equal to the first root, use of the method described previously will lead to division by zero. Therefore, we remove the factor $(p + 1)$ from $D(p)$ and obtain the particular integral as

$$y_p(t) = \left[\frac{1}{p^2 + 6p + 25}\right]_{p=-2} 4te^{-2t} = \frac{4}{17}te^{-2t} \tag{1.68}$$

■

Drill Problem 1.8

Determine the particular integrals for the following differential equations

(a) $\dfrac{d^2y}{dt^2} + 6\dfrac{dy}{dt} + 8y = 10e^{-4t}$ *Answer*: $-5te^{-4t}$

(b) $\dfrac{d^2y}{dt^2} + 10\dfrac{dy}{dt} + 41y = 50e^{-5t}\cos 4t$ *Answer*: $6.25te^{-5t}\sin 4t$

 Although this method does not apply to all input functions, it is useful for most functions encountered in engineering problems. In Chapter 5, we shall discuss a more general method using Laplace transforms.

1.5.5 THE COMPLETE SOLUTION

The complete solution to the differential equation consists of the sum of the complementary function and the particular integral with the n arbitrary constants in the complementary function evaluated so that the given initial conditions are satisfied. As stated previously, a unique solution can be obtained only if n boundary conditions are known; these may be the values of y and its $n - 1$ derivatives for some value of t. If these are known for $t = 0$ (initial conditions), it is called an *initial value problem*. Basically, it requires solving n linear simultaneous equations for the unknown constants. The procedure will be illustrated by the following example.

Example 1.10

Consider the differential equation, which was discussed in Examples 1.4 and 1.6. As shown there, the complete solution is of the form

$$y(t) = A_1e^{-2t} + A_2e^{-3t}\cos 4t + A_3e^{-3t}\sin 4t - 0.25e^{-3t} \tag{1.69}$$

where the constants A_1, A_2, and A_3 are to be evaluated to satisfy the initial conditions. Let us assume the following initial conditions:

$$y(0) = 1$$

$$\frac{dy}{dt}(0) = 2$$

$$\frac{d^2y}{dt^2}(0) = 1 \qquad (1.70)$$

Differentiating equation 1.69 twice and setting $t = 0$, the following equations are obtained to satisfy the initial conditions indicated by equation 1.70:

$$y(0) = A_1 + A_2 - 0.25 = 1$$

$$\frac{dy}{dt}(0) = -2A_1 - 3A_2 + 4A_3 + 0.75 = 2$$

$$\frac{d^2y}{dt^2}(0) = -4A_1 - 7A_2 - 24A_3 - 2.25 = 1 \qquad (1.71)$$

Solving these, we get

$$A_1 = \frac{42}{17}, \quad A_2 = \frac{-83}{68}, \quad \text{and} \quad A_3 = \frac{43}{68}. \qquad \blacksquare$$

It is apparent that the entire procedure is rather tedious, since we have to go through three distinct steps: namely, (1) determination of the complementary function, (2) evaluation of the particular integral for the given input function, and (3) solution of a set of linear simultaneous equations to satisfy the given initial conditions. A more direct approach for obtaining the complete solution, using Laplace transforms, will be presented in Chapter 5.

Drill Problem 1.9

Determine the complete solution for each of the following differential equations:

(a) $\dfrac{d^2y}{dt^2} + 6\dfrac{dy}{dt} + 25y = 50$,   with $y(0) = 4$, $\dfrac{dy}{dt}(0) = 2$

Answer: $y(t) = 2 + 2e^{-3t}\cos 4t + 2e^{-3t}\sin 4t$

(b) $\dfrac{d^2y}{dt^2} + 10\dfrac{dy}{dt} + 24y = 50e^{-2t}\cos 3t$,   with $y(0) = 4$, $\dfrac{dy}{dt}(0) = 1$

Answer: $y(t) = \dfrac{36}{13}e^{-2t}\sin 3t - \dfrac{2}{13}e^{-2t}\cos 3t + \dfrac{225}{26}e^{-4t} - \dfrac{9}{2}e^{-6t}$

1.6   SOLUTION OF LINEAR DIFFERENCE EQUATIONS

In Section 1.4, it was seen that a linear difference equation of order n can be written as

$$y(i) + a_1 y(i - 1) + \cdots + a_n y(i - n)$$
$$= b_0 u(i) + b_1 u(i - 1) + \cdots + b_n u(i - n) \qquad (1.72)$$

It can also be rearranged as below, where the ith sample of the output is expressed as a linear combination of the present and n past values of the input as well as the n past values of the output.

$$y(i) = \sum_{k=0}^{n} b_k u(i - k) - \sum_{k=1}^{n} a_k y(i - k) \qquad (1.73)$$

It is evident that the $y(i)$ can be easily calculated for any given input sequence $u(i)$ if the past n values of the output sequence $y(i)$ are known. Although this method provides a simple "brute force" solution, it does not give much insight into the nature of the output sequence. It would be more desirable to put the solution into a *closed form*. The most common approach for obtaining such a solution is very similar to that discussed in the previous section for differential equations. First we note that by using the operator notation we may write equation 1.72 as

$$\left(1 + a_1 q^{-1} + \cdots + a_n q^{-n}\right) y(i) = \left(b_0 + b_1 q^{-1} + \cdots + b_n q^{-n}\right) u(i)$$
$$(1.74)$$

where q is the unit advance operator.

As we discussed for the case of differential equations, the complete solution will consist of two components: the complementary solution and the particular solution. We first consider the complementary solution, which is then followed by the study of the particular solution.

1.6.1   DETERMINING THE COMPLEMENTARY SOLUTION

Consider the homogeneous equation, obtained by replacing the right-hand side of equation 1.71 with zero. Let r be any root of the auxiliary polynomial

$$q^n + a_1 q^{n-1} + \cdots + a_n = 0 \qquad (1.75)$$

Then, it can be easily verified (by direct substitution) that the sequence, $y(i) = Ar^i$, where A is any constant, is a solution of this equation. Since the auxiliary polynomial has n roots, it follows that, when the roots are distinct, the complementary solution will be of the form

$$y_c(i) = \sum_{k=1}^{n} A_k y_k(i) = \sum_{k=1}^{n} A_k r_k^i \qquad (1.76)$$

Multiple or complex roots can be handled in the same manner as was used for determining the complementary functions of differential equations.

As before, we can formulate the following procedure for determining the complementary solution.

1. Calculate the n roots of the auxiliary polynomial. Let these be denoted by r_k, $k = 1, 2, \ldots, n$.
2. For each distinct real root r_k, the sequence $y_k(i)$ is r_k^i.
3. For each pair of complex conjugate roots $a \pm j\beta$, the sequences are of the form $(\alpha \pm j\beta)^i$. Often it is more convenient to express the complex number $\alpha \pm j\beta$ in the polar form, $re^{+j\phi}$. In that instance the two sequences corresponding to the pair of complex conjugate roots may also be written as $r^i \cos i\phi$ and $r^i \sin i\phi$.
4. For each multiple real root, r, of multiplicity m, the sequences are $r^i, ir^i, i^2 r^i, \ldots, i^{m-1} r^i$.
5. For each pair of complex conjugate roots $\alpha \pm j\beta$ of multiplicity m, the sequences are $(\alpha \pm j\beta)^i, i(\alpha \pm j\beta)^i, i^2(\alpha \pm j\beta)^i, \ldots, i^{m-1}(\alpha \pm j\beta)^i$. Expressing the roots in the polar form $re^{\pm j\phi}$, the sequences are of the form, $r^i \cos i\phi, r^i \sin i\phi, ir^i \cos i\phi, ir^i \sin i\phi, i^2 r^i \cos i\phi, i^2 r^i \sin i\phi, \ldots, i^{m-1} r^i \cos i\phi, i^{m-1} r^i \sin i\phi$.

Example 1.11

Consider the homogeneous difference equation

$$y(i) - 8y(i-1) + 37y(i-2) - 50y(i-3) = 0 \qquad (1.77)$$

The resulting auxiliary equation is given by

$$q^3 - 8q^2 + 37q - 50 = 0 \qquad (1.78)$$

The roots are located at 2 and $3 \pm j4$. Expressing the complex roots in the polar form $(3 + j4 = 5e^{j0.9273})$, the complementary solution is given by the following sequence

$$y_c(i) = A_1 2^i + A_2 5^i \cos 0.9273i + A_3 5^i \sin 0.9273i \qquad (1.79)$$

∎

Example 1.12

Consider the homogeneous difference equation

$$y(i+3) - 7y(i+2) + 16(y+1) - 12y(i) = 0 \qquad (1.80)$$

The resulting auxiliary equation is given by

$$q^3 - 7q^2 + 16q - 12 = 0 \qquad (1.81)$$

The roots are located at 2, 2, and 3. Since the root at $q = 2$ has multiplicity two, the complementary solution is given by

$$y_c(i) = A_1 2^i + A_2 i 2^i + A_3 3^i \qquad (1.82)$$

∎

Drill Problem 1.10

Determine the complementary solutions for the difference equations given below.

(a) $y(i) + 0.6y(i - 1) + 0.08y(i - 2) = 0$ *Answer*: $A_1 0.2^i + A_2 0.4^i$

(b) $y(i) + 0.6y(i - 1) + 0.25y(i - 2) = 0$ *Answer*: $A_1 0.5^i \cos i\theta$

$$+ A_2 0.5^i \sin i\theta$$

(c) $y(i) + 0.06y(i - 1) + 0.09y(i - 2) = 0$ *Answer*: $A_1 0.3^i + A_2 i 0.3^i$

1.6.2 DETERMINING THE PARTICULAR SOLUTION

The particular solution of the difference equation depends on the forcing function and is also called the *forced response*. As for differential equations, it is possible to determine the particular solution very easily for the special case of complex exponential sequences. The following example illustrates the procedure for an exponential sequence.

Example 1.13

Consider the following difference equation, which has the same operator as in Example 1.11.

$$y(i + 3) - 8y(i + 2) + 37y(i + 1) - 50y(i) = 8(0.5)^i \quad (1.83)$$

Using the operator notation, we may write this as

$$\left(q^3 - 8q^2 + 37q - 50\right)y(i) = 8(0.5)^i \quad (1.84)$$

Since the input is an exponential sequence, the particular solution is readily obtained by replacing q with 0.5. This gives us

$$y_p(i) = \frac{8(0.5)^i}{0.125 - (8 \times 0.25) + (37 \times 0.5) - 50} = -\frac{64}{267}(0.5)^i \quad (1.85)$$
∎

Drill Problem 1.11

Determine the particular solution for each of the following difference equations.

(a) $y(i) + 0.6y(i - 1) + 0.08y(i - 2) = 4$ *Answer*: $\dfrac{50}{21}$

(b) $y(i) + 0.6y(i - 1) + 0.25y(i - 2) = 4(0.4)^i$ *Answer*: $\dfrac{64}{65}(0.4)^i$

(c) $y(i) + 0.6y(i - 1) + 0.09y(i - 2) = 4\cos\dfrac{i}{3}$

Answer: $2.387\cos\dfrac{i}{3} - 0.367\sin\dfrac{i}{3}$

1.6.3   THE COMPLETE SOLUTION

The complete solution of a difference equation can be obtained in the same way as was shown for differential equations. First we obtain the complementary solution and then the particular solution as described in the previous section. Finally, the unknown constants in the complete solution are determined in such a way that all of the boundary conditions are satisfied. In an *initial value* problem we must be given n initial conditions for a difference equation of order n. The following example illustrates the procedure.

Example 1.14

Consider the difference equation

$$y(i + 3) - 8y(i + 2) + 37y(i + 1) - 50y(i) = 8(0.5)^i \quad (1.86)$$

which is required to satisfy the boundary conditions

$$y(0) = 2, \quad y(1) = 3, \quad \text{and} \quad y(2) = 5$$

The complementary solution for this system was obtained in Example 1.11 and the particular solution was obtained in Example 1.13. The complete solution will have the form:

$$y(i) = A_1 2^i + A_2 5^i \cos 0.9273i + A_3 5^i \sin 0.9273i - \frac{64}{267}(0.5)^i \quad (1.87)$$

The constants A_1, A_2, and A_3 must be determined so that the given boundary conditions are satisfied. Therefore, substituting 0, 1, and 2 for i in equation 1.87, we obtain

$$A_1 + A_2 - \frac{64}{267} = 2$$

$$2A_1 + 5A_2 \cos 0.9273 + 5A_3 \sin 0.9273 - \frac{32}{267} = 3$$

$$4A_1 + 25A_2 \cos 1.8546 + 25A_3 \sin 1.8546 - \frac{16}{267} = 5$$

Solving these linear simultaneous equations for the unknown coefficients, we get

$$A_1 = 2.1886$$
$$A_2 = 0.05108$$
$$A_3 = -0.35666 \qquad \blacksquare$$

As with differential equations, the process is rather tedious and involves three distinct steps. A more direct approach for obtaining the complete solution of difference equations using z-transforms will be presented in Chapter 6.

Drill Problem 1.12

Obtain the complete solution for each of the difference equations given below if $y(0) = 2$ and $y(1) = 5$.

(a) $y(i) + 0.6y(i - 1) + 0.08y(i - 2) = 4$

Answer: $\dfrac{50}{21} + \dfrac{259}{21}(-0.2)^i - \dfrac{267}{21}(-0.4)^i$

(b) $y(i) + 0.6y(i - 1) + 0.25y(i - 2) = 4(0.4)^i$

Answer: $\dfrac{64}{65}(0.4)^i + \dfrac{699}{65}(0.5)^i \sin(i\theta) + \dfrac{66}{65}(0.5)^i \cos(i\theta)$

where $\theta = \tan^{-1}\dfrac{4}{3}$

(c) $y(i) + 0.6y(i - 1) + 0.09y(i - 2) = 4\cos\dfrac{i}{3}$

Answer: $2.387\cos\dfrac{i}{3} - 0.367\sin\dfrac{i}{3} - (0.387 + 9.161i)(-0.3)^i$

1.7 REALIZATION OF CONTINUOUS-TIME SYSTEMS

In some of the preceding sections of this chapter, we learned how linear continuous-time systems can be represented by differential equation models. We also studied methods for solving these equations. It is desirable, however, to maintain contact with reality through simulations. The basic idea is to set up another system on a computer that satisfies the same differential equation as the system under study and is subject to the same input as well as initial conditions. This is called an analog of the original system. One advantage of simulation is that one can easily study the effect of changes in the parameters of the actual system by varying these on the analog.

A continuous-time system can be represented very conveniently on an electronic analog computer. Other types of analogs can also be used. Our task of realizing a continuous-time system on an analog computer is quite straightforward if we assume the existence of three basic devices. These are (1) an *integrator*, (2) a *summing device* or *adder*, and (3) a *constant multiplier*. The block diagrams for these devices are shown in Figure 1.8. The input and output of the integrator are related through the equation

$$y(t) = \int_0^t x(\tau)\, d\tau + y(0) \tag{1.88}$$

The adder can add several inputs as shown, so that its output is given by

$$y(t) = x_1(t) + x_2(t) + \cdots + x_n(t) \tag{1.89}$$

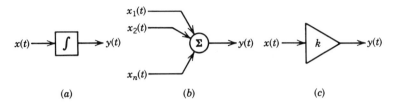

(a)   (b)   (c)

Figure 1.8   Basic devices of realization. (a) Integrator. (b) Adder. (c) Constant multiplier.

The constant amplifier multiplies the input by the constant k to give

$$y(t) = kx(t) \tag{1.90}$$

In electronic analog computers these devices are easily realized through the use of operational amplifiers, resistors, capacitors, and potentiometers. Furthermore, the parameters of the analogous system can be easily adjusted by changing the potentiometer settings. For our purpose, however, it will be sufficient to study the procedures to be used for realizing linear systems utilizing these basic components.

It may be observed at this point that instead of an integrator, in theory at least, it is also possible to use a differentiator as a component for simulation. This is not done in practice, because electronic operational amplifiers are affected very much by noise generated in their various components when these are used as differentiators. On the other hand, integration has a smoothing effect on noise.

1.7.1   DIRECT REALIZATION

We now study the use of these basic elements for realization of continuous-time systems. The main idea is illustrated through a simple example. Let us first consider a system represented by the following third-order differential equation:

$$\frac{d^3y}{dt^3} + 8\frac{d^2y}{dt^2} + 37\frac{dy}{dt} + 50y = u(t) \tag{1.91}$$

Rearranging it so that only the highest derivative term is on the left-hand side, we get

$$\frac{d^3y}{dt^3} = -8\frac{d^2y}{dt^2} - 37\frac{dy}{dt} - 5y + u(t) \tag{1.92}$$

The block diagram shown in Figure 1.9 forces the highest derivative of y to satisfy equation 1.92, where y and its lower order derivatives are obtained through successive integration. The only restriction is that the right-hand side of the differential equation has been constrained to be $u(t)$.

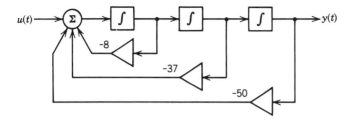

Figure 1.9 Realization of system described by equation 1.91.

As a more general case, let us consider the situation when the system function is given by the linear operator

$$L(p) = \frac{N(p)}{D(p)} = \frac{b_0 p^n + b_1 p^{n-1} + \cdots + b_n}{p^n + a_1 p^{n-1} + \cdots + a_n} \qquad (1.93)$$

where the operator p represents differentiation with respect to time, as before. Equivalently, the system can be represented by the following differential equation:

$$\frac{d^n y}{dt^n} + a_1 \frac{d^{n-1}y}{dt^{n-1}} + \cdots + a_n y$$

$$= b_1 \frac{d^{n-1}u}{dt^{n-1}} + \cdots + b_{n-1}\frac{du}{dt} + b_n u(t) \qquad (1.94)$$

To realize this sytem, first we consider the denominator polynomial alone and replace the numerator by 1. This modified system is given by the differential equation

$$\frac{d^n x}{dt^n} + a_1 \frac{d^{n-1}x}{dt^{n-1}} + \cdots + a_n x(t) = u(t) \qquad (1.95)$$

The similarity between equations 1.95 and 1.91 makes it evident that this system can be realized with n integrators, in a manner similar to that shown in Figure 1.9. The realization diagram for this case is shown in Figure 1.10.

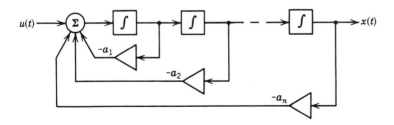

Figure 1.10 Realization of system described by equation 1.95.

Next we note that the output of the system given by equation 1.93 is related to that of the system given by equation 1.95 through the relationship

$$y(t) = N(p)x(t) \qquad (1.96)$$

In other words, the system equation 1.92, which may be written as

$$D(p)y(t) = N(p)u(t) \qquad (1.97)$$

has been separated into the following two equations

$$D(p)x(t) = u(t) \qquad (1.98)$$

and

$$y(t) = N(p)x(t) \qquad (1.99)$$

This is justified because in both the cases,

$$y(t) = D^{-1}(p)N(p)u(t) \qquad (1.100)$$

It would appear from equation 1.99 that to obtain $y(t)$ from the realization diagram of Figure 1.10, $(n - 1)$ differentiative of $x(t)$ will be necessary. However, we may note that $x(t)$ and its $n - 1$ derivatives are already available from the outputs of the integrators. Thus, we only need include an adder to the diagram of Figure 1.10.

Example 1.15

Consider a linear continuous-time system described by the following differential equation:

$$\frac{d^3y}{dt^3} + 8\frac{d^2y}{dt^2} + 37\frac{dy}{dt} + 50y = 3\frac{du}{dt} + 5u(t) \qquad (1.101)$$

The diagram for realizing this sytem is shown in Figure 1.11. It will be seen that it is similar to that of Figure 1.9, except for an extra adder. ∎

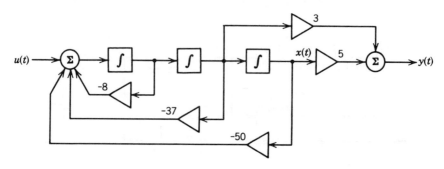

Figure 1.11 Direct realization of system described by equation 1.101.

The method described above is often called *direct realization*. Several other procedures are possible. Two of these will now be presented.

1.7.2 CASCADE REALIZATION

Given the system function $L(p)$ we may first factor it so that

$$L(p) = L_1(p)L_2(p) \cdots L_m(p) \qquad (1.102)$$

Thus, the system can be viewed as a cascade connection of m subsystems, where the order of each subsystem may be 1 or 2. Each of the subsystems can now be simulated by using the method described in the previous section. The output of the first subsystem acts as the input to the second subsystem and so on. The subsystems, however, must be selected in such a manner that their system functions are proper, that is, the degree of the numerator polynomial does not exceed that of the denominator for each of the factors. This restriction is imposed by the need to avoid the use of a differentiator.

Example 1.16

For the system described by equation 1.101, we have

$$L(p) = \frac{3p + 5}{p^3 + 8p^2 + 37p + 50} = \frac{1}{p + 2} \frac{3p + 5}{p^2 + 6p + 25} \qquad (1.103)$$

The realization diagram for this case is shown in Figure 1.12. ∎

1.7.3 PARALLEL REALIZATION

Another approach is to perform a partial fraction expansion of the system function so that it may be written as

$$L(p) = L_1(p) + L_2(p) + \cdots + L_m(p) \qquad (1.104)$$

where each term of the form $L_i(p)$ represents either a first- or a second-order proper rational function, depending on whether the denominator polynomial for the respective term has real or complex roots.

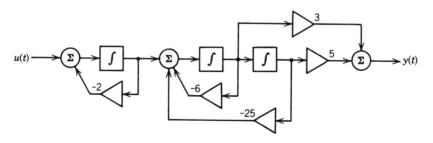

Figure 1.12 Cascade realization of system described by equation 1.103.

Example 1.17

Consider the system discussed in Example 1.15. By using partial fraction expansion of the system function, we get

$$L(p) = \frac{3p + 5}{p^3 + 8p^2 + 37p + 50} = \frac{-\dfrac{1}{17}}{p + 2} + \frac{\dfrac{p}{17} + \dfrac{55}{17}}{p^2 + 6p + 25} \qquad (1.105)$$

The simulation diagram for this case is shown in Figure 1.13.   ■

Many other approaches to analog simulation are possible, including combinations of the three methods described in this section. It is also possible to simulate continuous-time systems on digital computers, utilizing methods for numerical solution of differential equations.

1.7.4   INITIAL CONDITIONS

As mentioned earlier, a unique solution for a differential equation can be obtained only if the boundary conditions are given. For example, if the differential equation is of order n, then we must be given the initial values of the output and its $n - 1$ derivatives. It follows that to obtain the response of a system to a given input and specified initial conditions through simulation, it is necessary that the outputs of the integrators must satisfy these initial conditions. This was also implied in equation 1.88, which defined the relationship between the input and output of an integrator.

In some instances, the initial values of the output and its derivatives are not identical to the outputs of the integrators. For example, consider the simulation in Example 1.15. Here the output $y(t)$ is obtained as a linear

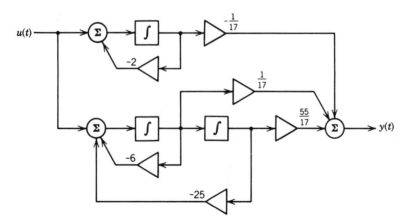

Figure 1.13   Parallel realization of system described by equation 1.105.

combination of the outputs of two integrators, that is,

$$y(t) = 3\frac{dx}{dt} + 5x \tag{1.106}$$

Therefore, the outputs of the three integrators are different from the output of the system and its first two derivatives. It is possible, however, to find the initial conditions of x and its first two derivatives from those of y and its first two derivatives. First we note that setting $t = 0$ in equation 1.106 gives us

$$y(0) = 3\frac{dx}{dt}(0) + 5x(0) \tag{1.107}$$

If we differentiate both sides of equation 1.106 with respect to t and set $t = 0$, we get

$$\frac{dy}{dt}(0) = 3\frac{d^2x}{dt^2}(0) + 5\frac{dx}{dt}(0) \tag{1.108}$$

Differentiating both sides of equation 1.106 twice with respect to t and setting $t = 0$, we obtain

$$\frac{d^2y}{dt^2}(0) = 3\frac{d^3x}{dt^3}(0) + 5\frac{d^2x}{dt^2}(0) \tag{1.109}$$

The third derivative of x in equation 1.108 can be eliminated by using the original differential equation. Consequently, we have

$$\frac{d^2y}{dt^2}(0) = -19\frac{d^2x}{dt^2}(0) - 111\frac{dx}{dt}(0) - 150x(0) + 3u(0) \tag{1.110}$$

Equations 1.107, 1.108, and 1.109 can now be used to solve for the initial values of x and its first two derivatives. Note that this also requires the knowledge of the initial value of $u(t)$.

Drill Problem 1.13

A linear system described by the following differential equation is to be simulated on an analog computer. Show how this can be done by using direct realization.

$$\frac{d^3y}{dt^3} + 4\frac{d^2y}{dt^2} + 11\frac{dy}{dt} + 15y = 2\frac{du}{dt} + 5u(t) \tag{1.111}$$

Drill Problem 1.14

Repeat using cascade and parallel realizations.

1.8 REALIZATION OF DISCRETE-TIME SYSTEMS

The realization of discrete-time system can be carried out exactly as in the case of continuous-time systems, with the difference that the *integrator must be replaced by a delay element* that introduces a delay equal to T seconds, where T is the sampling interval. This follows easily from the fact that the system functions for the two types of systems differ only in that the operator p for the continuous-time system is replaced by the operator q in the case of discrete-systems. All the methods described in the previous section can be used with this modification.

Example 1.18

A discrete-time system described by the difference equation

$$y(i + 3) - 8y(i + 2) + 37y(i + 1) - 50y(i) = 3u(i + 1) + 5u(i)$$
(1.112)

has the following system function

$$L(q) = \frac{3q + 5}{q^3 - 8q^2 + 37q - 50}$$
(1.113)

The direct realization of this system is shown in Figure 1.14. It would be instructive to compare it with Figure 1.11 ∎

Drill Problem 1.15

A discrete-time system is described by the difference equation given below. Draw diagrams for direct, cascade, and parallel realizations of this system.

$$y(k) + 3y(k - 1) + 5y(k - 2) + 7y(k - 3) = 6u(k) + 4u(k - 1)$$

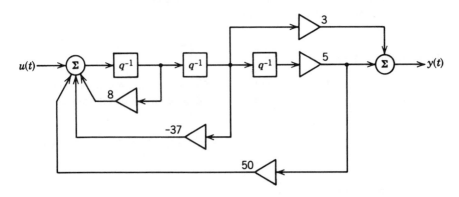

Figure 1.14 Direct realization of system described by equation 1.112.

1.9 STABILITY OF LINEAR SYSTEMS

The concept of stability is very important in system theory. A system is said to be *stable* if the output remains bounded for all bounded inputs.

Although the subject will be studied in great detail in Chapters 5 and 6, on the basis of our studies in this chapter, we can make the following observation:

1. The natural response of a linear time-invariant continuous-time system will remain bounded if and only if all the roots of $D(p)$, the denominator of the system function, satisfy the following conditions:
   (i) The real parts of all simple roots must be less than or equal to zero, and
   (ii) The real parts of all multiple roots must be less than zero.

2. The natural response of a linear time-invariant discrete-time system will remain bounded if and only if all the roots of $D(q)$, the denominator of the system function, satisfy the following conditions:
   (i) The magnitude of all simple roots must be less than or equal to one, and
   (ii) The magnitude of all multiple roots must be less than one.

Since the complete output consists of both the natural response (complementary function) and the forced response (particular solution), the conditions given above guarantee that the former will remain bounded for all initial conditions. For stability in the general bounded-input bounded-output (BIBO) sense, the following statements can be made.

1. A linear time-invariant continuous-time system is
   (i) Stable in the BIBO sense if all roots of $D(p)$ have negative real parts,
   (ii) Unstable if the real part of any root is greater than or equal to zero.

2. A linear time-invariant discrete-time system is
   (i) Stable in the BIBO sense if all roots of $D(q)$ have magnitude less than one,
   (ii) Unstable if the magnitude of any roots is greater than or equal to one.

Note that in these conditions for stability, we have excluded simple roots of $D(p)$ with zero real parts for continuous-time systems (and similarly simple roots of $D(q)$ with magnitude equal to one for discrete-time systems). The reason is that a bounded natural response does not necessarily imply stability. For example, simple roots of $D(p)$ with zero real parts will cause a bounded sinusoid in the natural response, but the particular solution will grow out of bounds if the forcing function is a sinusoid of the same frequency. The following example will demonstrate this fact.

Example 1.19

Consider the system described by the following differential equation

$$\frac{d^2y}{dt^2} + 4y = u(t) \tag{1.114}$$

The complementary function for this case is easily seen to be

$$y_c(t) = A\cos 2t + B\sin 2t \tag{1.115}$$

Evidently, this is bounded, However, if the input $u(t)$ is of the form

$$u(t) = 2\cos 2t \tag{1.116}$$

the particular integral is found to be (please refer to the discussion just before Example 1.9)

$$y_p(t) = 0.5t\sin 2t \tag{1.117}$$

which will be unbounded although the input itself is bounded.   ■

It should also be noted that if a system satisfies the conditions of stability stated above, the complementary function will decay with time. Thus, it can be called the *transient* component of the solution. In such situations, if the forcing function is a sinusoid, the particular solution of a linear system will be a sinusoid of the same frequency, but will generally have different magnitude and phase. It is customary to call this solution the *steady-state* response for the given input. We shall be returning to this concept in Chapters 3 and 4 in connection with the steady-state response of linear systems to periodic inputs.

1.10 SUMMARY

This chapter introduces the reader to the basic concepts of systems. A system can be defined as "a collection of objects arranged in an ordered form, which is, in some sense, purpose or goal directed." It is characterized by "an input," which may be regarded the cause, and "an output," which may be considered the effect. System theory attempts to develop relationships between these variables so that the behaviour of the system under different conditions may be understood. Systems that are physically very different may have similar mathematical models. Consequently, such models are very useful for understanding and predicting the behavior of a system under different operating conditions.

Systems can be static, dynamic, causal, anticipatory, linear, nonlinear, time-varying, time-invariant, deterministic, stochastic, lumped-parameter, distributed-parameter, continuous-time, and discrete-time. In this book we shall study only linear, time-invariant, deterministic, and lumped-parameter systems, which may be either of the continuous-time or the discrete-time type. Linear systems satisfy the property of superposition and are modeled by linear differential or difference equations. These systems can be character-ized by their operational transfer functions, using the operator p for continu-ous-time systems and the operator q for discrete-time systems.

In this chapter we studied the classical methods for solving linear differential or difference equations. A great deal of similarity was noted in this study. This was followed by a brief discussion of methods for realizing continuous-time as well as discrete-time systems. Here again, a direct parallel between the two types of systems was observed in that the ideal integrator for continuous-time systems was replaced by the ideal delay for discrete-time systems. The chapter was concluded with a brief discussion of the concept of stability of linear systems, and the conditions for bounded-input bounded-output stability were described.

1.11 PROBLEMS

1.1 Obtain the complete solution of each of the differential equations given below with initial conditions as specified.

(a) $\dfrac{d^2y}{dt^2} + 8\dfrac{dy}{dt} + 12y = 6,$ $y(0) = 2,$ $\dfrac{dy}{dt}(0) = 5$

(b) $\dfrac{d^2y}{dt^2} + 8\dfrac{dy}{dt} + 16y = 6e^{-2t},$ $y(0) = 1,$ $\dfrac{dy}{dt}(0) = 0$

(c) $\dfrac{d^2y}{dt^2} + 8\dfrac{dy}{dt} + 25y = 6\sin 2t,$ $y(0) = 1,$ $\dfrac{dy}{dt}(0) = 0$

1.2. Determine the system operator for the electrical network shown in Figure 1.15 where the input is the applied voltage $u(t)$ and the output is the voltage $v(t)$ across the capacitor.

1.3. Draw a simulation diagram for the system operator determined in the previous problem using direct realization.

1.4. Repeat Problem 1.3 by using cascade realization.

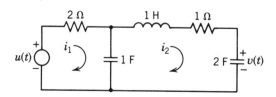

Figure 1.15 Electrical Network for problem 1.2.

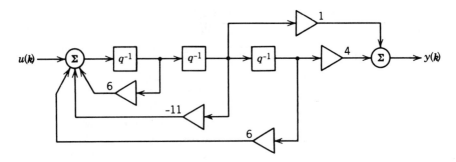

Figure 1.16   Realization diagram for a discrete-time system.

1.5.   Repeat Problem 1.3 using parallel realization.

1.6.   The realization diagram for a discrete-time system is shown in Figure 1.16. Find the corresponding difference equation.

1.7.   For the system given in the previous problem, determine the output sequence if the input sequence is given by $u(k) = 3(2)^k$. Assume zero initial conditions.

1.8.   Repeat the previous problem if $y(0) = 2$, $y(1) = 3$, and $y(2) = 5$.

1.9.   Obtain a cascade realization for the discrete-time system shown in Figure 1.14.

1.10.   Repeat Problem 1.9 by using parallel realization.

1.11.   Consider a savings account started with an initial deposit of $y(0)$ dollars. The interest rate is r percent per annum and the interest is compounded every month. The depositor is allowed to make additional deposits every month, say $u(1)$, $u(2)$, $u(3)$, and so on. Write an equation that will model the balance at the end of any month, expressing it in terms of the previous balance, the amount deposited during the month, and the interest accrued during the month. Draw a simulation diagram for this model.

1.12.   Write a computer program for solving the difference equation obtained for the previous problem. It is to be used for finding the total balance after 5 years if a person starts with an initial deposit of $500.00 on the first day of a given month and deposits $100.00 on the first day of every subsequent month. The interest rate may be taken as 10 percent per annum and is compounded on the last day of every month. For the purpose of this exercise, it may be assumed that the 12 months in the year are of equal length.

1.13.   Fibonacci numbers can be expressed through the following difference equation:

$$y(k) = y(k - 1) + y(k - 2), \quad \text{with} \quad y(0) = 1 \quad \text{and} \quad y(1) = 2$$

Obtain a general solution for $y(k)$ and determine $y(10)$.

1.14. Consider the growth of the population of rabbits in Australia. At the end of one month, each pair of rabbits produces a litter of four. Exactly two of these are male and the other two are female. Assuming that this process continues with each pair producing a litter of two pairs at the end of every month, and all the rabbits survive, obtain the difference equation that relates the population of rabbits after the $(k + 1)$th month to that at the end of k months. What will be the population after 12 months if initially there were two pairs?

1.15. Obtain the complete solution of each of the difference equation given below, with initial conditions as specified:
(a) $y(k) + 6y(k - 1) + 8y(k - 2) = 8$, $y(0) = 2$, $y(1) = 5$
(b) $y(k) + 6y(k - 1) + 9y(k - 2) = 3(2)^k$, $y(0) = 0$, $y(1) = 4$
(c) $y(k) + 6y(k - 1) + 13y(k - 2) = 4\sin(2k)$, $y(0) = 5$, $y(1) = 3$

1.16. Obtain the complete solution for the difference equation

$$y(k) + 8y(k - 1) + 80y(k - 2) = u(k) + 3u(k - 1)$$

given the initial conditions $y(0) = 1$, $y(1) = 2$, for the following input sequences:
(a) $u(k) = 3\cos(\pi k/3)$
(b) $u(k) = 4(0.3)^k$
(c) $u(k) = 2k(0.4)^k$

1.17. Repeat Problem 1.16 for the following difference equation with the same inputs and initial conditions:

$$y(k) + 6y(k - 1) + 9y(k - 2) = u(k) + 3u(k - 1)$$

1.18. The input $u(t)$ and the output $y(t)$ of a linear system are related through the following differential equation:

$$\frac{d^3y}{dt^3} + 4\frac{d^2y}{dt^2} + 11\frac{dy}{dt} + 15y = 2\frac{du}{dt} + 5u(t)$$

Assuming zero initial conditions, determine the complete solution for the output if $u(t) = 10$.

1.19. Repeat Problem 1.18 if $u(t) = 10e^{-2t}$.

1.20. Repeat Problem 1.18 if $u(t) = 10e^{-2t}\cos 3t$.

1.21. A d.c. servomotor is often used for positioning in automatic control systems. The input is a voltage v applied to the armature winding and the output is the angular potion θ of the shaft of the motor. These are related through the differential equation

$$\frac{d^2\theta}{dt^2} + 2\frac{d\theta}{dt} = 4v$$

Determine the output of the motor if $v = 1$, applied at $t = 0$. Assume that the motor is initially at rest.

1.22. The differential equation relating the position of the laser beam in a laserjet printer to the control input from the printer is given below.

$$\frac{d^2y}{dt^2} + 75\,\frac{dy}{dt} + 800y = 200\,\frac{du}{dt} + 800u$$

Determine the output, $y(t)$, if the input is given by $u(t) = t$. Assume zero initial conditions.

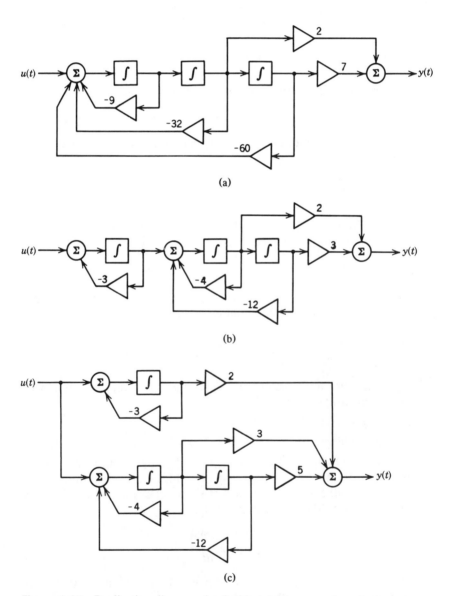

(a)

(b)

(c)

Figure 1.17 Realization diagrams for Problem 1.26.

1.23. Repeat Problem 1.22 if the initial conditions are

$$y(0) = 10, \qquad \frac{dy}{dt}(0) = 20$$

1.24. Two friends, Sam and Joseph, decide to deposit $2000 every year in a pension fund that pays interest at 10 percent per year, compounded annually. Sam is 40 years old and continues the deposits until he retires at the age of 65. Joseph is 25 years old and stops depositing money in the fund after 5 installments. Write suitable difference equations and utilize these to determine the value of the pension fund for Sam as well as Joseph at age 65.

1.25. Repeat Problem 1.24 for interest set at 11 percent per year, compounded annually.

1.26. Determine the differential equation corresponding to each of the realizations shown in Figure 1.17.

1.27. The system operators of some linear systems are given below. Examine each of these for stability in the bounded-input bounded-output sense.

(a) $L(p) = \dfrac{2p + 3}{p^3 + 5p^2 + 8p + 4}$

(b) $L(p) = \dfrac{2p + 3}{p^4 + 5p^3 + 8p^2 + 4p}$

(c) $L(p) = \dfrac{2p - 3}{p^3 + 5p^2 + 8p + 4}$

(d) $L(q) = \dfrac{q - 0.5}{q^2 - 1.1q + 0.3}$

(e) $L(q) = \dfrac{q - 0.5}{q^2 - 1.5q + 0.5}$

APPENDIX 1.1

Computer Solution of Linear Difference Equations

As stated in Section 1.6, the output sequence for any given linear difference equation of order n can be calculated easily if the input sequence and the past n values of the output sequence are known. A computer program for this purpose has been included with the book. It starts with asking the user the order of the difference equation, which is considered to have the same form as in equation 1.72. The coefficients a_i, $i = 1, 2, \ldots, n$, and b_i, $i = 0, 1, \ldots, n$, are then entered, either from the keyboard or from a file stored on a disk. The program then asks the user for the initial values of the output sequence, $y(i)$ for $i = 0, 1, \ldots, n - 1$. Finally, the input sequence is entered, either in the form of a formula or as the actual values (maximum length of the sequence may be 200). From these data, values of the output sequence for $i = n$, $n + 1$, $n + 2$, $\ldots$, are calculated and displayed. These can also be printed if a printer is connected to the computer, and they can be stored in a disk file if desired. This program is called DIFFCEQ.EXE.

Note that this program does not give an explicit solution for the difference equation. A more general solution can be obtained by determining the complementary function and the particular solution as shown in Section 1.6 and then finding the arbitrary constants that will satisfy the given initial conditions. Another alternative is to use z-transforms. This will be discussed in detail in Chapter 7.

APPENDIX 1.2

Computer Solution of Linear Differential Equations

Linear differential equations with constant coefficients can be solved in several different ways. Perhaps the most direct approach is the method described in Section 1.5.2. Complete solution requires the following steps:

(a) Evaluate the roots of the auxiliary equation to determine the complementary function.

(b) Determine the particular integral.

(c) Evaluate of the arbitrary constants in the complementary function to satisfy the initial conditions.

The disk included with the book has programs for performing all these steps separately. These programs are called Roots.EXE, Rational.EXE, and Simeq.EXE. The first can be used for determining the roots of the auxiliary equation $D(p)$ in order to obtain the complementary function. The second allows the evaluation of the rational function $L(p) = N(p)/D(p)$ for any real or complex p. Finally, the arbitrary constants in the complete solution are obtained by solving the set of linear simultaneous equations using the program Simeq.EXE, which solves equations of the form $\mathbf{Ax} = \mathbf{b}$, where $\mathbf{A}$ is a square nonsingular matrix of real numbers and $\mathbf{b}$ is a vector of real numbers.

A more efficient solution using Laplace transforms is discussed in Chapter 5 and a computer program for that purpose is also provided. This is described in Appendix 5.1.

Signals

2.1 INTRODUCTION

A signal may be defined as a function of time representing a physical variable associated with a system. The input to a system as well as its output are signals. For an electrical system, signals may represent currents or voltages, whereas for a mechanical system, signals may be forces and velocities. In some more complicated systems, signals may depend on several other independent variables in addition to time; such systems are modeled by partial differential equations. For example, in a chemical reactor, the signal of interest may be temperature, which may vary with time as well as along the spatial coordinates of the reactor. Since the input and output signals are, in general, different functions of time, it may be said that a system *processes* the input signal to produce the output signal.

Just as there are many different types of systems, signals can also be put into many classes. These will be described briefly in the following section.

2.2 CLASSIFICATION OF SIGNALS

Signals can be classified in several ways. For the purpose of this book, the most important distinction between signals is based on whether they are available for all values of time or only for discrete instants of time. This will be discussed in the next subsection.

2.2.1 CONTINUOUS-TIME AND DISCRETE-TIME SIGNALS

A signal is said to be of the *continuous-time* type if it is defined for every instant of time within a specified range. A typical example is an electrical voltage or a mechanical force that is available for all values of time. Note that this does not imply that the signal itself is a mathematically continuous function of time, but rather the fact that it has values for all instances of time. For example, consider the step function of time shown in Figure 2.1.

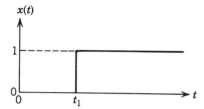

Figure 2.1 A step function.

Although this function has a step discontinuity at $t = t_1$, it is a continuous-time function, since it has values for all t (note that because of the discontinuity, it is undefined at $t = t_1$).

Alternatively, one may say that for a continuous-time signal, the time variable t takes its values from the set of real numbers.

The speech signal produced by a microphone that senses variations in acoustic pressure produced by sound waves and converts them into an electrical voltage is a common example of a continuous-time signal. The recording of a typical speech signal is shown in Figure 2.2.

A *discrete-time* signal has values for only discrete instants of time, that is, the domain of t is a discrete set of numbers. Consequently, such a signal will usually be denoted as $x(n)$, instead of $x(t)$, where n is an integer. Quite often, a discrete-time signal is obtained by *sampling* a continuous-time signal. In such cases, n may be replaced by kT, where k is an integer and T is called the sampling interval. If T is kept constant, the values of x are obtained at equally spaced values of time. Such a situation arises in digital telephony, where the speech signal is sampled at intervals of 125 μs (microseconds) (or 8000 times per second) to obtain a discrete-time signal. Although this is the most common case, there are situations where it may be desirable to vary the sampling interval. Discrete-time signals may also occur naturally in some areas of business, science, and engineering. For example, in a business application, the discrete-time variable may be a week, a month, three months, or a year. The weekly values of the Dow Jones average of the stock market, shown in Figure 2.3, form an example of a discrete-time signal.

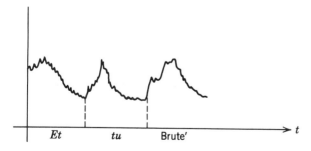

Figure 2.2 A speech signal.

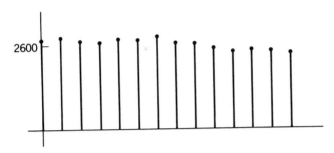

Figure 2.3 The weekly Dow Jones average for the first three months of 1990.

Another common example is the set of daily minimum (or maximum) temperatures recorded in a particular city.

A discrete-time signal $x(n)$ is often called a *sequence*, if n is a sequence of integers. Thus, the values of the weakly Dow Jones average shown in Figure 2.3 can be called the Dow Jones sequence for the first three months of 1990.

It is important to understand the difference between discrete-time and *quantized* signals. The latter arise when the values of the signal are limited to a countable set, for example, when these values must be in the form of eight binary digits. All discrete-time signals are not necessarily quantized. However, since a digital computer can handle numbers with only a finite number of digits, it is usually necessary to quantize signals if they are to be processed by such a computer.

2.2.2 PERIODIC AND APERIODIC SIGNALS

A continuous-time signal $x(t)$ is said to *periodic* if and only if

$$x(t + T) = x(t), \quad \text{for all } t \in (-\infty, \infty) \qquad (2.1)$$

The smallest positive value of T for which the above equation holds true is called the *period* of the signal. It follows that equation 2.1 will also hold true if T is replaced by kT, where k is any integer.

Similarly, a discrete-time signal $x(n)$ is said to be periodic if and only if

$$x(n + N) = x(n), \quad \text{for all } n \in (-\infty, \infty) \qquad (2.2)$$

where the smallest positive value of N for which the above equation holds is called the period of the signal.

Any signal that is not periodic is said to be *aperiodic*.

The most common example of a continuous-time periodic function is the familiar sinusoid, described by the equation

$$x(t) = A \cos(2\pi ft + \phi) \qquad (2.3)$$

where A, f, and ϕ are constants, called the *amplitude, frequency* in hertz (or cycles per second), and *phase in radians*, respectively. The angular frequency, expressed in radians per second, defined as

$$\omega = 2\pi f \tag{2.4}$$

is often more convenient to use. The *period T*, in seconds, is given by

$$T = \frac{1}{f} = \frac{2\pi}{\omega} \tag{2.5}$$

It follows that the sum of two sinusoids will be a periodic function if and only if the ratio of their respective periods is a rational number. For example, consider the following sinusoids:

$$x_1(t) = 10 \sin 3\pi t$$
$$x_2(t) = 20 \cos 7\pi t$$
$$x_3(t) = 10 \sin 32t \tag{2.6}$$

It can be seen that the sum of x_1 and x_2 will be a periodic function, since the period of x_1 is $\frac{2}{3}$ s and that of x_2 is $\frac{2}{7}$ s so that the ratio of the two periods is the rational fraction $\frac{3}{7}$. As a result, the period of the sum will be 2 s, which will comprise of 3 complete cycles of x_1 and 7 complete cycles of x_2. On the other hand, the sum of x_1 and x_3 will not be periodic, since the ratio of the respective periods, $\frac{2}{3}$ and $\pi/16$, is an irrational number.

The sinusoid in equation 2.3 may also be expressed in terms of complex exponentials using Euler's relationship

$$\exp(j\theta)^{\dagger} = \cos\theta + j\sin\theta \tag{2.7}$$

to obtain

$$A\cos(\omega t + \phi) = \mathrm{Re}\{A\exp[j(\omega t + \phi)]\} \tag{2.8}$$

where, as in Chapter 1, "Re" implies "real part of." Alternatively, we may write

$$A\cos(\omega t + \phi) = \frac{A}{2}\{\exp[j(\omega t + \phi)] + \exp[-j(\omega t + \phi)]\} \tag{2.9}$$

Both equations 2.8 and 2.9 imply the periodic nature of the complex exponential, characterized by the following expression, which holds true for any integer k. We utilize this property extensively in Chapters 3 and 4.

$$\exp[j(\omega t + \phi + 2k\pi)] = \exp[j(\omega t + \phi)] \tag{2.10}$$

Some other examples of common periodic continuous-time functions are shown in Figure 2.4.

---

†The notation $\exp(\ldots)$ instead of its alternative $e^{\cdots}$ will be used for greater readability where appropriate.

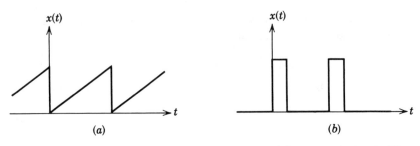

Figure 2.4 Some periodic continuous-time signals. (*a*) Saw-tooth signal. (*b*) Train of pulses.

An elementary example of a discrete-time periodic signal is the sinusoidal sequence of period N,

$$x(n) = A \sin\left(\frac{2\pi n}{N}\right) \tag{2.11}$$

where n and N are integers. Such a signal is shown in Figure 2.5, for the case when $N = 6$.

As for the continuous-time situation, we may express the periodic discrete-time signal in the form of a complex exponential. This gives us

$$x(n) = \mathrm{Re}\left\{ A \exp\left(\frac{j2\pi n}{N}\right) \right\} \tag{2.12}$$

Also, we may define the angular frequency as

$$\Omega = \frac{2\pi}{N} \tag{2.13}$$

It should be observed that since N is a dimensionless quantity, the unit for the angular frequency Ω is radians, whereas that of ω for the continuous-time case was seen to be radians per second. The significance of this difference will be discussed in Chapters 6 and 7.

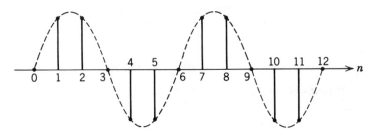

Figure 2.5 A sinusoidal sequence.

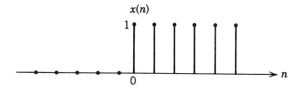

Figure 2.6 A step sequence.

An example of an aperiodic signal is the continuous-time step function, shown in Figure 2.1. A discrete-time step sequence $x(n)$, which is zero for $n < 0$ and 1 for $n \geq 0$, is shown in Figure 2.6.

Periodic signals are very important for engineers and will be discussed in detail in Chapters 3 and 4. Furthermore, aperiodic signals can be considered as limiting cases of periodic signals with an infinite period. This concept will be exploited in those chapters.

2.2.3 DETERMINISTIC AND RANDOM SIGNALS

Signals are said to be *deterministic* if they can be represented by known equations. In other words, a deterministic signal is described fully by its defining equation, so that all future values of the signal can be predicted on the basis of this equation. The sinusoid considered in the previous section is a good example of a deterministic signal.

On the other hand, a signal is said to be *random* if its future value cannot be predicted with certainty. A common example of a random signal is the noise voltage that is generated in an amplifier. Such signals can be described only in terms of probabilistic functions like their mean, variance, and distribution functions.

2.2.4 SINGULARITY FUNCTIONS

Some aperiodic signals have unique properties and are known as singularity functions because they are either discontinuous or have discontinuous derivatives. The simplest of these is the *unit step function* shown in Figure 2.7. It is

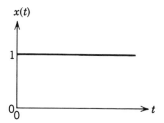

Figure 2.7 The unit step function.

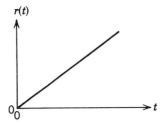

Figure 2.8 The unit ramp function.

defined as

$$x(t) = \begin{cases} 0 & t < 0 \\ 1 & t > 0 \end{cases} \qquad (2.14)$$

At $t = 0$ the value of the function jumps from 0 to 1. Therefore, it is discontinuous at that instant. This function is very important in the study of linear systems and is sometimes represented by the symbol $u_{-1}(t)$. In many books, the symbol $u(t)$ is used for this function. In this book, however, we reserve the symbol $u(t)$ for the input to a linear system, following the common practice in books on control systems. In view of the importance of the unit step function, we denote it by the special symbol $\gamma(t)$. A justification for this will follow later. Similarly, a delayed step function, that is, a function that changes from 0 to 1 at $t = t_1$, will be denoted by $\gamma(t - t_1)$. This function was shown in Figure 2.1.

Other singularity functions are defined through the relationship

$$u_{i-1}(t) = \int_{-\infty}^{t} u_i(\tau) \, d\tau \qquad (2.15)$$

that is, $u_{i-1}(t)$ is obtained by integrating $u_i(t)$. Alternatively, one may say that $u_i(t)$ is obtained by differentiating $u_{i-1}(t)$ with respect to t.

Integration of the unit step function gives the *unit ramp function*, $r(t)$, shown in Figure 2.8. Although, according to equation 2.15, the unit ramp function should be denoted by $u_{-2}(t)$, it is customary to use $r(t)$ to denote a ramp function. It should be noted that the slope of $r(t)$ is unity. A ramp function with slope m will be denoted by $mr(t)$ or $mu_{-2}(t)$.

Linear combinations of various singularity functions may be used to generate a large number of functions. Two common examples are given next.

Example 2.1

A rectangular pulse of duration T and height A, starting at time $t = t_0$ can be expressed as

$$x(t) = A\gamma(t - t_0) - A\gamma(t - t_0 - T) \qquad (2.16)$$

This is shown in Figure 2.9*a*. ∎

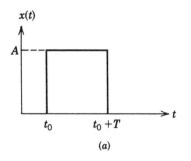
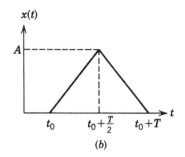

(a) (b)

Figure 2.9 Signals generated by singularity functions. (a) Rectangular pulse. (b) Triangular pulse.

Example 2.2

A triangular pulse of the form shown in Figure 2.9b can be expressed as

$$x(t) = \frac{2A}{T}\left[r(t - t_0) - 2r\left(t - t_0 - \frac{T}{2}\right) + r(t - t_0 - T)\right] \quad (2.17)$$

Many other functions can be generated in the same way. ∎

2.2.5 THE IMPULSE FUNCTION

An important singularity function is the *impulse* or *delta* function, $\delta(t)$. It can be defined as the function which after integration gives the unit step, $\gamma(t)$, that is,

$$\gamma(t) = \int_{-\infty}^{t} \delta(\tau)\, d\tau \quad (2.18)$$

Alternatively, we may look at the unit impulse as the time derivative of the unit step. This relationship was the main reason for our selecting the symbol $\gamma(t)$ for the unit step. In view of equation 2.15, we may also denote the unit impulse by $u_0(t)$. Because the unit step function is the integral of the delta function, the latter must satisfy the following equations:

(i) $\delta(t) = 0$ for $t \neq 0$ (2.19)

(ii) $\int_{-\infty}^{\infty} \delta(t)\, dt = 1$ (2.20)

From these two equations we conclude that the area of the impulse function is unity and is obtained over an infinitesimal interval around $t = 0$. This can be possible only if the height of the function approaches infinity at $t = 0$ while its width approaches zero. It also follows from the fact that since the unit impulse is the derivative of the unit step, it must be zero for all values of t except at $t = 0$, where it must be infinite.

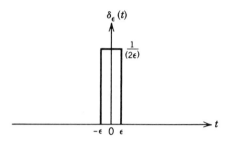

Figure 2.10 Rectangular pulse approximation to a unit impulse.

It is evident that the unit impulse is different from conventional functions. To develop an intuitive grasp of this function, we shall picture it through a limiting process. Consider a rectangular pulse of unit area extending from $t = -\varepsilon$ to $t = \varepsilon$ and zero elsewhere. The height of the pulse must be set equal to $1/(2\varepsilon)$ so that the area may be unity. This function, which we shall denote as $\delta_\varepsilon(t)$, is shown in Figure 2.10. In the limit, as $\varepsilon \to 0$, the unit area is obtained with an infinitesimal width around $t = 0$ and $\delta_\varepsilon(t) \to \delta(t)$.

Although it may appear that the impulse function is not real but is simply a mathematical fiction, in fact, several physical phenomena can be modeled appropriately with the impulse. The main property of these phenomena is that they happen in time intervals that are very short compared with the resolution of the measuring apparatus used, but they produce a measurable change in a physical quantity that is almost instantaneous. For example, if we connect an ideal resistance-free capacitor across the terminals of a battery, the voltage will change almost instantaneously. This is the result of a very large current flowing into the capacitor for a very small interval of time, that is, the current flowing into the capacitor is an impulse function. Another example arises when we hit the head of a nail with a hammer. In this instance, we are applying a large force for a very small amount of time, that is, the force applied to the head of the nail is an impulse function.

2.2.6 POWER AND ENERGY SIGNALS

Another method for classifying signals is based on whether they contain finite energy or finite average power. There are other signals that have neither finite energy nor finite average power.

We may define the energy content of a signal $x(t)$ as

$$E = \lim_{T \to \infty} \int_{-T}^{T} x^2(t)\, dt \tag{2.21}$$

Similarly, the average power content of a signal can be defined as

$$P = \lim_{T \to \infty} \frac{1}{2T} \int_{-T}^{T} x^2(t)\, dt \tag{2.22}$$

Note that if $x(t)$ is the current (in amperes) flowing through a 1-Ω resistor, then E is the total energy (in joules) dissipated in the resistor and P is the average power (in watts) content in the signal. Furthermore, if the average power content of the signal is finite and greater than zero then, in view of equation 2.21, its energy content will be infinite. Similarly, if the energy content of a signal is finite, then its average ower content must be zero.

In the light of these definitions, we may define power and energy signals as below:

1. $x(t)$ is a power signal if and only if its average power content P is finite and greater than zero, implying that its energy content is infinite.

2. $x(t)$ is an energy signal if and only if its energy content E is finite, implying that its power content is zero.

3. If $x(t)$ does not satisfy either of the two conditions stated above, then it is neither a power signal nor an energy signal.

As an example consider the signal

$$x(t) = Ae^{\alpha t}\gamma(t) \tag{2.23}$$

where $\gamma(t)$ is the unit step function and A and α are constants with $\alpha < 0$. In this case, it is easily shown that the energy content of the signal is given by

$$E = \frac{A^2}{2\alpha} \tag{2.24}$$

Thus, this is an energy signal.

On the other hand, if we set $\alpha = 0$, we get the step function, for which E is infinite, but the power content P is finite. Therefore, this is an example of a power signal.

The average power content of a periodic signal $x(t)$ with period T can be determined by performing the integration over one complete cycle, that is,

$$P = \frac{1}{T}\int_0^T x^2(t)\,dt \tag{2.25}$$

This follows from the periodic nature of the signal and will be discussed further in Chapter 3. The reader can verify (for example, for a sinusoid) that in this instance, P is finite if $x(t)$ is finite over the period.

Drill Problem 2.1

The equations for a number of signals are given below. Determine if they are (a) periodic or nonperiodic signals, and (b) energy or power signals. Calculate the average power or energy in each case.

(i) $x(t) = 20e^{-2t}\cos 100t$

(ii) $x(t) = 20\cos 2t + 10\sin 3\pi t$

(iii) $x(t) = 30\cos 4\pi t \cdot [\gamma(t) - \gamma(t - 1)]$

(iv) $x(t) = 4\cos 4\pi t + 6\sin 5\pi t$

(v) $x(t) = (4\cos 4\pi t + 6\sin 5\pi t)\,\gamma(t)$

(vi) $x(t) = 10e^{3t}\gamma(t)$

Answer: (i)   (a) Nonperiodic, (b) energy signal with total energy 50.02.

(ii)   (a) Nonperiodic, (b) power signal with average power 250.

(iii)   (a) Nonperiodic, (b) energy signal with total energy 450.

(iv)   (a) Periodic,   (b) power signal with average power 26.

(v)   (a) Nonperiodic, (b) causal power signal with average power 26.

(vi)   (a) Nonperiodic, (b) neither.

2.3   SOME COMMON SIGNALS

In the preceding section, several common signals encountered in system theory are mentioned. We now list the most important nonperiodic continuous-time as well as discrete-time signals along with the symbols used for them.

2.3.1   THE UNIT STEP, $\gamma(t)$

This is shown in Figure 2.7 and is described in Section 2.2.4. The response of a system to a unit step is easily obtained experimentally and is very useful for studying certain properties of the system, as will be described in subsequent chapters of the book. The symbol $g(t)$ will be used for the step response of a system.

2.3.2   THE UNIT RAMP, $r(t)$

The unit ramp function is obtained by integrating the unit step and is shown in Figure 2.8.

2.3.3   THE UNIT IMPULSE, $\delta(t)$

The unit impulse was described in Section 2.2.5. The response of a system to a unit impulse is important because it provides a great deal of information about the properties of the system. Throughout this book, the impulse response of a linear system will be denoted by the symbol $h(t)$. As we shall see later, it can also be utilized to determine the response of the system to any arbitrary input. The symbol for a unit impulse that occurs at time $t = t_0$ is $\delta(t - t_0)$. This function is depicted in Figure 2.11.

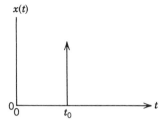

Figure 2.11 Impulse occurring at t_0.

2.3.4 THE RECTANGULAR PULSE, $AP_\Delta(t - t_k)$

The rectangular pulse $AP_\Delta(t - t_k)$ is shown in Figure 2.12. It is seen that it is a rectangle of height A, starting at $t = t_k$ and duration Δ. In the particular case when $A = 1/(\Delta)$, the area of the pulse will be equal to one and it will approach the unit impulse in the limit as $\Delta \rightarrow 0$.

2.3.5 THE DISCRETE-TIME UNIT STEP SEQUENCE, $\gamma(n)$

This function was shown in Figure 2.6. It can be formally defined by the equation

$$\gamma(n) = \begin{cases} 0 & n < 0 \\ 1 & n \geq 0 \end{cases} \tag{2.26}$$

2.3.6 THE DISCRETE-TIME UNIT IMPULSE, $\delta(n)$

This may be defined in a manner analogous to the definition of the unit impulse for the continuous-time case. The essential difference is that because of the discrete nature of the signal, the process of integration must be replaced by summation. Therefore, we get

$$\gamma(n) = \sum_{k=-\infty}^{n} \delta(k) \tag{2.27}$$

In view of the above definition and that of $\gamma(n)$, it follows immediately that

$$\delta(n) = \begin{cases} 0 & n \neq 0 \\ 1 & n = 0 \end{cases} \tag{2.28}$$

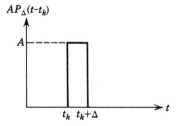

Figure 2.12 Rectangular pulse.

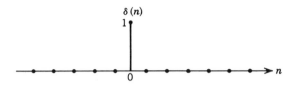

Figure 2.13 The discrete-time unit impulse, $\delta(n)$.

The discrete-time unit impulse is depicted in Figure 2.13. Note that there was no analytical difficulty in defining the discrete-time impulse function, in contrast with the situation for its continuous-time counterpart. Furthermore, in view of the definition of the discrete-time impulse function, it is easily seen that any discrete-time function $x(k)$ can be expressed as a weighted sum of such impulses. This will be discussed in greater detail in the Sections 2.5 and 2.8.

2.4 CONTINUOUS-TO-DISCRETE-TIME SIGNAL CONVERSION

Many signals occur naturally in the continuous-time form, but it is desirable to convert them into equivalent discrete-time signals in such a way that there is no loss of the information contained in the signal. This is also known as analog-to-digital conversion. There are many practical reasons for this conversion. Probably the most important reason is the convenience in storage and processing of signals after they are converted to the digital form. Another reason is the availability of inexpensive digital electronic hardware that makes it more attractive to convert analog signals to digital form for processing and then convert them back to the analog form. It may be noted that there is no loss of information in this conversion only if the signal and the sampling rate satisfy certain properties. This will be discussed in Chapter 4, along with the *sampling theorem*.

The block diagram of an analog-to-digital (A/D) converter is shown in Figure 2.14. The first component is a *sampler*, which obtains the values of the analog signal at the sampling instants. The output of the sampler is a discrete-time signal that can assume values from a continuous range. This is often referred to as a sampled-data signal, since the values of this signal are

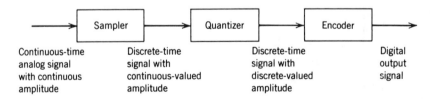

Figure 2.14 Analog-to-digital converter.

Switch closes at $t = kT$

Figure 2.15 An ideal sampler.

identical to those of the continuous-time (or analog) signal at the sampling instants. This signal is not suitable for use with a digital computer because the latter can accept only numbers that are limited to a given number of digits. The second component of the A/D converter is a *quantizer*, which changes the sample values from a continuous range into a range with a discrete set of values so that each sample value can be represented by a digital word of finite number of digits. The last component is the *encoder*, which converts each of the quantized sample values into a digital word that can be used on a digital computer. We shall now discuss each of these operations in detail.

2.4.1 SAMPLING

Given a continuous-time signal $x(t)$, the idea of sampling is to extract the values of x at $t = kT$, where T is called the sampling interval and k is an integer that indicates the position of each sample. A very simple approach is shown in Figure 2.15, where a sampling switch is closed for an infinitesimally short time at each of the sampling instants, $t = kT$. The output of the ideal sampler will therefore have a value equal to that of $x(t)$ at each of the sampling instants and zero at all other instants when the switch is open.

Such an ideal sampler cannot be obtained in practice, since no switch can be opened or closed in zero time. A more practical approach is that the switch be closed for a small interval at each of the sampling instants. A mathematical model for this operation is to assume that the signal $x(t)$ is multiplied by the periodic train of rectangular pulses $p(t)$, shown in Figure 2.16a to obtain the function $x^*(t)$. Note that each pulse is of unit height and duration Δ, centered around a sampling instant. As a result, we may write

$$x^*(t) = x(t)p(t) \tag{2.29}$$

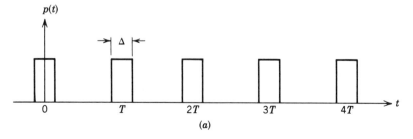

Figure 2.16a The sampling function.

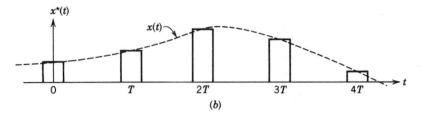

Figure 2.16b   The sampled function.

It is evident that the sampled function $x^*(t)$ will be a sequence of rectangular pulses. Each of these pulses has the same height as the value of $x(t)$ at the corresponding sampling instant, as shown in Figure 2.16b.

In the limit, as the width Δ of the pulse approaches zero, we get the special case when the sample function consists of a sequence of impulses. The effect of multiplication by $x(t)$ is, then, to make the *area* under each impulse equal to the value of $x(t)$ at that sampling instant. Although this is, again, an idealization, the model is very useful mathematically. In the rest of the book, we shall often idealize a sampled signal as consisting of a train of impulses as modeled above.

2.4.2   QUANTIZING AND ENCODING

The object of quantization is to round off a sampled value to the nearest of a finite set of values permitted by the number of digits that one can use. Encoding is the process of representing each of the permissible values of the samples, obtained by quantization, by a digital word. Assuming that the computer uses binary numbers and the digital word-length is n, the possible number of quantization levels is given by

$$\mu = 2^n \tag{2.30}$$

For example, if we are permitted to use numbers with 8 binary digits, the maximum number of quantization levels can only be 2^8, or 256. In this case, it can be said that we have an 8-bit A/D converter.

It is evident that the process of quantization introduces errors in the analog-to-digital conversion process. A quantitative measure of this error is easily derived, since the maximum error will be $\pm 0.5\Delta$, where Δ is the width of a quantization level. The value of Δ will be small if the number of quantization levels is large. Accordingly, it is reasonable to assume that the signal varies linearly within the quantization level for the period τ, during which it remains within the quantization level. Thus, the error in quantization at any time t within this period can be expressed as

$$\varepsilon(t) = \frac{2\Delta t}{\tau} \tag{2.31}$$

if it is assumed that τ is centered around the quantization level. The average power of the square error due to quantization is therefore given by

$$J = \frac{1}{\tau} \int_{-\tau/2}^{\tau/2} \varepsilon^2(t) \, dt = \frac{\Delta^2}{12} \tag{2.32}$$

It is interesting to note that, under the assumption made, the error is independent of τ.

2.5   REPRESENTATION OF A SIGNAL BY A CONTINUUM OF IMPULSES

An important application of the impulse function is the possibility of representing any arbitrary continuous-time signal as a continuum of impulses. Consider an arbitrary continuous-time function of time $x(t)$, which is defined over the interval $[-T, T]$. One possible approximation to the function can be obtained by representing it by a sequence of rectangular pulses of width Δ, where the height of each pulse is made equal to the value of $f(t)$ at the center of the pulse. This is shown in Figure 2.17.

It follows that the approximation gets better as the width of the pulses Δ is decreased. If we define the pulse of duration Δ at time $t = k\Delta$ as $P_\Delta(t - k\Delta)$, our approximation can be represented as

$$x(t) \approx \sum_{k=-N}^{N} x(k\Delta) P_\Delta(t - k\Delta) \tag{2.33}$$

where the total number of pulses is

$$2N + 1 = \frac{2T}{\Delta} \tag{2.34}$$

We can rearrange equation 2.33 as

$$x(t) \approx \sum_{k=-N}^{N} x(k\Delta) \frac{P_\Delta(t - k\Delta)}{\Delta} \Delta \tag{2.35}$$

Observe that as $\Delta \to 0$, the fraction in equation 2.34 approaches the unit impulse $\delta(t - k\Delta)$, which is an impulse occurring at $t = k\Delta$. Also, the value

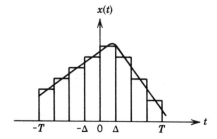

Figure 2.17 Approximation with sequence of rectangular pulses.

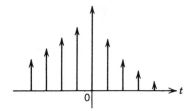

Figure 2.18 Approximation of $x(t)$ with a continuum of impulses.

of N approaches infinity. Thus, we may rewrite equation 2.35 as

$$x(t) \approx \sum_{k=-\infty}^{\infty} x(k\Delta)\delta(t - k\Delta)\,\Delta \qquad (2.36)$$

As $\Delta \to 0$, the summation in equation 2.36 can be replaced by an integral as shown below.

$$x(t) = \int_{-T}^{T} x(\tau)\delta(t - \tau)\,d\tau \qquad (2.37)$$

where we have replaced Δ by $d\tau$ and $k\Delta$ by τ. This is easily understood by the graphical interpretation of the integral in equation 2.37 as the area under $x(\tau)\delta(t - \tau)$, which would approach the area under the right-hand side of equation 2.33 as $\Delta \to 0$. Finally, the complete time function is obtained as $T \to \infty$, so that

$$x(t) = \int_{-\infty}^{\infty} x(\tau)\delta(t - \tau)\,d\tau \qquad (2.38)$$

Consequently, equation 2.38 represents the function $x(t)$ as the summation (integral) of a continuum of impulses, where the strength of each impulse is equal to the value of the function $x(t)$ at that instant. This equation is the result of an interesting property of the impulse function, called the *sifting property*, which states that the integral of the product of a signal and a unit impulse will be equal to the value of the signal at the time when the impulse occurs. This is because the impulse is zero for all other values of time and the area under the impulse itself is one. We shall be referring to this sifting property several times in this book.

The result of equation 2.38 is depicted in Figure 2.18, where the length of each vertical line represents the strength of the corresponding impulse. Although in this figure the spacing between the impulses has been shown as nonzero for clarity, it should actually have been the interval Δ, which is approaching zero.

2.6 IMPULSE RESPONSE OF CONTINUOUS-TIME SYSTEMS

It was shown in the previous section that any continuous-time signal can be represented by a continuum of impulses. Consequently, one can use the superposition theorem to determine the response to any input provided that the response of the system to a unit impulse is known. The same approach can also be used for discrete-time systems, where the input is exactly a sequence of discrete-time impulses. Thus, it is important for us to be able to calculate the response of a linear system to a unit impulse. This will be studied by first looking at a system described by a first-order differential equation. Because of the importance of the impulse response of a system, it is customary to denote this function as $h(t)$.

2.6.1 IMPULSE RESPONSE OF A FIRST-ORDER SYSTEM

Consider a system described by the differential equation

$$\frac{dx}{dt} + ax = u(t) \tag{2.39}$$

We would like to find the response of the system when the input $u(t)$ is the impulse function $\delta(t)$, assuming that $x = 0$ for $t < 0$. When we try to solve this differential equation in the usual manner, we run into the difficulty that the function $\delta(t)$ is zero for all values of $t > 0$, but goes through a large change during an infinitesimal interval of time centered around $t = 0$. The zero initial condition implies that $x = 0$ for $t = 0^-$. At $t = 0$, the impulse is applied so that at $t = 0^+$ the input $u(t)$ is again zero, after having gone through a large change at $t = 0$. Therefore, except for the infinitesimal interval $0^- < t < 0^+$, the right-hand side of equation 2.39 will always be zero, that is, for the case of the impulse input, we may rewrite equation 2.39 as

$$\frac{dx}{dt} + ax = 0, \qquad t > 0^+ \tag{2.40}$$

This homogeneous solution can be obtained easily, provided that the value of $x(0^+)$ is known. Since we do know that $x(0^-)$ is zero, we can determine the value of $x(0^+)$ by integrating both sides of equation 2.39 between $t = 0^-$ and $t = 0^+$, after multiplying both sides by dt, that is,

$$\int_{0^-}^{0^+} dx + \int_{0^-}^{0^+} ax\, dt = \int_{0^-}^{0^+} \delta(t)\, dt \tag{2.41}$$

Let us examine each of the integrals in equation 2.41. The first term is readily evaluated as $[x(0^+) - x(0^-)]$, and we know that $x(0^-) = 0$. The second term on the left-hand side will be zero, since $x(t)$ is known to be finite in this interval. Thus the left-hand side of equation 2.14 will be simply $x(0^+)$. The right-hand side of the integral of the unit impulse and is known to be one. Consequently, we must have $x(0^+) = 1$.

Therefore, the impulse response is given by

$$h(t) = e^{-at}\gamma(t) \tag{2.42}$$

where the unit step function $\gamma(t)$ has been included to emphasize that $x(t)$ is zero for $t < 0$.

The same result will now be derived by using another approach. We recall from Section 1.5.1 in Chapter 1 that the response of this system can be calculated by using equation 1.34, which is reproduced here, with the forcing function replaced with $\delta(t)$, that is,

$$x(t) = e^{-at}x(0^-) + e^{-at} \int_{0^-}^{t} e^{a\tau}\delta(\tau)\,d\tau \qquad (2.43)$$

Note that the lower limit of integration has been changed from 0 in equation 1.34 to 0^- in equation 2.43. This is necessary, since the initial value of x implies its value just before the instant $t = 0$ and also since the impulse function changes rapidly between 0^- and 0^+.

Because of the sifting property of the impulse function, the second term on the right-hand side will be one for any $t > 0$. Since $x(0^-) = 0$, taking the value of the integral into account, we get the impulse response as

$$h(t) = e^{-at}\gamma(t) \qquad (2.44)$$

It is interesting to observe that this is identical to the response of the unforced system with the initial condition $x(0^-)$ set to 1. This will be understood better through the following example.

Example 2.3

Consider the simple R-C network shown in Fig. 2.19, where it will be assumed that the input voltage is the unit impulse $\delta(t)$ and the voltage across the capacitor is initially zero.

Application of Kirchhoff's voltage law gives the differential equation

$$RC\frac{dv}{dt} + v(t) = \delta(t) \qquad (2.45)$$

Before the impulse is applied, the current in the circuit will be zero. Also, the voltage across the capacitor is known to be zero at $t = 0^-$. The application of the impulse voltage will cause the current in the circuit to be an impulse as well, since from equation 2.45

$$i(t) = C\frac{dv}{dt} = \frac{1}{R}[\delta(t) - v(t)] \qquad (2.46)$$

Because $v(t)$ is zero in that infinitesimal interval $0^- < t < 0^+$, it follows that the current $i(t)$ will be an impulse of area $1/R$. Thus, the capacitor will be charged from 0 to $1/RC$ V within this interval. As a result, the voltage across

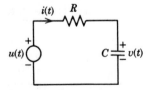

Figure 2.19   R-C network with impulse voltage input.

the capacitor for $t > 0^+$ will be given by

$$v(t) = \left(\frac{1}{RC}\right)e^{-t/RC}\gamma(t) \tag{2.47}$$

∎

In view of the above, we can formulate the rule that the *response of a first-order linear system to a unit impulse is identical to the response of the unforced system with the initial condition set to 1.*

Note that in the above rule it is assumed that the coefficient of the derivative term is equal to one. This can always be made valid by dividing both sides of the equation by that coefficient if it happens to be other than one, as it will certainly be nonzero; otherwise we do not have a first-order differential equation. We now extend our result to a linear system of order n.

2.6.2 IMPULSE RESPONSE OF HIGHER ORDER SYSTEMS

Let us now consider a linear system described by the equation

$$\frac{d^n x}{dt^n} + a_{n-1}\frac{d^{n-1}x}{dt^{n-1}} + \cdots + a_1\frac{dx}{dt} + a_0 x(t) = u(t) \tag{2.48}$$

It is desired to determine the response of the system when the input $u(t)$ is the unit impulse $\delta(t)$ with all the initial conditions set to zero (again using 0^- as the initial time), that is,

$$x(0^-) = 0$$

$$\frac{dx}{dt}(0^-) = 0$$

$$\frac{d^2 x}{dt^2}(0^-) = 0 \tag{2.49}$$

$$\vdots$$

$$\frac{d^{n-1}x}{dt^{n-1}}(0^-) = 0$$

As before, multiplying both sides of equation 2.48 by dt and integrating from 0^- to 0^+, we get

$$\frac{d^{n-1}x}{dt^{n-1}}(0^+) = 1 \tag{2.50}$$

Observe that this is consistent with the rule stated in the previous subsection. In fact, we can generalize it to state that *the response of a linear system of order n, described by equation 2.49, to a unit impulse is identical to the response of the unforced system with the initial condition of the (n − 1)th derivative set to 1, all the other initial conditions being zero.*

Example 2.4

Consider the system described by the following second-order differential equation:

$$\frac{d^2x}{dt^2} + 4\frac{dx}{dt} + 3x = u(t) \tag{2.51}$$

To determine its impulse response, we obtain the solution for the unforced system with the initial conditions that $x(0) = 0$ and the first derivative of x at $t = 0$ has the value of 1. First we note that the roots of the auxiliary polynomial are -1 and -3, so that the complementary function is given by

$$x_c(t) = Ae^{-t} + Be^{-3t} \tag{2.52}$$

The constants A and B must be obtained so that the initial conditions stated above are satisfied. Thus, we obtain the following equations

$$x_c(0) = A + B = 0$$

$$\frac{dx_c}{dt}(0) = -A - 3B = 1 \tag{2.53}$$

Solving these equations, we get $A = 0.5$ and $B = -0.5$. Consequently, the impulse response of this system is given by

$$h(t) = (0.5e^{-t} - 0.5e^{-3t})\gamma(t) \tag{2.54}$$

∎

We now consider the more general case when the system is described by the operator equation

$$D(p)y(t) = N(p)u(t) \tag{2.55}$$

where $D(p)$ is a polynomial of degree n in p and $N(p)$ is a polynomial of degree $(n - 1)$ or less. In such a case, the system function $L(p)$ is said to be a *strictly proper* rational function of p. Following the reasoning used in Section 1.7, we separate the system equation into two parts,

$$D(p)x(t) = u(t) \tag{2.56}$$

and

$$y(t) = N(p)x(t) \tag{2.57}$$

Therefore, we can first determine the impulse response corresponding to equation 2.56 and then perform the operation $N(p)$ on it to get the impulse response of the system described by equation 2.57.

Example 2.5

Consider the system described by the following second-order differential equation:

$$\frac{d^2y}{dt^2} + 4\frac{dy}{dt} + 3y = 2\frac{du}{dt} + 3u(t) \tag{2.58}$$

A comparison with Example 2.4 indicates that (with the notation used above)

$$x(t) = (0.5e^{-t} - 0.5e^{-3t})\gamma(t) \tag{2.59}$$

and the impulse response will be given by

$$h(t) = 2\frac{dx}{dt} + 3x$$

$$= (0.5e^{-t} + 1.5e^{-3t})\gamma(t) \tag{2.60}$$

∎

In the cases considered above, it was assumed that the degree of $N(p)$ is less than that of $D(p)$, that is, the system function $L(p)$ is a strictly proper rational function of p. If this is not the case, then the impulse response will contain the impulse function and its derivatives, as determined by performing the operation of long division of $N(p)$ by $D(p)$. This will be shown through the following example.

Example 2.6

Consider the system described by the equation

$$\frac{dx}{dt} + 3x(t) = \frac{du}{dt} + 4u(t) \tag{2.61}$$

In this instance the system operator may be written as

$$L(p) = \frac{p+4}{p+3} = 1 + \frac{1}{p+3} \tag{2.62}$$

Application of the superposition theorem will lead to the following impulse response:

$$h(t) = \delta(t) + e^{-3t} \tag{2.63}$$

In other words, we have added the impulse responses of the two parts of the system operator shown on the right-hand side of equation 2.62. This will be evident from Figure 2.20, which shows a scheme for direct realization of the system operator given by equation 2.63. The impulse on the right-hand side of equation 2.63 is caused by the direct path from the input to the output, as shown in Figure 2.20. ∎

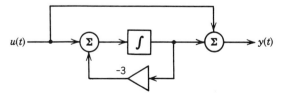

Figure 2.20 Direct realization of $L(p)$ given by equation 2.62.

Drill Problem 2.2

Determine the impulse response of the first-order system described by the differential equation

$$\frac{dx}{dt} + 4x = u(t) \qquad Answer: e^{-4t}$$

Drill Problem 2.3

Determine the impulse response of the second-order system described by the following differential equation:

$$\frac{d^2x}{dt^2} + 4\frac{dx}{dt} + 13x = u(t)$$

Answer: $\frac{1}{3}e^{-2t}\sin 3t$

Drill Problem 2.4

Repeat Drill Problem 2.3 for the following differential equation:

$$\frac{d^2x}{dt^2} + 4\frac{dx}{dt} + 13x = \frac{du}{dt} + 5u(t)$$

Answer: $e^{-2t}(\cos 3t + \sin 3t)$

Drill Problem 2.5

A linear system is described by the following operational equation. Determine its impulse response.

$$(p^2 + 6p + 25)x(t) = (2p^2 + 14p + 60)u(t)$$

Answer: $2\delta(t) + e^{-3t}(2\cos 4t + \sin 4t)$

2.7 IMPULSE RESPONSE SEQUENCE FOR DISCRETE-TIME SYSTEMS

We now consider the response of a discrete-time system to a unit impulse. Since this will also be a discrete-time function, it will be called the impulse response sequence and will be denoted as $h(k)$. Consider first a discrete-time system described by the difference equation

$$y(k) + a_1y(k-1) + a_2y(k-2) + \cdots + a_ny(k-n) = u(k) \quad (2.64)$$

where $u(k)$ is the impulse function $\delta(k)$.

By the definition given in equation 2.28, $\delta(k)$ is equal to 0 for $k \neq 0$ and 1 for $k = 0$. Furthermore, for a causal system, $h(k)$ must be zero for $k < 0$.

Since the sequence $h(k)$ must satisfy equation 2.64 for all k, we can write

$$h(k) + a_1 h(k-1) + a_2 h(k-2) + \cdots + a_n h(k-n) = \delta(k)$$

As all the terms on the left-hand side, except the first, will be zero for $k = 0$, the above equation simplifies to

$$h(0) = 1 \qquad (2.65)$$

Similarly, for $k = 1$, all terms except the first two are zero and we have

$$h(1) + a_1 h(0) = 0 \qquad (2.66)$$

Proceeding in this manner, we can obtain n linear equations through which we easily determine all the initial conditions $h(0), h(1), \ldots, h(n-1)$. We now have to obtain the general expression for $h(k)$.

In view of the fact that $\delta(k)$ is nonzero only for $k = 0$, $h(k)$ will be the unforced response of the system described by equation 2.63, which can be calculated as the complementary solution for the difference equation. The n arbitrary constants can then be calculated to satisfy the initial conditions, $h(0), h(1), h(2), \ldots, h(n-1)$ obtained above.

Example 2.7

We use the procedure described above to determine the impulse response sequence for the system described by the difference equation

$$y(k) - 2y(k-1) + 1.31y(k-2) - 0.28y(k-3) = u(k) \qquad (2.67)$$

The first step will be to find the complementary solution. The roots of the auxiliary polynomial

$$q^3 - 2q^2 + 1.31q - 0.28 = 0 \qquad (2.68)$$

are found to be 0.5, 0.7, and 0.8. Hence, the complementary solution is

$$y_c(k) = A(0.5)^k + B(0.7)^k + C(0.8)^k \qquad (2.69)$$

To evaluate the constants in the impulse response sequence, we need the initial conditions. Following the reasoning given earlier in this section, we get

$$h(0) = 1$$
$$h(1) - 2h(0) = 0$$
$$h(2) - 2h(1) + 1.31h(0) = 0 \qquad (2.70)$$

Solving these we obtain, $h(0) = 1$, $h(1) = 2$, and $h(2) = 2.69$. We can now evaluate A, B, and C by substituting these values in equation 2.69. The following equations are obtained:

$$A + B + C = 1$$
$$0.5A + 0.7B + 0.8C = 2$$
$$0.25A + 0.49B + 0.64C = 2.69 \qquad (2.71)$$

Finally, solving the simultaneous equations 2.71, we get the values of A, B, and C as $25/6$, $-49/2$, and $64/3$, respectively. The resulting impulse response sequence is given by

$$h(k) = \frac{25}{6}(0.5)^k - \frac{49}{2}(0.7)^k + \frac{64}{3}(0.8)^k \qquad (2.72)$$

∎

The following example will show how to use this method for the more general case when the right-hand side of the difference equation includes some operations on the input sequence.

Example 2.8

Let us consider the discrete-time system described by the difference equation

$$y(k) - 2y(k - 1) + 1.31(k - 2) - 0.28y(k - 3) = u(k) + 3u(k - 2) \qquad (2.73)$$

The left-hand side of equation 2.73 is identical to that of equation 2.67 in Example 2.7, but the right-hand side contains two terms. The simplest way to obtain the impulse response sequence in this instance is to use superposition, since equation 2.73 implies that the input to the system is $\delta(k) + 3\delta(k - 2)$ instead of simply $\delta(k)$. We have already found the effect of application of the impulse $\delta(k)$ in Example 2.7. In adding the effect of the two impulses, we must be careful to note that, because of causality, the effect of the impulse $\delta(k - 2)$ is not felt until $k = 2$. As a result, we obtain

$$h(k) = \begin{cases} \dfrac{25}{6}(0.5)^k - \dfrac{49}{2}(0.7)^k + \dfrac{64}{3}(0.8)^k & k = 0, 1 \\ \dfrac{325}{6}(0.5)^k - \dfrac{349}{2}(0.7)^k + \dfrac{364}{3}(0.8)^k & k > 1 \end{cases} \qquad (2.74)$$

∎

The application of superposition theorem in this example leads us to the powerful concept of convolution. This will be discussed in the next two sections.

Drill Problem 2.6

Determine the impulse response sequence for the linear difference equation given below:

$$y(k) - 0.8y(k - 1) + 0.15y(k - 2) = u(k)$$

Answer: $2.5(0.5)^k - 1.5(0.3)^k$

2.8 CONVOLUTION SUM FOR DISCRETE-TIME SYSTEMS

An important problem in system theory is to determine the response of a system to a given input function that cannot be expressed in terms of standard functions like exponentials and sinusoids. There may even be instances where it may not be possible to write an analytical expression for the input function. In this and the following section, we study an approach that enables us to obtain the response of the system to any given arbitrary excitation, if we know its response to either a unit impulse or a unit step input. This result, called the convolution theorem, is a consequence of the application of the principle of superposition to linear systems. It may be noted that although the theorem is usually expressed in terms of the impulse response of the system, it can easily be related to the step response, which can be obtained experimentally without much difficulty.

Recall that the superposition theorem states that the zero-state response of a linear system to the sum of two or more inputs is equal to the sum of the responses of the system to each input acting alone. This result is very useful whenever a given input can be expressed as the sum of elementary functions the responses to which are known. First, we study discrete-time systems where the system input is a sequence of impulses. This will be extended in the next section to continuous-time systems where we utilize the idea of representing an arbitrary function by a continuum of impulses.

Consider a discrete-time system with the impulse response sequence given by $h(k)$. For convenience, we denote the sequence as

$$\{h_0, h_1, h_2, \ldots, h_k, h_{k+1}, \ldots\}$$

where h_i represents $h(i)$.

Our object is to determine the output sequence of the system for the input sequence

$$\{u_0, u_1, u_2, \ldots, u_k, u_{k+1}, \ldots\}$$

where u_i represents $u(i)$. First we note that the input sequence can be expressed as a sequence of impulses, of strength (or area) u_i, as below

$$u(k) = \sum_{i=0}^{\infty} u_i \delta(k - i) \tag{2.75}$$

Consequently, we can use the superposition property to determine the total output at the kth sampling instant as the sum of the responses to each of the individual impulses that have occurred up to that instant. Thus, we obtain

$$y_k = u_0 h_k + u_1 h_{k-1} + \cdots + u_k h_0 \tag{2.76}$$

Equation 2.76 is called the convolution sum. Note that the first term on the right-hand side is the contribution of the impulse that occurred at $i = 0$ and is the product of u_0 and h_k. Similarly, the second term is the effect of the impulse that occurred at $i = 1$ and is the product of u_1 and h_{k-1}, and so on. It can be written in a more compact form as

$$y_k = \sum_{i=0}^{k} u_k h_{k-i} \tag{2.77}$$

Note that for a causal system, h_i is zero for $i < 0$. Therefore, we can change the upper limit of the summation to ∞ without affecting the result. Furthermore, it is not necessary that the input sequence be also causal, that is, u_i may not be zero for $i < 0$. In such cases we must change the lower limit from 0 to $-\infty$. Accordingly, for the general case, we obtain

$$y_k = \sum_{i=-\infty}^{\infty} u_i h_{k-i} \tag{2.78}$$

Equations 2.77 and 2.78 are known as the convolution sum. It is often convenient to denote this as

$$y(k) = h(k) * u(k) \tag{2.79}$$

which is read as $y(k)$ equals $h(k)$ convolved with $u(k)$. It should be noted that because of the *symmetry* of these equations, we may write

$$h(k) * u(k) = u(k) * h(k) \tag{2.80}$$

that is, *the convolution operation is commutative*. This is obvious from the fact that equation 2.76 could also have been written in the following form instead of as in equation 2.77:

$$y_k = \sum_{i=0}^{k} h_i u_{k-i} \tag{2.81}$$

Similarly, the arguments of $h(\cdot)$ and $u(\cdot)$ can be interchanged in equation 2.78 without affecting the overall expression for the output sequence.

Example 2.9

The impulse response sequence of a given discrete-time system is

$$\begin{aligned} h(k) &= 0.5^k \\ &= \{1, 0.5, 0.25, 0.125, 0.0625, 0.03125, \dots\} \end{aligned} \tag{2.82}$$

It is required to find the output sequence if the input sequence is given by

$$u(k) = \{1, 0, -1, 1, 1, 0\} \tag{2.83}$$

In this case, since we have an input sequence of finite length, we set the initial input at $k = 0$. Hence, we can apply equation 2.76 to obtain the output sequence for various values of k. The following values are obtained:

$$y(0) = h(0)u(0) = 1$$
$$y(1) = h(0)u(1) + h(1)u(0) = 0.5$$
$$y(2) = h(0)u(2) + h(1)u(1) + h(2)u(0) = -0.75$$
$$y(3) = h(0)u(3) + h(1)u(2) + h(2)u(1) + h(3)u(0) = 0.625$$

and so on. ∎

The importance of the convolution sum is obvious immediately, because it allows us to determine the response to any arbitrary input sequence if we

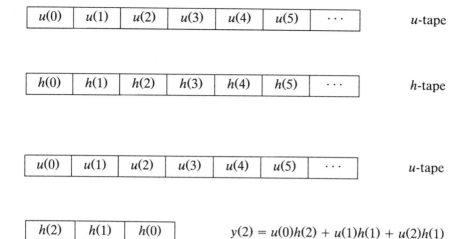

| $u(0)$ | $u(1)$ | $u(2)$ | $u(3)$ | $u(4)$ | $u(5)$ | $\cdots$ | u-tape |

| $h(0)$ | $h(1)$ | $h(2)$ | $h(3)$ | $h(4)$ | $h(5)$ | $\cdots$ | h-tape |

| $u(0)$ | $u(1)$ | $u(2)$ | $u(3)$ | $u(4)$ | $u(5)$ | $\cdots$ | u-tape |

| $h(2)$ | $h(1)$ | $h(0)$ | $y(2) = u(0)h(2) + u(1)h(1) + u(2)h(1)$ |

Figure 2.21 Sliding-tape algorithm of convolution sum. (*a*) The data tapes. (*b*) The h-tape folded at $i = 2$.

know the response of the system to a unit impulse. A better understanding of convolution is therefore very important, especially for the most common situation when both the input and the system are causal. One computational procedure, which gives a good intuitive grasp of the convolution operation, will now be described. Following Lathi,* we present the "sliding-strip" method in Figure 2.21.

1. Let each of the sequences $h(k)$ and $u(k)$ be listed on a tape, as shown in Figure 2.21*a*.

2. Fold the h-tape and align the entry $h(0)$ with $u(i)$, as shown in Figure 2.14*b* for $i = 2$, to determine the output $y(i)$.

3. The output $y(i)$ is then obtained by multiplying the aligned elements of the tape and adding the results.

The result is identical to equation 2.76 for $k = 2$.

Another algorithm, which is more convenient, is based on arranging the data in an array, following Gabel and Roberts.†

---

*See *Signals, Systems and Controls* by B. P. Lathi (New York: Intext Educational Publishers, 1974), Chapter 2, pp. 73–74.

†See *Signals and Linear Systems* by Robert A. Gabel and Richard A. Roberts (New York: John Wiley & Sons, 3rd ed., 1987), pp. 51–53.

	$u(0)$	$u(1)$	$u(2)$	$u(3)$	$u(4)$
$h(0)$	$h(0)u(0)$	$h(0)u(1)$	$h(0)u(2)$	$h(0)u(3)$	$h(0)u(4)$
$h(1)$	$h(1)u(0)$	$h(1)u(1)$	$h(1)u(2)$	$h(1)u(3)$	$h(1)u(4)$
$h(2)$	$h(2)u(0)$	$h(2)u(1)$	$h(2)u(2)$	$h(2)u(3)$	$h(2)u(4)$
$h(3)$	$h(3)u(0)$	$h(3)u(1)$	$h(3)u(2)$	$h(3)u(3)$	$h(3)u(4)$
$h(4)$	$h(4)u(0)$	$h(4)u(1)$	$h(4)u(2)$	$h(4)u(3)$	$h(4)u(4)$

Figure 2.22 The array algorithm.

The input sequence and the impulse response sequence are arranged in horizontal and vertical arrays, respectively, as shown in Figure 2.22. This is followed by multiplying each of the elements in the various rows and columns to get a table as shown in the figure.

To obtain $y(k)$ for any value of k, we add the terms on a diagonal of the matrix starting from the entry to the right of the corresponding value of $h(k)$ and proceeding toward the right and top. For instance, to find $y(3)$, we start with the entry $h(3)u(0)$ and proceed along the diagonal that contains the elements $h(2)u(1)$, $h(1)u(2)$, and $h(0)u(3)$. It is easily verified that the sum of these elements is, in fact, $y(3)$.

Example 2.10

We reconsider Example 2.9 and work it out by using the array algorithm. From the values of $u(k)$ and $h(k)$ given there, we obtain the following matrix:

	1.0	0.0	-1.0	1.0	1.0	0.0
1.0000	1.000	0.000	-1.000	1.000	1.000	0.000
0.500	0.500	0.000	-0.500	0.500	0.500	0.000
0.250	0.250	0.000	-0.250	0.250	0.250	0.000
0.125	0.125	0.000	-0.125	0.125	0.125	0.000
0.0625	0.0625	0.000	-0.0625	0.0625	0.0625	0.000
0.03125	0.500	0.000	-0.500	0.500	0.500	0.000

Figure 2.23 Array for Example 2.10.

From the array shown in Figure 2.23, we can obtain the following values of the output sequence:

$$y(0) = 1.000$$

$$y(1) = 0.500 + 0.000 = 0.500$$

$$y(2) = 0.250 + 0.000 - 1.000 = -0.750$$

$$y(3) = 0.125 + 0.000 - 0.500 + 1.000 = 0.625$$

and so on.

These values are identical to those calculated in Example 2.9. ∎

Drill Problem 2.7

The impulse response sequence $h(k)$ of a linear discrete-time system is nonzero only for $0 \le k \le 5$ and is given in the following table:

k	0	1	2	3	4	5
$h(k)$	5	3	1	0	−1	−1

Determine its response to the input sequence

$$u(k) = 1$$

Answer: $5, 8, 9, 9, 8, 7, 7, 7, 7, 7, 7, \ldots$

Drill Problem 2.8

Repeat Drill Problem 2.7 for the following input sequence:

k	0	1	2	3	4	5	6	7	8
$u(k)$	1	1	−1	−1	0	0	0	0	0

Answer: $5, 8, -1, -7, -5, -2, -3, 0, 2, 1, 0, 0, 0, \ldots$

2.9 CONVOLUTION INTEGRAL FOR CONTINUOUS-TIME SYSTEMS

We now extend the concept of convolution to continuous-time systems. In this instance we do not have a sequence of impulses. However, in view of our discussion in Section 2.5, a continuous-time signal $u(t)$ can be approximated by a sum of impulses as shown in equation 2.36, which is repeated below, with $x(t)$ replaced by $u(t)$.

$$u(t) \approx \sum_{k=-\infty}^{\infty} u(k\Delta)\delta(t - k\Delta)\,\Delta \qquad (2.36)$$

This approximation improves as $\Delta \to 0$, and in the limit we obtain the integral

$$u(t) = \int_{-\infty}^{\infty} u(\tau)\delta(t - \tau)\,d\tau \tag{2.84}$$

Applying the superposition theorem, the following approximation is obtained for $y(t)$ from equation 2.36:

$$y(t) \approx \sum_{k=-\infty}^{\infty} u(k\Delta)h(t - k\Delta)\,\Delta \tag{2.85}$$

Equation 2.85 states that the total response $y(t)$ is the sum of responses to the various impulses $u(k\Delta)\delta(t - k\Delta)$. In the limit, as $\Delta \to 0$, the convolution sum expressed in equation 2.85 becomes the convolution integral as we replace Δ with $d\tau$, $k\Delta$ with τ, and $u(k\Delta)\delta(\tau - k\Delta)$ with $u(\tau)$. Consequently, the output $y(t)$ is given by

$$y(t) = \int_{-\infty}^{\infty} u(\tau)h(t - \tau)\,d\tau \tag{2.86}$$

or, symbolically,

$$y(t) = u(t) * h(t) = h(t) * u(t) \tag{2.87}$$

It is important to note the simplifications that are introduced if both the input $u(t)$ and the impulse response $h(t)$ are causal. As a result of the former, the lower limit of the integral can be changed to 0 from $-\infty$, since $u(\tau)$ will be zero for negative τ. Similarly, causality of the impulse response can be utilized to change the upper limit of the integral in equation 2.86 to t from ∞, since $h(t - \tau)$ will be zero for $\tau > t$. This fact is especially useful in giving a graphical interpretation to convolution in a manner similar to that used for the discrete-time case.

Example 2.11

We use the convolution integral to find the response of the system given in Example 2.4 to the causal input

$$u(t) = 3e^{-2t}\gamma(t) \tag{2.88}$$

By using the impulse response of the system evaluated in Example 2.4 and given in equation 2.54, we get the output as

$$y(t) = \int_{0}^{t} 3e^{-2\tau}[0.5e^{(\tau - t)} - 0.5e^{(3\tau - 3t)}]\,d\tau \tag{2.89}$$

where the limits of integration emphasize the causal nature of the input and the impulse response.

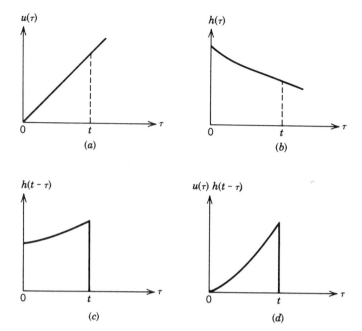

Figure 2.24 Graphical interpretation of convolution. (a) The input. (b) The impulse response. (c) The folded and shifted impulse response. (d) The product of (a) and (c).

Evaluating the integral we get

$$y(t) = (1.5e^{-t} - 3e^{-2t} + 1.5e^{-3t})\gamma(t) \qquad (2.90)$$

We now give a graphical interpretation to the convolution integral. The integrand in equation 2.86 is the product of two functions, $u(\tau)$ and $h(t - \tau)$. To obtain the second term, first we fold back the impulse response $h(\tau)$ on the τ-axis and then shift it to the right to the value of t at which the output is desired. Then we multiply the functions $u(\tau)$ and the folded (and shifted) impulse response $h(t - \tau)$ and integrate the product over the period 0 to t. Note that both the convolution sum and the convolution integral require

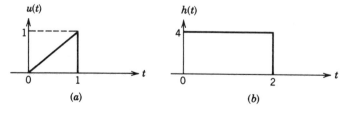

Figure 2.25 Input and impulse response for Example 1.2. (a) Input. (b) Impulse response.

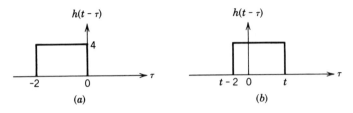

Figure 2.26   Folding and shifting the impulse response. (a) Response folded at 0. (b) Folded response shifted by t.

multiplication of the forcing function with the folded impulse response, but summation in the former is replaced with integration in the latter.

This graphical interpretation of convolution makes it possible to visualize the process much better, as illustrated in Figure 2.24.

Figure 2.24a shows the input $u(\tau)$, and Figure 2.24b shows the impulse response $h(\tau)$. Figure 2.24c shows the function $h(t - \tau)$ folded at 0 and shifted by t. Figure 2.24d depicts the product of the functions shown in (a) and (c). Note that for a causal system and a causal input, this product must be zero for $\tau < 0$ and for $\tau < t$. The output $y(t)$ is then obtained by integrating the product over the interval 0 to t. Evidently, if either of the functions is zero over any subinterval between 0 and t, it does not contribute to the integral in the evaluation of $y(t)$.   ■

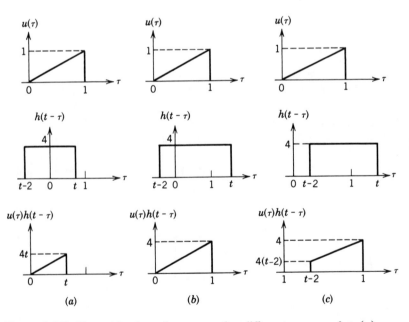

Figure 2.27   Determination of response for different ranges of t. (a) $0 \le t \le 1$. (b) $1 \le t \le 2$. (c) $2 \le t \le 3$.

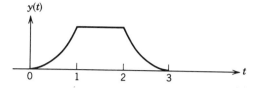

Figure 2.28 Response for Example 2.21.

Example 2.12

To further illustrate graphical convolution, let us consider the situation when $u(t)$ and $h(t)$ are as shown in Figure 2.25.

The folded function $h(t - \tau)$ is shown in Figure 2.26a for the case when $t = 0$. As t is increased, the rectangle representing the folded function moves to the right, as shown in Figure 2.26b.

To determine the response $y(t)$ for any given t, we must multiply the functions $u(\tau)$ and $h(t - \tau)$ and integrate the product between the limits 0 and t. For this example, the integration can be carried out by evaluating the area under the curve representing the product from 0 to t. Clearly, the product $u(\tau)h(t - \tau)$ is zero for all τ for $t \le 0$ and for $t \ge 3$. Therefore, we need consider only the following cases: (i) $0 \le t \le 1$, (ii) $1 \le t \le 2$, and (iii) $2 \le t \le 3$. These are shown in Figures 2.27a, 2.27b, and 2.27c, respectively. For Figure 2.27a and 2.27b the response $y(t)$ is determined as the area of a triangle, while for Figure 2.27c, we have to evaluate the area of a trapezoid. Calculations of these areas from the three parts of Figure 2.27 yields the following expressions:

$$y(t) = \begin{cases} 2t^2 & 0 \le t \le 1 \\ 2 & 1 \le t \le 2 \\ 2(t - 1)(3 - t) & 2 \le t \le 3 \end{cases} \qquad (2.91)$$

A plot of the resulting response is shown in Figure 2.28. ∎

Drill Problem 2.9

The impulse response of a system is given by

$$h(t) = 3e^{-4t} \cos 3t \; \gamma(t)$$

Use the convolution integral to determine its response to the input

$$u(t) = \gamma(t)$$

Answer: $(0.48 - 0.48e^{-4t} \cos 3t + 2.08e^{-4t} \sin 3t) \; \gamma(t)$

2.10 DECONVOLUTION

As we pointed out in the two previous sections, the convolution sum is represented by the equation

$$u(k) * h(k) = y(k) \qquad (2.92)$$

whereas the convolution integral is represented as

$$u(t) * h(t) = y(t) \qquad (2.93)$$

In both instances, the objective is to determine the output of the system, given its impulse response and the input. Often there are situations where we need to go the other way, that is, given the input and the output, we need to find the impulse response, or given the output and the impulse response, we need to find the input. This is called *deconvolution, which may be regarded as the inverse of convolution.* Note that owing to the commutative nature of convolution, these two problems are not different as far as the mathematical procedure is concerned.

There are many applications of deconvolution. For instance, one way to obtain a model for a linear system is to measure its output for a given input. From these input–output data, we can use deconvolution to determine the impulse response of the system and, hence, the system model. This is called the problem of *system identification.* The other problem of determining the input for given impulse response and output is very important for *control* systems, where the objective is to force the system to have a specified output by applying the input that will cause that output. Both of these are useful practical applications.

Deconvolution can be carried out very conveniently for discrete-time systems. This is evident if we write the equations for the output of a causal system to a causal input, assuming that the initial conditions are zero. From the convolution sum discussed in Section 2.8, we obtain the following set of equations relating the input and output sequences of the system:

$$y(0) = h(0)u(0)$$

$$y(1) = h(1)u(0) + h(0)u(1)$$

$$y(2) = h(2)u(0) + h(1)u(1) + h(0)u(2)$$

$$y(3) = h(3)u(0) + h(2)u(1) + h(1)u(2) + h(0)u(3)$$

$$\vdots \qquad (2.94)$$

Let us first consider the problem of identification, that is, that of determining the impulse response sequence $h(k)$, given the input and output sequences. Because of their special form, equations 2.94 are readily solved to obtain the following expressions for the sequence $h(k)$:

$$h(0) = \frac{y(0)}{u(0)}$$

$$h(1) = \frac{y(1) - h(0)u(1)}{u(0)}$$

$$h(2) = \frac{y(2) - h(1)u(1) - h(0)u(2)}{u(0)}$$

$$h(3) = \frac{y(3) - h(2)u(1) - h(1)u(2) - h(0)u(3)}{u(0)}$$

$$\vdots \qquad\qquad\qquad\qquad (2.95)$$

Note that if we were to write equations 2.94 by using the matrix notation, that is, in the form $y = Uh$, then U will be a lower triangular matrix.

For the control problem, we need to solve for $u(k)$, given the impulse response and output sequences. Utilizing the symmetry of the convolution sum, we may simply interchange $u(i)$ and $h(i)$ in equations 2.95. The resulting equations are given below.

$$u(0) = \frac{y(0)}{h(0)}$$

$$u(1) = \frac{y(1) - u(0)h(1)}{h(0)}$$

$$u(2) = \frac{y(2) - u(1)h(1) - u(0)h(2)}{h(0)}$$

$$u(3) = \frac{y(3) - u(2)h(1) - u(1)h(2) - u(0)h(3)}{h(0)}$$

$$\vdots \qquad\qquad\qquad\qquad (2.96)$$

The following example will illustrate the use of deconvolution.

Example 2.13

The input and output sequences for a linear system are given below. It is required to determine the impulse response sequence.

$$u(0) = 1, \quad u(1) = 0, \quad u(2) = -1, \quad u(3) = 1, \quad u(4) = 1, \quad u(5) = 0$$

$$y(0) = 1, \quad y(1) = 0.5, \quad y(2) = -0.75, \quad y(3) = 0.625, \quad y(4) = 1.3125$$

Using equation 2.95, the impulse response sequence is obtained as below:

$$h(0) = \frac{1}{1} = 1$$

$$h(1) = \frac{(0.5 - 1 \times 0)}{1} = 0.5$$

$$h(2) = \frac{[-0.75 - 0.5 \times 0 - 1 \times (-1)]}{1} = 0.25$$

$$h(3) = \frac{[0.625 - 0.25 \times 0 - 0.5 \times (-1) - 1 \times 0]}{1} = 0.125$$

$$h(4) = \frac{[1.3125 - 0.125 \times 0 - 0.25 \times (-1) - 0.5 \times 1 - 1 \times 1]}{1} = 0.0625$$

∎

Drill Problem 2.10

The impulse response sequence $h(k)$ of a linear discrete-time system is nonzero only for $0 \le k \le 5$ and is given in the following table:

k	0	1	2	3	4	5
$h(k)$	5	3	1	0	-1	-1

Determine the input sequence that produces the following output sequence under zero initial conditions:

k	0	1	2	3	4	5	6	7
$y(k)$	5	8	9	9	8	7	7	7

Answer: $u(k) = 1$.

2.11 RELATION BETWEEN IMPULSE RESPONSE AND RESPONSE TO A UNIT STEP

The practical usefulness of convolution methods may appear to be limited because it is not convenient to determine the response of a system to a unit impulse experimentally. Not only is it not possible to generate a true impulse, but it is also undesirable to apply an impulse to an actual system. For example, applying an impulse voltage function to an electrical circuit may cause some serious problems.

On the other hand, it is a lot easier to apply an input that will be a close approximation to a unit step. Therefore, it would be desirable to find some way to relate the step response of a linear system to its impulse response. This is done readily by applying the convolution theorem. We shall derive these useful relationships for both continuous-time and discrete-time systems.

2.11.1   STEP AND IMPULSE RESPONSES OF CONTINUOUS-TIME SYSTEMS

Consider a linear continuous-time system with impulse response given by $h(t)$. Also, let the response of the same system to a unit step input be denoted by $g(t)$. Then, using convolution, we get

$$g(t) = \int_{-\infty}^{\infty} \gamma(\tau)h(t - \tau)\, d\tau \qquad (2.97)$$

where $\gamma(t)$ represents the unit step. Owing to the causal nature of the input and the impulse response, we can replace the lower limit by 0 and the upper limit by t. Furthermore, because of the commutative nature of convolution, we can interchange the roles of the input and the impulse response. Consequently, equation 2.97 can be modified as

$$g(t) = \int_0^t h(\tau)\gamma(t - \tau)\, d\tau \qquad (2.98)$$

Finally, since between the limits of integration, that is, for $0 \le \tau \le t$, the function $\gamma(t - \tau)$ is equal to 1, we can simplify equation 2.98 to

$$g(t) = \int_0^t h(\tau)\, d\tau \qquad (2.99)$$

It is evident from equation 2.99 that the *response of a system to unit step at a particular instant of time* t, is the integral of its response to a unit impulse evaluated between 0 and t. This integral is often called the *running integral*. Alternatively, it may be said that the impulse response can be obtained by differentiating the step response with respect to time. Thus we have a practical way of determining the impulse response of a system experimentally from its response to a unit step. This important result is intuitively obvious if we recall that the unit impulse is the derivative of the unit step.

The input–output relationship can also be expressed directly in terms of the step response $g(t)$. Let us first rewrite the convolution integral in the form

$$y(t) = \int_{-\infty}^{\infty} h(\tau)u(t - \tau)\, d\tau \qquad (2.100)$$

and then integrate it by parts, using the relationship in equation 2.99. The following equation is obtained:

$$y(t) = g(\tau)u(t - \tau)\Big|_{-\infty}^{\infty} - \int_{-\infty}^{\infty} g(\tau)\frac{du(t - \tau)}{d\tau}\, d\tau \qquad (2.101)$$

If we assume that both the input and the system are causal, then the first term vanishes, since $g(-\infty) = 0$ and $u(t - \tau) = 0$ for $\tau > t$. The following result is then obtained:

$$y(t) = -\int_{-\infty}^{\infty} g(\tau)\frac{du(t-\tau)}{d\tau}\, d\tau \qquad (2.102)$$

By interchange of variables, this may also be written as

$$y(t) = \int_{-\infty}^{\infty} g(t-\tau)\frac{du(\tau)}{d\tau}\, d\tau \qquad (2.103)$$

These equations are useful, since they enable us to obtain the output of the system to any input if its response to a unit step input is known. As stated earlier, the step response can be measured experimentally without much difficulty. In practice, it may be more convenient to use equation 2.103 except when the input function has jump discontinuities for some values of t. In such cases, differentiation of the input will give rise to impulses. This is not a problem if one recalls the sifting property of the impulse, first shown in Section 2.5.

$$\int_{-\infty}^{\infty} f(\tau)\delta(t-\tau)\, d\tau = f(t) \qquad (2.104)$$

Therefore, the corresponding integral can easily be evaluated for this case.

2.11.2 STEP AND IMPULSE RESPONSES OF DISCRETE-TIME SYSTEMS

As pointed out in Section 2.2.2, the discrete-time equivalent of the step input is the step sequence $\gamma(k) = 1$ for all $k \geq 0$. Denoting the impulse response sequence of such a system by $h(k)$ and the step response by $g(k)$, and applying the convolution theorem, we obtain

$$g(k) = \gamma(0)h(k) + \gamma(1)h(k-1) + \cdots + \gamma(k)h(0)$$

$$= \sum_{i=0}^{k} h(i) \qquad (2.105)$$

since $\gamma(i) = 1$ for all $i \geq 0$.

Equation 2.105 is the discrete-time equivalent of equation 2.99 that was derived for continuous-time systems. Note that the operation of integration for $0 \leq \tau \leq t$ has been replaced by the operation of summation for $0 \leq i \leq k$, which is called the *running sum*.

Similarly, just as the impulse response of a continuous-time system can be obtained by differentiating the response to a unit step, for a discrete-time system, the impulse response sequence can be determined by taking successive differences of the step response sequence.

Example 2.14

The impulse response sequence of a discrete-time system is given by

$$h(k) = 10(0.8)^k$$

We use equation 2.91 to determine the step response sequence. This leads to

$$g(k) = \sum_{i=0}^{k} 10(0.8)^i$$

$$= 10 \frac{1 - 0.8^{k+1}}{1 - 0.8}$$

$$= 50(1 - 0.8^{k+1}) = 50 - 40(0.8)^k \quad \blacksquare$$

Drill Problem 2.11

The response of a system to a unit step is given by

$$g(t) = (0.48 - 0.48e^{-4t}\cos 3t + 0.36e^{-4t}\sin 3t)\gamma(t)$$

Determine its impulse response.

Answer: $h(t) = 3e^{-4t}\cos 3t$

2.12 SUMMARY

In this chapter we studied signals associated with systems. In fact, a system may be looked on as a device that processes an input signal to produce an output signal. Signals can be classified in many ways. They can be continuous-time or discrete-time, periodic or aperiodic, deterministic or random, power or energy signals. Singularity functions form an important class of signals. The unit step, ramp, and impulse functions are some examples of singularity functions. In this chapter, we also had an introduction to sampling and the approximation of a continuous-time signal by a discrete-time signal. The related ideas of analog-to-digital conversion and quantization were discussed briefly. This was followed by a discussion of the representation of continuous-time signal by a continuum of impulses. Determination of the impulse response of a continuous-time as well as a discrete-time system was then presented. This led to the study of the convolution sum and the convolution integral for determining the response of the system to any arbitrary input from a knowledge of its impulse response. The concept of deconvolution was introduced and discussed in detail for discrete-time systems. Finally, the relation between the impulse response of a system and its response to a unit step was derived for continuous-time as well as discrete-time systems. This relationship is especially useful since, in practice, it is much easier to approximate a step input and determine the response of a system to this input experimentally.

2.13 PROBLEMS

2.1 Express each of the signals shown in Figure 2.29 in terms of singularity functions.

2.2 Let $x_1(t)$ and $x_2(t)$ be two periodic signals, with periods T_1 and T_2, respectively.
   (a) Under what circumstances will the sum of these two signals be periodic and what will be the period of the resulting signal if it is periodic?
   (b) Under what circumstances will the product of these two signals be periodic and what will be the period of the resulting signal if it is periodic?

2.3 Evaluate the following integrals
   (a) $\int_{-\infty}^{\infty} e^{10t}\delta(t - 5)\,dt$ (b) $\int_{0}^{\infty} e^{-2t}\cos 3t\,dt$
   (c) $\int_{-\infty}^{\infty} \cos 4t\,\delta(t - 2)\,dt$ (d) $\int_{-\infty}^{\infty} e^{-2t}\cos 3t\,\gamma(t - 1)\,dt$

2.4 Determine the voltage $v(t)$ across the capacitor in the network shown in Figure 2.30 if the input is an impulse applied at $t = 0$. Assume that the voltage across the capacitor was zero prior to the application of the impulse.

2.5 Determine the voltage $v(t)$ across the capacitor in the network shown in Figure 2.31, if the input $u(t)$ is an impulse of voltage applied at $t = 0$. Assume that initially the voltage across the capacitor and the current through the inductor are zero.

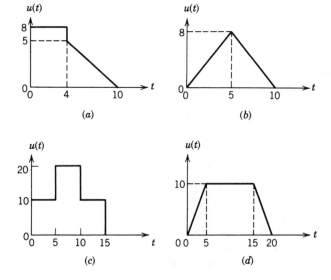

Figure 2.29 Signals for Problem 2.21.

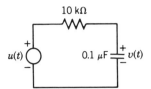

Figure 2.30   R-C network with impulse voltage input.

2.6   Determine the impulse response of each of the following continuous-time systems, given their system operator $L(p)$:

(a) $L(p) = \dfrac{1}{p^2 + 5p + 6}$ (b) $L(p) = \dfrac{2p + 3}{p^2 + 5p + 6}$

(c) $L(p) = \dfrac{1}{p^2 + 4p + 8}$ (d) $L(p) = \dfrac{2p + 3}{p^2 + 4p + 8}$

(e) $L(p) = \dfrac{1}{p^2 + 4p + 4}$ (f) $L(p) = \dfrac{2p + 3}{p^2 + 4p + 4}$

(g) $L(p) = \dfrac{1}{(p + 2)(p^2 + 4p + 8)}$

(h) $L(p) = \dfrac{2p + 3}{(p + 2)(p^2 + 4p + 8)}$

2.7   Show that the response of a continuous-time system to a unit ramp input can be obtained by integrating its response to a unit step input.

2.8   Determine the impulse response sequence of each of the discrete-time systems for which the system function $L(q)$ is given below:

(a) $L(q) = \dfrac{1}{q^2 - 1.4q + 0.48}$ (b) $L(q) = \dfrac{2q + 3}{q^2 - 1.4q + 0.48}$

(c) $L(q) = \dfrac{1}{q^2 - 1.2q + 1}$ (d) $L(q) = \dfrac{2q + 3}{q^2 - 1.2q + 1}$

(e) $L(q) = \dfrac{1}{q^2 - 2q + 1}$ (f) $L(q) = \dfrac{2q + 3}{q^2 - 2q + 1}$

(g) $L(q) = \dfrac{2q^2 + 3q + 4}{(q - 0.6)(q^2 - q + 0.1)}$

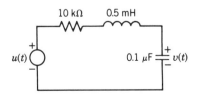

Figure 2.31   RLC network with impulse voltage input.

2.9 Use convolution to calculate the response of each of the systems in Problem 2.6 to a unit step input.

2.10 Repeat Problem 2.9 if the input is a unit ramp, that is, $u(t) = t$.

2.11 Determine the relationship between the response sequence of a discrete-time system to the inputs $u(k) = 1$ and $u(k) = k$, where $k \geq 0$.

2.12 Determine the response of each of the systems described in Problem 2.8 to the sequence $u(k) = 1$ for all $k \geq 0$, using convolution.

2.13 Repeat Problem 2.12 for $u(k) = k$ for all $k \geq 0$.

2.14 The impulse response of a causal discrete-time system is given by

$$h(k) = (0.5)^k \qquad \text{for } k \geq 0$$

Determine its response to the input $u(k) = k$ for all $k \geq 0$.

2.15 A small dc motor (called a servomotor) is often used in control systems. With a constant field excitation, a voltage applied to the armature of the motor causes it to rotate. The response of the device to a unit step voltage input is given below:

$$\omega = 2.5(1 - e^{-0.25t})$$

where ω is the angular velocity in radians per second.
(a) Determine the response of the motor if the applied voltage is the unit ramp function, that is, $u(t) = r(t)$.
(b) Repeat part (a) if $u(t) = 2\cos 0.5t \ \gamma(t)$.

2.16 The response of a continuous-time system to a unit impulse is given by $h(t) = e^{-2t}\cos 3t \ \gamma(t)$.
(a) Determine its response, for all $t \geq 0$, to a unit step input.
(b) Repeat part (a) for a unit ramp input.
(c) Repeat part (a) if the input is given by $u(t) = 3[\gamma(t) - \gamma(t - 1)]$.

2.17 The response of a continuous-time system to a step input is given by

$$g(t) = 1 - e^{-t}\left(\cos 3t + \frac{1}{3}\sin 3t\right)\gamma(t)$$

Determine the response of this system to the following inputs
(a) $u(t) = \gamma(t) - \gamma(t - 1)$
(b) $u(t) = r(t) - 2r(t - 1) + r(t - 2)$

2.18 The impulse response $h(t)$ of a continuous-time system is shown in Figure 2.32a. Determine the response of this system to the input shown in Figure 2.32b.

2.19 The response of a discrete-time system to the sequence $u(k) = 1$, $k \geq 0$, is given by

$$g(k) = 32(0.8)^k - 10(0.5)^k - 20$$

(a) Determine the impulse response sequence.
(b) Determine the output sequence for the causal input $u(k) = k$.

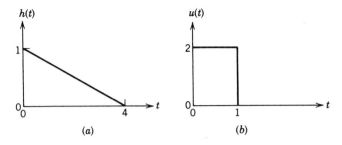

Figure 2.32 (*a*) Impulse response. (*b*) Input.

2.20 The impulse response of a continuous-time system is given by

$$h(t) = 2[\gamma(t) - \gamma(t - 1)]$$

Determine its response to the input $u(t) = \gamma(t) - \gamma(t - 2)$.

2.21 Repeat Problem 2.20 for the input $u(t) = t$.

2.22 Draw a realization diagram for a system that has the impulse response $h(t) = 3e^{-2t}\gamma(t)$.

2.23 The impulse response of a linear system is given by

$$h(t) = e^{-2t}\cos 3t \ \gamma(t)$$

Show one method for realizing this system.

2.24 The impulse response sequence of a discrete-time system is given by

$$h(k) = 2.5(0.5)^k - 1.5(0.3)^k$$

Show how this system can be realized.

2.25 The realization diagram for a discrete-time system is shown in Figure 2.33. Determine its impulse response sequence.

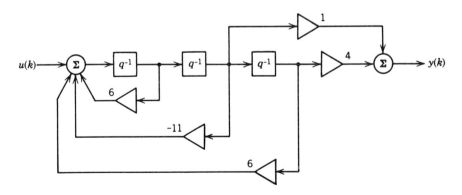

Figure 2.33 Realization diagram for problem 2.25.

2.26 Determine the response of the system shown in Figure 2.33 to the unit step sequence $\gamma(k)$.

2.27 Repeat for the unit ramp sequence, defined as

$$r(k) = k, \quad \text{for } k \geq 0$$

2.28 Determine the impulse response of each of the linear systems corresponding to the realization diagrams shown in Figure 2.34.

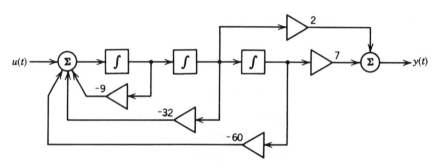

Figure 2.34a Realization Diagram (direct realization).

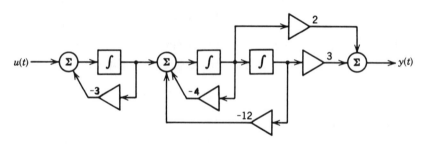

Figure 2.34b Realization Diagram (cascade realization).

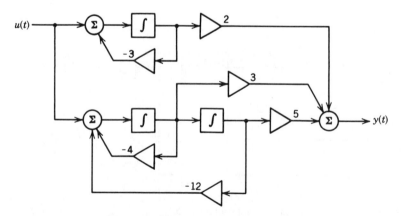

Figure 2.34c Realization diagram (parallel realization).

APPENDIX 2.1

Calculation of the Convolution Sum

The convolution sum, given the input sequence $u(k)$ and the impulse response sequence $h(k)$, can be calculated most conveniently on a computer by first storing the two sequences as vectors $\mathbf{u}$ and $\mathbf{h}$, respectively, as defined below and then multiplying the lower triangular matrix $\mathbf{H}$ with the vector $\mathbf{u}$ to get the vector $\mathbf{y}$ of the output sequence,

$$\mathbf{u} = \begin{bmatrix} u(0) \\ u(1) \\ \vdots \\ u(N) \end{bmatrix}, \quad \mathbf{h} = \begin{bmatrix} h(0) \\ h(1) \\ \vdots \\ h(N) \end{bmatrix}, \quad \mathbf{y} = \begin{bmatrix} y(0) \\ y(1) \\ \vdots \\ y(N) \end{bmatrix}$$

The computer program supplied with the book starts with the vectors $\mathbf{u}$ and $\mathbf{h}$, which may be input either through the keyboard or from files stored on a disk. They may also be entered in the form of functions. The matrix $\mathbf{H}$ is then formed as follows:

$$\mathbf{H} = \begin{bmatrix} h(0) & 0 & 0 & \cdots & 0 \\ h(1) & h(0) & 0 & \cdots & 0 \\ h(2) & h(1) & h(0) & \cdots & 0 \\ \hdotsfor{5} \\ h(N) & h(N-1) & \cdots & & h(0) \end{bmatrix}$$

The output sequence is now obtained simply from the equation

$$\mathbf{y} = \mathbf{Hu}$$

APPENDIX 2.2

Computer Program for Deconvolution

Deconvolution can be carried out on a computer in the same manner as described for the calculation of the convolution sum. For example, we first consider the case when it is desired to find the input sequence that will provide a specified output sequence from a system with given impulse response sequence. We can again use the equation

$$\mathbf{y} = \mathbf{Hu}$$

except that now we have to calculate $\mathbf{u}$, given $\mathbf{H}$ and $\mathbf{y}$. This requires solving a set of simultaneous equations. However, one can take advantage of the triangular nature of $\mathbf{H}$ to simplify the calculations. The computer program used for this purpose is based on L-U decomposition and utilizes this fact to reduce the amount of computation.

The problem of determining the impulse response sequence can be solved in the same manner if we note that the roles of the sequences $h(k)$ and $u(k)$ can be changed in the convolution sum. Consequently, this time we form a lower triangular matrix $\mathbf{U}$ from the input sequence, exactly in the same way as $\mathbf{H}$ was formed from the impulse response sequence for the other problem. We can now solve the equation

$$\mathbf{y} = \mathbf{Uh}$$

to obtain the vector $\mathbf{h}$, which gives us the impulse response sequence.

The computer program included with the book combines the solution to both problems. It starts by asking the user whether deconvolution is to be used for finding the impulse response sequence or the input sequence. The relevant data are then requested and after the input, the desired sequence is displayed. It may be printed if so requested by the user.

APPENDIX 2.3

Calculation of the Convolution Integral

The convolution integral can be calculated numerically on a digital computer by using the process of discretization. We start by selecting a small positive number T and set $t = kT$, where k is an integer variable. The convolution integral can then be approximated by the following summation (it is assumed that the input is causal; otherwise, the upper limit of summation must be changed):

$$y(kT) = T \sum_{i=0}^{k} h(iT)u(kT - iT)$$

In general, the accuracy of the approximation will improve as the value of T is decreased. The computer program supplied with the book uses this procedure to obtain the approximate solution with $h(t)$ and $u(t)$ given as functions of time. The user is asked for the time interval over which the solution is desired. It then selects T such that the maximum value of k is 1024 and calculates $y(kT)$ at all these points. The program included with the book computes the samples $y(kT)$, using the efficient FFT algorithm described in Chapter 4.

Fourier Analysis of Continuous-Time Signals

3.1 INTRODUCTION

In Chapter 2, the notion of periodic signals was introduced, and it was pointed out that the sinusoid is the simplest periodic function. It was also noted in Chapter 1 that the steady-state response of a stable linear system to a sinusoidal input, which is also the particular integral of the system differential equation for that input, will always be a sinusoid of the same frequency. In this chapter, we introduce the fundamental concept of the frequency spectrum of continuous-time signals and note that the sinusoid plays a very important role.

We begin our discussions with the Fourier series. It is named after the French physicist Jean Baptiste Fourier (1768–1830), who proved that almost any periodic function can be represented as the sum of sinusoids with integrally related frequencies. Both the trigonometric and the complex exponential forms of Fourier series will be studied. We also examine the effects of different types of symmetry.

The work of Fourier has had a profound impact on the theory of linear systems as well as on communication theory. Not only does it enable us to get a better understanding of periodic signals through their frequency spectra but, as we shall learn later in this chapter, the basic idea can be extended to a large class of aperiodic signals as well, through the use of Fourier transforms. We also introduce in our discussion the concepts of convolution (as viewed from the frequency domain) and modulation, two very important ideas in communication theory.

The contribution of Fourier can be summarized by the statement that most signals encountered in engineering can be represented in both the time and the frequency domain. Moreover, these representations are uniquely related, so that altering the signal in one domain will alter its representation in the other domain as well.

3.2 FOURIER SERIES FOR PERIODIC SIGNALS

Let us start by recalling that a signal $x(t)$ is said to be *periodic* if the following equation is satisfied for some value of T,

$$x(t + T) = x(t) \tag{3.1}$$

The smallest positive value of T for which equation 3.1 is satisfied is called the period of the signal. The quantity $f_0 = 1/T$ is called the *fundamental frequency of the signal in Hertz* and $\omega_0 = 2\pi f_0$ is the fundamental frequency in radians per second. A sinusoid of frequency nf_0, where n is a positive integer, is said to be the *nth harmonic*; it is called an *odd* harmonic if n is odd and an *even* harmonic if n is even.

Many important periodic functions are nonsinusoidal. Some of these are shown in Figure 3.1. These include the square wave signal often used in the laboratory, shown in Figure 3.1a, the sawtooth waveform shown in 3.1b, which is used in an oscilloscope for sweeping the electron beam across the screen, and the rectified sine wave shown in 3.1c, which is often used in measuring instruments and other applications requiring conversion form alternating current to direct current. By using Fourier analysis, we are able to express each of these waveforms as the sum of a sinusoid and its harmonics.

We now present the trigonometric form of Fourier series.

3.2.1 TRIGONOMETRIC FORM OF FOURIER SERIES

If $x(t)$ is a periodic function with period T, then by Fourier's theorem, in almost every case, it can be expressed by the following equation:

$$x(t) = a_0 + \sum_{n=1}^{\infty} (a_n \cos n\omega_0 t + b_n \sin n\omega_0 t) \tag{3.2}$$

Equation 3.2 is called the Fourier series for $x(t)$. The constants a_i and b_i are called the Fourier coefficients. An examination of equation 3.2 tells us that it includes all sinusoidal waveforms that repeat after T seconds, where $T =$

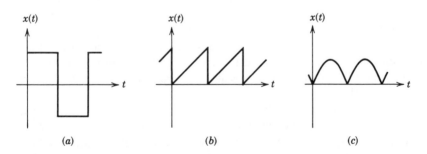

Figure 3.1 Some useful periodic signals.

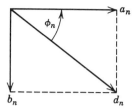

Figure 3.2
Relationship between
the coefficients of the
two forms.

$2\pi/\omega_0$. Equation 3.2 can also be expressed in the following form:

$$x(t) = a_0 + \sum_{n=1}^{\infty} d_n \cos(n\omega_0 t - \phi_n) \tag{3.3}$$

The coefficients a_n and b_n are uniquely related to d_n and ϕ_n as shown here:

$$a_n = d_n \cos \phi_n$$

$$b_n = d_n \sin \phi_n \tag{3.4}$$

Equation 3.4 can be visualized easily through the phasor relationship shown in Figure 3.2.

Calculation of these coefficients will now be discussed. These are based on certain properties of sinusoids, due to orthogonality. First we note a few important integrals, which can be easily derived.

For any t_0 and integers n and m

$$\int_{t_0}^{t_0+T} \sin n\omega_0 t \, dt = 0 \tag{3.5}$$

$$\int_{t_0}^{t_0+T} \cos n\omega_0 t \, dt = 0 \tag{3.6}$$

$$\int_{t_0}^{t_0+T} \sin n\omega_0 t \cos m\omega_0 t \, dt = 0 \tag{3.7}$$

$$\int_{t_0}^{t_0+T} \sin n\omega_0 t \sin m\omega_0 t \, dt = \begin{cases} 0 & \text{if } n \neq m \\ \dfrac{T}{2} & \text{if } n = m \end{cases} \tag{3.8}$$

$$\int_{t_0}^{t_0+T} \cos n\omega_0 t \cos m\omega_0 t \, dt = \begin{cases} 0 & \text{if } n \neq m \\ \dfrac{T}{2} & \text{if } n = m \end{cases} \tag{3.9}$$

We shall use these identities to derive equations for evaluating the Fourier coefficients. First we multiply both sides of equation 3.2 by dt and integrate over one complete period, say t_0 to $t_0 + T$. Then, in view of

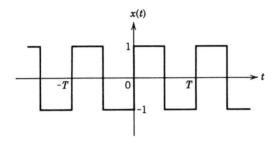

Figure 3.3 A square wave.

equations 3.5 and 3.6,* every term on the right-hand side will vanish, except that which contains a_0. Thus, we get the following equation:

$$a_0 = \frac{1}{T} \int_{t_0}^{t_0+T} x(t)\, dt \tag{3.10}$$

The right-hand side of equation 3.10 is the area under one complete cycle of the waveform, divided by the period. Therefore, it is evident that a_0 is the average (or dc) value of $x(t)$, taken over one complete period.

Similarly, multiplying both sides of equation 3.2 by $\cos n\omega_0 t$ and integrating over one complete cycle, we get

$$a_n = \frac{2}{T} \int_{t_0}^{t_0+T} x(t) \cos n\omega_0 t\, dt \tag{3.11}$$

and multiplication by $\sin n\omega_0 t$ followed by integration gives

$$b_n = \frac{2}{T} \int_{t_0}^{t_0+T} x(t) \sin n\omega_0 t\, dt \tag{3.12}$$

Equations 3.10, 3.11, and 3.12 can be utilized for evaluating the Fourier coefficients.

Example 3.1

Consider the square wave shown in Figure 3.3. Let us select $t_0 = 0$ for this case. By looking at the waveform, we can tell that its mean value over one

---

*Equations 3.5 and 3.6 are based on the fact that the area under an integral number of cycles of a sinusoid must be zero. The other three are obtained from the following trigonometric identities, followed by a similar reasoning.

$$2 \sin A \cos B = \sin(A - B) + \sin(A + B)$$
$$2 \cos A \cos B = \cos(A - B) + \cos(A + B)$$
$$2 \sin A \sin B = \cos(A - B) - \cos(A + B)$$

complete cycle is zero. Consequently,

$$a_0 = 0$$

Also

$$a_n = \frac{2}{T}\left[\int_0^{T/2} 1 \cdot \cos n\omega_0 t \, dt + \int_{T/2}^T (-1) \cos n\omega_0 t \, dt\right] = 0$$

and

$$b_n = \frac{2}{T}\left[\int_0^{T/2} 1 \cdot \sin n\omega_0 t \, dt + \int_{T/2}^T (-1) \sin n\omega_0 t \, dt\right] = \begin{cases} 0 & \text{for even } n \\ \dfrac{4}{n\pi} & \text{for odd } n \end{cases}$$

Thus, the Fourier series for the square wave shown in Figure 3.1 is

$$x(t) = \sum_{k=1}^{\infty} \frac{4}{(2k-1)\pi} \sin (2k-1)\omega_0 t \tag{3.13}$$

Note that this series contains only sine terms, consisting of the fundamental component and odd harmonics. ∎

It is interesting to observe how the square wave is synthesized by adding the various sine terms in equation 3.13. For example, the sum for the first 3, 5, and 10 terms is shown in Figure 3.4. From these, it would appear reasonable to assume that the sum of an infinite number of terms will converge to the square wave.

There is another important feature that should be noted. All sine and cosine terms are continuous functions with continuous derivatives of all orders. On the other hand, we are trying to approximate the square wave that has discontinuities. This is likely to cause some difficulties. In fact, this very question was raised by other mathematicians when Fourier had proposed his

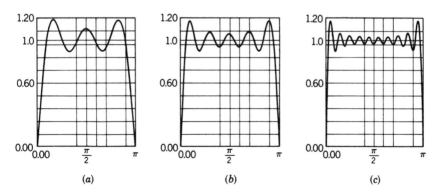

Figure 3.4 Convergence of the Fourier series of a square wave. (*a*) Three terms. (*b*) Five terms. (*c*) Ten terms.

theorem. The key point here is that the Fourier series will converge to the original function only when an infinite number of terms are included. We shall consider this matter later in this chapter when Gibbs phenomenon is discussed.

As is seen from Example 3.1, the evaluation of the Fourier coefficients for a periodic function requires three integrations. It is possible to reduce the amount of work by using the exponential form of the Fourier series, as will be seen in the next subsection.

Drill Problem 3.1

Determine the Fourier series for the square wave shown in Figure 3.5, which has been obtained by shifting the time origin of Figure 3.3 to the right by $T/4$.

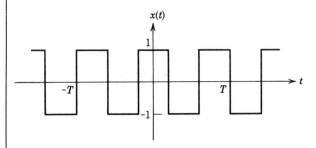

Figure 3.5   A square wave.

Answer: $a_n = \dfrac{4}{n\pi} \sin\left(\dfrac{n\pi}{2}\right), \qquad b_n = 0$

3.2.2   EXPONENTIAL FORM OF FOURIER SERIES

The exponential form of the Fourier series is based on Euler's identity, which may be written as

$$\cos n\omega_0 t = \frac{\exp(jn\omega_0 t) + \exp(-jn\omega_0 t)}{2} \qquad (3.14)$$

$$\sin n\omega_0 t = \frac{\exp(jn\omega_0 t) - \exp(-jn\omega_0 t)}{2j} \qquad (3.15)$$

Substituting these expressions into equation 3.2 we get the following form of the Fourier series after a little rearrangement.

$$x(t) = a_0 + \frac{1}{T} \sum_{n=1}^{\infty} \left[(a_n - jb_n)\exp(jn\omega_0 t) + (a_n + jb_n)\exp(-jn\omega_0 t) \right]$$

$$(3.16)$$

This can be simplified further with the following substitutions

$$c_0 = a_0 \tag{3.17}$$

$$c_n = \frac{(a_n - jb_n)}{2} \tag{3.18}$$

$$c_{-n} = \frac{(a_n + jb_n)}{2} \tag{3.19}$$

to obtain the very compact form

$$x(t) = \sum_{n=-\infty}^{\infty} c_n \exp(jn\omega_0 t) \tag{3.20}$$

It is also shown, by substituting the integrals for a_n and b_n from equations 3.11 and 3.12, that

$$c_n = \frac{1}{T} \int_{t_0}^{t_0+T} x(t) \exp(-jn\omega_0 t) \, dt \tag{3.21}$$

Equations 3.20 and 3.21 define the exponential form of the Fourier series. It is customary to call equation 3.21 the *analysis* equation, since it enables us to analyze a periodic function into its Fourier components. Similarly, equation 3.20 is called the *synthesis* equation, since it can be utilized to synthesize a waveform from its Fourier components. In addition to their compactness, these equations are also more convenient, since in many cases the integral represented by equation 3.21 will be much easier to evaluate than the integrals in equations 3.11 and 3.12. Furthermore, the alternative trigonometric form of the Fourier series shown in equation 3.3 can be related to this form by noting that

$$d_n e^{-j\phi_n} = a_n - jb_n = 2c_n \tag{3.22}$$

The use of the exponential form is illustrated through Example 3.2.

Example 3.2

We reconsider the square wave shown in Figure 3.3. Here

$$c_n = \frac{1}{T} \left[\int_0^{T/2} \exp(-jn\omega_0 t) \, dt - \int_{T/2}^{T} \exp(-jn\omega_0 t) \, dt \right]$$

$$= \frac{1}{T} \left[\frac{\exp(-jn\omega_0 t)}{-jn\omega_0} \bigg|_0^{T/2} + \frac{\exp(-jn\omega_0 t)}{jn\omega_0} \bigg|_{T/2}^{T} \right]$$

$$= \left[\frac{\exp(-jn\pi) - 1}{-j2n\pi} + \frac{\exp(-j2n\pi) - \exp(-jn\pi)}{j2n\pi} \right]$$

$$= \begin{cases} 0 & \text{for even } n \\ \dfrac{-j2}{n\pi} & \text{for odd } n \end{cases} \tag{3.23}$$

This is consistent with the result obtained in Example 3.1 since, from equation 3.18, we again get $a_n = 0$ and $b_n = 4/(n\pi)$ for odd n. ∎

Example 3.3

Consider the periodic train of rectangular pulses shown in Figure 3.6. The height of each pulse is A and duration Δ seconds. From equation 3.21 if we select $t_0 = -T/2$, we get

$$c_n = \frac{1}{T} \int_{-T/2}^{T/2} A \exp(-jn\omega_0 t)\, dt$$

$$= \frac{1}{T} \int_{-\Delta/2}^{\Delta/2} \exp(-jn\omega_0 t)\, dt$$

$$= \frac{A}{-jn\omega_0 T} \left[\exp(-jn\omega_0\Delta/2) - \exp(jn\omega_0\Delta/2) \right]$$

$$= \frac{A\Delta}{2T} \frac{\sin(n\omega_0\Delta/2)}{n\omega_0\Delta/2} \tag{3.24}$$

For the special case when $n = 0$, we can use l'Hôpital's rule to obtain

$$c_0 = \frac{A\Delta}{2T} \tag{3.25}$$

Equations 3.21 and 3.22 can also be utilized to obtain the trigonometric form of the Fourier series, which is given by

$$x(t) = \frac{A\Delta}{2T} + \sum_{n=1}^{\infty} \frac{A\Delta}{T} \frac{\sin(n\omega_0\Delta/2)}{n\omega_0\Delta/2} \cos n\omega_0 t \tag{3.26}$$

(*Note*: In these derivations use has been made of the relationship $\omega_0 T = 2\pi$.)
At this point, it is desirable to define the function

$$\text{sinc } \theta \triangleq \frac{\sin \theta}{\theta} \tag{3.27}$$

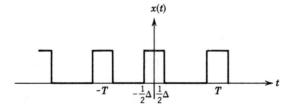

Figure 3.6 A periodic train of rectangular pulses.

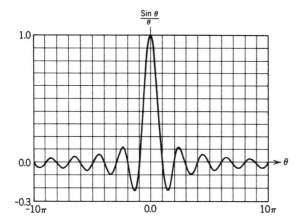

Figure 3.7   A plot of the sinc function.

since $\text{sinc}(n\omega_0\Delta/2)$ has already appeared twice; we shall see this again many times. A plot of the sinc function is shown in Figure 3.7.   ■

In addition to the ease in mathematical manipulation, the complex form of the Fourier series is more useful for physical interpretation in terms of phasors. Some of these aspects will be evident in the later sections of this chapter.

Drill Problem 3.2

Determine the exponential form of the Fourier series for the square wave shown in Figure 3.5 and considered in Drill Problem 3.1.

Answer:

$$c_n = \begin{cases} 0 & \text{for even } n \\ -j2\exp\left(\dfrac{jn\pi}{2}\right)/(n\pi) & \text{for odd } n \end{cases}$$

3.2.3 EFFECT OF SYMMETRY

Calculation of the coefficients of the Fourier series of a given periodic function can be further simplified by taking advantage of various forms of symmetry in the waveform. For example, we saw that the Fourier series for the square wave of Figure 3.3 contained only the odd harmonics of sine terms whereas the cosine terms as well as the constant term were absent. Similarly, the Fourier series for the square wave shown in Figure 3.5 (for Drill Problem 3.2) contained only cosine terms, while the sine terms were absent. These are caused by certain types of symmetry in the waveform and will now be described.

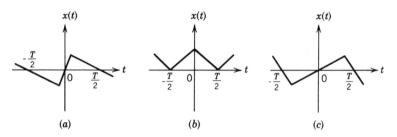

Figure 3.8 Examples of odd and even functions. (a) An odd function. (b) An even function. (c) Another odd function.

A periodic signal is said to be *even* if it satisfies the following equation:

$$x(t) = x(-t) \qquad (3.28)$$

It is said to be *odd* if

$$x(t) = -x(-t) \qquad (3.29)$$

Equation 3.24 implies that an even function is symmetrical about the vertical axis at $t = 0$, whereas from equation 3.25 it follows that an odd function is antisymmetric about that axis. Thus, the square wave shown in Figure 3.3 is an odd function of time, whereas that shown in Figure 3.5 is an even function. Some other examples of odd and even functions are shown in Figure 3.8.

It may be noted that $\sin n\omega t$ is odd while $\cos n\omega t$ is even for all values of n. Furthermore, any sum of odd functions will remain odd, and any sum of even functions will be even. Therefore, *the Fourier series for any periodic function that is odd can contain only sine terms.* Similarly, *the Fourier series for any even periodic function can contain only cosine terms and possibly a constant.* The constant term will be zero if the area under the positive half-cycle is equal to that under the negative half-cycle. If we use the exponential form of the Fourier series, the coefficients turn out to be purely imaginary for odd functions and purely real for even functions. This follows since $c_n = (a_n - jb_n)/2$, so that for an odd waveform containing only sine terms, a_n must be zero. Similarly, for an even waveform, b_n must be zero.

In view of the foregoing, if a periodic signal has either odd or even symmetry, then it is sufficient to integrate over only one half of the period to evaluate the Fourier coefficients, since the integral over the other half will be identical. For example, the square wave considered in Examples 3.1 and 3.2 has odd symmetry; hence, we could integrate only from 0 to $T/2$ and multiply the result by 2 to get the complete integral.

A periodic function is said to have *half-wave symmetry* if

$$x\left(t + \frac{T}{2}\right) = -x(t) \qquad (3.30)$$

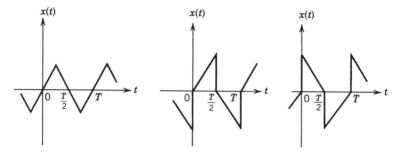

Figure 3.9   Some waveforms with half-wave symmetry.

This type of symmetry can be visualized by noting that if the negative half-cycle of the wave form is shifted by half of the period then this will be the mirror image of the positive half-cycle about the time axis. Some other waveforms that have half-wave symmetry are shown in Figure 3.9.

The square wave considered in Examples 3.1 and 3.2 has this type of symmetry. It can easily be shown that the Fourier series for a signal that satisfies equation 3.30 can contain only odd harmonics. This is evident from the fact that any even harmonic will complete one full cycle during one half of the period of the fundamental waveform and, therefore, will satisfy the following equation instead of equation 3.30:

$$x\left(t + \frac{T}{2}\right) = x(t) \tag{3.31}$$

It follows that the Fourier series for any waveform that satisfies equation 3.30 cannot contain even harmonics. Evidently, the constant term in the Fourier series must also be zero for such signals.

If a waveform has half-wave symmetry, then any of the integrals for calculating the Fourier coefficients of the odd harmonics need be evaluated over only a half-cycle and the result multiplied by two. The integral over the other half-cycle will be identical because of the relationship expressed by equation 3.30.

Furthermore, if a waveform has half-wave symmetry and is either odd or even, then it is necessary to integrate over only a quarter-cycle and the result multiplied by four to evaluate the odd harmonics. It is evident that the integrals over each of the other quarter-cycles will be identical.

There is an important difference between the two types of symmetry that we have discussed in this section. It is often possible to change an odd function into an even function, or vice versa, by shifting the origin on the time axis. For example, although the square wave shown in Figure 3.3 is an odd function of time, it can be converted into an even function by a shift of $T/4$ along the time axis. This also follows from the observation that a sine curve can be obtained by delaying a cosine curve by one fourth of its period. On the other hand, the property of half-wave symmetry is independent of the shift in time but does depend on shifting the horizontal axis. For instance, it is possible to produce half-wave symmetry in some waveforms by subtracting the average value of the signal, as shown in the following example. It may be noted that even symmetry of a waveform is not affected by a shift of this type.

Example 3.4

Consider the triangular waveform shown in Figure 3.10a. This waveform is obtained by integrating the square wave of the type shown in Figure 3.3, with amplitude 4 and period 10. It is an even function but does not have half-wave symmetry. If we subtract its average value from the function, the resulting waveform, shown in Figure 3.10b, does have half-wave symmetry. We can take advantage of this fact in calculating the Fourier coefficients for the triangular waveform.

Since the function shown in Figure 3.10b is even and also has half-wave symmetry, it can be expressed by a Fourier series of the following form:

$$x(t) - 10 = \sum_{k=1}^{\infty} a_{2k-1} \cos(2k-1)\omega_0 t \qquad (3.32)$$

where

$$a_{2k-1} = \frac{8}{10} \int_0^{2.5} (4t - 10) \cos(2k-1)\omega_0 t \, dt \qquad (3.33)$$

Integration of equation 3.33 and substitution of the limits, while noting that $10\omega_0 = 2\pi$, leads to

$$a_{2k-1} = -\frac{80}{(2k-1)^2 \pi^2} \qquad (3.34)$$

∎

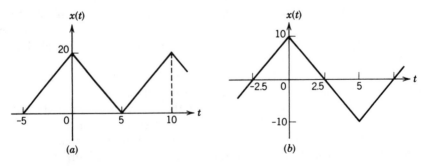

Figure 3.10 Half-wave symmetry produced by subtracting dc component. (a) Original waveform. (b) Waveform with axis shifted.

Drill Problem 3.3

Determine the Fourier series for the waveform shown in Figure 3.10b if the origin is moved to the left by a quarter-cycle, that is, 2.5 s.

Answer: $a_n = 0$, $b_n = \dfrac{80}{n^2 \pi^2} \sin\left(\dfrac{n\pi}{2}\right)$

3.2.4 SOME PROPERTIES OF THE FOURIER SERIES

In this section we discuss some important properties of the Fourier series that make it easier to determine the Fourier series of many periodic signals. Furthermore, these properties will enable us to examine the relationships between the Fourier series of time functions that are related to each other in some way. We begin with the familiar operations of differentiation and integration.

3.2.4.1 Differentiation and Integration of Periodic Signals

If the Fourier series for a periodic signal is known, then that of the derivative or the integral of this signal can be determined if we differentiate or integrate each term of the series, respectively. For instance, if we differentiate both sides of the complex Fourier series given in equation 3.20 we get

$$\frac{dx}{dt} = \frac{d}{dt} \sum_{n=-\infty}^{\infty} c_n \exp(jn\omega_0 t) = \sum_{n=-\infty}^{\infty} jn\omega_0 c_n \exp(jn\omega_0 t) \quad (3.35)$$

We see from equation 3.35 that the effect of differentiation is to multiply the Fourier coefficients of the original signal by $jn\omega_0$. In other words, if the coefficients of the complex Fourier series of $x(t)$ are denoted by c_n, then those of its derivative are given by $jn\omega_0 c_n$. It follows that the effect of differentiation will be to increase the magnitude of the higher harmonics. In particular, as n increases, the corresponding harmonic is multiplied by a very large number.

Since integration is the inverse of differentiation, it is evident that the effect of integration will be to divide the coefficients of the complex form of the Fourier series by $jn\omega_0$. Thus, integration has the effect of reducing the magnitudes of the higher harmonics of the waveform. With integration, one must also account for the constant of integration. This is, simply, the dc value of the integrated function obtained from the area under one complete cycle of this function.

Example 3.5

Consider the periodic train of impulses, each of strength 2, as shown in Figure 3.11. Note that this waveform would be obtained if we were to

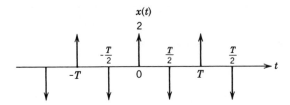

Figure 3.11 Derivative of a square wave.

differentiate the square wave shown in Figure 3.3. Recalling from equation 3.20, the Fourier coefficients for the square wave are given by

$$c_n = \begin{cases} 0 & \text{for even } n \\ \dfrac{-j2}{n\pi} & \text{for odd } n \end{cases} \tag{3.36}$$

Hence, the Fourier coefficients for the derivative function will be obtained by multiplying these by $j\omega_0 n$ or $j2\pi n/T$. Denoting these as c_n', we get

$$c_n' = \begin{cases} 0 & \text{for even } n \\ \dfrac{4}{T} & \text{for odd } n \end{cases} \tag{3.37}$$

We verify this result by finding the Fourier coefficient for this impulse train directly by applying equation 3.21. Selecting $t_0 = 0^-$, we get the following integral:

$$c_n' = \frac{1}{T} \int_{t_0}^{t_0 + T} \left[2\delta(t) - 2\delta\left(t - \frac{T}{2}\right) \right] \exp\left(-j\omega_0 t\right) dt \tag{3.38}$$

As pointed out in Chapter 2, an integral involving an impulse is obtained easily be recalling the following property (called the "sifting property") of the impulse:

$$\int_{t_2}^{t_1} f(t) \, \delta(t - a) \, dt = f(a) \tag{3.39}$$

provided that $t_1 \le a \le t_2$; otherwise the integral is zero. The integral in equation 3.38 is therefore given by

$$c_n' = \frac{1}{T}\left[2 - 2\exp\left(\frac{-jn\omega_0 T}{2}\right) \right] = \frac{2 - 2e^{-jn\pi}}{T}$$

$$= \begin{cases} 0 & \text{for even } n \\ \dfrac{4}{T} & \text{for odd } n \end{cases} \tag{3.40}$$

This result is seen to be identical to equation 3.37, as expected. ∎

This approach of differentiating a function (several times, if necessary) is very useful for finding the coefficients of the Fourier series for periodic functions that consist of singularity functions.

We now consider an example where integration of the waveform will be useful.

Example 3.6

If we integrate the square wave shown in Figure 3.12a, we obtain the triangular wave shown in Figure 3.12b. We now determine the Fourier series of the triangular wave from that of the square wave. We use the result of Example 3.2 to determine the Fourier series for the latter. The only difference is that the amplitude is now 4 and period 10. Thus, the Fourier coefficients of the square wave in Figure 3.12a are

$$c_n = \begin{cases} 0 & \text{for even } n \\ \dfrac{-j20}{n\pi} & \text{for odd } n \end{cases} \qquad (3.41)$$

taking into account the scaling in amplitude. Therefore, the Fourier coefficients for the waveform in Figure 3.12b are obtained by dividing those for the square wave by $jn\omega_0$. If we denote these coefficients by c_n'', then the following equation is readily obtained:

$$c_n'' = \begin{cases} 0 & \text{for even } n \\ \dfrac{-40}{n^2\pi^2} & \text{for odd } n \end{cases} \qquad (3.42)$$

The dc value of the signal is easily found from the area under one cycle of the triangular waveform and is seen to be 10. This gives us

$$c_0'' = 10 \qquad (3.43)$$

These values agree with the results obtained in Example 3.4 but were obtained here more easily. ∎

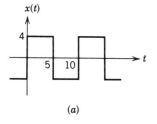 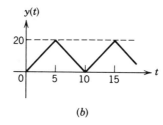

(a) (b)

Figure 3.12 A square wave and its integral. (a) Square wave of amplitude 4 and period 10. (b) Integral of the square wave shown in (a).

These examples also demonstrate some of the advantages of using the complex form of the Fourier series. Some other advantages will be seen in the subsequent sections.

3.2.4.2 Effect of Shift Along the Time-Axis of a Waveform

We often come across periodic functions that differ from each other only by a shift in the time-axis. It will be desirable to investigate the effect of this shift on the coefficients of the Fourier series.

Consider a signal $x(t)$ for which the Fourier series is

$$x(t) = \sum_{n=-\infty}^{\infty} c_n \exp(jn\omega_0 t) \tag{3.44}$$

Let us define another signal $y(t)$, related to $x(t)$ through the following equation:

$$y(t) = x(t - \tau) \tag{3.45}$$

The signals $x(t)$ and $y(t)$ are shown in Figure 3.13. It is evident that the latter can be obtained from the former by a simple transformation changing the variable t by $(t - \tau)$. Consequently, the Fourier series for $y(t)$ will be obtained by replacing t by $(t - \tau)$ in equation 3.44, that is,

$$y(t) = \sum_{n=-\infty}^{\infty} c_n \exp[jn\omega_0(t - \tau)] \tag{3.46}$$

The Fourier coefficients for the shifted function, which we shall denote by $\hat{c}_n$ are, therefore, obtained as

$$\hat{c}_n = c_n \exp(-jn\omega_0\tau) \tag{3.47}$$

It is evident that the two sets of Fourier coefficients are complex numbers with the same amplitude, but different arguments. This should be expected, since the shift in time changes only the phase of each frequency component.

For example, consider the square wave shown in Figure 3.14, which is obtained by shifting the square wave in Figure 3.3 in $T/4$.

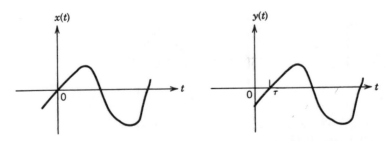

Figure 3.13 Shift along time-axis.

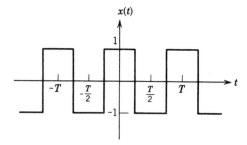

Figure 3.14 Square wave of Figure 3.3 after shift in time.

It was shown in Example 3.2 that the Fourier coefficients for the square wave of Figure 3.1 were given by

$$
c_n = \begin{cases} 0 & \text{for even } n \\ \dfrac{-j2}{n\pi} & \text{for odd } n \end{cases}
$$

Consequently, the Fourier coefficients for the waveform in Figure 3.5 are given by

$$
\hat{c}_n = \begin{cases} 0 & \text{for even } n \\ \dfrac{-j2e^{jn\pi/2}}{n\pi} & \text{for odd } n \end{cases} \tag{3.48}
$$

where we have used the fact that $\omega_0 T/4 = \pi/2$. It may also be noted that since $e^{jn\pi/2} = \pm j$ for odd n, the Fourier coefficients will now be purely real, whereas they were purely imaginary before the shift in time. As a result, it is evident that although the trigonometric form of the unshifted waveform had only sine terms, after the shift in time we get only cosine terms. This is also consistent with the even symmetry of the waveform of Figure 3.14.

3.2.4.3 Convergence of the Fourier series

It was stated in Section 3.2.1 that "in almost every case" a periodic function can be expressed in the form of a Fourier series. This is true for almost all signals that arise in engineering problems, but it would be desirable to know the conditions that are necessary for the series to converge to the given function. These are called the *Dirichlet conditions*, named after P. L. Dirichlet, who first derived them. If a function satisfies these conditions then the Fourier series, with infinite number of terms, is guaranteed to converge to the actual value of the signal for all values of t, with the exception of isolated points where the signal is discontinuous. These conditions are as follows.

1. The function is *absolutely integrable* over any period, that is,

$$\int_{t_0}^{t_0+T} |x(t)|\, dt < \infty \tag{3.49}$$

This condition guarantees that the integrals for evaluating the Fourier coefficients will exist and the coefficients will be finite.

2. The function must have a *finite number of maxima and minima* over one complete period.

3. The function must have a *finite number of discontinuities* over one complete period.

In fact, it can be proved that if a function satisfies these three conditions, then the *truncated Fourier series* (with N terms instead of an infinite number of terms) will be the best approximation to the original function, compared with any other harmonic function having the same number of terms. The criterion used for this comparison is the total squared-error magnitude over one period, defined as

$$J = \int_{t_0}^{t_0+T} [x(t) - x_N(t)]^2\, dt \tag{3.50}$$

where

$$x_N(t) = \sum_{n=-N}^{N} c_n \exp(jn\omega_0 t)\, dt \tag{3.51}$$

As stated previously, virtually all signals that arise in engineering will satisfy these conditions. Some functions that do not satisfy these conditions are given below:

(i)
$$x(t) = \frac{1}{t} \quad \text{for} \quad 0 < t < 1 \tag{3.52}$$

where $x(t)$ is periodic with period 1. A plot of one cycle of this function is shown in Figure 3.15*a*. It can be verified that this signal does not satisfy condition 1.

(ii)
$$x(t) = \sin\left(\frac{2\pi}{t}\right) \tag{3.53}$$

where $x(t)$ is periodic with period 1. A plot of one cycle of this function is shown in Figure 3.15*b*. It can be easily verified that it violates condition 2.

Fortunately, these functions are not known to arise in engineering practice. It may also be noted that Dirichlet conditions indicate that a periodic function need not be continuous for its Fourier series to exist. In fact, at a discontinuity, the series will converge to the average of the values of the function obtained from the left and the right of the discontinuity. This will be studied in the next section.

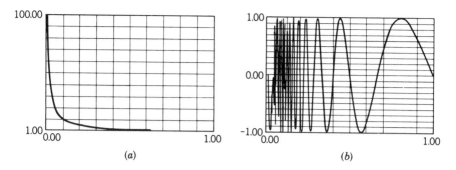

Figure 3.15 Some periodic signals that do not satisfy Dirichlet conditions. (a) $x(t) = 1/t$ and $0 < t < 1$. (b) $x(t) = \sin(2\pi/t)$ for $0 < t < 1$.

3.2.4.4 Gibbs Phenomenon

As pointed out earlier, although the Fourier series for a periodic function converges to the actual value of the function as the number of terms in the series is increased, there will always be some error at points of discontinuity. This is a basic limitation because all sine and cosine terms are continuous, and so any linear combination of these terms cannot exactly match a function at a point of discontinuity. Since a square wave is one of the simplest examples of a periodic function that has discontinuities, the properties of its Fourier approximation have been of great interest to investigators. In particular, it is interesting to observe how the truncated Fourier series approximates the step discontinuity as the number of terms N is increased. Originally it was thought that the approximation will get closer as N is increased, but this is only partially correct. It was shown by Josiah Gibbs in 1899 that for any finite N, no matter how large, the synthesized function had an overshoot of about 9 percent of the peak-to-peak value, although the overall approximation improved and the ripples moved closer to the discontinuity as N was increased. Two of these approximations are shown in Figure 3.16, for N equal to 10 and 50. It will be seen that for the latter case, the synthesized

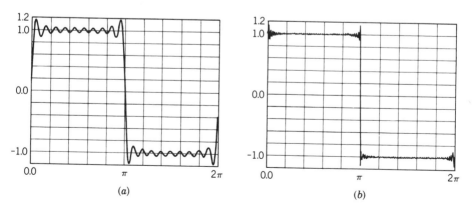

Figure 3.16 Gibbs phenomenon. (a) $N = 10$. (b) $N = 50$.

function is almost constant over the half-cycle, except at the beginning and end, where an overshoot of about 9 percent still exists. This peculiar property of the Fourier series is known as the *Gibbs phenomenon*.

Drill Problem 3.4

Determine the Fourier series for the triangular waveform shown in Figure 3.10b by considering it as the integral of a square wave of period 10 s.

Answer: See Example 3.4.

Drill Problem 3.5

Repeat Drill Problem 3.4 for the same waveform but start by differentiating it twice to obtain a periodic train of impulses similar to Figure 3.11.

3.3 SYSTEMS WITH PERIODIC INPUTS

We now study the response of systems to periodic inputs. The first step is to review the steady-state response of linear continuous-time systems to sinusoidal inputs. After that, the response to any periodic input will follow easily by applying the principle of superposition. The use of the complex Fourier series will again be especially helpful in calculating the responses.

3.3.1 STEADY-STATE RESPONSE TO SINUSOIDAL INPUTS

In Chapter 1 we had remarked that the particular solution of a linear differential equation for a sinusoidal forcing function was obtained very conveniently by using complex algebra. Electrical engineers have been using phasors for solving alternating current circuits for a long time. As we shall learn, these approaches are essentially identical and are based on replacing the differential operator p with $j\omega$, where ω is the frequency of the sinusoid in radians per second.

Consider a linear system described by the following differential equation, written in the operator notation

$$D(p)y(t) = N(p)u(t) \qquad (3.54)$$

where, as in Chapter 1, $D(p)$ and $N(p)$ are polynomials in the differential operator p. We are interested in the special case where the input function, $u(t)$ is a sinusoid, given by

$$u(t) = A \cos(\omega t + \phi) \qquad (3.55)$$

Let us use Euler's identity to write

$$u(t) = A \cos(\omega t + \phi) = Ue^{j\omega t} + U^*e^{-j\omega t} \qquad (3.56)$$

where

$$U = 0.5Ae^{j\phi}$$

and

$$U^* = 0.5Ae^{-j\phi} \tag{3.57}$$

Note that U and U^* are, in general, complex numbers and conjugates of each other. U is called the *phasor* representing the sinusoid; it contains information about both the magnitude and the phase of the sinusoid.

Following the discussions in Section 1.5.2.3, the steady-state component of $y(t)$ will be obtained, by using superposition, as

$$y(t) = \frac{N(p)}{D(p)}\bigg|_{p=j\omega} Ue^{j\omega t} + \frac{N(p)}{D(p)}\bigg|_{p=-j\omega} U^*e^{-j\omega t} \tag{3.58}$$

If we now define

$$\frac{N(p)}{D(p)}\bigg|_{p=j\omega} = Me^{j\theta} \tag{3.59}$$

where M is the *modulus* of the complex number and θ is its *argument*, we may rewrite equation 3.58 as

$$y(t) = Ye^{j\omega t} + Y^*e^{-j\omega t} \tag{3.60}$$

where the complex number

$$Y = Me^{j\theta}U = MAe^{j(\theta+\phi)} \tag{3.61}$$

and Y^* is its complex conjugate.

The two terms in equation 3.60 can now be combined to obtain $y(t)$ as a sinusoid. This gives the steady-state solution as

$$y_{ss}(t) = 2MA \cos\left(\omega t + \theta + \phi\right) \tag{3.62}$$

Notice that it is necessary to calculate M and ϕ only once, as the other term is its conjugate.

The following examples will illustrate the procedure.

Example 3.7

Consider a linear system described by the following equation:

$$\left(p^3 + 4p^2 + 6p + 11\right)y(t) = (3p + 5)u(t) \tag{3.63}$$

We are required to find the steady-state output for

$$u(t) = 10\cos\left(2t + \frac{\pi}{3}\right) \tag{3.64}$$

In this case, the phasor

$$U = 5e^{j\pi/3}$$

and

$$Y = \left. \frac{3p + 5}{\left(p^3 + 4p^2 + 6p + 11\right)} \right|_{p=j2} 5e^{j\pi/3}$$

$$= \frac{j6 + 5}{j4 - 5} 5e^{j\pi/3} = 6.0988e^{-j0.5436}$$

Consequently, the steady-state output is given by

$$y_{ss}(t) = 12.1976 \cos\left(2t - 0.5436\right) \tag{3.65}$$

∎

Example 3.8

Consider the R-C network shown in Figure 3.17. It is desired to find the steady-state output voltage $v_2(t)$ if the input voltage is

$$u(t) = 20 \cos\left(3t + \frac{\pi}{4}\right) \tag{3.66}$$

From the loop equations for the network as discussed in Chapter 1 (see Example 1.2 in Section 1.3.2 for the derivation of the system operator of this network from the loop equations), we may obtain the system operator of the network. Thus, we get

$$v_2(t) = \frac{1}{p^2 + 3p + 1} u(t)$$

The phasor for the output voltage is therefore given by

$$v_2 = \left. \frac{1}{p^2 + 3p + 1} \right|_{p=j3} 10e^{j\pi/4} = 0.83e^{-j1.512}$$

Hence, in the steady state,

$$v_2(t) = 1.66 \cos\left(3t - 1.512\right) \tag{3.67}$$

∎

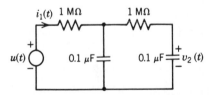

Figure 3.17   Two-loop network.

3.3.2 STEADY-STATE RESPONSE TO ANY PERIODIC INPUT

The method for obtaining the steady-state response to sinusoids, which was presented in the previous section, can easily be extended to the case of a general periodic input after its Fourier coefficients have been evaluated. Invoking the principle of superposition, we simply determine the steady-state response for each component separately and just add these to obtain the overall response. This will be illustrated through some examples.

Example 3.9

We reconsider the R-C network of Example 3.8, but the input will now be changed to

$$u(t) = 10 + 20\cos\left(3t + \frac{\pi}{4}\right) + 8\cos\left(6t - \frac{\pi}{3}\right) \tag{3.68}$$

In this instance, the input has three components, at radian frequencies 0, 3, and 6. Therefore, we first evaluate the system function at these frequencies and then multiply these values to the respective input phasors to obtain the corresponding phasors for the output.

$$\left.\frac{1}{p^2 + 3p + 1}\right|_{p=j0} = 1$$

$$\left.\frac{1}{p^2 + 3p + 1}\right|_{p=j3} = 0.830455e^{j2.2974}$$

$$\left.\frac{1}{p^2 + 3p + 1}\right|_{p=j6} = 0.025408e^{J2.66658}$$

The resulting steady-state output voltage is given by

$$v_2 = 10 + 16.609\cos\left(3t + \frac{\pi}{4} + 2.2974\right)$$

$$+ 0.0203264\cos\left(6t - \frac{\pi}{3} + 2.66658\right) \tag{3.69}$$

∎

The values of the operational transfer function calculated at different frequencies give the *frequency response* of the system. This topic is of great interest and will be studied in considerable detail in Chapters 5 and 7.

Example 3.10

We again refer to the R-C network shown in Figure 3.17 and determine the steady-state voltage v_2 if the input voltage is of the form of the square wave shown in Figure 3.3, with amplitude 5 V and period π s.

Using the result obtained in Example 3.2, the Fourier series for the input voltage may be written as

$$u(t) = \sum_{n=-\infty}^{\infty} c_n e^{j2nt} \qquad (3.70)$$

where

$$c_n = \begin{cases} 0 & \text{for even } n \\ \dfrac{-j10}{n\pi} & \text{for odd } n \end{cases} \qquad (3.71)$$

Since $\omega_0 = 2$ for this case, we calculate the nth harmonic component of the output by first evaluating the system operator at $\omega = 2n$.

$$\left. \frac{1}{p^2 + 3p + 1} \right|_{p=j2n} = \frac{1}{1 - 4n^2 + j6n} \qquad (3.72)$$

The Fourier coefficient of the nth harmonic of the steady-state output v_2, denoted by the symbol v_{2n}, is obtained by multiplying c_n with the value of the frequency response obtained from equation 3.72. After some complex arithmetic, we obtain

$$v_{2n} = \begin{cases} 0 & \text{for even } n \\ \dfrac{-60 + j10(4n - 1/n)}{\pi(1 + 28n^2 + 16n^4)} & \text{for odd } n \end{cases} \qquad (3.73)$$

Using the trigonometric form of the Fourier series, we get the steady-state output as

$$v_2(t) = \sum_{k=1}^{\infty} \frac{-6\cos(2k-1)2t - \left[4(2k-1) - \dfrac{1}{2k-1}\right]\sin(2k-1)2t}{0.05\pi\left[1 + 28(2k-1)^2 + 16(2k-1)^4\right]} \qquad (3.74)$$

It is possible to use equation 3.74 to obtain a plot of the waveform of the steady-state output by adding the various components. It can, however, be rather tedious unless it is done using a computer, since many terms must be added to obtain a good approximation to the correct waveform. A plot that was generated on a computer, after adding 50 terms of the Fourier series, is shown in Figure 3.18. A more direct approach, which does not require adding a large number of terms to get the waveform of the steady-state output, will be discussed in Chapter 5. This will be based on the use of Laplace transforms of causal functions that repeat every T s (as would be obtained by multiplying a periodic function with a unit step function) and a special technique for determining the steady-state component from the complete response. ∎

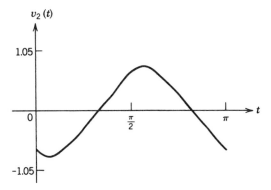

Figure 3.18 Plot of $v_2(t)$ from equation 3.74.

Drill Problem 3.6

Determine the steady-state output $v_2(t)$ of the network shown in Figure 3.17 if the input is given by

$$v_1(t) = 8 + 9\sin\left(t + \frac{\pi}{3}\right)$$

Answer: $8 + 3\sin(t - \frac{\pi}{6})$

3.4 SPECTRUM OF A PERIODIC SIGNAL

In general, a periodic function contains the fundamental sinusoid and a large (theoretically infinite) number of harmonics. The shape of the function depends on the relative values of the various harmonics. If we refer to the exponential form of the Fourier series, then c_n, which is in general a complex number, contains the information about the magnitude and the phase of each component of the waveform. If $|c_n|$, the magnitude of c_n, is plotted against $n\omega_0$, we obtain the *frequency spectrum* of the magnitude of the periodic function. In the same way, we could have plotted the frequency spectrum of the phase of c_n. By common usage, the spectrum of the magnitude of a periodic function is called its frequency spectrum, probably because it is invariant under time shift, whereas the spectrum of the phase changes with a shift along the time-axis. The magnitude spectrum of the square wave, derived in Example 3.2, is shown in Figure 3.19.

Note that the values of c_n have been shown only for positive n and hence only for positive values of ω. This is sufficient because for negative n we get the conjugate of c_n, with the same magnitude. It should also be noted that the frequency components are spaced ω_0 apart, although some of the components (even harmonics) have zero amplitude. Since the spectrum

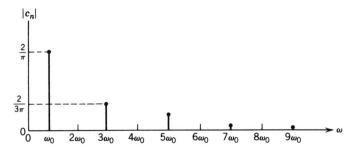

Figure 3.19 Magnitude spectrum of a square wave.

consists of discrete lines, it is called a *discrete spectrum*. This is characteristic of all periodic functions.

In Section 3.6 we extend this concept to aperiodic functions, which will be found to have continuous frequency spectra.

3.5 AVERAGE POWER OF A PERIODIC SIGNAL

It is customary to call the following integral the average power content of a periodic signal, $x(t)$:

$$P = \frac{1}{T}\int_{t_0}^{t_0+T} x^2(t)\, dt \qquad (3.75)$$

where T is the period of the signal. It will be seen that the quantity P would represent the actual average power delivered into a 1-Ω resistor if $x(t)$ is the current flowing through it or the voltage across it.

The property of orthogonality between the various harmonics in a Fourier series, shown in equations 3.7 and 3.9, makes it possible to find the average power in terms of the Fourier coefficients without performing the integration indicated in equation 3.75. It is easily shown, with the help of the integrals in equations 3.7 to 3.9, that

$$P = \frac{1}{T}\int_{t_0}^{t_0+T} x^2(t)\, dt = \sum_{n=-\infty}^{\infty} |c_n|^2 \qquad (3.76)$$

where c_n are the coefficients of the complex Fourier series for $x(t)$. This result is known as *Parseval's theorem*. It may also be expressed in terms of the coefficients of the trigonometric form of the Fourier series so that

$$P = a_0^2 + \frac{1}{2}\sum_{n=1}^{\infty} \left(a_n^2 + b_n^2\right) \qquad (3.77)$$

Note that the foregoing applies to power signals. In the case of energy signals, the average power is zero. Hence, for those signals we consider the total energy content of the signal. This will be discussed in Section 3.7.

Example 3.11

Consider the periodic signal described by the equation

$$x(t) = 10 + 20\cos 3t + 10\sin 3t + 8\cos 6t \qquad (3.78)$$

Using Parseval's theorem, the average power content is obtained as

$$P = 10^2 + \frac{(20^2 + 10^2 + 8^2)}{2} = 384$$

∎

Drill Problem 3.7

Use Parseval's theorem to prove that

$$\sum_{k=1}^{\infty} \frac{1}{(2k-1)^2} = \frac{\pi^2}{8}$$

(*Hint*: Use the Fourier series for a square wave of unit amplitude.)

3.6 THE FOURIER TRANSFORM

In Section 3.4 it was pointed out that the frequency spectrum of a periodic signal is discrete and can be obtained from its Fourier series. We now want to explore the possibility of extending the concept of frequency spectrum to aperiodic functions. This is very important because most of the time we come across signals that are aperiodic. One way to study this is to examine the effect of increasing the period of a signal. In the limit, when the period approaches infinity, we get an aperiodic signal. In other words, we are stipulating that an aperiodic signal can be regarded as a periodic signal with infinite period.

We start by recalling the two equations that were used for defining the exponential form of the Fourier series. Reproducing equations 3.20 and 3.21, we get

$$x(t) = \sum_{n=-\infty}^{\infty} c_n \exp(jn\omega_0 t) \qquad (3.79)$$

$$c_n = \frac{1}{T} \int_{t_0}^{t_0+T} x(t) \exp(-jn\omega_0 t)\, dt \qquad (3.80)$$

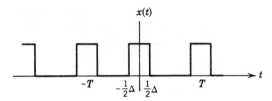

Figure 3.20 A periodic train of rectangular pulses.

where

$$\omega_0 = \frac{2\pi}{T} \tag{3.81}$$

As noted in Section 3.4, for a periodic function, we get a discrete spectrum, and the separation between the frequency components is equal to the fundamental frequency ω_0. For example, recall the periodic train of rectangular pulses that was considered in Example 3.3 and shown again in Figure 3.20.

It was shown in Example 3.3 that the coefficients c_n in the exponential Fourier series for this signal are given by

$$c_n = \frac{A\Delta}{2T} \operatorname{sinc} \frac{n\omega_0\Delta}{2} \tag{3.82}$$

where the sinc function was defined in equation 3.27 and a plot of the function was shown in Figure 3.7.

The frequency spectrum of this pulse train is the plot of the magnitude of c_n against ω and is nonzero for only integral multiples of the fundamental frequency ω_0. Since $\omega_0 = 2\pi/T$, we may write equation 3.82 as

$$c_n = \frac{A\Delta}{2T} \operatorname{sinc} \frac{n\pi\Delta}{T} \tag{3.83}$$

Evidently, the value of c_n for any given n will depend on the ratio of the duration of the pulse to the period Δ/T, and the sinc function will be the envelope of the spectrum. In other words, the Fourier coefficients will be equally spaced samples of the sinc function. Furthermore, the magnitudes of these samples will also depend on T. Therefore, to keep track of the effect of changes in the relative magnitudes and the spacing of the Fourier coefficients, we multiply both sides of equation 3.83 to obtain

$$c_n T = \frac{A\Delta}{2} \operatorname{sinc} \frac{n\pi\Delta}{T} \tag{3.84}$$

The plot of $c_n T$ versus ω is shown in Figure 3.21 for $\Delta/T = 0.4$ and in Figure 3.22 for $\Delta/T = 0.2$. Thus, we observe that as the period T is

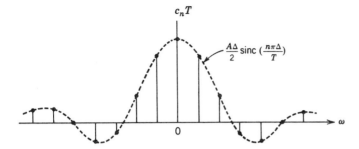

Figure 3.21 Frequency spectrum of the periodic train of rectangular pulses with $\Delta/T = 0.4$.

increased for a given Δ, the envelope of $c_n T$ is sampled with a closer spacing.

Let us now examine the effect of increasing the period T. In view of equation 3.82, this has the effect of reducing the value of the fundamental frequency ω_0. In the limit as T approaches infinity, we have

$$T \to \infty \qquad \omega_0 \to 0 \tag{3.85}$$

Therefore, the separation between the frequency components, which was ω_0 for the periodic case, will now be infinitesimally small. Let us denote this separation by $d\omega$. Consequently, *the discrete spectrum for the periodic function will be replaced with a continuous spectrum for an aperiodic function.* Also the summation, which was expressed by equation 3.79 for the complex form of the Fourier series, will have to be replaced by an integral. In view of these changes we shall modify equations 3.79 and 3.80 to obtain the following:

$$x(t) = \frac{1}{2\pi} \int_{-\infty}^{\infty} X(\omega) e^{j\omega t} \, d\omega \tag{3.86}$$

$$X(\omega) = \int_{-\infty}^{\infty} x(t) e^{-j\omega t} \, dt \tag{3.87}$$

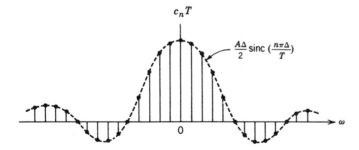

Figure 3.22 Frequency spectrum of the periodic train of rectangular pulses with $\Delta/T = 0.2$.

Equations 3.86 and 3.87 constitute the *Fourier transform pair* for aperiodic functions and are analogous to equations 3.79 and 3.80 for the Fourier series. First we compare equation 3.80 with equation 3.87. The former gives the value of the Fourier coefficient at a frequency $n\omega_0$ and the latter represents the value of the frequency component for a given ω. Note that the former requires division by the period T, but this division has been left out in the latter. It is natural to do so, since $T \to \infty$ for an aperiodic function and division by T would make the function zero. This implies that the magnitude of each frequency component approaches zero, and by avoiding the division by T we have obtained a function that preserves the relative magnitudes of the various frequency components of the signal. Thus both of these equations give the frequency spectra of the signals being considered and can be called the *analysis* equations, since they enable us to analyze the time functions into their frequency components. Similarly, we can call equations 3.79 and 3.86 the *synthesis* equations, since they enable us to synthesize the time function from its frequency components. The essential difference between these two equations is that the former is a summation due to the discrete nature of the spectrum of a periodic function, whereas the latter is an integral, since the spectrum of an aperiodic function has been shown to be continuous. It is customary to call the spectrum function $X(\omega)$ the *Fourier transform of* $x(t)$ whereas $x(t)$ is called the *inverse Fourier transform* of $X(\omega)$.

Just as for the Fourier series, the function $x(t)$ must satisfy the *Dirichlet conditions* in order for its Fourier transform to exist. These conditions ensure that the integral defined by equation 3.87 will converge for the particular function. They are as follows:

1. $x(t)$ must be absolutely integrable, that is,

$$\int_{-\infty}^{\infty} |x(t)|\, dt < \infty \tag{3.88}$$

2. $x(t)$ must have a finite number of maxima and minima within any finite interval of time.

3. $x(t)$ must have a finite number of discontinuities within any finite interval and each of these discontinuities must be finite.

It will be seen that these are quite similar to the Dirichlet conditions stated in Section 3.2.4.3 for the convergence of the Fourier series. In fact, these condition are sufficient for the existence of the Fourier transform, but can be relaxed if we are prepared to allow impulse functions in the transform. This will be discussed further in the sequel. First we shall consider some examples of Fourier transforms.

3.6.1   SOME FOURIER TRANSFORM PAIRS

In this section, we first derive the Fourier transforms for some common aperiodic functions. This is followed by the derivation of some inverse Fourier transforms. It is hoped that this will lead to some insight into the harmonic properties of these functions.

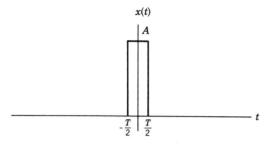

Figure 3.23   A rectangular pulse.

Example 3.12

Consider the rectangular pulse shown in Figure 3.23. Applying the definition given in equation 3.87, we get

$$X(\omega) = \int_{-T/2}^{T/2} Ae^{-j\omega t}\, dt = AT \operatorname{sinc}\left(\frac{\omega T}{2}\right) \tag{3.89}$$

The plot of $X(\omega)$ against ω is shown in Figure 3.24 at $AT = 1$.

It is interesting to compare the Fourier transform obtained above with the Fourier series of the periodic train of rectangular pulses obtained in Example 3.3, for which the frequency spectrum is shown in Figure 3.21. As expected, although the spectrum for the latter is discrete, its envelope is identical to the Fourier transform of the single rectangular pulse. ■

Example 3.13

Consider the exponential function

$$x(t) = e^{-at}\gamma(t) \tag{3.90}$$

A plot of this function is shown in Figure 3.25.

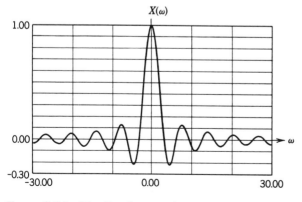

Figure 3.24   The Fourier transform of a rectangular pulse.

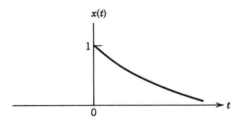

Figure 3.25 The function $x(t) = e^{-at}\gamma(t)$.

It is easily shown that this function will be absolutely integrable if and only if $a > 0$. In that case the Fourier transform will exist and is readily evaluated. From the definition given in equation 3.86 we obtain the following relationship

$$X(\omega) = \int_0^\infty e^{-at}e^{-j\omega t}\, dt = \frac{-1}{a + j\omega}e^{-(a+j\omega)t}\Big|_0^\infty$$

$$= \frac{1}{a + j\omega} \quad \text{for} \quad a > 0 \tag{3.91}$$

The Fourier transform for this function is complex. Expressing it in the polar form, we obtain the magnitude and the phase and plot these separately against ω, as shown in Figure 3.26. From equation 3.91, we get

$$X(\omega) = \frac{1}{\sqrt{(a^2 + \omega^2)}} \exp\left[-j\tan^{-1}\left(\frac{\omega}{a}\right)\right] \tag{3.92}$$

Example 3.14

We now determine the Fourier transform of the function

$$x(t) = Ae^{-a|t|}, a > 0 \tag{3.93}$$

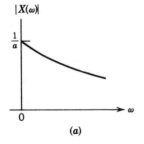

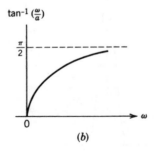

Figure 3.26 The Fourier transform of the function shown in Figure 3.25. (*a*) Plot of the magnitude. (*b*) Plot of the phase.

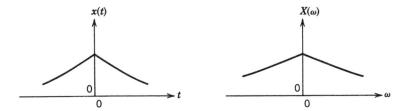

Figure 3.27 Fourier transform pair for Example 3.14.

which is an even function of time. From the basic definition we get

$$X(\omega) = \int_{-\infty}^{\infty} Ae^{-a|t|}e^{-j\omega t} \, dt$$

$$= \int_{0}^{\infty} Ae^{-at}e^{-j\omega t} \, dt + \int_{-\infty}^{0} Ae^{at}e^{-j\omega t} \, dt$$

$$= \frac{A}{a - j\omega} + \frac{A}{a + j\omega}$$

$$= \frac{2Aa}{a^2 + \omega^2} \tag{3.94}$$

Note that $X(\omega)$ is an even function and real for all ω in this case. Plots of $x(t)$ and $X(\omega)$ are shown in Figure 3.27. ∎

Example 3.15

Consider the unit impulse, $\delta(t - t_0)$, occurring at $t = t_0$. Because of the shifting property of the impulse function, which has been described in Section 2.5, its Fourier transform is obtained as

$$X(\omega) = \int_{-\infty}^{\infty} \delta(t - t_0)e^{-j\omega t} \, dt = e^{-j\omega t_0} \tag{3.95}$$

For the particular case when t_0 is zero, its value is 1. Plots of $x(t)$ and $|X(\omega)|$ for this case are shown in Figure 3.28. ∎

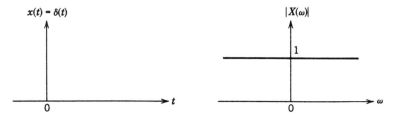

Figure 3.28 Fourier transform pair for Example 3.15.

It is interesting to observe that the magnitude of $X(\omega)$ is constant and equal to one for all values of t_0. The only effect of the timing of the impulse is on the phase of the Fourier transform. Furthermore, in the time domain, we have a very narrow function, an impulse that occurs at $t = t_0$ and is zero for all other values of time. On the other hand, in the frequency domain, its Fourier transform is spread uniformly over all frequencies. This is known as the *phenomenon of reciprocal spreading*, that is, if we compress the function in time, its frequency spectrum will be expanded, and if we expand the function in the time domain, its frequency spectrum will be compressed. We encounter this phenomenon in some other examples, and later we discuss this among the properties of Fourier transforms.

Example 3.16

We now determine the inverse Fourier transform of the function

$$X(\omega) = \delta(\omega) \tag{3.96}$$

which is a unit impulse in the frequency domain.
Using equation 3.86, we get

$$x(t) = \frac{1}{2\pi} \int_{-\infty}^{\infty} \delta(\omega) e^{j\omega t} \, d\omega = \frac{1}{2\pi} \tag{3.97}$$

Plots of $x(t)$ and $X(\omega)$ are shown in Figure 3.29.   ■

The corresponding time function is found to be a constant over the entire time domain, that is, for $-\infty < t < \infty$. This agrees with our intuitive idea that a constant for all time corresponds to zero frequency, so that its Fourier transform should be a unit impulse at $\omega = 0$. It also concurs with our observation in Example 3.15 regarding the phenomenon of reciprocal spreading. The situation here is just the opposite of that in the previous example, since a function that was spread uniformly in the time domain transforms into a narrow impulse in the frequency domain.

There is another important point about this example that should be noted. The time function in this case is not absolutely integrable, but we have seen that it does have a Fourier transform, which is an impulse. This will be

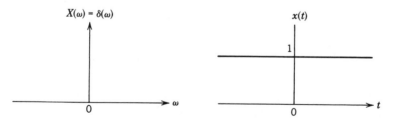

Figure 3.29   Fourier transform pair for Example 3.16.

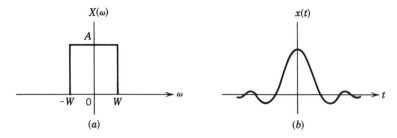

Figure 3.30 Fourier transform pair for Example 3.17.

brought up again in Example 3.19 when we discuss the properties of differentiation and integration in the time domain.

Example 3.17

We now determine the inverse Fourier transform for the case when $X(\omega)$ is a rectangular pulse in the frequency domain, as shown in Figure 3.30a.

To obtain the inverse transform, we again use equation 3.79. Thus, we have

$$x(t) = \frac{1}{2\pi} \int_{-\infty}^{\infty} X(\omega) e^{j\omega t} \, d\omega$$

$$= \frac{1}{2\pi} \int_{-W}^{W} A e^{j\omega t} \, d\omega = \frac{AW}{\pi} \frac{\sin Wt}{Wt} = \frac{AW}{\pi} \operatorname{sinc} Wt \qquad (3.98)$$

The time function in this case is a sinc function. It would be interesting to compare this result with that obtained in Example 3.13. In it we saw that a rectangular pulse in the time domain transformed into a sinc function in the frequency domain, whereas here a rectangular pulse in the frequency domain transformed into a sinc function in the time domain. Not only do we again see the phenomenon of reciprocal spreading but we may also observe the *property of duality* for Fourier transforms. This topic will be discussed in Section 3.6.2, along with several other interesting properties of Fourier transforms. ■

3.6.2 SOME PROPERTIES OF THE FOURIER TRANSFORM

In this section we consider some properties of the Fourier transform. These provide a considerable amount of insight into the transform and give us a better understanding of the relationship between the time-domain and frequency-domain representations of a signal. In addition, these properties can be used for obtaining the transforms more easily than is possible with direct application of the defining equations 3.86 and 3.87.

In these discussions we use, for convenience, the following short-hand notation to represent Fourier transformation,

$$X(\omega) = \mathscr{F}[x(t)] \text{ implies that } X(\omega)$$
$$\text{is the Fourier transform of } x(t) \tag{3.99}$$

and

$$x(t) = \mathscr{F}^{-1}[X(\omega)] \text{ implies that } x(t)$$
$$\text{is the inverse Fourier transform of } X(\omega) \tag{3.100}$$

3.6.2.1 Linearity

This property can be expressed as follows:
If

$$X_1(\omega) = \mathscr{F}[x_1(t)]$$

and

$$X_2(\omega) = \mathscr{F}[x_2(t)]$$

then

$$\mathscr{F}[a_1 x_1(t) + a_2 x_2(t)] = a_1 X_1(\omega) + a_2 X_2(\omega) \tag{3.101}$$

The proof of this property follows directly from the defining equations 3.86 and 3.87. It is very useful, since it allows us to obtain the Fourier transform of a linear combination of several functions as the same linear combination of their respective Fourier transforms. It can also be used for obtaining the inverse Fourier transform of a linear combination of several different functions, if the inverse transform of each of these is known. The following example will illustrate the procedure.

Example 3.18

Consider the following function for which the inverse Fourier transform has to be determined:

$$X(\omega) = \frac{12 + \omega^2}{4 + \omega^2} \tag{3.102}$$

By using the method of partial fraction expansion (described in detail in Chapter 5), this can be expressed as the sum of three standard functions as follows:

$$X(\omega) = 1 + \frac{2}{2 + j\omega} + \frac{2}{2 - j\omega} \tag{3.103}$$

The inverse transform is now easily obtained as

$$x(t) = \delta(t) + 2e^{-2|t|} \tag{3.104}$$

∎

3.6.2.2 Duality

In Section 3.6.1 it was seen that the Fourier transform of a rectangular pulse was the sinc function, whereas that of a sinc function was a rectangular pulse. Similarly, the Fourier transform of a constant was an impulse, whereas that of an impulse was a constant. These are summarized in Figure 3.31. This was called the phenomenon of reciprocal spreading. We now study the reason for this interesting and useful result.

An examination of equations 3.86 and 3.87 reveals that they are almost symmetrical in the variables t and ω, except for the factor 2π. This is the reason for the duality that we observed. An important advantage of this property is that we need not evaluate the integral in equation 3.86 if we have already obtained the same function by evaluating the integral in equation 3.87. The following relationship can be used for describing this property and will be proved.

$$\text{If } X(\omega) = \mathscr{F}\left[x(t)\right] \qquad \text{then} \qquad \mathscr{F}\left[X(t)\right] = 2\pi x(-\omega) \quad (3.105)$$

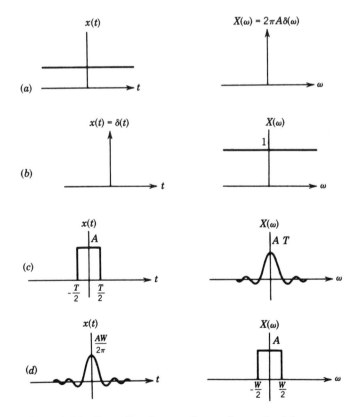

Figure 3.31 Some Fourier transform pairs emphasizing duality. (a) $x(t) = A$. (b) $x(t) = \delta(t)$. (c) $x(t)$ is a rectangular pulse. (d) $x(t)$ is a sinc function.

PROOF   By definition of the inverse Fourier transform

$$x(t) = \frac{1}{2\pi} \int_{-\infty}^{\infty} X(\omega)e^{j\omega t}\, d\omega$$

If we replace the variable ω by the dummy variable σ, we get

$$2\pi x(t) = \int_{-\infty}^{\infty} X(\sigma)e^{j\sigma t}\, d\sigma$$

The above equation will still be valid if we replace t by $-t$. Consequently,

$$2\pi x(-t) = \int_{-\infty}^{\infty} X(\sigma)e^{-j\sigma t}\, d\sigma$$

Let us now replace the variable t by ω. This gives us

$$2\pi x(-\omega) = \int_{-\infty}^{\infty} X(\sigma)e^{-j\sigma\omega}\, d\sigma = \mathscr{F}\left[X(t)\right]$$

where the last result has been obtained by replacing σ by t in the integral. This proves the relationship stated in equation 3.105.

In the particular case, when $x(t)$ is an even function, that is, when $x(-t) = x(t)$, we get $\mathscr{F}[X(t)] = 2\pi x(\omega)$. This is what we found in Examples 3.11 and 3.16. In the former, the time function was a rectangular pulse that was an even function of time. Its Fourier transform was found to be the sinc function, which was also an even function of ω. In Example 3.17 the inverse Fourier transform of the even rectangular pulse in the frequency domain was found to be the even sinc function in the time domain; in other words, the Fourier transform of the sinc function is the even rectangular pulse.

3.6.2.3   Differentiation and Integration in the Time Domain

Often we are required to determine the Fourier transform of a time function that is the derivative or integral of another time function for which the Fourier transform is already known. The following relationships are helpful in such instances.

If $\quad X(\omega) = \mathscr{F}\left[x(t)\right] \quad$ then $\quad \mathscr{F}\left[px(t)\right] = j\omega X(\omega)$

and

$$\mathscr{F}\left[\left(\frac{1}{p}\right)x(t)\right] = \left(\frac{1}{j\omega}\right)X(j\omega) + \pi X(0)\delta(\omega) \qquad (3.106)$$

The above equations imply that differentiation in the time domain is equivalent to multiplication by $j\omega$ in the frequency (or transform domain) and integration in the time domain is equivalent to division by $j\omega$ in the frequency domain, with the additional impulse term that reflects the dc or average value resulting from integration. We shall prove the equation for differentiation. Since integration is the inverse of differentiation, the other should follow.

PROOF From the definition of the inverse Fourier transform,

$$x(t) = \frac{1}{2\pi} \int_{-\infty}^{\infty} X(\omega) e^{j\omega t} \, d\omega$$

If we differentiate both sides of this equation with respect to time, we get

$$px(t) = \frac{1}{2\pi} \int_{-\infty}^{\infty} X(\omega) j\omega e^{j\omega t} \, d\omega$$

that is

$$px(t) = \mathscr{F}^{-1}[j\omega X(\omega)]$$

Example 3.19

In Example 3.15, we had seen that the Fourier transform of the unit impulse, occurring at time 0, is the constant 1. Also, the area under the impulse is one so that $X(0) = 1$. The Fourier transform of its integral, the unit step function, $\gamma(t)$, is therefore obtained as $1/(j\omega) + \pi\delta(\omega)$.

Note that the direct evaluation of the Fourier transform of the unit step is a little tricky, since the function does not satisfy the property of being absolutely integrable. The occurrence of the impulse in the Fourier transform also agrees with the result of Example 3.16 since the average or dc value of the unit step is 0.5. ∎

3.6.2.4 Time and Frequency Scaling

The phenomenon of reciprocal spreading was mentioned earlier. We now derive this from one of the properties of the Fourier transform.

If $\quad X(\omega) = \mathscr{F}[x(t)] \quad$ then $\quad \mathscr{F}[x(at)] = \frac{1}{|a|} X\left(\frac{\omega}{a}\right) \quad$ (3.107)

where a is a real constant.

PROOF From the definition of the Fourier transform,

$$X(\omega) = \int_{-\infty}^{\infty} x(t) e^{-j\omega t} \, dt$$

Let us now define a new variable $\sigma = at$, so that $d\sigma = a \, dt$. Substituting in the above, we get

$$\mathscr{F}\left[x(at)\right] = \int_{-\infty}^{\infty} x(at)e^{-j\omega t}\, dt = \int_{-\infty}^{\infty} x(\sigma)e^{-j\omega\sigma/a}\, d\sigma/a$$

$$= \int_{-\infty}^{\infty} \frac{1}{a}x(\sigma)e^{-j(\omega/a)\sigma}\, d\sigma = \frac{1}{a}X\!\left(\frac{\omega}{a}\right) \qquad \text{for } a > 0$$

$$\mathscr{F}\left[x(at)\right] = \int_{-\infty}^{\infty} x(at)e^{-j\omega t}\, dt = \int_{-\infty}^{\infty} x(\sigma)e^{-j\omega\sigma/a}\, d\sigma/a$$

$$= \int_{-\infty}^{\infty} -\frac{1}{a}x(\sigma)e^{-j(\omega/a)\sigma}\, d\sigma = -\frac{1}{a}X\!\left(\frac{\omega}{a}\right) \qquad \text{for } a < 0$$

This proves equation 3.107, which tells us that if we compress a function in the time domain by the factor a, its frequency spectrum will expand by the same factor. This also follows from the intuitive reasoning that when we compress the time duration of a signal, we make it change faster, thereby requiring higher frequency components. Similarly, when we expand the time duration of a signal, we make changes occur more slowly. Therefore, in this instance, we require lower frequency components. This provides us with a simple explanation for the phenomenon of reciprocal spreading that we had noticed earlier.

3.6.2.5 Time Shifting

It was seen in our discussion of periodic functions that a shift in time of the signal did not alter the magnitudes of the various harmonics but shifted their phase. It is therefore reasonable to expect a similar relationship in the case of the continuous frequency spectrum of aperiodic signals.

THEOREM

$$\text{If} \quad X(\omega) = \mathscr{F}\left[x(t)\right] \quad \text{then} \quad \mathscr{F}\left[x(t - t_0)\right] = e^{-j\omega t_0}X(\omega)$$

$$(3.108)$$

As expected, this theorem states that a delay in time by the amount t_0 causes a phase lag of ωt_0 for a frequency component of ω rad/s. As expected, the effect of the time shift is to change only the argument of the Fourier transform; the magnitude remains unchanged.

PROOF

$$\mathscr{F}\left[x(t - t_0)\right] = \int_{-\infty}^{\infty} x(t - t_0)\exp\left(-j\omega t\right)\, dt$$

$$= \int_{-\infty}^{\infty} x(\tau)\exp\left[-j\omega(\tau + t_0)\right]\, d\tau, \qquad \text{where } \tau = t - t_0$$

$$= \exp\left(-j\omega t_0\right)X(\omega)$$

Example 3.20

In Example 3.19 it was shown that the Fourier transform of the unit step function $\gamma(t)$ is given by $1/(j\omega) + \pi\delta(\omega)$. Consequently, it follows that the Fourier transform of the delayed unit step function $\gamma(t - t_0)$ will be $e^{-j\omega t_0}[1/(j\omega) + \pi\delta(\omega)]$. ∎

3.6.2.6 Frequency Shifting

Because of symmetry in the Fourier transform equations, we can expect a relationship similar to that derived in the last section, if there is a shift or translation in the spectrum of a signal, instead of in time. This is stated in the following theorem.

THEOREM

$$\text{If} \quad X(\omega) = \mathscr{F}\left[x(t)\right] \quad \text{then} \quad X(\omega - \omega_0) = \mathscr{F}\left[e^{j\omega_0 t}x(t)\right]$$

(3.109)

The proof of this theorem follows directly from the equation that defines the Fourier transform, where we just replace ω with $(\omega - \omega_0)$. It will be left as an exercise.

Frequency shifting also provides a simple mathematical explanation of modulation, where a time function is multiplied by a sinusoid, called the carrier signal. Since the sinusoid can be expressed as the sum of the two exponentials $e^{j\omega_0 t}$ and $e^{-j\omega_0 t}$, the effect of modulation is to shift the spectrum of the modulating signal as given by equation 3.109. Hence, the spectrum of the resulting signal is shifted and is centered around ω_0 as well as $-\omega_0$. This is illustrated in Figure 3.32.

3.6.2.7 Differentiation and Integration in the Frequency Domain

In Section 3.6.2.3, it was seen that differentiation in the time domain was equivalent to multiplication by $j\omega$ in the frequency domain and, as expected, integration in the time domain is equivalent to division by $j\omega$ in the

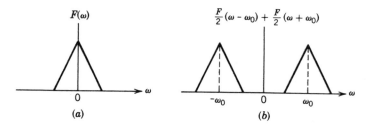

Figure 3.32 Spectra illustrating modulation. (*a*) Spectrum of modulating signal. (*b*) Spectrum of modulated signal.

frequency domain. In this section, we state similar results for differentiation and integration in the frequency domain.

THEOREM   If $X(\omega) = \mathscr{F}[x(t)]$ then

$$\frac{dX(\omega)}{d\omega} = \mathscr{F}[-jtx(t)] \tag{3.110}$$

that is, differentiation of the Fourier transform of a signal with respect to ω gives the Fourier transform of the original signal multiplied by $-jt$.

This is proved by simply differentiating the equation defining the Fourier transform with respect to ω.

Similarly, integration of the Fourier transform of a signal with respect to ω gives the Fourier series of the original signal divided by $-jt$. This follows easily, since integration is the inverse of differentiation.

These relations will be quite useful in extending our table of Fourier transform pairs, as will be seen in Section 3.6.4.

Drill Problem 3.8

Determine the Fourier transform of a single cycle of a sine wave, given by the equation

$$f(t) = A\sin\left(\frac{2\pi t}{T}\right) \quad \text{for} \quad 0 \le t \le T, \quad \text{and 0 otherwise}$$

Answer: $\dfrac{4\pi A/T}{(2\pi/T)^2 - \omega^2}\sin\left(\dfrac{\omega T}{2}\right)\exp\left[\dfrac{j(\pi - \omega T)}{2}\right]$

Drill Problem 3.9

Determine the Fourier transform of the function given below.

$$x(t) = A\left(1 - \frac{t}{T}\right) \quad \text{for} \quad 0 \le t \le T, \quad \text{and 0 otherwise}$$

Answer: $\dfrac{A[(1 + \cos\omega t) + j(\sin\omega T - \omega T)]}{(\omega^2 T)}$

3.6.3   CONVOLUTION

The concept of convolution was studied in Chapter 2 and had been found very useful, since it allows us to determine the response of a system to an arbitrary input from the knowledge of its impulse response. However, we also observed that the evaluation of the convolution integral is often quite tedious. In this section, we shall show that the Fourier transform may be used to find the response without evaluating the convolution integral. This is convolution in the time domain. Moreover, because of symmetry in the

Fourier transform equations, convolution in the frequency domain is also possible and has many applications. We start with the former.

3.6.3.1 Convolution in the Time Domain

This theorem may be stated as follows.

THEOREM Let $X(\omega) = \mathscr{F}[x(t)]$, $H(\omega) = \mathscr{F}[h(t)]$, and $Y(\omega) = \mathscr{F}[y(t)]$, where $x(t)$, $h(t)$, and $y(t)$ are related through the convolution integral

$$y(t) = \int_{-\infty}^{\infty} x(\tau)h(t - \tau)\, d\tau \tag{3.111}$$

then

$$Y(\omega) = H(\omega)X(\omega) \tag{3.112}$$

It will be noted that the operation of convolution in the time domain can be replaced by multiplication of the Fourier transforms of the input and the impulse response. The product is the Fourier transform of the output. To determine the corresponding time function we would therefore have to obtain the inverse Fourier transform of this product. Thus, we have been able to replace the need for evaluating the convolution integral with the need for finding the inverse transform of the product. This process will require much less effort, provided that we have suitable tables of transform pairs that can be utilized for obtaining the various Fourier transforms and their inverses. We shall also be able to give a meaning to the Fourier transform of the impulse response, which will provide us further insight.

PROOF From the definition of the Fourier transform

$$Y(\omega) = \int_{-\infty}^{\infty} y(t)e^{-j\omega t}\, dt = \int_{-\infty}^{\infty} e^{-j\omega t}\left[\int_{-\infty}^{\infty} x(\tau)h(t - \tau)\, d\tau\right] dt$$

$$= \int_{-\infty}^{\infty} x(\tau)\left[\int_{-\infty}^{\infty} h(t - \tau)e^{-j\omega t}\, dt\right] d\tau$$

For the integral inside the brackets, let $\sigma = t - \tau$ so that $d\sigma = dt$. Hence,

$$Y(\omega) = \int_{-\infty}^{\infty} x(\tau)\left[\int_{-\infty}^{\infty} h(\sigma)e^{-j\omega(\sigma + \tau)}\, d\sigma\right] d\tau$$

$$= \int_{-\infty}^{\infty} x(\tau)H(\omega)e^{-j\omega\tau}\, d\tau$$

$$= X(\omega)H(\omega)$$

This completes the proof.

The function $H(\omega)$, which is the Fourier transform of the impulse response of the system, can be given a very useful interpretation. From our discussions in Section 2.6.2, we recall that the impulse response of a system is obtained by solving the system differential equation, which was of order n, without any forcing function, but with the initial condition of the $(n - 1)$th derivative set to 1. In Section 3.2 we found that the steady-state response of the system to a sinusoidal input was obtained by replacing the operator p by $j\omega$ in the system function of the system and evaluating the resulting complex number for a given ω. This complex number was interpreted as the frequency response for that ω; the magnitude gave the ratio of the amplitudes of the output and input sinusoids, whereas the argument gave the phase shift between the output and the input. The Fourier transform of the impulse response of the system turns out to be just the operational transfer function with p replaced with $j\omega$. This should not be surprising, since we saw in Section 3.5.2 that differentiation in the time domain is equivalent to multiplying the Fourier transform by $j\omega$. It is a very useful result, since it tells us that the Fourier transform of the impulse response is also the frequency response function, obtained by replacing p with $j\omega$ in the operational transfer function of the system. It is also often a simpler way to obtain the impulse response, since we just have to obtain the inverse Fourier transform of the frequency response function $H(\omega)$. For this reason, $H(\omega)$ is also called the *transfer function* of the system. The following example will illustrate the procedure.

Example 3.21

Consider a linear system described by the following differential equation, where we have used the operator p to represent d/dt.

$$(p^2 + 6p + 8)y(t) = (2p + 3)u(t) \tag{3.113}$$

The transfer function of the system is given by

$$H(\omega) = \frac{2j\omega + 3}{(j\omega)^2 + 6j\omega + 8} \tag{3.114}$$

We first obtain the impulse response of the system from the inverse Fourier transform of $H(\omega)$. This is followed by the evaluation of the response of this system to the input $u = 3e^{-t}\gamma(t)$, using equation 3.109 instead of convolution. Both of these require inverse transformation, which will be done by partial fraction expansion. The detailed procedure for obtaining the partial fraction expansion will be discussed in Chapter 5, in connection with inverse Laplace transformation. First we note that

$$H(\omega) = \frac{2.5}{j\omega + 4} - \frac{0.5}{j\omega + 2} \tag{3.115}$$

Therefore, the impulse response is obtained as

$$h(t) = (2.5e^{-4t} - 0.5e^{-2t})\gamma(t) \tag{3.116}$$

The Fourier transform of the input is given by

$$U(\omega) = \frac{3}{j\omega + 1} \tag{3.117}$$

Therefore, the Fourier transform of the output is given by

$$Y(\omega) = \frac{3(2j\omega + 3)}{(j\omega + 1)(j\omega + 4)(j\omega + 2)}$$

$$= \frac{1}{j\omega + 1} - \frac{2.5}{j\omega + 4} + \frac{1.5}{j\omega + 2} \qquad (3.118)$$

Finally, taking the inverse Fourier transform yields

$$y(t) = e^{-t} - 2.5e^{-4t} + 1.5e^{-2t} \qquad (3.119)$$

■

This method requires much less effort than the evaluation of the convolution integral provided that the inverse Fourier transforms can be readily obtained. Having an exhaustive table of Fourier transform pairs of standard functions is, therefore, quite helpful.

The symmetry in the Fourier transform equations can be utilized for proving the convolution theorem in the frequency domain. This will be studied in the next section. As we shall learn in Section 3.8, it has many important applications, especially in the area of telecommunications.

3.6.3.2 Convolution in the Frequency Domain

This theorem makes it possible to obtain the transform of the product of two time functions by convolution in the frequency domain.

THEOREM   Let $X(\omega) = \mathcal{F}[x(t)]$ and $Y(\omega) = \mathcal{F}[y(t)]$. Then

$$\mathcal{F}[x(t)y(t)] = \frac{1}{2\pi} \int_{-\infty}^{\infty} X(u)Y(\omega - u) \, du \qquad (3.120)$$

PROOF   We prove this theorem by taking the inverse transform of the right-hand side of equation 3.120.

$$\mathcal{F}^{-1}\left[\frac{1}{2\pi} \int_{-\infty}^{\infty} X(u)Y(\omega - u) \, du\right]$$

$$= \frac{1}{(2\pi)^2} \int_{-\infty}^{\infty} e^{j\omega t} \int_{-\infty}^{\infty} X(u)Y(\omega - u) \, du \, d\omega$$

$$= \frac{1}{(2\pi)^2} \int_{-\infty}^{\infty} X(u)\left[\int_{-\infty}^{\infty} Y(\omega - u)e^{j\omega t} \, d\omega\right] du$$

$$= \frac{1}{(2\pi)^2} \int_{-\infty}^{\infty} X(u)\left[\int_{-\infty}^{\infty} Y(\sigma)e^{j(\sigma + u)t} \, d\sigma\right] du$$

$$(\text{where } \sigma = \omega - u, \, d\sigma = d\omega)$$

$$= \frac{1}{2\pi} \int_{-\infty}^{\infty} X(u)y(t)e^{jut} \, du$$

$$= x(t)y(t)$$

This proves the theorem.

Convolution in the frequency domain allows us to determine the spectrum of a modulated signal. In radio communication, a common practice is to allow a low-frequency signal to control the amplitude of a high-frequency carrier signal. This amounts to multiplying the two signals. The Fourier transform of the modulated signal produced in this manner is readily obtained through convolution of the Fourier transforms of the modulating signal and the carrier signal.

An important application of this theorem arises in the case when a continuous-time signal is sampled to obtain a discrete-time signal. Since this process can be regarded as multiplication in the time domain of the given continuous-time signal with a periodic train of impulses, the frequency spectrum of the resulting discrete-time signal can be obtained by convolution in the frequency domain. This will be discussed in detail in Chapter 4 and will be utilized for proving the well-known sampling theorem.

Drill Problem 3.10

A linear system is described by the following differential equation, written using the operational notation:

$$(p^2 + 5p + 6)y(t) = u(t)$$

Use the Fourier transform to determine the impulse response $h(t)$ of this system.

Answer: $(e^{-2t} - e^{-3t})\gamma(t)$

3.6.4 FOURIER TRANSFORMS OF PERIODIC FUNCTIONS

The functions for which we have obtained Fourier transforms thus far (with the exception of the unit step) have been *energy signals*, which contain a finite amount of energy over the interval $-\infty < t < \infty$ and are therefore absolutely integrable. Periodic functions, on the other hand, are *power signals* and are not absolutely integrable. We may recall that such functions do have a Fourier series representation, provided that they satisfy the condition of being absolutely integrable over one complete period and have a finite number of maxima, minima, and discontinuities in one period. Many periodic functions do have Fourier transforms, if we allow the transform to include impulse functions and, in some instance, higher order singularity functions.

In this section, we derive the Fourier transforms of some common periodic functions.

3.6.4.1 Fourier Transform of a Constant

In Example 3.17, it was shown that the inverse Fourier transform of the unit impulse function $\delta(\omega)$ was the constant $1/(2\pi)$. Therefore, it follows that the Fourier transform of a constant A must be $2\pi A\delta(\omega)$.

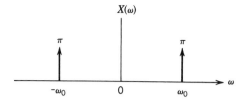

Figure 3.33 Fourier transform of $\cos \omega_0 t$.

3.6.4.2 Fourier Transform of a Sinusoid

The Fourier transform of a sinusoid can be determined by first expressing it in the form of complex exponentials, that is,

$$\cos \omega_0 t = \frac{\exp(j\omega_0 t) + \exp(-j\omega_0 t)}{2} \tag{3.121}$$

$$\sin \omega_0 t = \frac{\exp(j\omega_0 t) - \exp(-j\omega_0 t)}{2j} \tag{3.122}$$

Consequently, to evaluate the Fourier transforms of these functions, we must first obtain the Fourier transform of the exponential function $e^{j\omega_0 t}$. We do this by finding the inverse Fourier transform of the impulse function $\delta(\omega - \omega_0)$. By using equation 3.86 we get

$$x(t) = \frac{1}{2\pi} \int_{-\infty}^{\infty} \delta(\omega - \omega_0)e^{j\omega t} \, d\omega = \frac{1}{2\pi} e^{j\omega_0 t}$$

Therefore,

$$\mathscr{F}[e^{j\omega_0 t}] = 2\pi\delta(\omega - \omega_0) \tag{3.123}$$

Using equations 3.121 and 3.122, we immediately obtain the desired Fourier transforms

$$\mathscr{F}[\cos \omega_0 t] = \pi[\delta(\omega + \omega_0) + \delta(\omega - \omega_0)] \tag{3.124}$$

and

$$\mathscr{F}[\sin \omega_0 t] = j\pi[\delta(\omega + \omega_0) - \delta(\omega - \omega_0)] \tag{3.125}$$

These are shown in Figures 3.33 and 3.34 respectively.

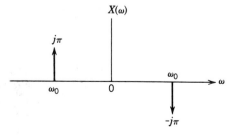

Figure 3.34 Fourier transform of $\sin \omega_0 t$.

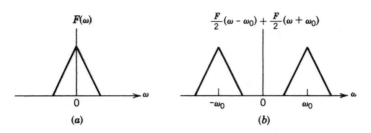

Figure 3.35 Spectra illustrating modulation. (a) Spectrum of modulating signal. (b) Spectrum of modulated signal.

TABLE 3.1 Fourier Transform Pairs

$x(t)$	$X(\omega)$	Comments
1. $A\delta(t - t_0)$	$Ae^{-j\omega t_0}$	Impulse at $t = t_0$
2. A	$2\pi A\delta(\omega)$	Constant
3. $A\gamma(t)$	$A\left[\dfrac{1}{j\omega} + \pi\delta(\omega)\right]$	Step function
4. $Ae^{-at}\gamma(t)$	$\dfrac{A}{j\omega + a}$	Valid only for $a > 0$
5. $Ae^{-a|t|}$	$\dfrac{2Aa}{a^2 + (j\omega)^2}$	Valid only for $a > 0$
6. $Ae^{-at}\cos \omega_0 t\,\gamma(t)$	$\dfrac{A(j\omega + a)}{(j\omega + a)^2 + \omega_0^2}$	Valid only for $a > 0$
7. $Ae^{-at}\sin \omega_0 t\,\gamma(t)$	$\dfrac{A\omega_0}{(j\omega + a)^2 + \omega_0^2}$	Valid only for $a > 0$
8. $Ate^{-at}\gamma(t)$	$\dfrac{A}{(j\omega + a)^2}$	Valid only for $a > 0$
9. $Ae^{j\omega t}$	$2A\pi\delta(\omega - \omega_0)$	
10. $A \cos \omega_0 t$	$A\pi[\delta(\omega + \omega_0) + \delta(\omega - \omega_0)]$	
11. $A \sin \omega_0 t$	$jA\pi[\delta(\omega + \omega_0) - \delta(\omega - \omega_0)]$	
12. $AP_T(t)$	$AT \text{ sinc}\left(\dfrac{\omega T}{2}\right)$	Rectangular pulse of height A for $-\dfrac{T}{2} < t < \dfrac{T}{2}$
13. $\dfrac{AW}{(2\pi)} \text{ sinc}\left(\dfrac{Wt}{2}\right)$	$AP_W(\omega)$	Sinc function

These results provide us with another approach to explain the modulation property. Multiplication of the modulating signal with the sinusoidal carrier leads to convolution in the frequency domain. Since the spectrum of the modulating signal is being convolved with the impulses at ω_0 and $-\omega_0$, the modulated signal must be shifted so that the original spectrum is centered around both ω_0 and $-\omega_0$, as illustrated in Figure 3.35. It should also be noted that the amplitude of the spectrum of the modulated signal is half of that of the modulating signal.

3.6.4.3 Fourier Transform of Any Periodic Signal

The results obtained above can be used directly to obtain the Fourier transform of any periodic signal. We start with the exponential form of the Fourier series of the signal and obtain the Fourier transform of each component using equation 3.123. Therefore, it follows that the Fourier transform for such a signal will consist of impulses located at the various harmonic frequencies of the signal. Furthermore, it is evident that any periodic signal that can be expressed by a Fourier series will have a Fourier transform of this type.

3.6.5 A SHORT TABLE OF FOURIER TRANSFORM PAIRS

In this section, we present a short table of Fourier transform pairs. (Table 3.1) Most have already been derived. The rest are easily obtained.

TABLE 3.2 Fourier Transform Theorems

1. Linearity	$\mathscr{F}[a_1 x_1(t) + a_2 x_2(t)] = X_1(\omega) + X_2(\omega)$
2. Duality	$\mathscr{F}[X(t)] = 2\pi x(-\omega)$
3. Time domain differentiation	$\mathscr{F}[p^n x(t)] = (j\omega)^n X(\omega)$
4. Time domain integration	$\mathscr{F}\left[\int_{-\infty}^{t} x(\tau)\, d\tau\right] = \dfrac{X(\omega)}{j\omega} + \pi X(0)\delta(\omega)$
5. Time or frequency scaling	$\mathscr{F}[x(at)] = \dfrac{1}{|a|}X\left(\dfrac{\omega}{a}\right)$
6. Time domain convolution	$\mathscr{F}\left[\int_{-\infty}^{\infty} x(\tau)h(t-\tau)\, d\tau\right] = X(\omega)H(\omega)$
7. Frequency convolution	$\mathscr{F}[x(t)y(t)] = \dfrac{1}{2\pi}\int_{-\infty}^{\infty} X(u)Y(\omega-u)\, du$
8. Time shifting	$\mathscr{F}[x(t-t_0)] = \exp(-j\omega t_0)X(\omega)$
9. Frequency shifting	$X(\omega - \omega_0) = \mathscr{F}[\exp(j\omega_0 t)x(t)]$
10. Frequency differentiation	$\mathscr{F}[tx(t)] = j\dfrac{dX(\omega)}{d\omega}$
11. Frequency integration	$\mathscr{F}\left[\left(\dfrac{1}{t}\right)x(t)\right] = j\int_{\omega}^{\infty} X(u)\, du$

3.6.6 SHORT TABLE OF FOURIER TRANSFORM THEOREMS

In this section we list in Table 3.2 the various theorems that were discussed as useful properties of Fourier transforms. These can be used effectively to obtain more pairs of transforms.

3.7 ENERGY CONTENT OF A SIGNAL

The *energy content* of a signal $x(t)$ is defined as

$$E = \int_{-\infty}^{\infty} x^2(t)\, dt \tag{3.126}$$

This integral represents the total energy that would be dissipated in a one-ohm resistor with the current $x(t)$ flowing through it or the voltage $x(t)$ across it.

Just as the power content of a periodic signal can be obtained from the coefficients of its Fourier series, we now show that the energy content of an aperiodic energy signal can be obtained from its Fourier transform. Using the definition of the inverse Fourier transform, we may write equation 3.126 as

$$E = \int_{-\infty}^{\infty} x(t) \left[\frac{1}{2\pi} \int_{-\infty}^{\infty} X(\omega) e^{j\omega t}\, d\omega \right] dt$$

$$= \frac{1}{2\pi} \int_{-\infty}^{\infty} X(\omega) \left[\int_{-\infty}^{\infty} x(t) e^{j\omega t}\, dt \right] d\omega$$

$$= \frac{1}{2\pi} \int_{-\infty}^{\infty} X(\omega) X(-\omega)\, d\omega \tag{3.127}$$

Since $x(t)$ is a real function of time, $X(-\omega) = X^*(\omega)$. Hence, we get

$$E = \int_{-\infty}^{\infty} x^2(t)\, dt = \frac{1}{2\pi} \int_{-\infty}^{\infty} |X(\omega)|^2\, d\omega \tag{3.128}$$

Equation 3.128 represents the generalized form of Parseval's theorem for aperiodic real functions of time with finite energy content.

The function $|X(\omega)|^2$ is known as the energy spectral density function of the signal $x(t)$, since it is a measure of the distribution of the total energy of the signal with frequency.

Drill Problem 3.11

Use the energy content of a rectangular pulse together with Parseval's theorem to evaluate the integral

$$\int_{-\infty}^{\infty} \text{sinc}^2(t)\, dt$$

Answer: π

Drill Problem 3.12

Use Parseval's theorem to determine the energy content of the function

$$x(t) = 10e^{-2t}\gamma(t)$$

Answer: 25

Drill Problem 3.13

Repeat Drill Problem 3.12 for the following functions

(a) $x(t) = 4e^{-2t}\cos 3t\,\gamma(t)$

(b) $x(t) = (5e^{-3t} + 3e^{-3t}\sin 2t)\gamma(t)$

Answer: (a) $\frac{2}{3}$ (b) $\frac{31}{240}$

3.8 SOME APPLICATIONS OF FOURIER TRANSFORMS

The Fourier transform has been applied widely for the analysis and design of communication systems. In this section we study two of the most important applications, modulation and demodulation, which are used in the transmission and reception of radio signals.

Signals produced by human voice and music are band-limited so that the Fourier transform of any audio signal will be negligibly small above the frequency of 20 kHz. Even if there is any component above this frequency, the human ear is incapable of detecting it. In fact, if components above 10 kHz are removed, most of us will be unable to find any difference. In telephone systems everything above 2.5 kHz is eliminated. Although the resulting signal is still intelligible, distortion is quite noticeable.

Electrical signals required to reproduce television pictures, on the other hand, are in the range of 7.5 kHz to 4 MHz. In North American practice, 525 lines are drawn on the screen 30 times a second. Thus, if we assume the same resolution in the vertical direction, we require a frequency of 525 × 525 × 30 ÷ 2, or 4,134,375 Hz, which is approximately 4 MHz, to be able to scan the complete picture 30 times per second. These are commonly called *video* signals.

Neither audio nor video signals are in the frequency range to be radiated efficiently for propagation through the atmosphere. The main reason is that the size of the antenna should be approximately one quarter of the wavelength of an electromagnetic wave. Since the product of the frequency and wavelength is the velocity of light, the wavelength at 4 MHz is given by

$$\lambda = \frac{3 \times 10^8}{4 \times 10^6} = 75 \text{ m} \tag{3.129}$$

which is rather large. For audio frequencies, this value is increased by a factor of 2000, that is, 150,000 m.

Consequently, to transmit audio or video signals through the atmosphere in an efficient manner, it is essential that these signals be moved up in frequency, without losing their information content. This is the process of modulation and requires the use of a high-frequency *carrier wave*, which is modified in some way to include the information content of the original signal. At the receiving end, the signals have to brought back to their original frequency range. This is the process of demodulation. We shall discuss modulation in the next subsection. It will be followed by a study of the process of demodulation.

3.8.1 MODULATION

The basic idea in modulation is to modify the carrier wave in such a way that it contains the information in the input signal. As a result, a general expression of this modified waveform is given by

$$m(t) = f(t) \cos\left[\omega_c t + \phi(t)\right] \tag{3.130}$$

where ω_c is the radian frequency of the carrier waveform, $f(t)$ is its amplitude, and $\phi(t)$ is its phase. Note that both the amplitude and the phase of the modulated signal are assumed to be time-varying in equation 3.130. We consider two special cases here. If $\phi(t)$ is kept constant but $f(t)$ is allowed to vary according to the modulating signal, the resulting expression is said to be an amplitude modulated (AM) signal. On the other hand, if we keep the amplitude constant and allow $\phi(t)$ to vary in some way according to the modulating signal, we get a phase modulated (PM) signal. A special case of phase modulation is called frequency modulation or FM. We shall discuss amplitude modulation first.

3.8.1.1 Amplitude Modulation

Consider the case when $\phi(t)$ is set to a constant value, say 0, and the amplitude of the modulated signal is expressed as

$$f(t) = A + \lambda f_m(t) \tag{3.131}$$

where A and λ are constants and $f_m(t)$ is the modulating signal. Therefore, the resulting modulated signal is given by the expression

$$m(t) = \left[A + \lambda f_m(t)\right] \cos \omega_c t \tag{3.132}$$

Note that the information is contained only in the modulating signal $f_m(t)$. Plots of the unmodulated and modulated carrier are shown in Figure 3.36. It will be seen that although the unmodulated carrier is a pure sinusoid, after modulation, its envelope takes the shape of the modulating signal.

From equation 3.132 it is evident that the modulated signal is made up of two terms. The first is the carrier signal $A \cos \omega_c t$, while the second term is the product of the modulating signal $f_m(t)$ and the carrier signal $\lambda \cos \omega_c t$. The frequency spectrum of the second term can be obtained through convolution of the modulating signal and carrier in the frequency domain. This was

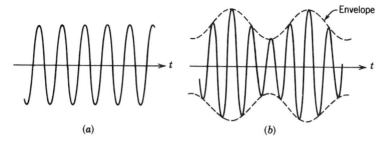

Figure 3.36 Waveforms of the unmodulated and modulated carrier. (*a*) Unmodulated carrier. (*b*) Carrier after amplitude modulation.

considered in Section 3.6.4.2, where it was shown that if the spectrum of the modulating signal is given by $F_m(\omega)$, then the spectrum of the product will be given by

$$M(\omega) = \tfrac{1}{2}F_m(\omega - \omega_c) + \tfrac{1}{2}F_m(\omega + \omega_c) \qquad (3.133)$$

as illustrated in Figure 3.35.

Thus, we note that the effect of amplitude modulation is to produce two *sidebands* of the carrier frequency, as shown in Figure 3.35, and that the complete information is contained in either of the sidebands. The procedure for recovering the information from the sidebands will be discussed in the subsection on demodulation.

3.8.1.2 Frequency Modulation

Let us now consider the case when the amplitude of the modulated signal is held constant, say equal to A, but its phase $\phi(t)$ varies with time according to the relationship

$$\phi(t) = \lambda \int_0^t f_m(\tau)\,d\tau \qquad (3.134)$$

Consequently, the modulated signal may be written as

$$m(t) = A \cos\left(\omega_c t + \lambda \int_0^t f_m(\tau)\,d\tau\right) \qquad (3.135)$$

Let us now define an angle $\theta(t)$ as

$$\theta(t) = \omega_c t + \lambda \int_0^t f_m(\tau)\,d\tau \qquad (3.136)$$

Note that $\theta(t)$ is the instantaneous phase of the modulated signal $m(t)$ in equation 3.135. We can determine the instantaneous frequency of $m(t)$ by differentiating $\theta(t)$ with respect to t. Hence, we obtain

$$\omega(t) = \omega_c + \lambda f_m(t) \qquad (3.137)$$

From equation 3.137 we conclude that now the frequency is varying with time

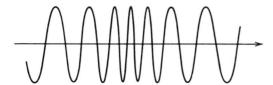

Figure 3.37 A frequency modulated signal.

in accordance with the modulating signal $f_m(t)$. Thus, the resulting signal $m(t)$ is said to be frequency modulated. A typical frequency modulated signal is shown in Figure 3.37.

Phase modulation is obtained if we vary the phase ϕ according the modulating signal, as shown here:

$$\phi(t) = \lambda f_m(t) \tag{3.138}$$

The modulated signal, $m(t)$ is therefore given by

$$m(t) = A \cos \left[\omega_c t + \lambda f_m(t) \right] \tag{3.139}$$

Thus, for this case, we have

$$\theta(t) = \omega_c t + \lambda f_m(t) \tag{3.140}$$

and the resulting instantaneous frequency is obtained by differentiating θ with respect to time as before. This gives us

$$\omega(t) = \omega_c + \lambda \frac{df_m(t)}{dt} \tag{3.141}$$

It will be seen that frequency modulation and phase modulation are closely related. In both cases, the amplitude of the modulated signal is held constant and the frequency is allowed to vary around the carrier. For frequency modulation, the instantaneous frequency varies according to the modulating signal, whereas for phase modulation the instantaneous frequency varies according to the time derivative of the modulating signal.

Spectrum analysis for frequency and phase modulated signals is a little more involved than for amplitude modulation. Therefore, we consider only the case of frequency modulation with a sinusoidal modulating signal so that

$$f_m(t) = B \cos \omega_m(t) \tag{3.142}$$

where B is a constant and ω_m is the angular frequency of the modulating signal. The angular frequency of the modulated signal is given by

$$\omega(t) = \omega_c + \lambda B \cos \omega_m(t) \tag{3.143}$$

Thus, the instantaneous frequency of the modulated signal varies sinusoidally between $\omega_c + \lambda B$ and $\omega_c - \lambda B$. Let us define

$$\Delta \omega = \lambda B \tag{3.144}$$

as the *frequency deviation*. We now obtain the following expression for the modulated signal by substituting equations 3.142 to 3.144 into 3.135:

$$m(t) = A \cos \left[\omega_c t + \lambda \int_0^t B \cos \omega_m(t) \, dt \right]$$

$$= A \cos \left[\omega_c t + \frac{\Delta \omega}{\omega_m} \sin \omega_m t \right] \qquad (3.145)$$

Defining the factor $\Delta \omega / \omega_m$ as the *modulation index* m_i, we may rewrite and simplify equation 3.145 as

$$m(t) = A \cos \left(\omega_c t + m_i \sin \omega_m t \right)$$

$$= A \cos \omega_c t \cos \left(m_i \sin \omega_m t \right) - A \sin \omega_c t \sin \left(m_i \sin \omega_m t \right) \quad (3.146)$$

Equation 3.146 leads to an easy interpretation for the special case (called narrow-band FM) when the modulation index m_i is small compared with one (of the order of 0.1), since in that case, we have

$$\cos \left(m_i \sin \omega_m t \right) \approx 1 \qquad (3.147)$$

and

$$\sin \left(m_i \sin \omega_m t \right) \approx m_i \sin \omega_m t \qquad (3.148)$$

Consequently, equation 3.146 may be simplified to yield

$$m(t) \approx A \cos \omega_c t - A m_i \sin \omega_c t \sin \omega_m t$$

$$\approx A \cos \omega_c t - 0.5 A m_i \left[\cos \left(\omega_c - \omega_m \right) t - \cos \left(\omega_c + \omega_m \right) t \right]. \quad (3.149)$$

It is evident from equation 3.149 that the modulated signal contains sinusoids at frequencies ω_c, $\omega_c - \omega_m$, and $\omega_c + \omega_m$. The Fourier transform of $m(t)$, shown in Figure 3.38, is seen to be similar to that obtained by amplitude modulation with a sinusoidal modulating signal, but now the carrier differs in phase with the modulated carrier by $\pi/2$.

The analysis presented above does not apply for *wide-band FM*, the case when m_i is not small. The spectrum of the modulated signal for this case depends on both the amplitude and spectrum of the modulating signal. For a

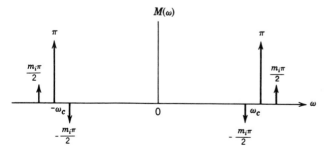

Figure 3.38 Approximate spectrum for narrow-band FM.

sinusoidal modulating signal, the spectrum of the modulated signal can be determined from equation 3.146. It may be noted that this equation contains terms $\cos(m_i \sin \omega_m t)$ and $\sin(m_i \sin \omega_m t)$, which are periodic signals with fundamental frequency ω_m. The Fourier coefficients of the resulting Fourier series for these two periodic signals involve Bessel functions of the first kind. Without getting into the details, we can easily see that the modulated signal $m(t)$ in equation 3.146 will contain many frequency components of the form $\omega_c + k\omega_m$, $k = 0, 1, 2, \ldots$, because these periodic signals are multiplied by the carrier signal. In practice, the components for $k > m_i$ can be considered negligible. Thus, the total bandwidth of the frequency modulated signal is approximately equal to $2m_i\omega_m$, centered around the carrier frequency.

In general, the bandwidth of FM signals is larger than that of AM signals, but they are less affected by noise. However, it is necessary that the frequency of the carrier be tightly controlled. This is often achieved by using a phase-locked loop, which is a feedback method for "locking" the phase. The interested reader is referred to a suitable book on communication systems to learn more about these methods.

3.8.2 DEMODULATION

Demodulation is the process by which the original information-bearing signal is extracted from the modulated signal. This is carried out at the receiver and can be regarded as bringing the spectrum of the message signal back down to its original low-frequency location. Thus demodulation is the inverse operation of modulation.

Demodulation can be accomplished in many ways and also depends on the method used for modulation. For example, an amplitude modulated signal is easily demodulated if we multiply it at the receiving end with the carrier signal and then pass it through a low-pass filter. This is known as *coherent* or *synchronous* demodulation, since it requires that the carrier frequency signal used at the receiver should be locked in phase with the carrier signal at the transmitter. The basic idea behind this method is evident immediately by recalling that the spectrum of the amplitude modulated signal is, as shown in Figure 3.39a, centered around the frequencies $-\omega_c$ and ω_c. Multiplication of this signal by a sinusoid at the frequency of the carrier will again produce components at frequencies obtained by adding $\pm\omega_c$ to the frequencies of the modulated carrier. The frequency spectrum of the resulting signal is shown in Figure 3.39b. It is easily seen that it has components at the modulating frequency as well as at frequencies obtained by adding $\pm 2\omega_c$ to the modulating frequency. The low-pass filter effectively removes the high-frequency components and recovers the modulating signal.

There are many other methods for modulation and demodulation. A very popular method of modulation is based on sampling the modulating signal with a periodic sequence of pulses. This is called *pulse modulation* and can be done in several ways. The basic idea behind this approach will be discussed in the next chapter, where we also present the sampling theorem.

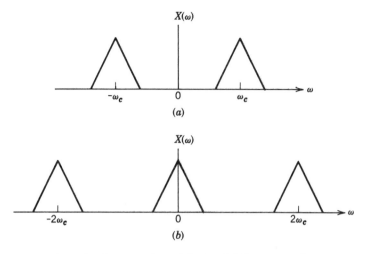

Figure 3.39 Synchronous demodulation. (*a*) Spectrum of amplitude modulated signal. (*b*) Spectrum after multiplication by $\cos \omega_c t$.

3.9 SUMMARY

In this chapter we have studied the representation of signals as a sum of sinusoids. For periodic functions, we obtain a sum of sinusoids with integrally related frequencies, known as the fundamental component and the harmonics. Both the trigonometric and the exponential forms of the Fourier series were studied along with the method of evaluation of Fourier coefficients. The effects of symmetry as well as some properties of the Fourier series were discussed. These led to the study of the steady-state response of linear systems to periodic inputs; it was found that the exponential form of the Fourier series enabled us to extend the use of phasors to nonsinusoidal periodic inputs. The concept of frequency response of linear systems follows as a direct consequence of this observation. The section on Fourier series concluded with the notion of the frequency spectrum of a signal; it was observed that the frequency spectrum of periodic functions is discrete, with components only at integral multiples of the fundamental frequency.

The study was then extended to aperiodic functions, which were found to have a continuous frequency spectrum. The Fourier transform was then introduced as the limiting form of the Fourier series. Some very interesting properties of the Fourier transform were discussed. These include the phenomenon of reciprocal spreading, convolution in the time and frequency domains, time and frequency scaling, effects of differentiation and integration in the time and frequency domain, and shifting in time and frequency. Many of these concepts have interesting practical applications.

This was followed by the study of Parseval's theorem and energy spectral density of a signal. The chapter concluded with a brief description of modulation and demodulation as examples of application of the Fourier transform to communication systems.

Our studies in this chapter emphasize that a signal has a unique representation in both time and frequency domains. Furthermore, these two representations are related so that altering the signal in the time domain will also alter its frequency domain counterpart. For many applications, the latter is more useful and provides us with a great deal of information about the signal that can be utilized in applications like filtering, modulation, and signal processing.

3.10 PROBLEMS

3.1 The waveforms of one cycle of several periodic functions are shown in Figure 3.40. Determine the trigonometric form of the Fourier series for each case.

3.2 Determine the exponential form of the Fourier series for each of the waveforms shown in Figure 3.40.

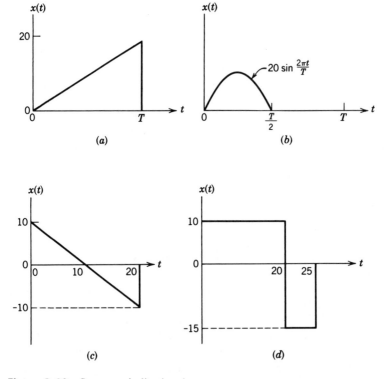

Figure 3.40 Some periodic signals.

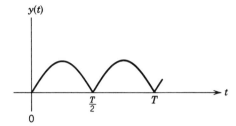

Figure 3.41   Waveform of a full-wave rectifier.

3.3   Determine the Fourier series of a periodic train of triangular pulses spaced T seconds apart. Each pulse is shaped like an isosceles triangle of height A and width Δ, with the base coinciding with the time axis.

3.4   A dc power supply uses a full-wave rectifier that can be described by the input–output equation $y(t) = |x(t)|$. The waveform is shown in Figure 3.41. Obtain the Fourier series for $y(t)$ if $x(t) = 200 \sin 377t$.

3.5   Repeat the previous problem if $x(t) = 200 \cos 377t$.

3.6   Consider the square wave shown in Figure 3.3. Determine the Fourier series in the trigonometric form if the wave is shifted to the left by a quarter period. What will be the Fourier series in the exponential form?

3.7   Repeat Problem 3.6 if the waveform in Figure 3.3 is shifted to the right by $T/3$.

3.8   Determine the Fourier series for a signal $x(t)$ of period 10 s if it is given by $x(t) = 10e^{-2t}$ during the first half-cycle, starting at $t = 0$, and is zero in the second half-cycle.

3.9   A signal $x(t)$ has a period of 10 s. The following equations describe the function during the period $0 \le t \le 10$.

$$x = 4e^{0.2t}, \qquad \text{for} \quad 0 < t < 5$$

$$x = 4e^{0.2(6-t)}, \qquad \text{for} \quad 5 < t < 10$$

(a)   Sketch the signal against time for the full period. Does it have any discontinuities?

(b)   Determine the Fourier series for this signal.

3.10   An electronic amplifier has a gain of 10, but it saturates when the input exceeds 1. In mathematical terms, the output of the amplifier is related to the input through the following equation:

$$y = \begin{cases} 10x & \text{if } |x| \le 1 \\ 10\,\text{sgn}\,(x) & \text{if } |x| > 1 \end{cases}$$

where $\text{sgn}\,(x)$ is the signum function, which has the value 1 if $x \ge 0$ and

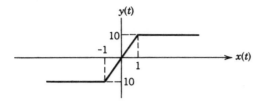

Figure 3.42 Amplifier with saturation.

-1 if $x < 0$. The relationship between $x(t)$ and $y(t)$ is shown in Figure 3.42. Determine the Fourier series for $y(t)$ if $x(t) = 1.5 \sin \omega_0 t$.

3.11 Repeat Problem 3.10 if $x(t) = 2 \sin \omega_0 t$.

3.12 The differential equation for a linear system is given below, using the operator notation.

$$(p^2 + 4p + 13)y(t) = (3p + 2)u(t)$$

Determine the steady-state solution for $y(t)$ if
(a) $u(t) = 10 \cos 3t$
(b) $u(t) = 5 + 3 \cos\left(2t + \dfrac{\pi}{6}\right) + 4 \cos\left(4t - \dfrac{\pi}{3}\right)$

3.13 The differential equation for a third-order low-pass filter is given below.

$$(p + 1)(p^2 + p + 1)y(t) = u(t)$$

Determine the steady-state output if the input is given by
(a) $u(t) = 2 \cos 0.5t$
(b) $u(t) = 2 \cos t$
(c) $u(t) = 2 \cos 1.4t$
(d) $u(t)$ is a square wave of period 2π s and amplitude 10. (*Hint:* Use only the first three terms of the Fourier series to approximate the input.)

3.14 Consider the R-C network shown in Figure 3.17. Determine the steady-state output $v_2(t)$ if the input voltage is given by

$$u(t) = 4 + 10 \cos\left(2t + \frac{\pi}{6}\right)$$

3.15 Repeat Problem 3.14 if the input voltage is of sawtoothed waveform, as shown in Figure 3.40a. Take the period $T = 2\pi$ s.

3.16 Find the Fourier transform of the signum function shown in Figure 3.43. (See Problem 3.10 for the definition of the signum function.)

3.17 Obtain the Fourier transforms of the following signals
(a) $x(t) = A[\gamma(t) - \gamma(t - 1)]$
(b) $x(t) = Ae^{-at}[\gamma(t) - \gamma(t - 1)]$

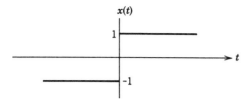

Figure 3.43 The signum function.

3.18 Determine the Fourier transforms of the signals shown in Figure 3.44. In each case, use the properties of Fourier transforms to minimize the effort required.

3.19 Use the results of the previous problem to determine the signals that have the Fourier transforms shown in Figure 3.45.

3.20 Determine the Fourier transform of a triangular pulse of height A and duration Δ. It is shaped like an isosceles triangle with the base coinciding with the time axis and centered around $t = 0$ as shown in Figure 3.46.

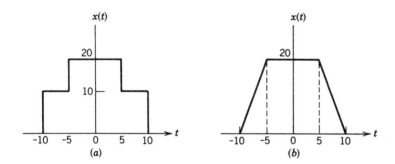

Figure 3.44 Some aperiodic time functions.

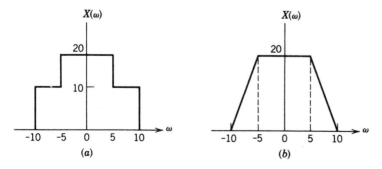

Figure 3.45 Some Fourier transforms.

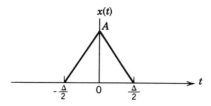

Figure 3.46 Waveform for Problem 3.20.

3.21 The Fourier transform of a continuous-time signal is shaped like the triangular pulse described in the previous problem. The width of the pulse is B and it is centered around the origin at the ω-axis. Determine the inverse Fourier transform.

3.22 The Fourier transform of a continuous-time signal $x(t)$ is given by

$$X(\omega) = \frac{10}{j\omega + 4}$$

Determine the Fourier transform $Y(\omega)$ of each of the signals given below:

(a) $y(t) = tx(t)$

(b) $y(t) = e^{-2t}x(t)$

(c) $y(t) = x(t)\cos 2t$

(d) $y(t) = \dfrac{d^2x}{dt^2}$

(e) $y(t) = x(2t - 3)$

(f) $y(t) = x^2(t)$

(g) $y(t) = \displaystyle\int_{-\infty}^{\infty} x(\tau)x(t - \tau)\,d\tau$

3.23 The voltage and current in an electrical network are given by the following equations

$$v(t) = 20 + 100\cos 377t + 50\cos\left(1131t + \frac{\pi}{3}\right)$$

$$i(t) = 5 + 7\cos\left(377t - \frac{\pi}{10}\right) + 4\cos\left(1131t + \frac{\pi}{4}\right)$$

Determine the average power supplied to the network.

3.24 Obtain the energy spectral densities of the signals described in Problem 3.17.

3.25 Use Parseval's theorem to determine the energy spectral densities of the signals shown in Figure 3.44.

3.26 The autocorrelation function $\phi(\tau)$ of a function $f(t)$ may be defined as

$$\phi(\tau) = \int_{-\infty}^{\infty} f(t)f(t - \tau)\,dt$$

(a) Show that $\phi(\tau)$ is an even function of τ.

(b) The Fourier transform of $\phi(\tau)$ is called the spectral density of $f(t)$ and is denoted by $\Phi(\omega)$. Prove that $\Phi(\omega)$ is given by

$$\Phi(\omega) = F(\omega)F(-\omega) = |F(\omega)|^2$$

(c) Is it possible to find $f(t)$ uniquely from $\Phi(\omega)$? Justify your answer.

(d) Determine the autocorrelation function and the spectral density of each of the following functions: (i) $e^{-t}\gamma(t)$, (ii) $e^{-t}\gamma(-t)$, and (iii) a rectangular pulse of height A, width Δ, and centered around $t = 0$.

APPENDIX 3.1

Fourier Series for Some Common Waveforms

1. Square wave
(odd symmetry)

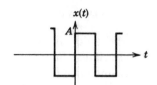

$$x(t) = \sum_{\substack{n=1 \\ (\text{odd } n)}}^{\infty} \frac{4A}{n\pi} \sin n\omega_0 t$$

2. Square wave
(even symmetry)

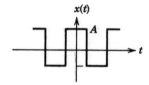

$$x(t) = \sum_{n=1}^{\infty} \frac{4A}{n\pi} \sin\left(\frac{n\pi}{2}\right) \cos n\omega_0 t$$

3. Sawtooth wave

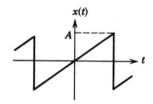

$$x(t) = \sum_{n=1}^{\infty} (-1)^{n+1} \frac{2A}{n\pi} \sin n\omega_0 t$$

4. Triangular wave

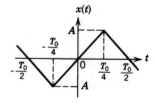

$$x(t) = \sum_{n=1}^{\infty} \frac{8A}{n^2\pi^2} \sin \frac{n\pi}{2} \sin n\omega_0 t$$

5. Pulse train

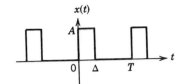

$$x(t) = \sum_{n=-\infty}^{\infty} \frac{A}{n\pi} \sin \frac{n\pi\Delta}{T} \exp\left[jn\omega_0\left(\frac{t-\Delta}{2}\right)\right]$$

6. Full-wave rectifier

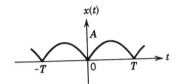

$$x(t) = \frac{2A}{\pi} + \sum_{n=1}^{\infty} \frac{4A}{\pi(1-4n^2)} \cos n\omega_0 t$$

7. Half-wave rectifier

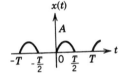

$$x(t) = \frac{A}{\pi} + \frac{A}{2} \sin \omega_0 t + \sum_{n=1}^{\infty} \frac{2A}{\pi(1-n^2)} \cos 2n\omega_0 t$$

8. Backward sawtooth

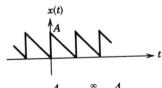

$$x(t) = \frac{A}{2} + \sum_{n=1}^{\infty} \frac{A}{\pi n} \sin n\omega_0 t$$

Fourier Analysis of Discrete-Time Signals

4.1 INTRODUCTION

In Chapter 3 we learned how periodic continuous-time signals can be represented as a superposition of sinusoids in the form of a Fourier series. This was extended to nonperiodic signals through the use of Fourier transforms. In both cases, the given signal was viewed through its frequency spectrum, which was found to be discrete for periodic functions and continuous for nonperiodic functions. It was seen that this frequency domain representation of signals has several advantages. These include convenience in evaluating the response of a linear system to a general periodic or nonperiodic input as well as a better understanding of the nature of the input and output signals. Therefore, it is natural that we attempt to extend these concepts to the class of discrete-time signals.

In this chapter we shall study the discrete-time counterpart of the theory studied in the previous chapter. In the next section we shall start with the Fourier series representation of periodic discrete-time signals. This will be followed by a study of the discrete-time version of the Fourier transform and the frequency spectra of periodic and aperiodic discrete-time signals. This will allow us to get a good understanding of the sampling theorem, which will be proved in Section 4.4. In the following section we shall study the discrete Fourier transform (DFT). It is different from the discrete-time Fourier transform (DTFT), which is a continuous function of frequency, in that here we consider time-limited discrete-time signals. The resulting transform (DFT) is a discrete function of a finite number of frequencies. This transform is more suitable for use with digital computers and, hence, is used extensively in digital signal processing. In Section 4.6 we study one version of an efficient algorithm for computing the DFT, popularly known as the fast Fourier transform (FFT) algorithm. Properties of the DFT are presented in Section 4.7. Finally, some applications of the DFT are discussed in Section 4.8.

The subject material in this chapter is relatively new. It has assumed great importance in recent years because of the availability of low-cost

156

microprocessors, which are now used as components in a variety of systems. This has led to a great deal of interest in digital signal processing, which has attracted a lot of attention during the last 25 years. In this chapter we propose to lay the foundation for this important subject.

4.2 FOURIER SERIES FOR PERIODIC DISCRETE-TIME SIGNALS

In Chapter 2 a discrete-time signal $x(n)$ was defined as being periodic if for some positive integer N,

$$x(n) = x(n + N) \tag{4.1}$$

The smallest value of N for which equation 4.1 is satisfied is defined as the period of the signal. It was also pointed out that, just as for the case of continuous-time signals, the simplest periodic sequence is the sinusoid, of the form

$$x(n) = a_n \cos\left(\frac{2\pi n}{N}\right) \tag{4.2}$$

or

$$x(n) = b_n \sin\left(\frac{2\pi n}{N}\right) \tag{4.3}$$

We defined the angular frequency for discrete-time periodic signals as

$$\Omega = \frac{2\pi}{N} \tag{4.4}$$

and pointed out that Ω has the unit of radians, whereas for continuous-time signals the angular frequency ω had the dimension of radians per second.

Some other important differences between periodic continuous-time and discrete-time signals will now be pointed out. First we note that the requirement that the period N be an integer implies that the $\Omega/(2\pi)$ is the reciprocal of an integer and thus a rational number. For example, the sequence $\cos(n/5)$ will not be periodic, whereas the sequence $\cos(2\pi/7)$ will be periodic. Both of these sequences are shown in Figure 4.1. Note that although the former is not periodic, it has a periodic envelope.

From the above, we see that the angular frequency Ω cannot assume all possible values, whereas for continuous-time periodic functions, there was no restriction on the possible values of ω. Furthermore, we note that

$$\cos(\Omega + 2k\pi)n = \cos\Omega n \tag{4.5}$$

where k is any integer. This implies that identical sinusoidal sequences are obtained for frequencies separated by 2π. This is a very important property of periodic discrete-time sequences. A consequence of this result is that there will be only a finite number of independent harmonics.

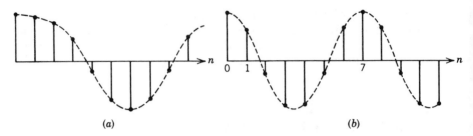

Figure 4.1 Discrete-time sinusoids. (a) $x(n) = \cos(n/5)$. (b) $x(n) = \cos(2\pi n/7)$.

We now investigate the possibility of expressing $x(n)$ in the form of a Fourier series. In Chapter 3 we first used the trigonometric form of the series with terms like $a_n \cos(n\omega_0 t)$ and $b_n \sin(n\omega_0 t)$, where n is an integer and the fundamental angular frequency ω_0 is determined from the period T of the signal through the relationship $\omega_0 = 2\pi/T$. For n equal to one, we had the fundamental component of the Fourier series, and an infinite number of harmonics could be defined for n varying from 2 to ∞. In the same way, in the case of periodic discrete-time signals, we may use the trigonometric form of the series having terms like $a_k \cos(k\Omega_0 n)$ and $b_k \sin(k\Omega_0 n)$, where Ω_0 is the fundamental angular frequency, defined through the relationship

$$\Omega_0 = \frac{2\pi}{N} \qquad (4.6)$$

and k is an integer. An important difference is that there are only N independent harmonics in this case, for $k = 0$ to $N - 1$. This follows from equation 4.5 which leads us to the following equations:

$$\begin{aligned}
\cos(N\Omega_0 n) &= \cos(2\pi n) = \cos(0\Omega_0 n) \\
\cos[(N + 1)\Omega_0 n] &= \cos(\Omega_0 n) \\
\cos[(N + 2)\Omega_0 n] &= \cos(2\Omega_0 n) \\
&\cdots\cdots\cdots\cdots\cdots\cdots\cdots\cdots \\
\cos[(N + k)\Omega_0 n] &= \cos(k\Omega_0 n)
\end{aligned} \qquad (4.7)$$

Similar relationships are easily established for harmonics of the form $\sin[(N + k)\Omega_0 n]$.

Alternatively, one may use the exponential form of the Fourier series. In Chapter 3 it was seen that the exponential form of the series was not only more compact but also was directly related to the frequency spectrum of the signal. Therefore, in this chapter we prefer to use the complex exponential form of the Fourier series, with terms of the form $a_n \exp(jk\Omega_0 n)$ for periodic discrete-time signals, where n and k are integers, and Ω_0 is the angular frequency, defined in equation 4.6. Furthermore, both n and k will be in the range 0 to $N - 1$, because of the periodic nature of $x(n)$ and the periodicity of the harmonics.

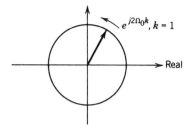

Figure 4.2 Graphical interpretation of N roots of unity.

4.2.1 EXPONENTIAL FORM OF FOURIER SERIES FOR DISCRETE-TIME SIGNALS

Before proceeding further, we must determine whether it is possible to represent a periodic discrete-time signal by a Fourier series. We can start by recognizing that the complex exponential $e^{j\Omega_0 n}$ is periodic, with period N. We shall also show that $e^{jk\Omega_0}$ is an Nth root of unity, where k is any integer between 0 and $N - 1$. This follows easily from the relationship

$$\left[\exp\left(jk\Omega_0\right)\right]^N = \left[\exp\left(\frac{j2\pi k}{N}\right)\right]^N = \exp\left(j2\pi k\right) = 1 \qquad (4.8)$$

where k is any integer between 0 and $N - 1$. Thus, as k proceeds from 0 to N, we move along the unit circle and return to the starting point when $k = N$. A graphical interpretation is shown in Figure 4.2 for $N = 6$. For notation convenience, we denote the Nth root of one by the symbol w_N, that is,

$$w_N \triangleq \exp\left(\frac{j2\pi}{N}\right) = \exp\left(j\Omega_0\right) \qquad (4.9)$$

Furthermore, the set of all discrete-time complex exponential signals that are periodic with period N is given by

$$w_N^k = \exp\left(\frac{j2\pi k}{N}\right), \qquad k = 0, \pm 1, \pm 2, \ldots \qquad (4.10)$$

All of these signals have frequencies that are multiples of the fundamental frequency w_N, that is, they are the harmonics. Furthermore, they satisfy the orthogonality relationship,

$$\sum_{k=m}^{m+N-1} \left(w_N^j\right)^k \left(w_N^i\right)^{-k} = \begin{cases} 0 & \text{if } i \neq j \\ N & \text{if } i = j \end{cases} \qquad (4.11)$$

where i, j, and m are integers.

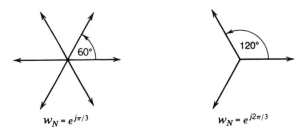

$w_N = e^{j\pi/3}$ $w_N = e^{j2\pi/3}$

Figure 4.3   Graphical interpretation of equation 4.12.

The last result follows easily from the fact that w_N^k, being Nth roots of unit for all k, satisfy the following relationship:

$$\sum_{k=i}^{i+N-1} w_N^k = \frac{w_N^i\left(w_N^N - 1\right)}{w_N^i - 1} = 0 \tag{4.12}$$

where i is any integer. A graphical interpretation of equation 4.12 is shown in Figure 4.3 for the case when $N = 6$.

We are now ready to establish that any periodic discrete-time signal of period N can be expressed by the following Fourier series:

$$x(n) = \sum_{k=0}^{N-1} a_k w_N^{kn}, \qquad n = 0, \pm 1, \pm 2, \ldots \tag{4.13}$$

where

$$a_k = \frac{1}{N} \sum_{n=0}^{N-1} x(n) w_N^{-kn}, \qquad k = 0, 1, 2, \ldots, N-1 \tag{4.14}$$

It is important to note that the *Fourier series for a discrete-time signal is a finite sum*, as shown in equation 4.13, in contrast with the Fourier series for continuous-time signals, which contains an infinite number of components. There is a dc component and the frequency of the fundamental component is $2\pi/N$. The frequencies of the harmonics are $2\pi k/N$, where $k = 2, 3, \ldots, N - 1$. The important point is that only N components of the series have to be evaluated. As we shall see in the next subsection, this property has a profound effect on the question of the convergence of the series. Not only will such a series exist for every periodic discrete-time sequence $x(n)$ but also the representation will be exact for each value of n.

4.2.2   PROOF OF THE FOURIER SERIES REPRESENTATION

The prove the validity of equations 4.13 and 4.14, we need only substitute the expressions for the coefficients a_i from equation 4.14 into equation 4.13 and verify that the right-hand side is equal to x_n for every n. To do this, we change the index of summation in equation 4.14 from n to m and insert this into equation 4.13. This gives us

$$\sum_{k=0}^{N-1} a_k w_N^{kn} = \frac{1}{N} \sum_{k=0}^{N-1} \sum_{m=0}^{N-1} x(m) w_N^{-km} w_N^{kn}$$

$$= \frac{1}{N} \sum_{m=0}^{N-1} x(m) \sum_{k=0}^{N-1} w_N^{-k(m-n)} \qquad (4.15)$$

In view of equation 4.11, the second summation on the right-hand side of equation 4.15 will be equal to N for $m = n$ and 0 otherwise. Consequently, the right-hand side of equation 4.15 will be equal to $x(n)$ for each value of n.

It is worth noting that since there are only a finite number of components in the discrete Fourier series, exact values of $x(n)$ are obtained for each value of n by *adding a finite series* consisting of N components. Thus we have exactly N equations for the N unknown coefficients for the discrete Fourier series. We could have evaluated the Fourier coefficients by solving the set of N simultaneous equations obtained by writing equation 4.13 for n ranging from 0 to $N - 1$. Equation 4.14 is preferable since it allows us to obtain the various coefficients explicitly by taking advantage of the orthogonality relationship described by equation 4.11. Note that we do not have to worry about the convergence of the series for discrete-time periodic signals and do not have the equivalent of the Gibbs phenomenon for such signals. These problems were due to the Fourier series of continuous-time periodic signals having an infinite number of terms.

Example 4.1

Consider the discrete-time equivalent of a square wave. In this case, for even N and $(N > 2)$, we have

$$x(n) = \begin{cases} A, n = 0, 1, \ldots \left(\dfrac{N}{2} - 1 \right) \\[2mm] -A, n = \dfrac{N}{2}, \left(\dfrac{N}{2} + 1 \right), \ldots, (N - 1) \end{cases} \qquad (4.16)$$

This signal is shown in Figure 4.4 for N equal to 8. Consequently, the Fourier

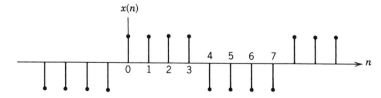

Figure 4.4   Discrete-time square wave.

coefficients are given by

$$a_k = \frac{1}{N} \sum_{n=0}^{N-1} x(n) w_N^{-kn}$$

$$= \frac{1}{N} \left[\sum_{n=0}^{N/2-1} A w_N^{-kn} - \sum_{n=N/2}^{N-1} A w_N^{-kn} \right]$$

$$= \begin{cases} \dfrac{4A/N}{1 - w_N^{-k}} & \text{for odd } k \\ 0 & \text{for even } k \end{cases} \tag{4.17}$$

As seen from equation 4.17, a_k is complex. This is more obvious if we rewrite equation 4.17 for odd k as follows:

$$a_k = \frac{4A/N}{1 - [\exp(-j2\pi k/N)]}$$

$$= \frac{4A/N}{1 - \cos(-2k\pi/N) - j \sin(-2k\pi/N)} \tag{4.18}$$

From equation 4.18, the magnitude of a_k for odd k can be evaluated as

$$|a_k| = \frac{2\sqrt{2}\,(A/N)}{[1 - \cos(-2k\pi/N)]^{0.5}} \tag{4.19}$$

A plot of $|a_k|$ is shown in Figure 4.5 for N equal to 8. ∎

It is easily verified that this series would give us the exact value of $x(n)$ for every value of n. It is interesting to compare the result of this example with that of Example 3.2, where the Fourier coefficients of a continuous-time square wave with odd symmetry were determined. Although the latter also contained only odd harmonics, these decreased monotonically, whereas for the discrete-time case, first they decrease and then increase. This should have

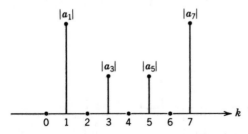

Figure 4.5 Fourier coefficients of discrete square wave.

been expected owing to the periodic nature of the coefficients of the discrete-time Fourier series.

4.2.3 STEADY-STATE RESPONSE TO PERIODIC INPUT

The steady-state response of a stable discrete-time system to a periodic input can be determined in a manner very similar to the procedure used for continuous-time systems. We recall that for the latter the steady-state response to a sine wave input was a sinusoid of the same frequency, but with a different magnitude and phase. The magnitude ratio and phase difference between the output and input were obtained by replacing the operator p by $j\omega$ in the system operator and evaluating it for the given ω. The resulting complex number was then expressed in the polar form to give the magnitude ratio M and phase shift ϕ. This simple procedure was then extended to any periodic function by applying superposition, that is, by adding the steady-state response to each frequency component of the input to get the total steady-state response.

The same idea is easily applied to discrete-time systems if we note that the effect of the operator q on a periodic signal of the form $Ae^{j\Omega_0 k}$ is to advance it by one sample, that is, to be multiplied by $\exp(j\Omega_0 k)$ or w_N^k. Consequently, for discrete-time systems subject to a periodic input of the form $A \exp(j2\pi nk/N)$, we replace q in the system function with w_N^k [or $\exp(j\Omega_0 k)$] and calculate the value of the complex number that gives us the magnitude ratio and phase shift (here, the number of samples of shift) for the given complex exponential. For the general case of a periodic function, we can apply superposition, as for the continuous-time case.

Example 4.2

Consider a discrete-time system, described by the following difference equation:

$$y(n + 2) - 0.7y(n + 1) + 0.1y(n) = u(n + 1) + 2u(n) \quad (4.20)$$

The input is a periodic sequence of period 10 and is given by

$$u(n) = 20 \exp\left(\frac{j2\pi n}{10}\right) \quad (4.21)$$

The steady-state output of the system will now be determined. First we note that the system function is given by

$$L(q) = \frac{q + 2}{q^2 - 0.7q + 0.1} \quad (4.22)$$

and the roots of the denominator are located at -0.2 and -0.5, indicating that the system is stable. Consequently, the steady-state output of the system will be of the same form as the input. Therefore, setting $q = \exp(j2\pi/10)$, we get

$$L\left[\exp\left(\frac{j2\pi}{10}\right)\right]$$

$$= \frac{\exp(j2\pi/10) + 2}{\exp(j4\pi/10) - 0.7\exp(j2\pi/10) + 0.1}$$

$$= \frac{(\cos 0.2\pi + 2) + j\sin 0.2\pi}{(\cos 0.4\pi - 0.7\cos 0.2\pi + 0.1) + j(\sin 0.4\pi - 0.7\sin 0.2\pi)}$$

$$= 5.1059\exp(-j1.6482)$$

Therefore, the steady-state output is given by

$$y_{ss}(n) = 102.118\exp(j0.2\pi n - 1.6482) \tag{4.23}$$

∎

Example 4.3

Consider the same system that was described in Example 4.2, but with the following input:

$$u(n) = 20\exp\left(\frac{j2\pi n}{10}\right) + 10\exp\left(\frac{j4\pi n}{10}\right) \tag{4.24}$$

The input signal in equation 4.24 contains two terms, a fundamental component and its second harmonic. Furthermore, the fundamental component is identical to the input given by equation 4.21 and thus response due to this component alone will be as given by equation 4.23. Therefore, we need only calculate the response due to the second harmonic. To do this, we shall set $q = e^{j0.4\pi}$ in the system function given by equation 4.22. This yields

$$L\left[\exp\left(\frac{j4\pi}{10}\right)\right] = 2.6892\exp(j3.4483) \tag{4.25}$$

The steady-state response to this component of the input is, thus, given by

$$y_{2ss}(n) = 26.892\exp(j0.4\pi n + 3.4483) \tag{4.26}$$

Finally, applying superposition, the complete steady-state response is obtained as

$$y_{ss}(n) = 102.118\exp(j0.2\pi n - 1.6482)$$
$$+ 26.892\exp(j0.4\pi n + 3.4483) \tag{4.27}$$

∎

Drill Problem 4.1

A discrete-time system is defined by the following difference equation:

$$y(n + 2) - 0.8y(n + 1) + 0.15y(n) = u(n)$$

Determine its steady-state response for the periodic input sequence

$$u(n) = 5 + 2\exp\left(\frac{j2\pi n}{10}\right)$$

Answer: $14.286 + 3.873\exp\left[j\left(\frac{2\pi n}{10} - 1.94\right)\right]$

4.3 THE DISCRETE-TIME FOURIER TRANSFORM

In this section, we generalize the theory of Fourier series representation of discrete-time signals to the aperiodic case. This will proceed in a manner analogous to that used for the continuous-time case.

Let $x(n)$ be a discrete-time signal that will be assumed zero outside the range $0 \le n \le N_1$. Thus, $x(n)$ is a *time-limited* signal. We can construct a periodic signal $\tilde{x}(n)$, with period $N > N_1$, such that it is equal to $x(n)$ for $0 \le n \le N_1$. These signals are shown in Figure 4.6. Using the procedure developed in Section 4.2, the Fourier series for $\tilde{x}(n)$ can be written as

$$\tilde{x}(n) = \sum_{n=0}^{N-1} a_k \exp\left(jk\Omega_0 n\right) \tag{4.28}$$

where

$$a_k = \frac{1}{N} \sum_{n=0}^{N-1} \tilde{x}(n)\exp\left(-jk\Omega_0 n\right) \tag{4.29}$$

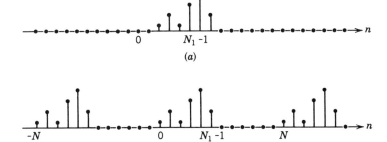

Figure 4.6 A periodic signal from a finite duration aperiodic signal. (*a*) Aperiodic signal $x(n)$. (*b*) Periodic signal $\tilde{x}(n)$.

Since $\tilde{x}(n)$ is zero for $n > N_1$, we may express equation 4.29 in terms of $x(n)$, as shown below:

$$a_k = \frac{1}{N} \sum_{n=0}^{N_1-1} x(n) \exp(-jk\Omega_0 n) \tag{4.30}$$

Finally, since $x(n)$ is nonzero only for $0 \le n \le N_1$, equation 4.30 may be further modified as

$$a_k = \frac{1}{N} \sum_{n=-\infty}^{\infty} x(n) \exp(-jk\Omega_0 n) \tag{4.31}$$

It should be noted that the fundamental frequency in equations 4.28 to 4.31 is given by

$$\Omega_0 = \frac{2\pi}{N} \tag{4.32}$$

Let us now examine the effect of increasing N. From the definition of $\tilde{x}(n)$, it follows that it will approach $x(n)$ as N is increased, that is,

$$\lim_{N \to \infty} \tilde{x}(n) = x(n) \tag{4.33}$$

As $N \to \infty$, however, the fundamental frequency, $\Omega_0 \to 0$. Consequently, the separation between the various harmonics decreases, until in the limit, the discrete frequency spectrum is replaced by a continuous frequency spectrum. To determine this continuous spectrum, let us first obtain an expression for the envelope of the discrete spectrum given by equation 4.31. Define

$$X(\Omega) \triangleq Na_k = \sum_{n=-\infty}^{\infty} x(n) \exp(-j\Omega n) \tag{4.34}$$

where Ω replaces $k\Omega_0$, so that the coefficients a_k are given by

$$a_k = \frac{1}{N} X(\Omega) \tag{4.35}$$

We may now express equation 4.28 in terms of $X(\Omega)$ to obtain

$$\tilde{x}(n) = \sum_{n=0}^{N} \frac{1}{N} X(k\Omega_0) \exp(jk\Omega_0 n) \tag{4.36}$$

Substituting for N from equation 4.32, we may rewrite equation 4.36 as

$$\tilde{x}(n) = \sum_{n=0}^{N} \frac{\Omega_0}{2\pi} X(k\Omega_0) \exp(jk\Omega_0 n) \tag{4.37}$$

As $N \to \infty$, $\Omega_0 \to 0$ and $\tilde{x}(n) \to x(n)$ for any finite value of n. Consequently, the separation between the frequency components will change from Ω_0 to

$d\Omega$, and equation 4.37 changes into the following integral:

$$x(n) = \frac{1}{2\pi} \int_0^{2\pi} X(\Omega) \exp(j\Omega n) \, d\Omega \qquad (4.38)$$

This can be understood clearly if we note that after taking out the constant $1/(2\pi)$, each term in the summation in equation 4.37 can be regarded as the area of a rectangle of height $X(k\Omega_0) \exp(jk\Omega_0 n)$ and width Ω_0. Therefore, as we make $\Omega_0 \to 0$, this total area under summation will be represented by the integral on the right-hand side of equation 4.38.

Equations 4.34 and 4.38 define the discrete-time Fourier transform (DTFT) and the inverse discrete-time Fourier transform (IDTFT), respectively. It will be observed that these equations are very similar to those defining the Fourier transform pair for continuous-time aperiodic signals. However, there are some important differences. The most important differences are that the discrete-time transform $X(\Omega)$ is periodic and that the interval of integration is finite. Both of these are consequences of the fact that we have noted earlier: discrete-time complex exponentials differing in frequency by integral multiples of 2π are identical. This is the reason why the Fourier coefficients of a periodic discrete-time signal are periodic and the Fourier series is a finite sum. This is also the reason for the periodicity of $X(\Omega)$ for aperiodic discrete-time signals as well as for the fact that the synthesis equation 4.38 is an integral over the finite frequency interval of length 2π.

The following examples will give us a better understanding of the discrete-time Fourier transform.

Example 4.4

Consider the time-limited sequence

$$x(n) = \begin{cases} 1 & \text{for } -N_1 \le n \le N_1 \\ 0 & \text{otherwise} \end{cases} \qquad (4.39)$$

This signal is the discrete-time counterpart of a rectangular pulse and is shown in Figure 4.7. The discrete-time Fourier transform of this sequence is

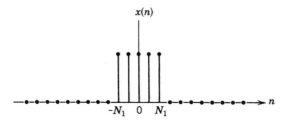

Figure 4.7 Discrete-time rectangular pulse.

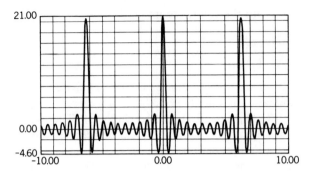

Figure 4.8 Discrete-time Fourier transform of rectangular pulse.

given by

$$X(\Omega) = \sum_{n=-N_1}^{N_1} \exp(-jn\Omega)$$

$$= \exp(-jN_1\Omega)\left[1 + \exp(j\Omega) + \cdots + \exp(j2N_1\Omega)\right]$$

$$= \exp(-jN_1\Omega)\frac{1 - \exp\left[-j(2N_1 + 1)\Omega\right]}{1 - \exp(-j\Omega)}$$

$$= \exp(-j2N_1\Omega)\frac{\sin(N + 1/2)\Omega}{\sin(\Omega/2)} \tag{4.40}$$

This is the discrete-time counterpart of the sinc function that was found to be the Fourier transform of the continuous-time rectangular pulse. It is seen to be periodic. A plot of the magnitude of the transform given by equation 4.40 is shown in Figure 4.8 for $N = 10$. ∎

It can easily be verified that if we obtain the inverse discrete-time Fourier transform of equation 4.40 using the relationship of equation 4.38, we get the sequence given by equation 4.39.

The DTFT for a signal $x(n)$ exists if the sum on the right-hand side of equation 4.34 converges for all real values of Ω. Therefore, a sufficient condition for $x(n)$ to have a DTFT is that the sum be absolutely convergent, that is,

$$\sum_{n=-\infty}^{\infty} |x(n)| < \infty \tag{4.41}$$

although, as for continuous-time signals, there will be some instances where a DTFT will exist, if we allow impulses. This will be illustrated through the example of the discrete-time constant or dc signal.

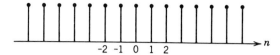

Figure 4.9 Discrete-time constant signal.

Example 4.5

Consider the sequence

$$x(n) = 1 \qquad \text{for all integers } n \qquad (4.42)$$

which is shown in Figure 4.9. Evidently, this infinite sequence is not absolutely summable. However, its DTFT is given by

$$X(\Omega) = \sum_{n=-\infty}^{\infty} 2\pi \, \delta(\Omega - 2\pi n) \qquad (4.43)$$

Thus, the DTFT of this sequence will be the periodic impulse train shown in Figure 4.10. Each impulse has strength 2π and is located at $\Omega = 2k\pi$. This fact is easily verified by taking the IDFT of equation 4.43. Using the relationship in equation 4.38, we obtain

$$x(n) = \frac{1}{2\pi} \int_0^{2\pi} \sum_{k=-\infty}^{\infty} 2\pi \, \delta(\Omega - 2\pi k) \, d\Omega = 1 \qquad \text{for all } n \quad (4.44)$$

This last result follows from the sifting property of the impulse that was first seen in Chapter 2 and has been utilized a number of times. ∎

Drill Problem 4.2

Determine the discrete-time Fourier transform of the time-limited sequence given below:

$$x(n) = \begin{cases} 1 & \text{if } n \text{ is even and } -5 \le n \le 5 \\ -1 & \text{if } n \text{ is odd and } -5 \le n \le 5 \\ 0 & \text{otherwise} \end{cases}$$

Answer: $1 - 2\cos\Omega + 2\cos 2\Omega - 2\cos 3\Omega + 2\cos 4\Omega - 2\cos 5\Omega$

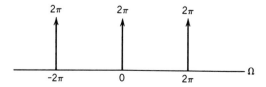

Figure 4.10 DTFT of the constant sequence.

4.3.1   DISCRETE-TIME FOURIER TRANSFORM OF PERIODIC SIGNALS

As was seen for the continuous-time case, the discrete-time Fourier transform of a periodic signal will contain impulses. For example, consider the basic complex exponential

$$x(n) = A e^{j\Omega_0 n} \tag{4.45}$$

Its Fourier transform is given by

$$X(\Omega) = \sum_{k=-\infty}^{\infty} 2\pi \delta(\Omega - \Omega_0 - 2\pi k) \tag{4.46}$$

This can easily be verified by taking the inverse Fourier transform of the right-hand side of equation 4.46.

We now determine the DTFT for periodic cosine and sine sequences. For the cosine sequence, we have

$$x(n) = A \cos \Omega_0 n = \frac{A}{2}(e^{j\Omega_0 n} + e^{-j\Omega_0 n}) \tag{4.47}$$

Therefore, using the results of equations 4.45 and 4.46, we obtain

$$X(\Omega) = \pi \sum_{k=-\infty}^{\infty} \delta(\Omega - \Omega_0 - 2\pi k) + \delta(\Omega + \Omega_0 - 2\pi k) \tag{4.48}$$

A plot of $X(\Omega)$ is shown in Figure 4.11.

It is interesting to compare Figure 4.11 with Figure 3.33, since the latter depicts the Fourier transform of the continuous-time periodic cosine function. The latter has just two impulses of strength π at $-\omega_0$ and ω_0 whereas in Figure 4.11 we have a periodic train of impulses of strength π, at $-\Omega_0$ and Ω_0 in the region $-\pi \leq \Omega \leq \pi$ and repeated with a period of 2π. As expected, this is due to the periodic nature of the DTFT.

Similarly, we can show that DTFT of the periodic sinusoid

$$x(n) = A \sin \Omega_0 n = \frac{A}{(2j)}(e^{j\Omega_0 n} - e^{-j\Omega_0 n}) \tag{4.49}$$

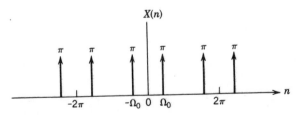

Figure 4.11   The DTFT of a periodic cosine sequence.

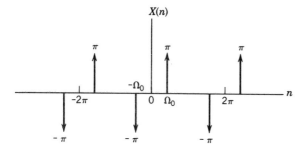

Figure 4.12 The DTFT of a periodic sine sequence.

is given by

$$X(\Omega) = -j\pi \sum_{k=-\infty}^{\infty} \left[\delta(\Omega - \Omega_0 - 2\pi k) - \delta(\Omega + \Omega_0 - 2\pi k) \right] \quad (4.50)$$

A plot of $X(\Omega)$ is shown in Figure 4.12.

As expected, Figure 4.12 is similar to Figure 3.34 for the continuous-time sinusoid, with the difference that the DTFT is periodic.

4.3.2 SOME PROPERTIES OF THE DTFT

We now present some important properties of the DTFT. Many of them are similar to those of the continuous-time Fourier transform. We shall, therefore, just state these. The properties that are different are discussed in detail.

4.3.2.1 Periodicity

An important feature of the DTFT is its periodicity, that is,

$$X(\Omega + 2\pi) = X(\Omega) \quad (4.51)$$

This follows from the fact that

$$e^{-j2\pi n} = 1 \quad \text{for all integers } n \quad (4.52)$$

Consequently, the spectrum of $X(\Omega)$ is determined completely by computing it over any finite interval of length 2π. Moreover, since $X(\Omega)$ is periodic, so are the related magnitude and phase spectra.

This property was discussed earlier and is one of the important differences between the Fourier transforms of continuous-time and discrete-time signals.

4.3.2.2 Linearity

Just as for the continuous-time case, the DTFT also satisfies the property of linearity, that is,

$$\text{If} \quad \mathscr{F}[x_1(n)] = X_1(\Omega) \quad \text{and} \quad \mathscr{F}[x_2(n)] = X_2(\Omega)$$
$$\text{then} \quad \mathscr{F}[a_1 x_1(n) + a_2 x_2(n)] = a_1 X_1(\Omega) + a_2 X_2(\Omega) \quad (4.53)$$

This is easily proved by direct substitution.

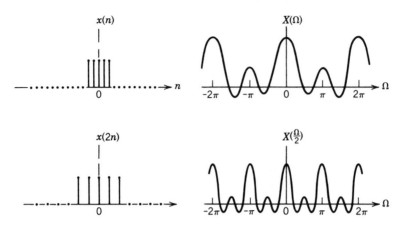

Figure 4.13   Time and frequency scaling.

4.3.2.3   Time Shifting and Frequency Shifting

These are also analogous to the continuous-time case and can be derived by direct substitution.

If $\mathscr{F}[x(n)] = X(\Omega)$ then $\mathscr{F}[x(n - n_0)] = e^{-j\Omega n_0}X(\Omega)$ (4.54)

If $\mathscr{F}[x(n)] = X(\Omega)$ then $\mathscr{F}[\exp(j\Omega_0 n)x(n)] = X(\Omega - \Omega_0)$

   (4.55)

4.3.2.4   Time and Frequency Scaling

If $\mathscr{F}[x(n)] = X(\Omega)$ then $\mathscr{F}[x(nk)] = X(\Omega/k)$ (4.56)

where $k > 1$, is an integer.

PROOF

$$\mathscr{F}[x(nk)] = \sum_{n=-\infty}^{\infty} x(nk)e^{-jn\Omega} = \sum_{n=-\infty}^{\infty} x(nk)\exp\left[-jnk\left(\frac{\Omega}{k}\right)\right] = X\left(\frac{\Omega}{k}\right)$$

Equation 4.56 reminds us of the phenomenon of reciprocal spreading that we had observed for continuous-time signals. Here again, as the signal is expanded in time, its frequency spectrum is compressed by the same ratio. This is shown in Figure 4.13 for the case of a rectangular pulse.

4.3.2.5   Differencing and Summation

If $\mathscr{F}[x(n)] = X(\Omega)$ then

$$\mathscr{F}[x(n) - x(n - 1)] = (1 - e^{-j\Omega})X(\Omega)$$ (4.57)

and

$$\mathscr{F}\left[\sum_{m=-\infty}^{n} x(m)\right] = \frac{1}{1 - e^{-j\Omega}}X(\Omega) + \pi X(0)\sum_{k=-\infty}^{\infty} \delta(\Omega - 2\pi k)$$ (4.58)

These are, again, seen to be similar to the properties of differentiation and integration obtained in the case of Fourier transforms for continuous-time signals. Equation 4.57 is obtained easily by using the properties of linearity and time shifting. Equation 4.58 can be derived in a similar manner, except for the impulse train on the right-hand side, which is caused by the dc or average value of the signal (see Example 4.5), which may result from the process of summation. This should be compared with equation 3.106 for continuous-time signals.

4.3.2.6 Differentiation in Frequency

$$\text{If} \quad \mathscr{F}[x(n)] = X(\Omega) \quad \text{then} \quad \mathscr{F}[nx(n)] = j\frac{dX(\Omega)}{d\Omega} \quad (4.59)$$

which is seen to be similar to the property of differentiation with respect to frequency for the continuous-time case. This property is useful for obtaining the DTFT of a sequence multiplied by n, which is analogous to multiplication by t for a continuous-time signal.

4.3.2.7 Parseval's Equation

$$\text{If} \quad \mathscr{F}[x(n)] = X(\Omega) \quad \text{then} \quad \sum_{n=-\infty}^{\infty} |x(n)|^2 = \frac{1}{2\pi}\int_0^{2\pi} |X(\Omega)|^2 \, d\Omega$$

$$(4.60)$$

As for continuous-time signals, the sum on the left-hand side is called the energy in $\{x(n)\}$ and the expression $|X(\Omega)|^2$ is called the *energy spectral density* of the signal.

4.3.2.8 Convolution

Let $\mathscr{F}[x(n)] = X(\Omega)$, $\mathscr{F}[y(n)] = Y(\Omega)$, and $\mathscr{F}[h(n)] = H(\Omega)$ where $x(n)$, $y(n)$, and $h(n)$ are related through the convolution sum

$$y(n) = \sum_{k=-\infty}^{\infty} x(k)h(n-k) \quad (4.61)$$

then

$$Y(\Omega) = H(\Omega)X(\Omega) \quad (4.62)$$

This is analogous to the property of convolution for the case of continuous-time signals and the proof will be omitted here. As before, $H(\Omega)$ is called the system function. This is a very valuable property because it can be utilized to calculate the response of a discrete-time system to any input by obtaining the inverse transform of the product $H(\Omega)X(\Omega)$, where $X(\Omega)$ is the Fourier transform of the input. Also, the impulse response $h(n)$ can be calculated as the inverse transform (IDTFT) of $H(\Omega)$ which, in turn, can be obtained from the system equations.

4.3.2.9   Periodic Convolution

The convolution property described in equations 4.61 and 4.62 cannot be used directly for periodic discrete-time signals, since in that case the convolution will not converge. This difficulty can be overcome by considering the convolution sum of two periodic signals $x_1(n)$ and $x_2(n)$, where it is assumed that *both of them have the same period N*. We can now obtain a sequence $y(n)$ through the following convolution sum:

$$y(n) = \sum_{k+1}^{k+N} x_1\langle m \rangle x_2 \langle n - m \rangle \qquad (4.63)$$

where k is any integer and the expression $\langle r \rangle$ implies r Modulo N, for any integer r.

It may be noted that the summation is carried over one complete period only. Consequently, this process is called *periodic convolution*. It can be used very efficiently for calculating $y(n)$ for different values of n. The procedure is similar to the sliding tape algorithm described in Section 2.8, with the difference that each of the tapes is replaced by a wheel and the given sequences are represented along the circumference of the two wheels (equally spaced), one of these being in the reversed order. To obtain the value of $y(n)$ for a given n, one of the wheels is rotated relative to the other so that the displacement between them is equal to n. The value of $y(n)$ is then obtained as the sum of the N terms obtained by multiplying elements in adjacent locations. Owing to this analogy, periodic convolution is also known as *circular convolution*, whereas the convolution sum expressed by equation 4.61 is called *linear convolution*.

Example 4.6

Consider two sequences $x_1(n)$ and $x_2(n)$, each of period 4, as given below:

$$x_1 = \{1, 2, 0, -1\} \qquad (4.64)$$

$$x_2 = \{3, 1, -1, 2\} \qquad (4.65)$$

We perform periodic convolution to obtain the sequence $y(n)$, which will also have the same period. We start with the two wheels shown in Figure 4.14a, where there is no displacement. Note that the entries for the inner wheel are in the counterclockwise direction, whereas those for the outer wheel are in the clockwise direction. Thus, we get

$$y(0) = 3 - 1 + 0 + 4 = 6 \qquad (4.66)$$

To obtain $y(1)$, we advance the inner wheel by 1 space (90° in this case) in the clockwise direction, as shown in Figure 4.14b. Hence, we get

$$y(1) = 6 + 1 + 1 + 0 = 8 \qquad (4.67)$$

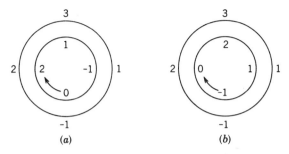

Figure 4.14 Circular convolution for $n = 0$ and 1.
(a) $n = 0$. (b) $n = 1$.

Proceeding in this manner, we get the complete sequence

$$y = \{6, 8, -1, -3\} \tag{4.68}$$

∎

An important application of circular convolution will be seen in the section on the discrete Fourier transforms (DFT), where it is used for fast convolution.

4.4 THE SAMPLING THEOREM

The sampling theorem is of great practical importance in all instances where a discrete-time signal is obtained from the samples of a continuous-time signal. The main objective in this process is to select the sampling rate in such a way that there is no loss of information in this process. As will be seen, this is possible only if the continuous-time signal is *band-limited*, that is, it does not contain any component above a certain frequency. This can be done by passing the signal through a suitable low-pass filter. As an example, the voice signal that is transmitted on telephone wires is limited to an upper frequency of 4 kHz. The frequency spectrum of a band-limited signal $x(t)$ is shown in Figure 4.15a. Note that this has been taken as triangular only for simplicity and convenience in drawing; the only requirement is that it be zero outside the frequency band $-\omega_b \leq \omega \leq \omega_b$. We now examine the effect of sampling the signal at a given rate, say f_s times per second. It will be assumed that the samples are spaced uniformly so that the sampling interval, in seconds, will be given by

$$T = \frac{1}{f_s} = \frac{2\pi}{\omega_s}$$

The process of sampling can be considered as multiplication of the given continuous-time signal with a periodic train of unit impulses with period T. We shall use this fact to determine the frequency spectrum of the resulting

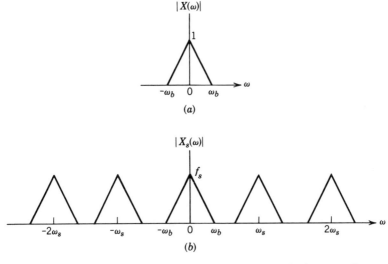

Figure 4.15 Amplitude spectra of a signal before and after sampling. (*a*) Amplitude spectrum of a band-limited signal. (*b*) Amplitude spectrum of the sampled signal obtained from the band-limited signal in (*a*).

discrete-time signal. Recalling our discussion in Section 3.6.3, this spectrum can be obtained by frequency domain convolution of the spectrum of the continuous-time signal and that of the periodic train of unit impulses. Let us denote this train of impulses as

$$p(t) = \sum_{n=-\infty}^{\infty} \delta(t - nT) \tag{4.69}$$

Since $p(t)$ is periodic, we determine its spectrum by finding its Fourier series. This is a discrete spectrum with values only at integral multiples of the sampling frequency ω_s. Using the exponential form we get

$$c_n = \frac{1}{T} \int_{-T/2}^{T/2} \delta(t) \exp\left(-j2\omega_s t\right) dt = \frac{\omega_s}{2\pi} = f_s \tag{4.70}$$

where the last equality follows from the sifting property of the impulse function and the fact that $\omega_s T = 2\pi$.

It follows from equation 4.70 that the discrete frequency spectrum of $p(t)$ will have the constant value f_s at all integral multiples of the sampling frequency ω_s. Using Table 3.1 in Section 3.6.5, its Fourier transform is readily obtained as

$$P(\omega) = \omega_s \sum_{n=-\infty}^{\infty} \delta(\omega - n\omega_s) \tag{4.71}$$

and will consist of a train of impulses of strength ω_s, located at integral multiples of the sampling frequency.

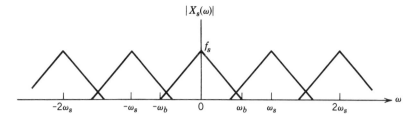

Figure 4.16 Amplitude spectra of the signal in Figure 4.15a for $\omega_s < 2\omega_b$.

The frequency spectrum of the sampled signal $x_s(t)$ can now be obtained by complex convolution of the two spectra, as described in Section 3.5.3. Thus, we obtain

$$X_s(\omega) = \frac{1}{2\pi} \int_{-\infty}^{\infty} X(\omega) \sum_{n=-\infty}^{\infty} \omega_s \delta(\omega - n\omega_s - u)\, du \qquad (4.72)$$

Although the expression in equation 4.72 looks complicated, it is easily evaluated by utilizing the sifting property of the impulse and is given below:

$$X_s(\omega) = \frac{\omega_s}{2\pi} \sum_{n=-\infty}^{\infty} X(\omega - \omega_s) \qquad (4.73)$$

It is very simple to see from equation 4.73 that the spectrum of the sampled signal is composed of the spectrum of the original continuous-time system, scaled by the constant $\omega_s/(2\pi)$ and translated to each harmonic of the sampling frequency ω_s. Consequently, the frequency spectrum of the sampled signal will be as shown in Figure 4.15b.

It is evident from Figure 4.15 that the spectra will overlap causing distortion or *aliasing* if the sampling frequency ω_s is less than twice the bandwidth ω_b, as shown in Figure 4.16.

It also follows that in the former case ($\omega_s > 2\omega_b$) it is possible to completely recover the original signal by passing the sampled signal through a low-pass filter (called a reconstruction filter) of bandwidth ω_b. On the other hand, this cannot be done for the latter case ($\omega_s < 2\omega_b$), because of the distortion produced by overlapping of the spectra.

This leads us to the sampling theorem, which can be stated as follows:

A band-limited signal having no frequency component above ω_b is completely described by uniformly spaced samples if the sampling frequency ω_s is greater than twice ω_b.

The frequency $\omega_s = 2\omega_b$ is called the *Nyquist rate*.

It is important to note that in practical situations, no signal is strictly band-limited. As a result, it is not possible to sample a signal and then reconstruct the original signal from the samples without any error. In most practical situations, however, the energy content of a signal is negligible beyond a certain frequency. Consequently, this frequency may be taken as the bandwidth. Furthermore, ideal reconstruction filters do not exist, and there is always a finite slope in the frequency response curve of the filter beyond the nominal cutoff frequency. Therefore, it is customary to make the sampling frequency significantly higher than the Nyquist rate.

It should also be noted that, in practice, ideal samplers do not exist, and the best we can do is to replace the impulse train with a train of pulses of very small width.

4.5   DISCRETE FOURIER TRANSFORM

Although the theory of the discrete-time Fourier transform is very useful in understanding the sampling process and has many applications, we cannot place $X(\Omega)$ into the memory of a computer since it is a continuous function of frequency. For implementation on a digital computer we have to discretize the frequency. This leads to the concept of the discrete Fourier transform (DFT), which we study in this section. As will be seen in the following sections, the DFT has approached a great deal of importance owing to a large number of applications in digital signal processing.

Consider a discrete-time signal $x(n)$, which is zero for all $n < 0$ and for all $n \geq N$. The discrete Fourier transform of $x(n)$ is defined by

$$X(k) = \sum_{k=0}^{N-1} x(n) \exp\left(\frac{-j2\pi kn}{N}\right), \qquad k = 0, 1, \ldots, N-1 \quad (4.74)$$

It is seen from equation 4.74 that the discrete Fourier transform $X(k)$ is a function of the integer variable k. We may also write

$$X(k) = X(\Omega)|_{\Omega = 2\pi k/N} = X\left(\frac{2\pi k}{N}\right) \qquad (4.75)$$

where $X(\Omega)$ is the DTFT of $x(n)$, as defined in equation 4.34. Thus the DFT of $x(n)$ can be considered to contain the samples of its DTFT.

The inverse DFT is given by

$$x(n) = \frac{1}{N} \sum_{n=0}^{N-1} X(k) \exp\left(\frac{j2\pi kn}{N}\right), \qquad n = 0, 1, 2, \ldots, N-1 \quad (4.76)$$

The difference between the DTFT and the DFT can also be stated in the following way. For the former, we have a *timed-limited but nonperiodic sequence* $x(n)$ of duration N. We obtain a continuous frequency spectrum for this sequence by making N approach infinity and assuming that the period of the sequence is infinity. This was the reason that the DTFT turned out to be a continuous function of frequency. On the other hand, *for the DFT, we assume that the sequence* $x(n)$ *is periodic, with period N, where N is finite.* This results in the DFT, which is a discrete function of frequency, since all the frequency components are integral multiples of the fundamental frequency

$\Omega_0 = 2\pi/N$. Thus, it will be seen that the DFT is very similar to the discrete Fourier series, since for the latter also we had a periodic sequence $x(n)$ of period N. Consequently, the frequency spectrum of $x(n)$ was discrete, with values only at integral multiples of the fundamental frequency Ω_0. This similarity is further reinforced by comparing equations 4.74 and 4.76 with the corresponding equations for the discrete-time Fourier series, that is, equations 4.14 and 4.13, respectively. The only difference that we notice is that the DFT is N times the value of the coefficient of the Fourier series for a periodic-time signal with period N. This also accounts for the fact that the right-hand side of equation 4.13 is N times the right-hand side of equation 4.76.

The notation can be simplified, as in the case of the discrete Fourier series, by replacing $e^{j2\pi/N}$ by w_N, denoting the nth root of unity. This leads to the following equations defining the discrete Fourier transform and the inverse discrete Fourier transform:

$$X(k) = \sum_{n=0}^{N-1} x(n)w_N^{-kn}, \qquad k = 0, 1, 2, \ldots, N-1 \qquad (4.77)$$

and

$$x(n) = \frac{1}{N} \sum_{k=0}^{N-1} X(k)w_N^{kn}, \qquad n = 0, 1, 2, \ldots, N-1 \qquad (4.78)$$

These equations (and the corresponding equations for the discrete-time Fourier series) are readily programmed on a digital computer. Furthermore, a comparison between equation 4.77 and equation 4.78 tells us that once we have developed a good algorithm for calculating the forward transform, the same algorithm can also be used for calculating the inverse transform with only a minor modification. It may be noted, however, that for computing each value of $X(k)$, we would require N multiplications if we use equation 4.77 directly. Hence, for computing the values of $X(k)$ for $k = 0$ to $N - 1$, the number of multiplications needed will be N^2. In fact, each of these will, in general, be multiplication between two complex numbers and will normally require four multiplications and two additions of real numbers.* It follows, therefore, that the number of real multiplications required for the computation of the DFT is of the order of $4N^2$. This number becomes very large as N is increased. For example, for a sequence of length 4096, the algorithm would require more than 67 million multiplications. It is possible to reduce the number of real multiplications to $2N \log_2 N$ by using one of a group of computational algorithms known as the fast Fourier transform. This implies

---

*There are special techniques for multiplications of complex numbers that require only three real multiplications and five real additions. For example, see the book *Digital Filters*, by N. K. Bose (North-Holland, 1985), page 109. Also see Problem 4.21 at the end of this chapter.

that for a sequence of length 4096, we shall require only 98,304 real multiplications with such an algorithm. This will be the topic for the next section.

4.6 FAST FOURIER TRANSFORM ALGORITHMS

Starting with the first published work of Cooley and Tukey in 1965, there has been a great deal of activity in the application of the DFT to signal processing and has resulted in the discovery of a number of computational algorithms, which have come to be known as *fast Fourier transform*, or simply FFT algorithms. All these algorithms exploit the symmetry and periodicity of the complex sequence $w_N^{kn} = \exp[j(2\pi/N)kn]$. In this book, our objective is not to cover in detail all the computational aspects of the FFT, but just to explain the main idea that leads to the dramatic savings in computation.

The basic principle utilized in all these algorithms is that of decomposing the computation of the discrete Fourier transform of a sequence of length N into successively smaller discrete Fourier transforms. A variety of algorithms have been developed, depending on the way in which this principle is implemented. In general, the FFT algorithms can be put into two basic classes. These are known as *decimation in time* and *decimation in frequency*. Algorithms that are based on decimation in time derive their name from the fact that in the process of arranging the computations into smaller transformations, the sequence $x(n)$ is decomposed into successively smaller subsequences. Algorithms that utilize decimation in frequency are so named because the sequence of discrete Fourier transform coefficients $X(n)$ is decomposed into successively smaller subsequences. Here, we describe, in detail, an algorithm based on decimation in time. For simplicity, it is assumed that the number of samples N is an integral power of 2. If this is not the case, one may simply "pad" the sequence with a number of zeros to increase the number to the nearest integral power of 2. It may be added that although there are FFT algorithms that utilize radixes different from 2, it is desirable to stay with the simplest case for the purpose of this book. It should be noted, however, that algorithms with radixes different from 2 can often be very efficient, especially when used with computers that utilize parallel processing.

Suppose that we have $2N$ samples of the signal $x(n)$. The first step is to separate them into an "odd" and an "even" sequence, that is,

$$b(0) = x(0), \quad b(1) = x(2), \ldots, b(N-1) = x(2N-2)$$
$$c(0) = x(1), \quad c(1) = x(3), \ldots, c(N-1) = x(2N-1) \quad (4.79)$$

We now show that to find the DFT of $x(n)$, it is easier to find the DFTs of $b(n)$ and $c(n)$ by proving the following theorem.

THEOREM The DFT $X(k)$ of $\{x(n)\}$ is given by

$$X(k) = B(k) + w_{2N}^{-k}C(k), \quad k = 0, 1, \ldots, 2N-1 \quad (4.80)$$

where

$$B(k) = \sum_{m=0}^{N-1} b(m)w_N^{-mk} \quad \text{and} \quad C(k) = \sum_{m=0}^{N-1} c(m)w_N^{-mk} \quad (4.81)$$

are the DFTs of order N of the even components $b(n)$ and the odd components $c(n)$ of $x(n)$, respectively. Also note that, according to our definition of w_N as the Nth root of unity, $e^{j2\pi/N}$, the term w_{2N} is the $2N$th root of unity. Thus $w_{2N}^2 = w_N$.

PROOF If we replace N by $2N$ in equation 4.77 and separate the odd and even terms, we get

$$X(k) = \sum_{n=0}^{2N-1} x(n)w_{2N}^{-nk} = \sum_{m=0}^{N-1} x(2m)w_{2N}^{-2mk} + \sum_{m=0}^{N-1} x(2m+1)w_{2N}^{-(2m+1)k}$$

$$= \sum_{m=0}^{N-1} b(m)w_N^{-mk} + w_{2N}^{-k}\sum_{m=0}^{N-1} c(m)w_N^{-mk}$$

$$= B(k) + w_{2N}^{-k}C(k)$$

The main advantage of this procedure is that it reduces the number of multiplications from $(2N)^2$ to $2(N^2 + N)$, that is, N^2 multiplications for $B(m)$, N^2 multiplications for $C(m)$, and $2N$ multiplications for computing the product term $w_{2N}^{-m}C(m)$.

Further reduction in the number of multiplications required for calculating the transform is obtained if we compute $X(m)$ using equation 4.80 for m from 0 to $N - 1$ and the remaining values of $X(m)$ from N to $2N - 1$ by using the following equations:

$$X(k + N) = B(k) - w_{2N}^{-k}C(k), \quad k = 0, 1, \ldots, N - 1 \quad (4.82)$$

These are identical to the last N equations in 4.80. In fact, if we were to replace k by $k + N$ in equation 4.80, we would obtain equation 4.82, since

$$B(k + N) = B(k), \quad C(k + N) = C(k) \quad \text{and} \quad w_{2N}^{-(k+N)} = -w_{2N}^{-k}$$

and as k varies from 0 to $N - 1$, $k + N$ varies from N to $2N - 1$.

Equation 4.82 implies that it is possible to combine two of the calculations, since both of them involve multiplication of the same two terms and the only difference is that the product is either added to or subtracted from another term. This is done by using an arrangement called *butterfly* and will be explained in more detail later. It may be pointed out that although the butterfly arrangement is valid only for radix-2, it is possible to extend this to the multidimensional case, say for radix-4, and obtain an algorithm that involves fewer multiplications or memory cycles than for the case of radix-2 operations.

Using the foregoing scheme causes the number of multiplications to be reduced to $2N^2 + N$ from $2N^2 + 2N$, since we need only N multiplications

TABLE 4.1 The FFT Algorithm for $N = 8$

$N = 2$	$N = 4$	$N = 8$
$X_2^1(0) = x(0) + x(4)$	$X_4^1(0) = X_2^1(0) + X_2^2(0)$	$X(0) = X_4^1(0) + X_4^2(0)$
$X_2^1(1) = x(0) - x(4)$	$X_4^1(1) = X_2^1(1) + w_4^{-1}X_2^2(1)$	$X(1) = X_4^1(1) + w_8^{-1}X_4^2(1)$
$X_2^2(0) = x(2) + x(6)$	$X_4^1(2) = X_2^1(0) - X_2^2(0)$	$X(2) = X_4^1(2) + w_8^{-2}X_2^2(2)$
$X_2^2(1) = x(2) - x(6)$	$X_4^1(3) = X_2^1(1) - w_4^{-1}X_2^2(1)$	$X(3) = X_4^1(3) + w_8^{-3}X_4^2(3)$
$X_2^3(0) = x(1) + x(5)$	$X_4^2(0) = X_2^3(0) + X_2^4(0)$	$X(4) = X_4^1(0) - X_4^2(0)$
$X_2^3(1) = x(1) - x(5)$	$X_4^2(1) = X_2^3(1) + w_4^{-1}X_2^4(1)$	$X(5) = X_4^1(1) - w_8^{-1}X_4^2(1)$
$X_2^4(0) = x(3) + x(7)$	$X_4^2(2) = X_2^3(0) - X_2^4(0)$	$X(6) = X_4^1(2) - w_8^{-2}X_4^2(2)$
$X_2^4(1) = x(3) - x(7)$	$X_4^2(3) = X_2^3(1) - w_4^{-1}X_2^4(1)$	$X(7) = X_4^1(3) - w_8^{-3}X_4^2(3)$

to find the product $w_{2N}^{-k}C(k)$ and this product is the same in equations 4.63 and 4.65.

If the total number of data points is 2^r, we can repeat the above process of dividing the data into odd and even parts and continue until we obtain $N = 2$. This results in a significant reduction in the number of multiplications to be performed. Before we estimate the total number of multiplications required for the complete algorithm, we shall explain the steps carefully for the case when we have $N = 2^3 = 8$ data points. This should enable us to fully understand the algorithm. An example will follow.

In this case, since we have 8 data points, we first subdivide them into 2 groups of 4 and then into 4 groups of 2 data points. In order to keep track of changing orders, the following notation is used:

$$X_N(k) \text{ represents a DFT of order } N$$

and if several DFTs of the same order are calculated, we include a superscript to distinguish them from each other, that is,

$$X_N^i(k) \text{ represents the } i\text{th DFT of order } N,$$

while the index k has the usual meaning.

The various steps involved in computation are shown in detail in Table 4.1.

By using the notation given above, equations 4.76 and 4.78 can be written as

$$X_{2N}(k) = X_N^1(k) + w_{2N}^{-k}X_N^2(k)$$

$$X_{2N}(k + N) = X_N^1(k) - w_{2N}^{-k}X_N^2(k) \qquad \text{for } k = 0, 1, \ldots, N - 1 \quad (4.83)$$

These equations are shown graphically in Figure 4.17, which depicts the butterfly arrangement. All butterfly operations for Table 4.1 are shown in Figure 4.18. There are $r = \log_2 N = 3$ columns and each column has $N/2$ or 4 butterflies. Each butterfly requires only one multiplication. The data appear in their natural order, that is, $x(0), x(1), x(2), \ldots, x(7)$, only in the

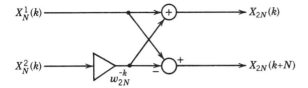

Figure 4.17 The butterfly arrangement.

last column. In other columns, they are the even and odd components of the data to their right, as in equation 4.75. The order in which the data appear in the first column is determined very easily if we write the value of k in the binary form. In the extreme left we have these numbers written in the natural order, whereas in the next column these are written in the reverse order of binary digits. This *reversed bit order* is used for the elements in the first

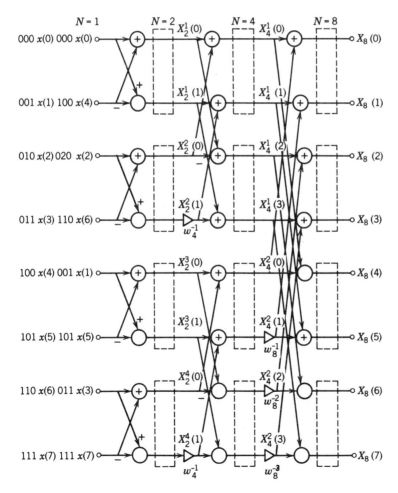

Figure 4.18 All butterfly operations for $N = 8$.

TABLE 4.2 Example of FFT Calculations

$N = 2$	$N = 4$	$N = 8$
$X_2^1(0) = 3$	$X_4^1(0) = 0 + j0$	$X_8(0) = 1 + j0$
$X_2^1(1) = -1$	$X_4^1(1) = -1 - j3$	$X_8(1) = 3.9497 - j5.1213$
$X_2^2(0) = -3$	$X_4^1(2) = 6 + j0$	$X_8(2) = 6 - j1$
$X_2^2(1) = 3$	$X_4^1(3) = -1 + j3$	$X_8(3) = -5.9497 + j0.8787$
$X_2^3(0) = 1$	$X_4^2(0) = 1 + j0$	$X_8(4) = -1 + j0$
$X_2^3(1) = 5$	$X_4^2(1) = 5 + j2$	$X_8(5) = -5.9497 - j0.8787$
$X_2^4(0) = 0$	$X_4^2(2) = 1 - j0$	$X_8(6) = 6 + j1$
$X_2^4(1) = -2$	$X_4^2(3) = 5 - j2$	$X_8(7) = 3.9497 + j5.1213$

column for computations (under $N = 2$). For the general case of 2^r samples of data, we would have a binary number of r digits and we would proceed in the same manner.

Example 4.7

Consider the following sequence

$$x(0) = 1, \quad x(1) = 3, \quad x(2) = 0, \quad x(3) = -1, \quad x(4) = 2,$$
$$x(5) = -2, \quad x(6) = -3, \quad x(7) = 1$$

By using the reversed bit ordering described earlier, the starting order of these samples will, therefore, be 1, 2, 0, -3, 3, -2, -1, and 1.

The results obtained using the procedure outlined in Table 4.1, are shown in Table 4.2. Advantage has been taken of the fact that $w_4^1 = j$ and $w_8^1 = \cos \pi/4 + j \sin \pi/4$. These values have been used in the complex multiplications required for the procedure. All computations were done to an accuracy of nine significant figures, but rounded off to retain only four figures after the decimal point for entering into the table. Note that this procedure requires several multiplications and additions with complex numbers.

The algorithm described above is based on decimation in time. For decimation in frequency, the subdivision is carried out on the output rather than the input. The butterfly operations for this case will be similar to those shown in Figure 4.18, but with all arrows reversed and the input and output interchanged. As a result, both of the approaches require precisely the same number of arithmetic operations.

We are now ready to determine the number of arithmetic operations required for the FFT algorithm if $N = 2^r$. As seen in Figure 4.18, the total number of columns in the algorithm is given by

$$r = \log_2 N \tag{4.84}$$

In each column, there are $N/2$ butterflies and each butterfly requires one

TABLE 4.3 Comparison of FFT with Direct Computation

N	256	512	1,024	4,096
N^2	65,536	261,244	1,048,576	16,777,216
$\frac{1}{2}N \log_2 N$	1,024	2,304	5,120	24,576

multiplication. Hence, the total number of multiplications required for the entire algorithm is given by

$$M = \tfrac{1}{2} \log_2 N \qquad (4.85)$$

Table 4.3 shows the number of computations required with the direct method and the FFT for different values of N. The advantage of the FFT algorithm is evident, especially when the number of data points is large. For this reason, this algorithm has been very popular and has found many applications.

It should be observed, however, that most of these multiplications are performed with complex numbers. As mentioned earlier, multiplication of two complex numbers requires at least three multiplications and five additions of real numbers. Therefore, if we count only real multiplications, then the numbers in the table should be multiplied by three.

4.7 SOME PROPERTIES OF THE DFT

In this section, we discuss some useful properties of the discrete Fourier transform. As expected, they are very similar to those of the discrete Fourier series and can be proved in the same manner as for the latter or for the discrete-time Fourier transform. Consequently, we shall omit the proofs and just give a short table of these properties, where the following notation will be used:

$$\mathscr{F}[x(n)] = X(k), \qquad k = 0, 1, 2, \ldots, N \qquad (4.86)$$

implies that the DFT of the sequence $x(n)$ is given by the sequence $X(k)$. It is assumed that the length of the sequence as well as the size of the DFT is N. Also, we shall represent $e^{j2\pi/N}$ by w_N.

All the properties given in Table 4.4 should be familiar to the reader, with the possible exception of circular convolution, which was discussed in Section 4.3.2.9 as *periodic convolution*. Although equation 4.63 looks a little different from the relationship given above, a little reflection will show that the two give the same answer. We verify this by working out Example 4.6 using the relationship for circular convolution given above.

Example 4.8

Let two sequences, each of length 4, be given by

$$x(n) = (1, 2, 0, -1) \qquad (4.87)$$

TABLE 4.4 Properties of the DFT

1. Linearity	$\mathcal{F}[a_1 x_1(n) + a_2 x_2(n)] = a_1 X_1(k) + a_2 X_2(k)$
2. Shift in time	$\mathcal{F}[x(n - m)] = X(k) w_N^{-km}$
3. Shift in frequency	$\mathcal{F}[x(n) w_N^{-mn}] = X(k - m)$
4. Duality	$\mathcal{F}[X(k)] = Nx(-n)$
5. Circular convolution	$\mathcal{F}\left[\sum_{i=0}^{N-1} x[(n - i) \bmod N] y(i) \right] = X(k) Y(k)$
6. Multiplication	$\mathcal{F}[x(n) y(n)] = N^{-1} \left[\sum_{i=0}^{N-1} X[(k - i) \bmod N] Y(i) \right]$
7. Parseval's theorem	$N \sum_{n=1}^{N-1} |x(n)|^2 = \sum_{k=1}^{N-1} |X(k)|^2$

and

$$y(n) = (3, 1, -1, 1) \tag{4.88}$$

Our object is to determine the DFT of the product $x(n)y(n)$. We can do it by first multiplying the two sequences and then obtaining the DFT. We can also first determine the DFT of each of the sequences and then obtain the DFT of the product by circular convolution of the DFTs of the two sequences. We now verify that both methods lead to the same result.

By direct multiplication we obtain the product

$$z(n) = x(n) y(n) = (3, 2, 0, -1) \tag{4.89}$$

Since in this case we have only four samples, the DFT for each of the sequences can be calculated directly by using equation 4.77. Noting that $w_4 = j$, we obtain

$$X(0) = x(0) + x(1) + x(2) + x(3) = 2$$

$$X(1) = x(0) + (-j)\dot{x}(1) + (-j)^2 x(2) + (-j)^3 x(3) = 1 - j3$$

$$X(2) = x(0) + (-j)^2 x(1) + (-j)^4 x(2) + (-j)^6 x(3) = 0$$

$$X(3) = x(0) + (-j)^3 x(1) + (-j)^6 x(2) + (-j)^9 x(3) = 1 + j1$$

Similarly,

$$Y(0) = y(0) + y(1) + y(2) + y(3) = 4$$

$$Y(1) = y(0) + (-j)y(1) + (-j)^2 y(2) + (-j)^3 y(3) = 4$$

$$Y(2) = y(0) + (-j)^2 y(1) + (-j)^4 y(2) + (-j)^6 y(3) = 0$$

$$Y(3) = y(0) + (-j)^3 y(1) + (-j)^6 y(2) + (-j)^9 y(3) = 4$$

and

$$Z(0) = z(0) + z(1) + z(2) + z(3) = 4$$

$$Z(1) = z(0) + (-j)z(1) + (-j)^2 z(2) + (-j)^3 z(3) = 3 - j3$$

$$Z(2) = z(0) + (-j)^2 z(1) + (-j)^4 z(2) + (-j)^6 z(3) = 2$$

$$Z(3) = z(0) + (-j)^3 z(1) + (-j)^6 z(2) + (-j)^9 z(3) = 3 + j3$$

Finally, we calculate the DFT of the sequence $z(n)$ by using circular convolution of $X(k)$ and $Y(k)$. From Table 4.4, we obtain

$$Z(0) = \frac{1}{4} \sum_{i=0}^{3} X[(0 - i) \bmod 4] Y(i)$$

$$= \frac{[X(0)Y(0) + X(1)Y(1) + X(2)Y(2) + X(3)Y(3)]}{4} = 4$$

$$Z(1) = \frac{1}{4} \sum_{i=0}^{3} X[(1 - i) \bmod 4] Y(i)$$

$$= \frac{[X(1)Y(0) + X(0)Y(1) + X(3)Y(2) + X(2)Y(3)]}{4} = 3 - j3$$

$$Z(2) = \frac{1}{4} \sum_{i=0}^{3} X[(2 - i) \bmod 4] Y(i)$$

$$= \frac{[X(2)Y(0) + X(1)Y(1) + X(0)Y(2) + X(3)Y(3)]}{4} = 2$$

$$Z(3) = \frac{1}{4} \sum_{i=0}^{3} X[(3 - i) \bmod 4] Y(i)$$

$$= \frac{[X(3)Y(0) + X(2)Y(1) + X(1)Y(2) + X(0)Y(3)]}{4} = 3 + j3$$

The two sets of DFTs of $z(n)$ are seen to be identical. Evidently, in this case it is easier to first obtain the product $z(n) = x(n)y(n)$ and then determine its DFT. The main application of this property is in the calculation of $Z(k)$ if $X(k)$ and $Y(k)$ are given. ∎

The reader may verify that the values of $Z(k)$, obtained by using the circular convolution algorithm described in Section 4.3.2.9, will be the same as those obtained above.

4.8   SOME APPLICATIONS OF THE DFT

Discrete Fourier transforms have many applications, specially when an FFT algorithm is used for computing the forward or inverse transform. These applications are found in many fields, including digital filtering, convolution, deconvolution, estimation of the power spectrum of a signal, digital communications, and system identification. In this section we discuss some of these applications.

4.8.1   CALCULATION OF FOURIER TRANSFORMS

An important application of the FFT algorithm is the calculation of the Fourier transform of a given function of time. This is very useful because often we find that analytical evaluation of the Fourier transform integral is either very involved or not possible. In such cases, we can get a close approximation to the Fourier transform fairly easily by using the FFT.

The main idea is to evaluate the integral numerically. This is done by first calculating the values of the given signal, $x(t)$, at equally spaced values of t. These samples are then used for calculating the DFT of the signal at equally spaced values of ω. A good approximation will be obtained if the sampling interval is chosen suitably. In particular, if the signal is band-limited, one may use the sampling theorem to ensure that the sampling frequency is somewhat greater than the Nyquist rate. We now explain the mathematical details.

The Fourier transform $X(\omega)$ of a causal signal $x(t)$ is given by

$$X(\omega) = \int_0^\infty x(t)e^{j\omega t}\, dt \tag{4.90}$$

Selecting a suitable sampling interval T, we can rewrite equation 4.90 in the following form:

$$X(\omega) = \sum_{n=0}^\infty \int_{nT}^{nT+T} x(t)e^{j\omega t}\, dt \tag{4.91}$$

For sufficiently small T, it is possible to replace $x(t)$ with $x(kT)$ in the above integral, that is, we assume that $x(t)$ is constant over the sampling interval. Therefore, we integrate only the exponential function to obtain

$$X(\omega) = \sum_{n=0}^\infty \left[\int_{nT}^{nT+T} e^{j\omega t}\, dt \right] x(nT)$$

$$= \frac{e^{-j\omega T} - 1}{j\omega} \sum_{n=0}^\infty e^{-jn\omega t}x(nT) \tag{4.92}$$

The upper limit in the above summation may be changed from ∞ to N if $x(nT)$ is almost zero for $n \geq N$, where N is a sufficiently large positive integer. Thus, we obtain the following approximation for $X(\omega)$

$$X(\omega) = \frac{e^{-j\omega T} - 1}{j\omega} \sum_{n=0}^{N-1} e^{-jn\omega t}x(nT) \tag{4.93}$$

Furthermore, we may replace ω by $k\Omega$, where $\Omega = 2\pi/(NT)$. The following relationship is then obtained:

$$X(k\Omega) = \frac{e^{-jk\Omega T} - 1}{jk\Omega} \sum_{n=0}^{N-1} e^{-jnk\Omega t} x(nT)$$

$$= \frac{e^{-jk\Omega T} - 1}{jk\Omega} X(k) \qquad (4.94)$$

Note that the variable Ω is the angular frequency corresponding to the period NT. Thus, our choice of T and N limits the minimum separation between the various values of the angular frequency ω at which we can use equation 4.94 for calculating the Fourier transform $X(k\Omega)$.

Therefore, we may first calculate $X(k)$, for $k = 0, 1, 2, \ldots, N - 1$, using the FFT algorithm and then utilize equation 4.94 to calculate $X(k\Omega)$.

It should be emphasized that equation 4.94 is an approximation. Consequently, it gives only approximate values of the Fourier transform. However, these will be quite close to the actual values, especially if the sampling interval T is sufficiently small. As stated earlier, a good choice is to select T such that the sampling frequency is somewhat greater than the Nyquist rate if the signal is band-limited. In practice, it is generally desirable to make the sampling frequency sufficiently greater than twice the estimated bandwidth of the signal.

4.8.2 FAST CONVOLUTION

If we have an input sequence $x(n)$, which is nonzero for $0 \geq n > N$, and a system with impulse response $h(n)$, which is nonzero for $0 \geq n > M$, then we can determine the output sequence through the convolution sum, as discussed in Chapter 2. The number of multiplications required to obtain the output sequence using the convolution sum will be of the order of

$$M_1 = 0.5(M + N)^2 + 1.5(M + N) \qquad (4.95)$$

It is possible to use the FFT algorithm for calculating the output sequence with the number of multiplications reduced to the order of

$$M_2 = 1.5(M + N) \log_2 (M + N) + M + N \qquad (4.96)$$

This is done by first adding M zeros to the input sequence and N zeros to the impulse response sequence, so that both of them have the same number of entries. The FFT algorithm is then used to obtain the respective DFTs, given by $X(k)$ and $H(k)$. The DFT of the output sequence $y(n)$ is given by

$$Y(k) = X(k)H(k) \qquad (4.97)$$

After obtaining $Y(k)$ as above, we then determine its inverse DFT, again using the FFT algorithm. This gives $y(n)$.

Note that the calculation of the inverse DFT can be carried out by using the FFT algorithm since equations 4.77 and 4.78 are almost identical, the only difference being in the sign of the exponent and division by N. The computer program for convolution of two real sequences that is included with this book is based on the FFT algorithm and the procedure described above.

The following table presents a comparison of the values of M_1 and M_2 for several values of M and assuming that $M = N$. These fully illustrate the savings in computation brought about by the use of the FFT algorithm for computing the convolution sum.

M	128	256	512
M_1	33,152	131,840	525,824
M_2	647	1,289	2,570

4.8.3   SYSTEM IDENTIFICATION

We came across the system identification problem in Chapter 2 as an application of deconvolution, and it was shown in Section 2.10 that one can determine the impulse response sequence of a linear system if the input and output sequences $x(n)$ and $y(n)$ are known. One can also use the FFT algorithm to obtain the DFTs $X(k)$ and $Y(k)$, respectively. The DFT $H(k)$ of the impulse response sequence is then known immediately through equation 4.97, that is, for any given value of k,

$$H(k) = \frac{Y(k)}{X(k)} \tag{4.98}$$

If desired, one can determine the impulse response sequence $h(n)$ by calculating the inverse DFT of $H(k)$.

In view of the foregoing, the FFT algorithm is often used to determine the model of a system from its input–output data. It must, however, be noted that the results thus obtained can be significantly affected by the presence of noise in the input–output data. The results can usually be improved by prefiltering the data before using the FFT algorithm.

4.8.4   ENERGY SPECTRAL DENSITY AND AUTOCORRELATION SEQUENCE

Given a sequence $x(n)$ of length N, its energy content is defined as

$$E = \sum_{n=0}^{N-1} |x(n)|^2 \tag{4.99}$$

Using Parseval's theorem, we can also express the energy in terms of $X(k)$, the DFT of $x(n)$. Thus, we obtain

$$E = \sum_{n=0}^{N-1} \frac{|X(k)|^2}{N} \qquad (4.100)$$

The expression inside the summation sign in equation 4.100 can be interpreted as the *energy spectral density function*, so that its sum over the entire range of frequencies gives the total energy content. Denoting this density function as $S_x(k)$, we may write

$$S_x(k) = \frac{1}{N} X(k) X^*(k) \qquad (4.101)$$

where $X^*(k)$ is the complex conjugate of $X(k)$.

It can be shown that the energy spectral density function is also the DFT of the *autocorrelation sequence* of $x(n)$, defined as

$$R_x(n) = \frac{1}{N} \sum_{m=0}^{N-n-1} x(m) x^*(m+n) \qquad (4.102)$$

We may therefore write

$$S_x(k) = \mathscr{F}[R_x(n)] \qquad (4.103)$$

Equation 4.103 is known as the *Wiener–Khintchine theorem* for discrete-time signals. Since the DFT can be calculated more efficiently, this theorem can be utilized for determining the autocorrelation sequence of such a signal by first calculating its DFT and then obtaining the IDFT of the corresponding energy density function.

A program for calculating the energy density function as well as the autocorrelation function of a finite sequence of real numbers, based on the FFT algorithm, is included on the disk supplied with this book. Since the length of the sequence should be an integral power of 2, it is "padded" with zeros, if necessary.

4.9 SUMMARY

In this chapter we have studied Fourier analysis of discrete-time signals. We started with the Fourier series representation of periodic discrete-time signals and extended the approach to nonperiodic signals to obtain the discrete-time version of the Fourier transform. We noticed that unlike its continuous-time counterpart, the discrete Fourier series is a finite sum. Thus, we do not have to truncate the series in this case and problems of convergence like the Gibbs phenomenon do not arise. It was shown that the discrete Fourier series can be applied to determine the steady-state response of a discrete-time linear system to a periodic input by using a procedure analogous to the one studied for continuous-time systems. The difference is that the unit advance operator q is replaced with w_N^k for the kth harmonic component of the input for the discrete-time case, corresponding to the replacement of the operator p with $j\omega n$ for the continuous-time case.

The discrete-time Fourier transform (DTFT) was, again, seen to be a direct counterpart of the Fourier transform of continuous-time signals, with analogous properties. An important difference was also noted: the DTFT is periodic. Furthermore, the integration for the inverse discrete-time Fourier transform (IDTFT) need be performed only over an interval of length 2π, instead of an infinite interval of frequencies. As a result, the spectrum of sampled signals is also periodic. This observation can be regarded as the key to the sampling theorem and explains why the sampling frequency must not be less than twice the bandwidth of the original unsampled signal if we expect to recover it from the samples. This was confirmed by a formal derivation of the frequency spectrum of the sampled signal, assuming that a train of impulses is used in the ideal sampler.

The discrete Fourier transform (DFT) was then introduced. It is almost identical to the discrete Fourier series; the two differ only by the factor N, which is the number of samples for DFT and the period for the discrete Fourier series. The DFT can be calculated very efficiently by using any version of the fast Fourier transform (FFT) algorithm. The latter can be based on either decimation in time or decimation in frequency and reduces the number of real multiplications from approximately $4N^2$ to $2N \log_2 N$. Consequently, it is applied extensively in digital signal processing and digital communications. Several important applications of the FFT algorithm were discussed in this chapter. These include calculation of Fourier transforms of functions that cannot be evaluated analytically, fast convolution, identification of systems by deconvolution, and determination of the energy spectral density, as well as the autocorrelation sequence of a discrete-time signal of finite length.

4.10   PROBLEMS

4.1   A periodic sequence is given below. Determine the discrete Fourier series for this sequence

$$x = \{1, 1, 1, 1, -1, -1, -1, -1\}$$

4.2   Repeat Problem 4.1 for the following sequence:

$$x = \{2, 1, 0, -2, 3, -1, 2, -2\}$$

4.3   The difference equation for a discrete-time system is given below:

$$y(k + 1) - 0.8y(k) = u(k)$$

Determine the steady-state response of this system if the input is
(a) $u(k) = 10 \sin (0.2\pi k)$.
(b) $u(k) = 10 \sin (0.2\pi k) - 5 \sin (0.4\pi k + \pi/3)$.
(c) $u(k)$ is the periodic sequence $\{1, 1, -1, -1\}$.
(d) $u(k)$ is the periodic sequence $\{1, -1, 0, -1, 2, -1\}$.

4.4   Repeat Problem 4.3 for the system defined by the following difference equation:

$$y(k + 2) - 1.2y(k + 1) + 0.45y(k) = 2u(k + 1) + 3u(k)$$

4.5   Let $x(k)$ denote a sequence with period N and $A(k)$ denote its discrete Fourier series coefficients. $A(k)$ is also a sequence with period N. Determine, in terms of $x(k)$, the discrete Fourier series coefficients of the sequence $A(k)$.

4.6   Determine the discrete-time Fourier transform of the sequence given in Problem 4.1, assuming the sequence is nonzero only for $0 < n < 8$.

4.7   Repeat Problem 4.6 for the sequence given in Problem 4.2.

4.8   The discrete-time Fourier transform of a signal $x(n)$ is given by

$$X(\Omega) = \frac{10}{j\Omega + 4}$$

Determine the Fourier transform $Y(\Omega)$ of each of the signals given below:
(a) $y(n) = nx(n)$
(b) $y(n) = x(2n - 3)$
(c) $y(n) = x(-n)$
(d) $y(n) = x(n) - x(n - 1)$
(e) $y(n) = (0.5)^n x(n)$
(f) $y(n) = x(n) \cos 2n$
(g) $y(n) = x^2(n)$
(h) $y(n) = \sum\limits_{k=0}^{\infty} x(k)x(n - k)$

4.9   Determine the inverse discrete-time Fourier transform for each of the following:
(a) $X(\Omega) = 10 \cos 2\Omega$
(b) $X(\Omega) = 20 \sin 3\Omega$
(c) $X(\Omega) = 10 + 20 \cos 2\Omega$
(d) $X(\Omega) = 10e^{-2|\Omega|} \cos 2\Omega$ for $-1 \le \Omega \le 1$, with period 2π
(e) $X(\Omega) = \begin{cases} 1 & \text{for } -1 \le \Omega \le 1 \\ 0 & \text{otherwise,} \quad \text{with period } \pi \end{cases}$
(f) $X(\Omega) = \begin{cases} e^{-j\Omega} & \text{for } -1 \le \Omega \le 1 \\ 0 & \text{otherwise,} \quad \text{with period } 2\pi \end{cases}$

4.10   Let $X(n)$ denote the N-point DFT of the N-point sequence $x(n)$.
(a)   Show that if $x(n) = -x(N - 1 - n)$ then $X(0) = 0$.
(b)   Show that if N is even and $x(n) = x(N - 1 - n)$ then $X(N/2) = 0$.

4.11   The impulse response of a linear system is given by the sequence

$$h = \{1, 0.5, 0.25, 0.125, 0.05, 0.025, 0.0125, 0.006\}$$

Determine the output sequence if the input sequence is given by

$$x = \{1, 1, -1, -1, 1, 1\}$$

Use convolution for this problem.

4.12   Repeat the previous problem using the fast convolution method.

4.13   Use the FFT algorithm to determine the DFT of $x(n)$, which is defined below:

$$x(n) = \begin{cases} 2 & \text{for } n = 0 \\ \dfrac{1}{n} & \text{for } n = 1, 2, 3, \ldots, 15 \\ 0 & \text{for } n > 15. \end{cases}$$

4.14   The discrete-time signal $x(n)$ described in Problem 4.11 is the input to a linear system having the following impulse response sequence:

$$h(n) = \{1, 0.4, 0.15, -0.2, -0.1, 0.05, 0.01, 0.001\}$$

Determine the output sequence.

4.15   A continuous-time function is given by

$$x(t) = \frac{\sin 2t}{2t}$$

This function is sampled at intervals of $\pi/2$ s. Determine and sketch the frequency spectrum of the sampled function.

4.16   Use the FFT algorithm to approximately determine the Fourier transform of the following signal:

$$x(t) = \frac{1}{\sqrt{(2\pi)}} e^{-t^2/2}$$

4.17   Repeat Problem 4.16 if $x(t)$ is a rectangular pulse of height 10 and duration 2 s, centred around $t = 0$.

4.18   Show that

$$\sum_{n=0}^{N-1} x(n)x^*(n) = \frac{1}{N} \sum_{n=0}^{N-1} X(n)X^*(n)$$

[*Hint*: Substitute for $x^*(n)$ in terms of the IDFT of $X(n)$]

4.19   Prove the multiplication property given in Table 4.4 by substituting for $X(n - i)$ in terms of the DFT of $x(n)$.

4.20   Prove the circular convolution property given in Table 4.4.

4.21   Given two complex numbers $(a + jb)$ and $(c + jd)$, their product can be calculated as

$$(a + jb)(c + jd) = (ac - bd) + j(ad + bc)$$

This, evidently, requires four real multiplications and two real additions. Show that it is possible to reduce the number of real multiplications from four to only three, while increasing the number of real additions to five, if we express

$$ad + bc = (a + b)(c + d) - (ac + bd)$$

4.22   The number of complex multiplications and complex additions required for calculating the DFT of a sequence of length $N = 2^r$, where r is a positive integer, are $\frac{1}{2}N \log_2 N$ and $N \log_2 N$, respectively.

(a)   Use these relationships to estimate the time required to compute the FFT of a sequence of length 1024 on a microcomputer, if each real multiplication requires 1 μs whereas each real addition requires 0.1 μs. Assume that a complex multiplication requires four real multiplications and two real additions.

(b)   Repeat if each complex multiplication requires only three real multiplications but five real additions.

4.23   Repeat the previous problem for a sequence of length 2048 assuming that the microcomputer is twice as fast, that is, it requires 0.5 μs for each real multiplication and 0.05 μs for each real addition.

4.24   Repeat Problem 4.22 for a microcomputer designed in such a way that real multiplication takes only twice as long as addition. Consider the time required for multiplication as 0.2 μs and that for addition as 0.1 μs.

APPENDIX 4.1

Computation of the Discrete Fourier Transform

The computer program on the disk enclosed with the book uses the FFT algorithm, with decimation in time, as described in this chapter, for calculating the discrete Fourier transform of a sequence $x(n)$ of either real or complex numbers. The length of the sequence is N, that is, $x(n)$ is nonzero only for $0 \leq n \leq (N - 1)$. It is assumed that $N = 2^r$, where r is an integer. If this condition is not satisfied for a given sequence, the program automatically "pads" it with additional zeros to increase the length of the sequence to the next highest number 2^r. The DFT sequence $X(n)$ will, in general, consist of complex numbers.

The program also uses the same algorithm for calculating the inverse discrete Fourier transform for a given DFT sequence.

The data either can be entered through the keyboard or can be read from a disk file. The output is normally shown on the console, but both the input and the output data can be printed as well as stored in disk files.

APPENDIX 4.2

Fast Convolution

This program calculates the convolution of two sequences of real numbers of finite length by using the FFT algorithm, as described in Section 4.8.2. The sequences are padded with zeros so that their lengths are equal to N, an integral power of 2. The convolution is obtained by first calculating the DFT of each of the two sequences, multiplying these term by term, and then calculating the IDFT of the result. The result of convolution is a sequence of length $2N$. As in the other programs, the input sequences can be either entered from the keyboard or read from disk files, and both the input and output data can be either printed or stored in disk files, if desired.

5
Laplace Transforms

5.1 INTRODUCTION

In Chapter 3 we studied the theory of the Fourier transform that enables us to understand the behavior of a system in the frequency domain by allowing a signal $x(t)$ to be represented as a continuous sum of complex exponentials. Although this representation provides us with a powerful analytical tool, it is restricted to only those functions for which the Fourier transform exists. A sufficient condition for the existence of the Fourier transform of a signal is that it be absolutely integrable. We learned that in some special situations, where the power in the signal was concentrated at specific frequencies, this requirement can be relaxed by allowing impulse functions in the frequency domain. Nevertheless, there are many important functions for which the Fourier transform cannot be obtained, even after allowing this extension. Some common examples are the ramp function and the positive real exponential. In such cases, the introduction of a convergence factor, in the form of a negative real exponential, into the Fourier transform integral leads to the well-known Laplace transform. Although all the results required for using Laplace transforms can be obtained by starting with a definition of the transform, without even mentioning the Fourier transform, much better insight can be obtained by proceeding from the Fourier transform to the Laplace transform and showing how the two are related. This is especially useful in providing a frequency domain interpretation of Laplace transform analysis.

In Section 5.2, we shall define the bilateral Laplace transform as an extension of the Fourier transform. This will be followed by a brief study of convergence of the bilateral Laplace transform in Section 5.3. In Section 5.4, the theory of the one-sided Laplace transform will be presented in detail, including the basic properties, a table of Laplace transform pairs, and their use in the solution of linear differential equations. The concept of the transfer function of a linear system will be introduced in Section 5.5 and will include a discussion of poles and zeros, stability, and frequency response from transfer functions. This will be followed in Section 5.6 by the study of Laplace transforms of causal repeating functions and their application to finding the steady-state response of a linear system to any periodic input as an alternative approach to the use of the Fourier series. Finally, the inversion of bilateral Laplace transforms will be discussed in Section 5.7.

5.2   DEFINITION OF THE BILATERAL LAPLACE TRANSFORM

We start by recalling the defining equations for the Fourier transform pair for a signal $x(t)$, as given in Chapter 3:

$$X(\omega) = \int_{-\infty}^{\infty} x(t)e^{-j\omega t}\, dt \tag{5.1}$$

$$x(t) = \frac{1}{2\pi}\int_{-\infty}^{\infty} X(\omega)e^{j\omega t}\, d\omega \tag{5.2}$$

Let us now define a function $y(t)$ as

$$y(t) = e^{-\sigma t}x(t) \tag{5.3}$$

The term $e^{-\sigma t}$ introduced in equation 5.3 is a *convergence factor*, so that with a proper choice of σ, $y(t)$ will be absolutely convergent, and its Fourier transform will exist for a large number of functions, although $x(t)$ does not satisfy this property. The Fourier transform of $y(t)$ is given by

$$Y(\omega) = \int_{-\infty}^{\infty} y(t)e^{-j\omega t}\, dt$$

$$= \int_{-\infty}^{\infty} e^{-\sigma t}x(t)e^{-j\omega t}\, dt$$

$$= \int_{-\infty}^{\infty} x(t)e^{-(\sigma+j\omega)t}\, dt \tag{5.4}$$

Equation 5.4 can also be written as

$$X(\sigma + j\omega) = \int_{-\infty}^{\infty} x(t)e^{-(\sigma+j\omega t)}\, dt \tag{5.5}$$

Similarly, the inverse transform can be written as

$$x(t) = \frac{1}{2\pi}\int_{-\infty}^{\infty} X(\sigma + j\omega)e^{(\sigma+j\omega t)}\, d\omega \tag{5.6}$$

Since σ and $j\omega$ occur together in equations 5.5 and 5.6, let us define the variable s as

$$s = \sigma + j\omega \tag{5.7}$$

It is customary to call s the *complex frequency variable*, since ω appears as the imaginary part of the complex variable s. The s-plane is depicted in

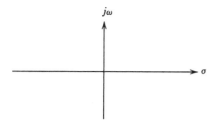

Figure 5.1   The s-plane.

Figure 5.1. Also, since $ds = j\,d\omega$, we may rewrite equations 5.5 and 5.6 as

$$X(s) = \int_{-\infty}^{\infty} x(t)e^{-st}\,dt \tag{5.8}$$

$$x(t) = \frac{1}{2\pi j}\int_{\sigma-j\infty}^{\sigma+j\infty} X(s)e^{st}\,ds \tag{5.9}$$

Note that the limits in equation 5.9 have been modified to account for the change in variable from ω to s.

Equations 5.8 and 5.9 define the *bilateral* or *two-sided Laplace transform pair*. Note that these are related to the Fourier transform pair simply through the substitution of s for $j\omega$, provided that $x(t)$ is absolutely integrable. In our development, we have multiplied the given function $x(t)$ by $e^{-\sigma t}$, where σ is a real number. This results in making the integral converge for a larger class of functions than is possible with Fourier transforms. Consequently, the Laplace transform exists for many functions that are not absolutely integrable. This is the main advantage of using the convergence factor $e^{-\sigma t}$. The choice of σ is very important for the convergence of the Laplace transform integral and will be discussed in further detail in the next section.

5.3 CONVERGENCE OF THE BILATERAL LAPLACE TRANSFORM

Existence of the Laplace transform of a given function depends on the convergence of the integral on the right-hand side of equation 5.8. It is evident that a sufficient condition for the integral to converge is that

$$\int_{-\infty}^{\infty}\left|x(t)e^{-\sigma t}\right|dt = \int_{-\infty}^{0}\left|x(t)\right|e^{-\sigma t}\,dt + \int_{0}^{\infty}\left|x(t)\right|e^{-\sigma t}\,dt \tag{5.10}$$

be finite. This will, indeed, be possible if we can find a real positive number

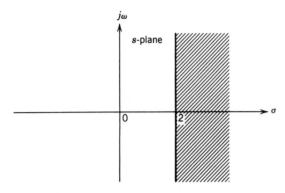

Figure 5.2 Region of convergence for Example 5.1.

A and real α and β such that

$$|x(t)| < \begin{cases} Ae^{\alpha t} & \text{for } t > 0 \\ Ae^{\beta t} & \text{for } t < 0 \end{cases} \tag{5.11}$$

then $X(s)$ converges as long as $\alpha < \sigma < \beta$. The following examples will illustrate the main idea.

Example 5.1

Consider the function

$$x(t) = 10e^{2t}\gamma(t) \tag{5.12}$$

The Fourier transform of this function does not exist, since it does not satisfy the condition of absolute integrability. We now determine its Laplace transform. Since this function is zero for $t < 0$, we have

$$X(s) = \int_0^\infty 10e^{2t}e^{-st}\, dt = \frac{10}{s-2}, \qquad \text{provided that } \sigma > 2 \quad (5.13)$$

Note that the integral will not converge if $\sigma \le 2$. Thus, we obtain a region of convergence in the s-plane for this function, which is any point to the right of the line $\sigma = 2$, as shown by the shaded area in Figure 5.2. ∎

Example 5.2

In the previous example, we considered a causal function. We now consider an anticausal function, one that exists for negative values of time only. Let

$$x(t) = 10e^{2t}\gamma(-t) \tag{5.14}$$

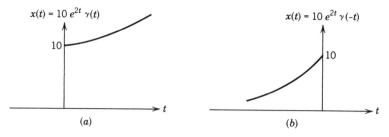

Figure 5.3 Causal and anticausal functions. (a) Causal function. (b) Anticausal function.

This function, as well as the causal function represented by equation 5.12 are shown in Figure 5.3. In this case, the Laplace transform is obtained as

$$X(s) = \int_{-\infty}^{0} 10e^{2t}e^{-st}\, dt = \frac{10}{s-2}, \qquad \text{provided that } \sigma < 2 \quad (5.15)$$

The region of convergence for this Laplace transform is shown in Figure 5.4. Two very interesting observations follow. First we note that the Laplace transform for this function will exist only if $\sigma < 2$. Also, the Laplace transforms of the causal function denoted by equation 5.12 and the anti-causal function denoted by equation 5.14 are identical, but the regions of convergence for the two functions in the s-plane are different. It is, evidently, very important to know the region of convergence in bilateral transforms if we want to obtain the correct inverse transform. ∎

For the more general case of functions, which are neither causal nor anti-causal, the region of convergence will be a strip in the s-plane. If this strip includes the $j\omega$-axis, then the Fourier transform can be obtained by merely replacing s with $j\omega$ in the expression for the Laplace transform.

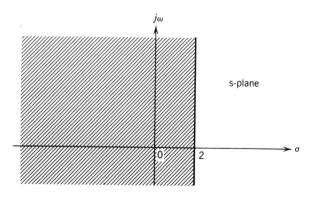

Figure 5.4 Region of convergence for Example 5.2.

In the majority of engineering applications, the time functions of interest are causal, that is, $x(t) = 0$ for $t < 0$. This is usually the case if a forcing function is applied to a system at $t = 0$. In practice, it is often permissible to select the time origin to satisfy the causality condition for the input signal. In such instances, we can change the lower limit in the Laplace transform integral to 0 from $-\infty$. It will be shown later that it is not necessary to specify the region of convergence if we are considering only causal functions. In those instances we get the *unilateral* or *one-sided Laplace transform*, which will be described in the following sections. One situation where the unilateral Laplace transform will not satisfy our needs arises when $x(t)$ is a random signal, since in such cases we require the Laplace transform of its autocorrelation function, which is an even function of time.

5.4 THE ONE-SIDED LAPLACE TRANSFORM

For causal signals, the equations defining the Laplace transform pair take the following form:

$$X(s) = \int_{0^-}^{\infty} x(t)e^{-st}\, dt \tag{5.16}$$

$$x(t) = \frac{1}{2\pi j} \int_{\sigma - j\infty}^{\sigma + j\infty} X(s)e^{st}\, dt \tag{5.17}$$

Note that the lower limit of integration in the defining equation 5.16 has been made 0^-. This has been done to ensure that if the time function $x(t)$ contains an impulse at $t = 0$, this is taken into account in the Laplace transform.

For notational convenience, the following symbols will be used to denote the one-sided Laplace transform pair:

$$X(s) = \mathscr{L}[x(t)] \tag{5.18}$$

and

$$x(t) = \mathscr{L}^{-1}[X(s)] \tag{5.19}$$

As before, the integral will converge if σ is selected so that

$$\lim_{t \to \infty} e^{-\sigma t} x(t) = 0 \tag{5.20}$$

For most functions it will be possible to select a positive and sufficiently large σ such that equation 5.20 will be satisfied. This will always be true with positive exponentials or with functions that increase at a slower rate than an exponential. There do exist some functions for which equation 5.20 cannot be satisfied for any value of σ. One example is the function e^{t^2}. However, such functions seldom arise in engineering problems. In the next section we present some useful properties of unilateral Laplace transforms. These properties also apply to bilateral transforms unless stated otherwise. Most of

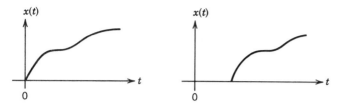

Figure 5.5 Effect of shifting a causal function to the right.

these are very similar to those of Fourier transforms presented in Chapter 3 and can be proved in the same way. Therefore, proofs will be given for only those properties that are different from the corresponding properties of Fourier transforms.

5.4.1 PROPERTIES OF LAPLACE TRANSFORMS

5.4.1.1 Linearity

If $X_1(s) = \mathscr{L}[x_1(t)]$ and $X_2(s) = \mathscr{L}[x_2(t)]$ then

$$\mathscr{L}[\alpha x_1(t) + \beta x_2(t)] = \alpha X_1(s) + \beta X_2(s) \qquad (5.21)$$

As for the case of Fourier transforms, this follows directly from linearity of integration. It applies to bilateral transforms as well.

5.4.1.2 Right Shift in Time

We first state and prove this property for unilateral Laplace transforms. Let $x(t)$ be a causal function, that is, $x(t) = 0$ for $t < 0$.
   If $X(s) = \mathscr{L}[x(t)]$ then

$$\mathscr{L}[x(t - \tau)\gamma(t - \tau)] = e^{-\tau s}X(s) \qquad (5.22)$$

where $\tau > 0$.
   Both $x(t)$ and the shifted function are shown in Figure 5.5.
   We shall prove this important property. From the definition of the unilateral Laplace transform,

$$\mathscr{L}[x(t - \tau)\gamma(t - \tau)] = \int_{0^-}^{\infty} x(t - \tau)\gamma(t - \gamma)e^{-st}\, dt$$

$$= \int_{\tau}^{\infty} x(t - \tau)\gamma(t - \tau)e^{-st}\, dt$$

$$= \int_{0^-}^{\infty} x(t_1)\gamma(t_1)\exp[-s(t_1 + \tau)]\, dt_1,$$

$$\text{where } t_1 = t - \tau$$

$$= e^{-s\tau}\int_{0^-}^{\infty} x(t_1)\gamma(t_1)e^{-st_1}\, dt_1$$

$$= e^{-s\tau}X(s)$$

This is a very useful property, since it will enable us to obtain the Laplace transforms of a wide variety of functions in terms of the Laplace transforms of some basic functions that will be described in Section 5.4.2.

Recall from Section 3.6.2.3 that the shifting property is also applicable to Fourier transforms. Thus, causality is not a requirement for this property, and it can be applied to bilateral Laplace transforms as well. However, the region of convergence for both $X(s)$ and $e^{-s\tau}X(s)$ must remain the same.

5.4.1.3   Multiplication by an Exponential (or Frequency Shift)

If $X(s) = \mathscr{L}[x(t)]$ then

$$\mathscr{L}\left[e^{at}x(t)\right] = X(s - a) \tag{5.23}$$

This is analogous to the frequency shifting property of the Fourier transform and is proved directly from the defining equation. Note that, as expected, $j\omega$ has been replaced by s. This property will be very useful for obtaining the Laplace transforms of some basic time functions multiplied by exponentials, as will be seen in Section 5.4.2.

5.4.1.4   Time and Frequency Scaling

If $X(s) = \mathscr{L}[x(t)]$ then

$$\mathscr{L}[x(at)] = \frac{1}{a}X\left(\frac{s}{a}\right) \tag{5.24}$$

where $a > 0$.

This is, again, analogous to the property of time and frequency scaling that was obtained for Fourier transforms in Chapter 3.

5.4.1.5   Differentiation with Respect to Time

If $X(s) = \mathscr{L}[x(t)]$ then

$$\mathscr{L}\left[\frac{dx}{dt}\right] = sX(s) - x(0^-) \tag{5.25}$$

This is a very useful property of unilateral Laplace transforms because it enables us to solve linear differential equations with much less effort. The main advantage of this approach is that the initial conditions can be taken into account directly, and we need not go through the rather tedious process of separately determining the complementary function and the particular integral and then evaluating the arbitrary constants that will satisfy the initial conditions, as discussed in Chapter 1. This will be presented in detail in Section 5.4.4. We now prove this property. From the definition of the Laplace transform,

$$\mathscr{L}\left[\frac{dx}{dt}\right] = \int_{0^-}^{\infty}\frac{dx}{dt}e^{-st}\,dt$$

Integrating by parts, we get

$$\mathscr{L}\left[\frac{dx}{dt}\right] = x(t)e^{-st}\Big|_{t=0^-}^{\infty} + s\int_{0^-}^{\infty} x(t)e^{-st}\,dt$$

$$= sX(s) - x(0^-)$$

A repeated application of the above may be used to generalize this property into the following form:

$$\mathscr{L}\left[\frac{d^n x}{dt^n}\right] = s^n X(s) - s^{n-1}x(0^-) - s^{n-2}\frac{dx}{dt}(0^-)$$

$$- \cdots - \frac{d^{n-1}x}{dt^{n-1}}(0^-) \tag{5.26}$$

Note that this property is slightly different from the corresponding property of the Fourier transform, which did not require the initial value. This is the result of our using the one-sided Laplace transform. Therefore, it is not applicable to bilateral Laplace transforms.

The following example will illustrate how this property can be used for solving differential equations.

Example 5.3

Consider the following differential equation:

$$\frac{d^2 x}{dt^2} + 4\frac{dx}{dt} + 8x(t) = u(t) \tag{5.27}$$

where the initial conditions are

$$x(0^-) = 10$$

$$\frac{dx}{dt}(0^-) = 2 \tag{5.28}$$

Taking the Laplace transform of both sides of equation 5.27 and using the property described in equation 5.26, we obtain

$$s^2 X(s) - 10s - 2 + 4[sX(s) - 10] + 8X(s) = U(s)$$

which can be rearranged as

$$(s^2 + 4s + 8)X(s) = 10s + 42 + U(s) \tag{5.29}$$

For a given $u(t)$, we can obtain the complete solution for $x(t)$ by simply finding the inverse transform of $X(s)$ from equation 5.29. The procedure for doing this will be discussed further in Section 5.4.3. As we can see, the main advantage is that initial conditions are also taken into account, together with the forcing function, in the same equation. Thus, we are spared the trouble of determining the complementary function and particular integral separately and then evaluating the constants in the complementary function to satisfy the initial conditions. ∎

5.4.1.6 Integration with Respect to Time

If $X(s) = \mathscr{L}[x(t)]$ then

$$\mathscr{L}\left[\int_{0^-}^t x(\tau)\, d\tau\right] = \frac{X(s)}{s} \tag{5.30}$$

and

$$\mathscr{L}\left[\int_{-\infty}^t x(\tau)\, d\tau\right] = \frac{X(s)}{s} + \int_{-\infty}^{0^-} x(\tau)\, d\tau \tag{5.31}$$

Like the property of differentiation with respect to time, this property, especially equation 5.31, applies only to unilateral Laplace transforms. Note that in equation 5.30 we start integrating $x(t)$ at $t = 0^-$, with the result that if $x(t)$ contains an impulse at $t = 0$, this is fully taken into account. Thus, these equations are different from the corresponding property of the Fourier transform, which requires an impulse at $\omega = 0$. These equations will be helpful in obtaining the transient solution of the integro-differential equations that arise for electrical networks that contain both inductors and capacitors. To prove equation 5.31, let us define

$$y(t) = \int_{-\infty}^t x(\tau)\, d\tau$$

so that

$$x(t) = \frac{dy}{dt}$$

Using the property of differentiation with respect to time, we obtain

$$X(s) = sY(s) - y(0^-)$$

so that

$$Y(s) = \frac{X(s)}{s} + \int_{-\infty}^0 x(\tau)\, d\tau$$

because

$$y(0^-) = \int_{-\infty}^{0^-} x(\tau)\, d\tau$$

5.4.1.7 Multiplication by t (Differentiation in the Frequency Domain)

If $X(s) = \mathscr{L}[x(t)]$ then

$$\mathscr{L}[tx(t)] = -\frac{dX(s)}{ds} \tag{5.32}$$

and

$$\mathscr{L}[t^n x(t)] = (-1)^n \frac{d^n X(s)}{ds} \qquad (5.33)$$

These equations are similar to the corresponding properties of the Fourier transform and also apply to bilateral Laplace transforms. Therefore, they will not be proved here. They will be helpful in determining Laplace transforms of some important signals.

5.4.1.8 Division by t (Integration in the Frequency Domain)

If $X(s) = \mathscr{L}[x(t)]$ then

$$\mathscr{L}\left[\frac{x(t)}{t}\right] = \int_s^\infty X(u)\, du \qquad (5.34)$$

This is also similar to the corresponding property of the Fourier transform and applies to bilateral Laplace transforms as well.

5.4.1.9 Convolution in the Time Domain

If $X_1(s) = \mathscr{L}[x_1(t)]$ and $X_2(s) = \mathscr{L}[x_2(t)]$ then

$$X_1(s) X_2(s) = \mathscr{L}\left[\int_{-\infty}^\infty x_1(\tau) x_2(t - \tau)\, d\tau\right] \qquad (5.35)$$

This is seen as being analogous to the result obtained with the Fourier transform. However, since the Laplace transform exists for a larger class of functions, it is often more convenient to evaluate the convolution integral by determining the inverse Laplace transform of $X_1(s)X_2(s)$.

5.4.1.10 Convolution in the Complex Frequency Domain

If $X_1(s) = \mathscr{L}[x_1(t)]$ and $X_2(s) = \mathscr{L}[x_2(t)]$ then

$$\mathscr{L}[x_1(t) x_2(t)] = \frac{1}{2\pi j} \int_{c-j\infty}^{c+j\infty} X_1(u) X_2(s - u)\, du \qquad (5.36)$$

This is the analog of convolution in the frequency domain for the Fourier transform. It will be especially useful for determining the Laplace transform of the product of two time functions when their individual Laplace transforms are known.

In the next subsection, we shall determine the unilateral Laplace transforms of some important time functions.

5.4.2 SOME UNILATERAL LAPLACE TRANSFORM PAIRS

In engineering problems some functions appear more frequently than others. We have come across many of these functions in the earlier chapters of this book. In practice, it will seldom be necessary to evaluate the Laplace transform of a function by integration using the definition given in equation 5.16, since most of the time it can be determined from the Laplace trans-

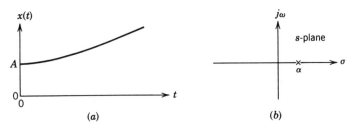

Figure 5.6 An exponential and its Laplace transform. (*a*) Plot of $x(t)$. (*b*) Pole-zero plot of $X(s)$.

forms of some basic functions with the help of the properties described in Section 5.4.1. We now derive the Laplace transforms of some of these functions. We shall find that for almost all of these, the Laplace transform will turn out to be a rational function, that is, a ratio of two polynomials in the complex frequency variable s. The roots of the numerator polynomial are called the *zeros* of the rational function, since for these values of s, the rational function is zero. The roots of the denominator polynomial are called the *poles* of the rational function. Consequently, the poles of $X(s)$ are the values of s for which $X(s)$ will be infinite. It is customary to show the poles and zeros of $X(s)$ in the s-plane by $\times$s and os, respectively. As we shall see later, the poles correspond to the components of complex frequency contained in the signal $x(t)$.

5.4.2.1 An Exponential Function of Time

Consider the causal exponential function of time, given by

$$x(t) = Ae^{\alpha t}\gamma(t) \tag{5.37}$$

Its Laplace transform is obtained as

$$\mathscr{L}[Ae^{\alpha t}] = \int_0^\infty Ae^{\alpha t}e^{-st}\,dt = \frac{A}{s - \alpha} \tag{5.38}$$

Both $x(t)$ and the s-plane pole–zero plot of $X(s)$ are shown in Figure 5.6.

The Laplace transform of the exponential is seen to have a pole at $s = \alpha$. This is valid for all α, which may be either real (positive or negative) or complex. For convergence of the integral, we must have σ, that is, the real part of s greater than the real part of α.

5.4.2.2 The Step Function

The step function can be regarded as a special case of the causal exponential function that was considered in the previous section, since it can be obtained by simply setting the exponent α to zero. Consequently, the Laplace transform in this case is given by

$$\mathscr{L}[A\gamma(t)] = \frac{A}{s} \tag{5.39}$$

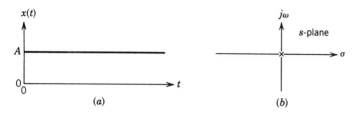

Figure 5.7 The step function and its Laplace transform. (a) Plot of $x(t)$. (b) Pole–zero plot of $X(s)$.

The step function and the s-plane pole–zero plot of its Laplace transform are shown in Figure 5.7. We see that $X(s)$ has a pole at the origin of the s-plane in this case. It is important to note that unlike the Fourier transform of the step function, its unilateral Laplace transform does not contain an impulse. We shall examine the relationship between the two transforms later in this chapter.

5.4.2.3 The Causal Cosine Function

We can again use the result for the exponential function to obtain the Laplace transform of the causal cosine function.

$$\mathscr{L}\left[A\cos\beta t\gamma(t)\right] = A\mathscr{L}\left[\frac{e^{j\beta t} + e^{-j\beta t}}{2}\right] = \frac{0.5A}{s - j\beta} + \frac{0.5A}{s + j\beta}$$

$$= \frac{As}{s^2 + \beta^2} \qquad (5.40)$$

The causal cosine function and the pole–zero plot of its Laplace transform are shown in Figure 5.8.

It is interesting to observe that the Laplace transform of the cosine function has a pair of imaginary poles at $s = \pm j\beta$. This agrees with our interpretation of s as the complex frequency variable. It was noted earlier that the Laplace transform of the step function had a pole at the origin and the Laplace transform of the exponential function $e^{\alpha t}$ had a pole at $s = \alpha$.

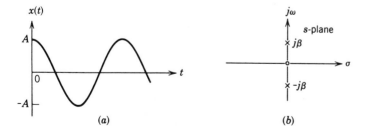

Figure 5.8 The causal cosine function and its Laplace transform. (a) Plot of $x(t) = A\cos\beta t$. (b) Pole–zero plot of $X(s)$.

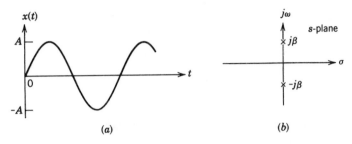

Figure 5.9 The causal sine function and its Laplace transform. (*a*) Plot of $x(t) = A \sin \beta t$. (*b*) Pole–zero plot of $X(s)$.

All of these lead us to interpret the poles of the Laplace transform as the frequency components of the corresponding function of time, provided that we use the complex frequency variable. With this terminology, imaginary values of s will imply sinusoids, whereas real values of s will lead to exponentials. Furthermore, if a pole is real and positive, it will lead to an increasing (or positive) exponential, while a negative real pole will cause the time function to be a decreasing exponential. Later, we shall extend this concept to the case of complex poles.

5.4.2.4 The Causal Sine Function

The Laplace transform of the causal sine function can be obtained in the same way.

$$\mathscr{L}[A \sin \beta t \gamma(t)] = A\mathscr{L}\left[\frac{e^{j\beta t} - e^{-j\beta t}}{2j}\right] = \frac{0.5A/j}{s - j\beta} - \frac{0.5A/j}{s + j\beta}$$

$$= \frac{A\beta}{s^2 + \beta^2} \tag{5.41}$$

The causal sine function and the pole–zero plot of its Laplace transform in the s-plane are shown in Figure 5.9. The poles are again located at $\pm j\beta$, but we do not have a zero at the origin as was the case for the cosine function. This will confirm our intuitive feeling that the poles of the Laplace transform of a signal are located at its frequency components.

5.4.2.5 The Causal Damped Cosine Function

We now consider the function

$$x(t) = e^{-\alpha t} \cos \beta t \gamma(t) \tag{5.42}$$

The Laplace transform can be obtained from that of the cosine function if we recall the frequency shifting property for Laplace transforms of functions multiplied by exponentials that was discussed in Section 5.4.1.3. Therefore, to determine the Laplace transform of the exponentially decaying cosine function, we simply replace s by $(s + \alpha)$ in the Laplace transform of the cosine

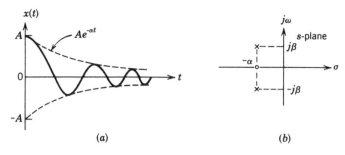

Figure 5.10 The causal damped cosine function and its Laplace transform. (a) Plot of $x(t) = Ae^{-\alpha t}\cos\beta t$. (b) Pole–zero plot of $X(s)$.

function. Thus, we have

$$\mathscr{L}\left[e^{-\alpha t}\cos\beta t\right] = \frac{s + \alpha}{(s + \alpha)^2 + \beta^2} \tag{5.43}$$

A plot of this function and the corresponding s-plane pole–zero plot of its Laplace transform are shown in Figure 5.10.

It may be observed that the poles and the zero of the Laplace transform of the cosine function have been *shifted to the left* by the distance α to obtain the poles and zeros of the damped cosine function. This is why it is called the frequency shifting property.

5.4.2.6 The Damped Sine Function

As for the damped cosine function, the Laplace transform in this case is obtained by shifting the poles and zeros of the Laplace transform of the undamped sine function, that is

$$\mathscr{L}\left[e^{-\alpha t}\sin\beta t\right] = \frac{\beta}{(s + \alpha)^2 + \beta^2} \tag{5.44}$$

The damped sine function and the pole–zero plot of its Laplace transform are shown in Figure 5.11. As expected, the pole–zero plot for this case is a simple translation to the left of the pole–zero plot of the undamped sine function by the distance α.

It follows that complex poles located in the left half of the s-plane, at $s = -\alpha \pm j\beta$, will give rise to damped sine and cosine functions of the form $e^{-\alpha t}\cos\beta t$ and $e^{-\alpha t}\sin\beta t$ in the time domain. Similarly, complex poles in the right half of the s-plane will cause the corresponding functions of time to be exponentially increasing cosine and sine functions. On the other hand, real poles in the s-plane give rise to exponentials in the time domain; those in the left half of the s-plane cause the time function to be a decaying exponential, whereas those in the right half of the s-plane give rise to increasing exponentials. Finally, poles on the $j\omega$-axis will cause the corresponding time function to be a sinusoid with constant amplitude. This gives

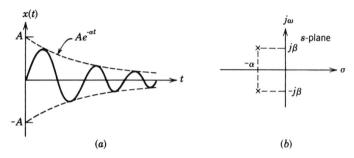

(a)   (b)

Figure 5.11 The causal damped sine function and its Laplace transform. (a) Plot of $x(t) = Ae^{-\alpha t} \sin \beta t$. (b) Pole–zero plot of $X(s)$.

us a complete picture of our interpretation of s as the complex frequency variable as depicted in Figure 5.12. These concepts will be particularly valuable when we discuss the topic of inverse Laplace transforms.

5.4.2.7 The Unit Ramp Function

The Laplace transform of the unit ramp function can be obtained from that of the unit step in two different ways. First we can consider the unit ramp as the integral of the unit step and use the integration property in the time domain. Alternatively, we can obtain the unit ramp function by multiplying the unit step function by t and use the property of frequency domain differentiation. The result with either procedure is

$$\mathscr{L}[r(t)] = \frac{1}{s^2} \tag{5.45}$$

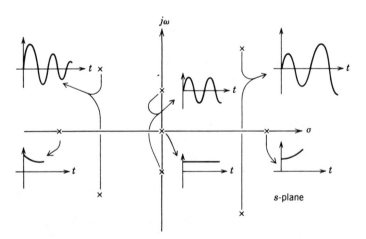

Figure 5.12 Time functions corresponding to pole locations in the s-plane.

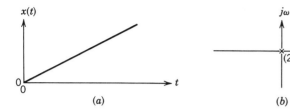

Figure 5.13 The ramp function and its Laplace transform. (*a*) Plot of $x(t) = t$. (*b*) Pole–zero plot of $X(s)$.

In this case we have a double pole at the origin of the s-plane. The function and the s-plane plot of its Laplace transform are shown in Figure 5.13.

5.4.2.8 The Unit Impulse Function

The Laplace transform of the unit impulse can be obtained either by direct evaluation from the defining integral or by using the fact that the unit impulse is the derivative of the unit step. Note that the use of 0^- as the lower limit in the defining integral makes it possible to include the impulse at $t = 0$. The following results are easily obtained.

$$\mathscr{L}[\delta(t)] = 1$$
$$\mathscr{L}[\delta(t - \tau)] = e^{-s\tau} \tag{5.46}$$

5.4.2.9 The Function $x(t) = Ate^{\alpha t}$

The Laplace transform of this function can be obtained from either the Laplace transform of At by using the frequency shifting property or that of $Ae^{\alpha t}$ by using differentiation in the frequency domain. These are shown below:

$$\mathscr{L}[At] = \frac{1}{s^2} \rightarrow \mathscr{L}[Ate^{\alpha t}] = \frac{1}{(s - \alpha)^2}$$

$$\mathscr{L}[Ae^{\alpha t}] = \frac{1}{s - \alpha} \rightarrow \mathscr{L}[Ate^{\alpha t}] = -\frac{d}{dt}\left[\frac{1}{s - \alpha}\right] = \frac{1}{(s - \alpha)^2} \tag{5.47}$$

5.4.2.10 A Short Table of Unilateral Laplace Transforms

We now present a brief table of Laplace transform pairs. Note that we were able to derive all of these, except for the case of the exponential, without actually using the defining integral. Along with the properties of the Laplace transform discussed in Section 5.4.1, Table 5.1 is especially useful for finding inverse Laplace transforms.

It will be shown in the following section that the inverse Laplace transform of most functions encountered in engineering problems is derived as some combination of the elementary functions listed in Table 5.1, after the Laplace transform is expanded into partial fractions.

TABLE 5.1 Laplace Transform Pairs

$x(t)$	$X(s)$	Comments
1. $A\delta(t - \tau)$	$Ae^{-s\tau}$	Impulse at $t = \tau$
2. $A\gamma(t)$	$\dfrac{A}{s}$	Pole at the origin
3. $Ae^{-\alpha t}\gamma(t)$	$\dfrac{A}{s + \alpha}$	Pole at $s = -\alpha$
4. $A\cos\beta t\gamma(t)$	$\dfrac{A}{s^2 + \beta^2}$	Poles at $s = \pm j\beta$
5. $A\sin\beta t\gamma(t)$	$\dfrac{A\beta}{s^2 + \beta^2}$	Poles at $s = \pm j\beta$
6. $Ae^{-\alpha t}\cos\beta t\gamma(t)$	$\dfrac{A(s + \alpha)}{(s + \alpha)^2 + \beta^2}$	Poles at $s = -\alpha \pm j\beta$
7. $Ae^{-\alpha t}\sin\beta t\gamma(t)$	$\dfrac{A\beta}{(s + \alpha)^2 + \beta^2}$	Poles at $s = -\alpha \pm j\beta$
8. $t\gamma(t)$	$\dfrac{1}{s^2}$	Two poles at the origin
9. $t^n e^{-\alpha t}\gamma(t)$	$\dfrac{n!}{(s + \alpha)^{n+1}}$	$(n + 1)$ poles at $s = -\alpha$

Drill Problem 5.1

Determine the Laplace transforms of the following functions:

(a) $t^2\gamma(t)$

(b) $t\cos 3t\gamma(t)$

(c) $(1 - e^{-2t})\gamma(t)$

Answer: (a) $\dfrac{2}{s^3}$, (b) $\dfrac{s^2 - 9}{(s^2 + 9)^2}$, (c) $\dfrac{2}{s(s + 2)}$

5.4.3 INVERSION OF THE LAPLACE TRANSFORM

An effective use of the Laplace transform in system analysis requires inversion of the Laplace transform to obtain the corresponding function of time. This can be done in several ways. The most direct method will be to use the defining equation, that is,

$$x(t) = \frac{1}{2\pi j} \int_{\sigma - j\infty}^{\sigma + j\infty} X(s)e^{st}\, ds \qquad (5.48)$$

This integral can be evaluated by contour integration in the s-plane. It is usually much easier, especially if $X(s)$ is a rational functional of s (i.e., ratio of two polynomials in s), to reduce $X(s)$ to simpler functions by using the method of *partial-fraction expansion* and then obtain the inverse Laplace transform of each term by identifying the corresponding time function from the location of each pole. The basic procedure will be evident from the following examples.

Example 5.4

Consider the rational function

$$X(s) = \frac{20}{s(s^2 + 4s + 20)} = \frac{20}{s\left[(s + 2)^2 + 4^2\right]} \quad (5.49)$$

The first step is to determine the poles of $X(s)$ by finding the roots of the denominator polynomial. Since, in this case, the denominator is already in the factored form, we note that $X(s)$ has one pole at the origin and a pair of complex conjugate poles at $s = -2 \pm j4$. Consequently, we can expand $X(s)$ in the following form:

$$X(s) = \frac{A}{s} + \frac{Bs + C}{(s + 2)^2 + 4^2} \quad (5.50)$$

where the constants A, B, and C have to be determined. These can be evaluated by expanding the right-hand side of equation 5.50 to obtain its numerator and equating the coefficients with the corresponding terms of the numerator of $X(s)$. This is called the *method of undetermined coefficients*. Following this procedure, we obtain

$$A(s^2 + 4s + 20) + s(Bs + C) = (A + B)s^2 + (4A + C)s + 20A = 20 \quad (5.51)$$

Equating the coefficients of the various powers of s, we get

$$A + B = 0$$
$$4A + C = 0$$
$$20A = 20$$

These are readily solved to obtain

$$A = 1, \quad B = -1, \quad C = -4$$

Substituting these into equation 5.50, we have

$$X(s) = \frac{1}{s} - \frac{s + 4}{(s + 2)^2 + 4^2}$$

$$= \frac{1}{s} - \frac{s + 2}{(s + 2)^2 + 4^2} - \frac{2}{(s + 2)^2 + 4^2} \quad (5.52)$$

Since each term in equation 5.52 corresponds to a standard from in Table 5.1, we obtain the inverse Laplace transform as

$$x(t) = [1 - e^{-2t}\cos 4t - 0.5e^{-2t}\sin 4t]\gamma(t) \qquad (5.53)$$

∎

A more efficient approach for obtaining the partial fraction expansion will be described in the next section.

Example 5.5

Consider the following rational function:

$$X(s) = \frac{7s^3 + 60s^2 + 117s + 104}{s^4 + 6s^3 + 21s^2 + 26s} \qquad (5.54)$$

As before, the first step is to determine the poles of $X(s)$ by finding the roots of the denominator polynomial. These are located at 0, -2, and $-2 \pm j3$. The next step is to perform the partial fraction expansion. This time, we use linear factors for the complex poles as well. (The details of the procedure for performing the partial fraction expansion will be explained in the next section.) As a result, we obtain

$$X(s) = \frac{4}{s} - \frac{3}{s+2} + \frac{3+j4}{s+2+j3} + \frac{3-j4}{s+2-j3} \qquad (5.55)$$

The inverse Laplace transform can now be written by inspection from equation 5.55, since each term in the partial fraction expansion will give us an exponential in the time domain, as determined by the location of the pole, while the numerator of each of the fractions gives the corresponding multiplying factor. Furthermore, since the numerators of the fractions corresponding to the complex conjugate poles are also conjugates of each other, we may combine them to obtain real functions of time. The details are shown below, where it is implied that $x(t)$ is causal.

$$x(t) = 4 - 3e^{-2t} + (3+j4)e^{-(2+j3)t} + (3-j4)e^{-(2-j3)t}$$
$$= 4 - 3e^{-2t} + 3e^{-2t}(e^{-j3t} + e^{j3t}) + j4e^{-2t}(e^{-j3t} - e^{j3t})$$
$$= 4 - 3e^{-2t} + 6e^{-2t}\cos 3t + 8e^{-2t}\sin 3t \qquad (5.56)$$

∎

Drill Problem 5.2

Determine the inverse Laplace transforms of $X(s)$ given as follows:

$$X(s) = \frac{3}{s+2} + \frac{8}{s+5} + \frac{5+j4}{s+3+j4} + \frac{5-j4}{s+3-j4}$$

Answer: $[3e^{-2t} + 8e^{-5t} + e^{-3t}(10\cos 4t + 8\sin 4t)]\gamma(t)$

5.4.3.1 Partial Fraction Expansion

We now present an efficient method for expanding a rational function into partial fractions.

Consider the following:

$$X(s) = \frac{P(s)}{Q(s)} = \frac{a_m s^m + a_{m-1} s_{m-1} + \cdots + a_1 s + a_0}{s^n + b_{n-1} s^{n-1} + \cdots + b_1 s + b_0} \quad (5.57)$$

where the coefficients $a_m, a_{m-1}, \ldots, a_0, b_{n-1}, \ldots, b_0$ of the numerator and denominator polynomials are real numbers.

It will be assumed that the rational function $X(s)$ is strictly proper, that is, the degree m of the numerator $P(s)$ is less than n, the degree of the denominator $Q(s)$. This is not a limitation, since if $m \geq n$, we can always divide the numerator by the denominator to obtain a strictly proper rational function in addition to terms involving a constant and positive powers of s. The inverse Laplace transform of the latter will be the impulse functions (for the constant) and its derivatives (for the terms with higher powers of s). Accordingly, it will be sufficient for our purpose to limit ourselves to obtaining the partial fraction expansion for the case when $n > m$. Let the roots of $Q(s)$ be given by $p_1, p_2, \ldots, p_n$, so that we may express it in the factored form, as

$$Q(s) = (s - p_1)(s - p_2) \cdots (s - p_n) \quad (5.58)$$

It should be noted that roots of $Q(s)$, which are also the poles of $X(s)$, can be either real or complex. The complex roots must, however, occur in conjugate pairs, since all the coefficients of $Q(s)$ are real. Similarly, the roots of $P(s)$, which are the zeros of $X(s)$, must either be real or occur in complex conjugate pairs since all the coefficients of $P(s)$ are real. Some of the poles of $X(s)$ may be repeated, but we first consider the case when they are all distinct. In this case, $X(s)$ is said to have only *simple* poles and the partial fraction expansion of $X(s)$ is given by

$$X(s) = \frac{A_1}{s - p_1} + \frac{A_2}{s - p_2} + \cdots + \frac{A_k}{s - p_k} + \cdots + \frac{A_n}{s - p_n} \quad (5.59)$$

We now demonstrate a straightforward way of evaluating the A_i, for $i = 1, 2, \ldots, n$. Let us multiply both sides of equation 5.59 by $(s - p_k)$. This gives us

$$(s - p_k)X(s) = \frac{(s - p_k)A_1}{s - p_1} + \frac{(s - p_k)A_2}{s - p_2} + \cdots + A_k$$

$$+ \cdots + \frac{(s - p_k)A_n}{s - p_n}$$

Setting $s = p_k$ in the above equation, which is valid for all s, all the terms on the right-hand side vanish, with the exception of A_k. We may therefore rearrange it to obtain the following equation, which gives an explicit expression for A_k.

$$A_k = [(s - p_k)X(s)]_{s = p_k}, \qquad k = 1, 2, \ldots, n \qquad (5.60)$$

The constants $A_1, A_2, \ldots, A_n$ are called the *residues* at the poles, $p_1, p_2, \ldots, p_n$, respectively. The residue at a real pole will always be real, while that at a complex pole will, in general, be complex. Also, since the coefficients of the polynomials are real, residues at complex conjugate poles will also be the conjugates of each other.

We now return to the problem discussed in Example 5.5 to illustrate the procedure.

Example 5.6

The rational function in Example 5.5 may be written as

$$X(s) = \frac{7s^3 + 60s^2 + 117s + 104}{s(s + 2)(s + 2 + j3)(s + 2 - j3)} \qquad (5.61)$$

Consequently, the partial fraction expansion will have the following form:

$$X(s) = \frac{A}{s} + \frac{B}{s + 2} + \frac{C}{s + 2 + j3} + \frac{D}{s + 2 - j3} \qquad (5.62)$$

where the residues A, B, C, and D are to be evaluated.

Following the procedure indicated in equation 5.60, we get

$$A = \frac{7s^3 + 60s^2 + 117s + 104}{(s + 2)(s + 2 + j3)(s + 2 - j3)}\bigg|_{s=0} = 4 \qquad (5.63)$$

Similarly,

$$B = [(s - 2)X(s)]_{s=-2}$$
$$= \frac{7s^3 + 60s^2 + 117s + 104}{s(s + 2 + j3)(s + 2 - j3)}\bigg|_{s=-2} = -3 \qquad (5.64)$$

and

$$C = [(s + 2 + j3)X(s)]_{s=-2-j3}$$
$$= \frac{7s^3 + 60s^2 + 117s + 104}{s(s + 2)(s + 2 - j3)}\bigg|_{s=-2-j3}$$
$$= \frac{7(-2 - j3)^3 + 60(-2 - j3)^2 + 117(-2 - j3) + 104}{(-2 - j3)(-2 - j3 + 2)(-2 - j3 + 2 - j3)}$$
$$= 3 + j4 \qquad (5.65)$$

∎

The last equation requires arithmetic with complex numbers. This may become tedious if calculated by hand. However, we need not evaluate D, since it must be the conjugate with C.

We now consider the case when all the poles of $X(s)$ are not distinct, that is, some of them are repeated. These are also called *multiple* poles. If a pole is repeated r times, it is said to have multiplicity r. For the case when the ith pole p_i is repeated r times, the partial fraction expansion of $X(s)$ will take the following form:

$$X(s) = \frac{A_1}{s - p_1} + \cdots + \frac{A_{i,1}}{s - p_i} + \frac{A_{i,2}}{(s - p_i)^2} + \cdots$$

$$+ \frac{A_{i,r}}{(s - p_i)^r} + \cdots + \frac{A_n}{s - p_n} \qquad (5.66)$$

where the constants $A_{i,k}$ are obtained by multiplying both sides of equation 5.60 by $(s - p_i)^r$, differentiating $(r - k)$ times with respect to s and evaluating the resulting equation at $s = p_i$. Proceeding as before, we get the following equations*:

$$A_{i,r} = (s - p_i)^r X(s)\big|_{s=p_i}$$

$$A_{i,r-1} = \frac{d}{ds}\big[(s - p_i)^r X(s)\big]\bigg|_{s=p_i}$$

$$\cdots$$

$$A_{i,r-k} = \frac{1}{k!}\frac{d^k}{ds^k}\big[(s - p_i)^r X(s)\big]\big|_{s=p_i}$$

$$\cdots$$

$$A_{i,1} = \frac{1}{(r-1)!}\frac{d^{r-1}}{ds^{r-1}}\big[(s - p_i)^r X(s)\big]\bigg|_{s=p_i} \qquad (5.67)$$

The computer program included with this book and described in Appendix 5.1 performs all the arithmetic required for the evaluation of residues at real or complex poles, which may be either simple or multiple.

After the partial fraction expansion is completed, we can use the following relationship to obtain the inverse Laplace transform:

$$\mathscr{L}^{-1}\left[\frac{A}{(s+a)^k}\right] = \frac{A}{(k-1)!}t^{k-1}e^{-at} \qquad (5.68)$$

*It is not necessary to perform the differentiations indicated in equation 5.67 as the residues corresponding to repeated poles can also be evaluated by equating the two sides of equation 5.66 for some other values of s that do not correspond to pole locations. This will be illustrated as an alternative approach in Example 5.7.

Equation 5.68 can be derived by using the property described in Section 5.4.1.7, that multiplication by t in the time domain is equivalent to differentiation with respect to s in the frequency domain, followed by a change in sign.

The following examples will demonstrate the use of this procedure for obtaining the inverse Laplace transforms when the multiplicity of some of the poles is greater than one.

Example 5.7

Consider the rational function

$$X(s) = \frac{10(s + 2)}{(s + 1)^2(s + 3)} \tag{5.69}$$

The partial fraction expansion of $X(s)$ can be written in the following form:

$$X(s) = \frac{A_{1,1}}{s + 1} + \frac{A_{1,2}}{(s + 1)^2} + \frac{A_2}{s + 3} \tag{5.70}$$

Following the procedure outlined in equations 5.67, we get

$$A_{1,2} = \left[(s + 1)^2 X(s)\right]_{s = -1} = \left[\frac{10(s + 2)}{s + 3}\right]_{s = -1} = 5 \tag{5.71}$$

$$A_{1,1} = \frac{d}{ds}\left[(s + 1)^2 X(s)\right]\Big|_{s = -1} = \frac{d}{ds}\left[\frac{10(s + 2)}{s + 3}\right]\Big|_{s = -1}$$

$$= \left[\frac{10}{(s + 3)^2}\right]_{s = -1} = 2.5 \tag{5.72}$$

$$A_2 = \left[(s + 3)X(s)\right]_{s = -3} = -2.5 \tag{5.73}$$

We can determine $A_{1,1}$ without performing the differentiation indicated in equation 5.72. After evaluating $A_{1,2}$ and A_2, we substitute the values of the latter in equation 5.70 for some value of s that does not coincide with a pole. This gives an equation containing $A_{1,1}$ as the only unknown. For example, setting s equal to 0 in equation 5.70 and using the values of $A_{1,2}$ and A_2 calculated above, we obtain

$$\left[\frac{10(s + 2)}{(s + 1)^2(s + 3)}\right]_{s=0} = \frac{A_{1,1}}{1} + \frac{5}{1} - \frac{2.5}{3}$$

This equation is easily solved to obtain

$$A_{1,1} = 2.5$$

which agrees with the value in equation 5.72. The inverse transform is now obtained as

$$x(t) = 5te^{-t} + 2.5e^{-t} - 2.5e^{-3t} \tag{5.74}$$

∎

Example 5.8

Consider the following rational function:

$$X(s) = \frac{5s^5 + 94s^4 + 706s^3 + 2628s^2 + 4401s + 3750}{s(s + 2)(s^2 + 6s + 25)^2} \tag{5.75}$$

In this instance, $X(s)$ has simple poles at $s = 0$ and -2, but double complex poles at $s = -3 \pm j4$. Hence, the partial fraction expansion will be of the form

$$X(s) = \frac{A}{s} + \frac{B}{s + 2} + \frac{C + jD}{s + 3 + j4} + \frac{C - jD}{s + 3 - j4}$$

$$+ \frac{E + jF}{(s + 3 + j4)^2} + \frac{E - jF}{(s + 3 - j4)^2} \tag{5.76}$$

Evaluation of the residues proceeds as follows:

$$A = [sX(s)]_{s=0} = 3 \tag{5.77}$$

$$B = [(s + 2)X(s)]_{s=-2} = -2 \tag{5.78}$$

$$E + jF = [(s + 3 + j4)^2 X(s)]_{s=-3-j4} = 4 + j3 \tag{5.79}$$

$$C + jD = \frac{d}{ds}[(s + 3 + j4)^2 X(s)]\Big|_{s=-3-j4} = 2 + j3 \tag{5.80}$$

Accordingly, the inverse transform is obtained as

$$x(t) = 3 - 2e^{-2t} + (2 + j3)\exp[-(3 + j4)t] + (2 - j3)\exp[-(3 - j4)t]$$

$$+ (4 + j3)t\exp[-(3 + j4)t] + (4 + j3)t\exp[-(3 + j4)t]$$

$$= 3 - 2e^{-2t} + e^{-3t}(4\cos 4t + 6\sin 4t)$$

$$+ te^{-3t}(8\cos 4t + 6\sin 4t) \tag{5.81}$$

∎

   In the next section we get further practice with the inversion of Laplace transforms while solving linear differential equations.

Drill Problem 5.3

Obtain the partial fraction expansion of the following:

$$X(s) = \frac{17s^4 + 125s^3 + 395s^2 + 465s + 78}{s(s + 1)(s + 3)(s^2 + 4s + 13)}$$

Answer: $\dfrac{2}{s} + \dfrac{5}{s + 1} + \dfrac{4}{s + 3} + \dfrac{3 + j3}{s + 2 + j3} + \dfrac{3 - j3}{s + 2 - j3}$

Drill Problem 5.4

Obtain the partial fraction expansion of the following:

$$X(s) = \frac{10s + 12}{s(s + 2)^2}$$

Answer: $\dfrac{3}{s} - \dfrac{3}{s + 2} + \dfrac{4}{(s + 2)^2}$

5.4.3.2 Evaluation of Residues — A Graphical Interpretation

The procedure for evaluation of residues, described above, can be given an interesting graphical interpretation. This is based on the fact that a rational function $F(s)$ can be evaluated for a given value s_1 of s, by drawing vectors to the point s_1 in the s-plane from all the poles and zeros of $F(s)$. To understand this better, let us consider the case when

$$F(s) = \frac{12(s + 1)(s + 4)}{s(s + 2)(s + 1 + j2)(s + 1 - j2)} \tag{5.82}$$

and we want to evaluate $F(s)$ for $s = s_1 = -2 + j3$. This will be carried out by replacing s by $-2 + j3$ in the expression for $F(s)$:

$F(-1 + j2)$

$$= \frac{12(-2 + j3 + 1)(-2 + j3 + 4)}{(-2 + j3)(-2 + j3 + 2)(-2 + j3 + 1 + j2)(-2 + j3 + 1 - j2)} \tag{5.83}$$

Now consider the s-plane plot of the poles and zeros of $F(s)$, as shown in Figure 5.14. A little examination reveals that each of the bracketed terms in the numerator of equation 5.83 can be considered as a vector drawn from one of the zeros of $F(s)$ to the point s_1. For example, the first bracketed term in the numerator has the value $-1 + j3$ and is the length of the vector drawn from the zero at $s = -1$ to the point $s_1 = -2 + j3$. Similarly, each bracketed term in the denominator can be regarded as a vector drawn from one of the poles at s_1.

The reader can verify that each of the vectors drawn from the zeros of $F(s)$ in Figure 5.14 corresponds to a bracketed term in the numerator,

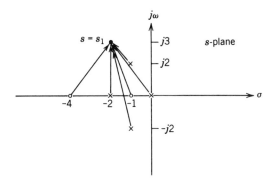

Figure 5.14 Graphical evaluation of $F(s)$ at $s = s_1$.

whereas each vector drawn from the poles corresponds to a bracketed term in the denominator of equation 5.83. The reason this works is evident from Figure 5.15, where the term $(s_1 - z_k)$ has been shown as the difference between two vectors, s_1 and z_k; each of these is drawn from the origin of the s-plane to the point given by the value of the corresponding complex number. The difference $(s_1 - z_k)$ is now obtained from the basic rules of addition and subtraction of vectors in the complex plane.

We can now generalize this result to state that if a rational function $F(s)$ is given by the equation

$$F(s) = \frac{K(s - z_1)(s - z_2) \cdots (s - z_m)}{(s - p_1)(s - p_2) \cdots (s - p_n)} \tag{5.84}$$

then the value of $F(s)$ at $s = s_1$ can be obtained as

$$F(s_1) = K \frac{\text{Product of directed distances from each zero to } s_1}{\text{Product of directed distances from each pole to } s_1} \tag{5.85}$$

The graphical interpretation given in Figure 5.14 and expressed in equation 5.84 is easily extended to the determination of the residue at a given

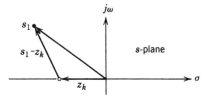

Figure 5.15 Evaluation of $(s_1 - z_k)$ in the s-plane.

pole p_k of $F(s)$. Following equation 5.60 this is given by

$$A_k = [(s - p_k)F(s)]_{s=p_k}$$

$$= K \frac{\text{Product of directed distances from each zero to } p_k}{\text{Product of directed distances from each pole to } p_k} \quad (5.86)$$

where it is implied that in the denominator, we use the directed distance from every pole except p_k, since the term $(s - p_k)$ has already been taken out of the expression and will be zero for $s = p_k$.

The following example will demonstrate the use of this method.

Example 5.9

Consider the function $F(s)$ that was given in equation 5.82. We now expand it into partial fractions using the graphical method discussed in this section. We may write

$$F(s) = \frac{12(s + 1)(s + 4)}{s(s + 2)(s + 1 + j2)(s + 1 - j2)}$$

$$= \frac{A}{s} + \frac{B}{s + 2} + \frac{C + jD}{s + 1 + j2} + \frac{C - jD}{s + 1 - j2}$$

The pole–zero plot for $F(s)$, with vectors drawn for calculating the residue at the pole at $s = -1 + j2$, is shown in Figure 5.16. From Figure 5.16, the residue is obtained as

$$C - jD = 12\frac{j2(3 + j2)}{(-1 + j2)(0 + j4)(1 + j2)} = \frac{-48 + j72}{-j20} = -3.6 - j2.4 \quad \blacksquare$$

In general, the calculation involves complex arithmetic that may get tedious if done manually. The reader may still find it easier to use the

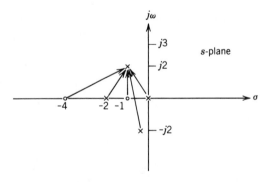

Figure 5.16 Graphical evaluation of residue at pole at $-1 + j2$.

computer program on the disk enclosed with the book for calculating the residues at real or complex poles. The main idea behind the presentation in this section is to give a graphical picture, which often gives better insight. We shall return to this graphical interpretation later for the calculation of frequency response from the transfer function.

5.4.4 SOLUTION OF LINEAR DIFFERENTIAL EQUATIONS

In Section 5.4.1.5, we observed that differentiation in the time domain is equivalent to multiplying the Laplace transform of the function by s. Furthermore, the initial value of the time function was also taken into account in the Laplace transform of the derivative. This property makes it very convenient to solve differential equations for linear time-invariant systems using Laplace transforms. Unlike the classical method described in Chapter 1, we do not have to divide the process into three steps which involve the evaluation of the complementary function, the particular integral, and the constants that will satisfy the initial conditions. Example 4.3 was used to demonstrate the procedure. In this section, we present some additional examples of solving integro-differential equations using the Laplace transform.

Example 5.10

Consider the R-C circuit shown in Figure 5.17. It is desired to determine the current $i(t)$ in the circuit if the switch S is closed at $t = 0$. The initial voltage across the capacitor is $v(0) = 15$ V. The Kirchhoff voltage law equation for the network is given by

$$Ri + \frac{1}{C} \int_0^t i(\tau)\, d\tau + 15 = 100\gamma(t) \quad \text{for} \quad t \geq 0, \quad \text{with } v(0) = 15$$

$$(5.87)$$

Taking the Laplace transforms of both sides of equation 5.87, we have

$$RI(s) + \frac{1}{C}\frac{I(s)}{s} + \frac{15}{s} = \frac{100}{s} \tag{5.88}$$

Solving equation 5.88 for $I(s)$, we get

$$I(s) = \frac{85C}{1 + sCR} = \frac{85 \times 10^{-6}}{s + 1} \tag{5.89}$$

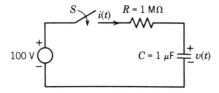

Figure 5.17 R-C network.

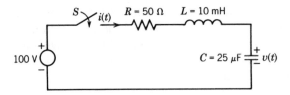

Figure 5.18 RLC network.

Taking the inverse Laplace transform, we get

$$i(t) = 85 \times 10^{-6}e^{-t} \text{ A}, \quad \text{for} \quad t \geq 0 \quad (5.90)$$

Note that we could have obtained equation 5.89 directly if we had used the notion of transform networks and written the Kirchhoff's voltage law equation in terms of the Laplace transform of the current. The initial voltage across the capacitor is regarded here as a constant voltage source equal to the value of $v(0)$. The impedance of the capacitor is then taken as $1/(sC)$. This leads to

$$I(s) = \frac{\dfrac{100}{s} - \dfrac{15}{s}}{R + 1/(sC)} = \frac{85C}{sCR + 1} \qquad \blacksquare$$

The following example further exploits the concept of the transform network.

Example 5.11

Consider the RLC network shown in Figure 5.18, where it is required to find the current $i(t)$ if the initial values are $i(0^-) = 1$ and $v(0^-) = 40$ and the switch S is closed at $t = 0^+$.

Note that since for this network $i(t)$ and $v(t)$ cannot change suddenly, their respective values at time 0^- and 0^+ will be identical. We shall, therefore, just use 0 as the initial time in this example.

Application of Kirchhoff's voltage law to the network gives us the following equation in the Laplace domain:

$$\left(sL + R + \frac{1}{sC}\right)I(s) = \frac{100}{s} - \frac{v(0)}{s} + Li(0) \qquad (5.91)$$

Incorporation of the initial conditions on the right-hand side of equation 5.91 should be noted. The initial voltage across the capacitor is replaced by an equivalent constant voltage source $v(0)/s$ in series with an uncharged capacitor and is given the negative sign because this voltage opposes the flow of the current $i(t)$. The initial current through the inductor can be considered as being equivalent to a constant current source of value $i(0)/s$ *in*

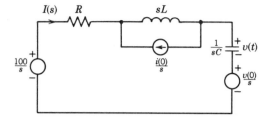

Figure 5.19 Transform network for Example 5.11.

parallel with the inductor, but can be changed into a voltage source of value $Li(0)$ *in series* with the inductor. In view of this discussion, we obtain the following equivalent *transform network*, shown in Figure 5.19, from which equation 5.91 could have been written by inspection. Note that the impedance of the inductor has been taken as sL and that of the capacitor as $1/(sC)$.

We now solve for $I(s)$ to obtain

$$I(s) = \frac{60/s + Li(0)}{sL + R + 1/(sC)} = \frac{60/L + si(0)}{s^2 + (R/L)s + 1/(LC)}$$

$$= \frac{s + 6000}{s^2 + 5000s + (4 \times 10^6)} = \frac{s + 6000}{(s + 1000)(s + 4000)}$$

$$= \frac{5/3}{s + 1000} - \frac{2/3}{s + 4000}$$

Taking the inverse transform, we get

$$i(t) = \frac{5}{3}e^{-1000t} - \frac{2}{3}e^{-4000t} \qquad \blacksquare$$

Example 5.12

In the previous example, we determined the value of the current $i(t)$ through the circuit. We now determine the voltage $v(t)$ across the capacitor. Utilizing the relationship with the current through the circuit, we have, from the transform network shown in Figure 5.19,

$$V(s) = \frac{I(s)}{sC} + \frac{v(0)}{s} = \frac{s + 6000}{s(s + 1000)(s + 4000) \times 25 \times 10^{-6}} + \frac{40}{s}$$

$$= \frac{60}{2} - \frac{200/3}{s + 1000} + \frac{20/3}{s + 4000} + \frac{40}{s}$$

The resulting inverse transform is

$$v(t) = 100 - \frac{200}{3}e^{-1000t} + \frac{20}{3}e^{-4000t}$$ ∎

Example 5.13

We repeat the previous problem, but the applied voltage is now a sinusoid given by $u = 100 \sin 1000t$. Here, since $I(s) = sC[V(s) - v(0)/s]$, we have

$$(1 + sCR + s^2LC)\left[V(s) - \frac{v(0)}{s}\right] = \frac{100 \times 1000}{s^2 + 1000^2} + Li(0) + \frac{v(0)}{s}$$

This equation can be simplified to obtain

$$V(s) = \frac{4 \times 10^{11}}{(s + 10^6)(s + 1000)(s + 4000)} + \frac{4 \times 10^4}{(s + 1000)(s + 4000)}$$

$$+ \frac{160 \times 10^6}{s(s + 1000)(s + 4000)} + \frac{40}{s}$$

Performing the partial fraction expansion and collecting terms with common denominators, we get

$$V(s) = \frac{80}{s} - \frac{0.002 + j19.99}{s - j1000} - \frac{0.002 - j19.99}{s + j1000} - \frac{53.335}{s + 1000} + \frac{13.339}{s + 4000}$$

Finally, taking the inverse Laplace transform we have

$$v(t) = 80 - 0.004\cos 1000t + 39.98\sin 1000t$$
$$- 53.335e^{-1000t} + 13.339e^{-4000t}$$ ∎

In the next section, we shall study some theorems that would allow us to determine the initial and final values of a function of time directly from its Laplace transform. Then, we shall return to these examples to check the results obtained here.

Drill Problem 5.5

A second-order differential equation is given below, along with the initial conditions. Determine the rational function $X(s)$.

$$\frac{d^2x}{dt^2} + 6\frac{dx}{dt} + 25x(t) = 10e^{-2t}; \quad x(0^-) = 5; \quad \frac{dx}{dt}(0^-) = 2$$

Answer: $X(s) = \dfrac{5s^2 + 42s + 74}{(s + 2)(s^2 + 6s + 25)}$

5.4.5 INITIAL AND FINAL VALUE THEOREMS

Often it is desirable to determine the initial and/or final values of a function of time from its Laplace transform without having to obtain the complete inverse Laplace transform. Sometimes these values can be determined for a given system by inspection. Even in such cases, it may be desirable to verify that the system equations have been formulated correctly by using the initial and final value theorems that will be described in this section.

5.4.5.1 Initial Value Theorem

If $\mathscr{L}[x(t)] = X(s)$ then

$$x(0^+) = \lim_{s \to \infty} sX(s) \tag{5.92}$$

PROOF We had seen in Section 5.4.1.5 that the Laplace transform of the derivative of x is given by

$$\int_{0^-}^{\infty} \frac{dx}{dt} e^{-st} dt = sX(s) - x(0^-) \tag{5.93}$$

If we now let $s \to \infty$, the integral on the left-hand side will vanish if $x(t)$ is continuous at $t = 0$. In that case, we immediately get equation 5.92, since we must have $x(0^+) = x(0^-)$ due to continuity. Note that since s is not a function of t we are justified in letting $s \to \infty$ before integrating.

If $x(t)$ is not continuous at $t = 0$, then its derivative dx/dt will contain an impulse, given by $[x(0^+) - x(0^-)]\delta(t)$. In this case, integration of the left-hand side of equation 5.93 yields

$$\lim_{s \to \infty} \int_{0^-}^{\infty} \frac{dx}{dt} e^{-st} dt = x(0^+) - x(0^-) = \lim_{s \to \infty} [sX(s) - x(0^-)]$$

This simplifies to

$$\lim_{s \to \infty} sX(s) = x(0^+) - x(0^-) + x(0^-) = x(0^+)$$

Example 5.14

We now apply the initial value theorem to the electrical network problem in Example 5.11, where the Laplace transform of the current was found to be

$$I(s) = \frac{s + 6000}{s^2 + 5000s + (4 \times 10^6)} \tag{5.94}$$

Applying the initial value theorem, we get

$$i(0^+) = \lim_{s \to \infty} sI(s) = \lim_{s \to \infty} \frac{s(s + 6000)}{s^2 + 5000s + (4 \times 10^6)} = 1 \tag{5.95}$$

This agrees with the initial value specified in the example. ∎

5.4.5.2   Final Value Theorem

If $\mathscr{L}[x(t)] = X(s)$ and $\lim_{t \to \infty} x(t)$ exists, then

$$\lim_{t \to \infty} x(t) = \lim_{s \to 0} sX(s) \qquad (5.96)$$

Note that the limit exists only if all the poles of $X(s)$ are in the left half of the s-plane, with the possible exception of a single pole at the origin. This is obvious, since poles in the right half of the s-plane will cause $x(t)$ to be infinite at t approaches infinity, whereas poles on the $j\omega$-axis will give rise to sinusoids, which are indeterminate as t approaches infinity.

PROOF   We again start with the Laplace transform of the derivative of $x(t)$ but this time we take the limit as $s \to 0$.

$$\lim_{s \to 0} \int_{0^-}^{\infty} \frac{dx}{dt} e^{-st} \, dt = \lim_{s \to 0} \left[sX(s) - x(0) \right] \qquad (5.97)$$

Taking limit before integration allows the integral on the left-hand side to be evaluated immediately. Hence,

$$\lim_{t \to \infty} x(t) - x(0) = \lim_{s \to 0} sX(s) - x(0) \qquad (5.98)$$

or

$$\lim_{t \to \infty} x(t) = \lim_{s \to 0} sX(s)$$

Example 5.15

We now apply the final value theorem to the electrical network solved in Example 5.12. From a close look at the network we can tell that the final value of the voltage across the capacitor will be 100. This is also verified from the inverse transform $v(t)$, given in equation 5.90. Application of the final value theorem gives us

$$\lim_{t \to \infty} v(t) = \lim_{s \to 0} sV(s) = 100 \qquad (5.99)$$

∎

The final value theorem is of limited importance, since the final value will be either zero or infinite, except when there is a single pole at the origin and all other poles are strictly in the left half of the s-plane. In this case the final value is simply the residue of $X(s)$ at the pole at the origin. This will be identical to the expression on the right-hand side of equation 5.96. This theorem is used extensively in the study of control systems.

Drill Problem 5.6

Determine the initial and final values of $x(t)$ if

$$X(s) = \frac{10s^3 + 30s^2 + 25s + 50}{s(s + 4)(s^2 + 8s + 100)}$$

Answer: $x(0) = 10$; $x(\infty) = 0.125$

5.4.6 TABLE OF LAPLACE TRANSFORM THEOREMS

Several properties of the one-sided Laplace transform were derived in Section 5.4.1, in addition to the initial and final value theorems, which were presented in Section 5.4.5. For ready reference, these theorems are listed in Table 5.2. They can be used to determine Laplace transforms of functions not listed in Table 5.1 as well as for inverse transformation.

TABLE 5.2 Laplace Transform Theorems

1. Linearity	$\mathscr{L}[a_1 x_1(t) + a_2 x_2(t)] = a_1 X_1(s) + a_2 X_2(s)$
2. Shift in time	$\mathscr{L}[x(t - \tau)] = e^{-s\tau} X^{(s)}$
3. Shift in s-plane	$\mathscr{L}[e^{\sigma t} x(t)] = X(s - a)$
4. Time scaling	$\mathscr{L}[x(at)] = \dfrac{1}{a} X\left(\dfrac{s}{a}\right)$
5. Differentiation	$\mathscr{L}\left[\dfrac{dx}{dt}\right] = sX(s) - x(0^-)$
6. Integration	$\mathscr{L}\left[\displaystyle\int_{-\infty}^{t} x(\tau)\, d\tau\right] = \dfrac{X(s)}{s} + \displaystyle\int_{-\infty}^{0} x(\tau)\, d\tau$
7. Multiplication by t	$\mathscr{L}[tx(t)] = -\dfrac{dX(s)}{ds}$
8. Division by t	$\mathscr{L}\left[\dfrac{x(t)}{t}\right] = \displaystyle\int_{s}^{\infty} X(u)\, du$
9. Convolution in time	$\mathscr{L}\left[\displaystyle\int_{-\infty}^{\infty} x_1(\tau) x_2(t - \tau)\, d\tau\right] = X_1(s) X_2(s)$
10. Convolution in frequency	$\mathscr{L}[x_1 x_2] = \dfrac{1}{2\pi j} \displaystyle\int_{c-j\infty}^{c+j\infty} X_1(u) X_2(s - u)\, du$
11. Initial value theorem	$x(0^+) = \lim\limits_{s \to \infty} sX(s)$
12. Final value theorem	$\lim\limits_{t \to \infty} x(t) = \lim\limits_{s \to 0} sX(s)$ (Valid only if $sX(s)$ has all its poles in the left half of the s-plane.)

5.5 TRANSFER FUNCTIONS OF LINEAR CONTINUOUS-TIME SYSTEMS

In Chapter 1 the concept of the operational transfer function of a linear system was introduced in terms of the operators p and q. It was also brought up in Chapter 3, where we learned that replacing p by $j\omega$ in the operational transfer function gave us the transfer function of the system that could be used to determine its frequency response. Furthermore, it was also observed that the transfer function was the Fourier transform of the impulse response of the system. These concepts are easily formalized with Laplace transforms.

5.5.1 DEFINITIONS OF THE TRANSFER FUNCTION

We shall start with a formal definition of the transfer function. The following are equivalent.

Definition 1:   The transfer function of a linear time-invariant continuous-time system is the Laplace transform of its impulse response.

Definition 2:   The transfer function of a linear time-invariant continuous-time system is the ratio of the Laplace transforms of the output and the input under zero initial conditions.

Both of these definitions of the transfer function are very useful as well as meaningful. The former is suitable whenever the impulse response of the system is known, whereas the latter is more suitable for determining the transfer function from the differential equation or block diagram of the system. For example, given an electrical network, the latter definition is very convenient for the determination of the transfer function. It should be emphasized that in both of these definitions the initial conditions are assumed to be zero. These definitions will be used in the following examples for determining the transfer function of a system.

Example 5.16

In sampled-data control systems, a continuous-time staircase signal of the form shown in Figure 5.20a is reconstructed from a sequence of impulses. A device called a zero-order hold is often used for this purpose. It can be described as a system that will generate an output equal to $x(kT)$ for the period $kT < t < (k + 1)T$ in response to an input given by the impulse $x(kT)\delta(t - kT)$. In other words, the impulse response of the zero-order hold has the form of a rectangular pulse of unit height and duration equal to T, the sampling interval, as shown in Figure 5.20b. This impulse response can be expressed mathematically as the difference between two unit step functions, one applied at $t = 0$ and the other applied at $t = T$. Accordingly, we may write

$$h(t) = \gamma(t) - \gamma(t - T) \tag{5.100}$$

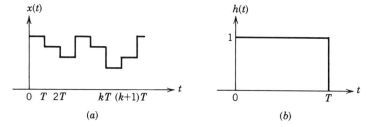

Figure 5.20 The impulse response of a zero-order hold. (*a*) Staircase input. (*b*) Impulse response.

The Laplace transform of $h(t)$ is readily evaluated to give

$$H(s) = \frac{1}{s}(1 - e^{-sT}) \qquad (5.101)$$

as the transfer function of the zero-order hold. ■

Example 5.17

Consider the R-C ladder network shown in Figure 5.21. We shall determine the transfer function relating the output voltage $v_2(t)$ to the input voltage $v_1(t)$.

Using the Laplace transforms of the various currents and voltages we can write the following loop equations for zero initial conditions,

$$\left(R + \frac{1}{sC}\right)I_1(s) - \frac{1}{sC}I_2(s) = V_1(s)$$

$$-\frac{1}{sC}I_1(s) + \left(R + \frac{2}{sC}\right)I_2(s) = 0 \qquad (5.102)$$

Solving these equations, we obtain

$$I_2(s) = \frac{sCV_1(s)}{s^2C^2R^2 + sCR + 1} \qquad (5.103)$$

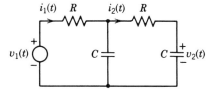

Figure 5.21 An R-C ladder network.

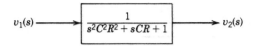

Figure 5.22 Block diagram of R-C network shown in Figure 5.21.

Finally, since $I_2(s) = sCV_2(s)$, we get the transfer function

$$H(s) = \frac{V_2(s)}{V_1(s)} = \frac{1}{s^2C^2R^2 + sCR + 1} \qquad (5.104)$$

∎

The second definition of the transfer function emphasizes the fact that the Laplace transform of the output of a system is the product of the transfer function of the system and the Laplace transform of the input. This also follows from the convolution theorem. Consequently, it is often useful to represent a system by a *block diagram* with the transfer function shown inside the block, as shown in Figure 5.22 for the R-C network in Example 5.1.

5.5.2 POLES AND ZEROS

The concept of poles and zeros was introduced in Section 5.4.2 as the roots of the denominator and numerator polynomials, respectively, of a rational function. These have special significance in relation to transfer functions.

Since the zero-state output of the system to any input can be obtained as the inverse transform of the product of the transfer function and the Laplace transform of the input, it follows that the poles of the transfer function are also its *natural frequencies*. The time functions corresponding to these poles will normally be present in the output of the system to any arbitrary excitation; the only exception will be when a pole of the transfer function is canceled by a zero in the Laplace transform of the input.

The zeros of a transfer function also have an important physical interpretation. These can be considered as the frequencies at which there will be no output; in other words, inputs at these frequencies will be *blocked* by the system.

It is customary to show the poles and zeros of a transfer function in the s-plane by ×s and os, respectively. For example, the pole–zero plot of the transfer function $H(s)$ given in equation 5.105, which represents a low-pass filter, is shown in Figure 5.23.

$$H(s) = \frac{20(s + 1)}{(s + 2)(s^2 + 4s + 13)} \qquad (5.105)$$

It may be noted that the pole–zero plot in the s-plane contains all the information in the transfer function, with the exception of the value of the

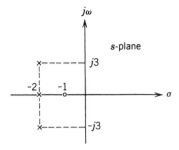

Figure 5.23 Pole–zero plot of
$H(s)$ in equation 5.105.

constant 20. Accordingly, it is possible to reconstruct the transfer function from the pole–zero plot, except for a scale factor.

The location of the poles of a transfer function has an important effect on the stability of the system. This will be discussed in the next section.

5.5.3 STABILITY OF LINEAR SYSTEMS

The concept of stability was introduced in Section 1.9, where a system was defined as being stable if the output remains bounded for all bounded inputs. It was seen that a continuous-time linear system is stable in the BIBO sense if and only if all of the roots of its characteristic polynomial have negative real parts.

From our study of transfer functions of continuous-time systems we can show that the following statements are equivalent.

1. A linear system is stable if and only if its impulse response is absolutely integrable.

2. A linear system is stable if and only if its impulse response $h(t)$ approaches zero as t approaches infinity.

3. A linear system is stable if and only if all the poles of its transfer function are located to the left of the $j\omega$-axis in the s-plane.

4. A linear system is stable if all roots of its characteristic polynomial have negative real parts.

Recall that the characteristic polynomial for a system described by a linear differential equation is identical to the denominator of the transfer function for that system, with the operator p replaced by the complex frequency variable s. The poles of the transfer function and the roots of the characteristic polynomial will therefore be identical. It also follows that if all of the poles of the transfer function are located in the left half of the s-plane, then every component of the impulse response, which is the inverse Laplace transform of the transfer function, will be either a decaying exponential or an exponentially decaying sinusoid. Thus, the impulse response for such a system will approach zero as t approaches infinity and will also be absolutely integrable.

In all cases, the response of the system to any arbitrary input can be separated into two components: (1) the natural response, and (2) the forced response. The natural response will depend on the poles of the transfer function and for a stable system, this will decay to zero with time. For stable systems, the natural response is also called the *transient response*. The forced response depends on the nature of the forcing function. If the forcing function is a sinusoid or any periodic function, the forced response will also be periodic for a stable system and is then known as the *steady-state response*. This topic will be discussed in further detail in the following section.

5.5.4 RESPONSE OF A SYSTEM TO AN ARBITRARY INPUT

The response of a linear system to any arbitrary input can be obtained in a very straightforward manner by using Laplace transforms. This approach makes it possible to account for nonzero initial conditions as well. Consider a system for which the input and output are related through the differential equation

$$D(p)y(t) = N(p)u(t) \tag{5.106}$$

where $D(p)$ and $N(p)$ are polynomials in the operator p. It may be recalled that the operator p denotes differentiation with respect to time. From our earlier discussions in this chapter, it follows that the transfer function for this system can be written as

$$H(s) = \frac{Y(s)}{U(s)} = \frac{N(s)}{D(s)} \tag{5.107}$$

where the polynomials $N(s)$ and $D(s)$ are obtained from the corresponding polynomials in equation 5.106 by merely replacing p with s. This is due to the property of Laplace transforms that differentiation with respect to time is equivalent to multiplication of the Laplace transform by s, provided that the initial conditions are zero. The case of nonzero initial conditions does not present any special problem. This was briefly illustrated in Example 5.3 in Section 5.4.1.5. We shall now continue with the same example.

Example 5.18

Consider the following differential equation:

$$\frac{d^2x}{dt^2} + 4\frac{dx}{dt} + 8x(t) = u(t) \tag{5.108}$$

where the initial conditions are

$$x(0) = 10$$

$$\frac{dx}{dt}(0) = 2 \qquad (5.109)$$

We determine the complete response of this system if the input is given by

$$u(t) = 10\cos 2t\gamma(t) \qquad (5.110)$$

Taking the Laplace transform of both sides of equation 5.108, we get

$$[s^2X(s) - 10s - 2] + 4[sX(s) - 10] + 8X(s) = \frac{10s}{s^2 + 4} \qquad (5.111)$$

Equation 5.111 can be rearranged to obtain

$$(s^2 + 4s + 8)X(s) = 10s + 42 + \frac{10s}{s^2 + 4} \qquad (5.112)$$

Solving equation 5.112 for $X(s)$, we get

$$X(s) = \frac{10s + 42}{s^2 + 4s + 8} + \frac{10s}{(s^2 + 4s + 8)(s^2 + 4)} \qquad (5.113)$$

Finally, taking the inverse transform, we obtain

$$x(t) = 9.5e^{-2t}\cos 2t + 9.5e^{-2t}\sin 2t + 0.5\cos 2t + \sin 2t \quad (5.114)$$

The above may also be written as

$$x(t) = 13.435e^{-2t}\cos(2t - 0.25\pi) + 1.118\cos(2t - 1.107) \quad (5.115)$$

∎

Note that the steady-state component of the output is a sinusoid of the same frequency as the input, but with different magnitude and phase. The nature of the transient response is determined by the poles of the transfer function of the system. This is the reason the poles are called the natural frequencies of the system. The magnitudes of the various components of the transient response must be such that the complete response satisfies the initial conditions. It was also seen in this example that the effect of nonzero initial conditions was to add extra terms to the right-hand side of equation 5.111. These may be considered as additional inputs.

5.5.4.1   Steady-state Response to Sinusoidal Inputs

The steady-state component of the response to a sinusoidal input can be obtained without the need for evaluating the inverse Laplace transform if we interpret the transfer function as the frequency response function. A formal proof will be given in Section 5.5.5. Here we just introduce the main idea, which is based on our observation in Chapter 1 that the steady-state response (particular solution) of a stable system to a sinusoid can be obtained by evaluating the system function $L(p)$ with p replaced by $j\omega$. This will be seen as equivalent to replacing s by $j\omega$ in the transfer function and evaluating $H(j\omega)$ for the desired value of ω. The following examples will demonstrate the procedure.

Example 5.19

We shall determine the steady-state response of the system in Example 5.18 by using this procedure. From equation 5.108, we obtain the transfer function of the system as

$$H(s) = \frac{1}{s^2 + 4s + 8} \tag{5.116}$$

Since the input to the system is given by

$$u(t) = 10\cos 2t \tag{5.117}$$

we evaluate $H(s)$ for $s = j2$. This gives us

$$H(j2) = \frac{1}{(j2)^2 + 4(j2) + 8} = 0.1118e^{-j1.107} \tag{5.118}$$

Consequently, the steady-state component of the output is given by

$$x_{ss}(t) = 1.118\cos(2t - 1.107) \tag{5.119}$$

This is seen to agree with the steady-state component of the result obtained in equation 5.115. ∎

Example 5.20

The transfer function of a linear system is given by

$$H(s) = \frac{200(s + 2)}{(s + 4)^2(s^2 + 2s + 10)} \tag{5.120}$$

It is desired to obtain the steady-state output of the system for the input

$$u(t) = 5 + 3\cos\left(3t + \frac{\pi}{4}\right) \tag{5.121}$$

In this case, the input consists of two sinusoids, with $\omega = 0$ for the first and $\omega = 3$ for the other. Hence, we evaluate

$$H(j0) = \frac{200 \times 2}{4 \times 4 \times 10} = 2.5 \tag{5.122}$$

$$H(j3) = \frac{200(j3 + 2)}{(j3 + 4)^2\left[(j3)^2 + (2 \times j3) + 10\right]} = 4.742e^{-j1.77} \tag{5.123}$$

Using superposition, the steady-state output is obtained as

$$x_{ss}(t) = 12.5 + 14.226 \cos(3t - 0.925) \qquad (5.124)$$

■

It should be noted that it would have required much more effort if we had first found the complete solution by inverse Laplace transformation and then discarded the transient component to obtain the steady-state solution.

5.5.5 FREQUENCY RESPONSE FROM TRANSFER FUNCTION

In the previous section we saw how the transfer function can be used for evaluating the steady-state response of the system to a sinusoidal input. In this section, we shall first prove this result formally and then introduce a graphical interpretation.

Let $H(s)$ be the transfer function of a system to which a sinusoidal input $u(t)$ is applied, where

$$u(t) = A \cos \omega_0 t \qquad (5.125)$$

The the Laplace transform of the output of the system will be given by

$$Y(s) = H(s)U(s) = H(s)\frac{As}{s^2 + \omega_0^2} \qquad (5.126)$$

As pointed out in Section 5.5.3, if the system is stable, all of the poles of $H(s)$ will lie strictly in the left half of the s-plane and will contribute to only transient components. Thus only the poles of $U(s)$, located at $s = \pm j\omega_0$, will contribute to the steady-state output. Consequently, for obtaining the steady-state response, we need to evaluate the residues of the right-hand side of equation 5.126 only at these poles. The residue at the pole located at $s = j\omega_0$ is given by

$$C = \left[H(s)\frac{As}{s + j\omega_0} \right]_{s=j\omega_0} = H(j\omega_0)\frac{Aj\omega_0}{j\omega_0 + j\omega_0} = Me^{j\phi}\frac{A}{2} \qquad (5.127)$$

where

$$H(j\omega_0) = Me^{j\phi} \qquad (5.128)$$

The residue at the other pole, $s = -j\omega_0$, must be the conjugate of C, since this pole is the conjugate of the pole at $s = j\omega_0$. Therefore, the steady-state response of the system will be given by

$$y_{ss}(t) = \mathcal{L}^{-1}\left[\frac{C}{s - j\omega_0} + \frac{C^*}{s + j\omega_0} \right] = \frac{1}{2}MAe^{j\phi}e^{j\omega_0 t} + \frac{1}{2}MAe^{-j\phi}e^{-j\omega_0 t}$$

$$= MA \cos(\omega_0 t + \phi) \qquad (5.129)$$

Thus, it will be seen that the steady-state output is a sinusoid of the same frequency as the input. Furthermore, the amplitude of the steady-state output is M times the amplitude of the input, and the phase of the output leads that of the input by ϕ radians. The values of M and ϕ can also be obtained by evaluating the transfer function $H(s)$ at $s = j\omega_0$, as shown in equation 5.128. The quantity M is called the *gain* of the system and ϕ, the phase shift at the frequency ω_0.

The *frequency response* of a system is obtained if we determine M and ϕ for different values of ω. Several types of frequency response plots can be obtained for depicting the values of the gain and phase shift against frequency. These will be discussed in detail in Chapter 7. In the next section we discuss a graphical interpretation of the frequency response in the s-plane.

5.5.5.1 Graphical Interpretation of Frequency Response Plots

An interesting graphical interpretation of the frequency response of a system can be given in terms of its poles and zeros in the s-plane. It will be similar to our discussion in Section 5.4.3.2 in connection with the evaluation of residues. Let the transfer function be denoted by

$$H(s) = \frac{K(s - z_1)(s - z_2) \cdots (s - z_m)}{(s - p_1)(s - p_2) \cdots (s - p_n)} \tag{5.130}$$

where $z_1, z_2, \ldots, z_m$ are the m zeros and $p_1, p_2, \ldots, p_n$ are the n poles of the transfer function. Then for $s = j\omega_1$, we get

$$H(j\omega_1) = \frac{K(j\omega_1 - z_1)(j\omega_1 - z_2) \cdots (j\omega_1 - z_m)}{(j\omega_1 - p_1)(j\omega_1 - p_2) \cdots (j\omega_1 - p_n)} \tag{5.131}$$

As pointed out in Section 5.4.3.2, each of the bracketed terms on the right-hand side of equation 5.131 can be considered as a directed distance from a pole or a zero to the point $s = j\omega_1$ on the $j\omega$-axis in the s-plane. In view of this interpretation, we can write equation 5.131 as below.

$$H(j\omega_1) = K \frac{\text{Product of directed distances from each zero to } s = j\omega_1}{\text{Product of directed distances from each pole to } s = j\omega_1} \tag{5.132}$$

Expressing each of the directed distances in equation 5.132 in the polar form, we can separate the moduli and the arguments to obtain

$$M = K \frac{\text{Product of lengths of vectors from each zero to } s = j\omega_1}{\text{Product of lengths of vectors from each pole to } s = j\omega_1} \tag{5.133}$$

and

$$\phi = \text{Sum of arguments of vectors from each zero to } s = j\omega_1$$
$$- \text{Sum of arguments of vectors from each pole to } s = j\omega_1 \tag{5.134}$$

where, as before, M is the ratio of the amplitudes of the output and the input sinusoids and ϕ is the angle by which the output leads the input.

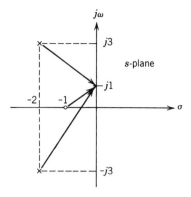

Figure 5.24 Frequency response calculation from pole–zero plot.

Example 5.21

Consider the linear system described by the transfer function

$$H(s) = \frac{20(s+1)}{s^2 + 4s + 13} = \frac{20(s+1)}{(s+2+j3)(s+2-j3)} \tag{5.135}$$

The pole–zero plot of the transfer function in the s-plane is shown in Figure 5.24, which also illustrates the calculation of $H(j1)$.

From Figure 5.24, we obtain

$$H(j1) = \frac{20(j1+1)}{(j1+2+j3)(j1+2-j3)} = \frac{20+j20}{12+j4}$$

$$= 2.236 \exp(j0.4636) \tag{5.136}$$

Thus, we get $M(j1) = 2.236$ and $\phi(j1) = 0.4636$. ∎

Equation 5.133 can be given a nice pictorial interpretation. Let us imagine a flexible rubber sheet suspended over the complex frequency plane. At the location of each pole, the sheet is poked up by a thin rod of infinite height, and at the location of each zero the sheet is tacked down to the plane. The height of the rubber sheet above any point in the s-plane will then represent the magnitude of $H(s)$ for that value of s. The curve displaying the magnitude of the frequency response against frequency will be represented by the cross section of the sheet along the imaginary axis of the s-plane. Using this interpretation, we obtain an approximate sketch of the variation of the magnitude of the frequency response $M(\omega)$, against ω, for the transfer function in this example, as shown in Figure 5.25. The response curve is seen to have a peak near $\omega = 3$, because of the vicinity of the pole at $j1$, and a trough at $\omega = 0$, because of the presence of the zero at $s = -1$.

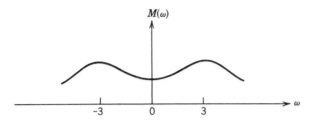

Figure 5.25 Approximation of frequency response from pole–zero plot.

5.6 LAPLACE TRANSFORMS OF CAUSAL REPEATING FUNCTIONS

In Chapter 3 we learned that the steady-state response of a stable linear system to a periodic input can be obtained if the input is expressed as a Fourier series. Although this approach is intuitively appealing, it is of practical value only in those instances when the Fourier series for a periodic input signal has a finite and small number of components. In cases where the Fourier series has an infinite number of components, for example, the Fourier series for a square wave, this method is at best tedious and does not lead to easy determination of the waveform of the output, except when a computer is used for adding the effect of a very large number of components. The Laplace transform method leads to a more direct solution in such circumstances.

We begin by showing how one can obtain the Laplace transform of a causal function, which repeats every T seconds for $t > 0$. Let us denote this function as $x(t)$ and define $X_1(s)$ as the Laplace transform of the first cycle of the function. This implies that

$$X_1(s) = \int_{0^-}^{T^-} x(t)e^{-st}\,dt \qquad (5.137)$$

Using the fact that all subsequent complete cycles of the function can be obtained by shifting the first cycle by $T, 2T, 3T, \ldots$, we can write the following expression for the Laplace transform of the entire function $x(t)$:

$$X(s) = X_1(s)(1 + e^{-sT} + e^{-2sT} + e^{-3sT} + \cdots)$$

$$= \frac{X_1(s)}{1 - e^{-sT}} \qquad (5.138)$$

The last equality follows from the properties of a geometric series that the sum

$$\sum_{n=0}^{\infty} e^{-nsT} = \frac{1}{1 - e^{-sT}} \qquad (5.139)$$

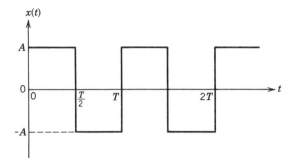

Figure 5.26 Periodic waveform for Example 5.22.

Note that this sum will converge only if $|e^{-sT}| < 1$, which will always be valid if σ, the real part of s, is positive. This defines the region of convergence for the Laplace transform denoted by equation 5.138 and is valid for all sinusoids. Thus, the Laplace transform of any causal repeating function will exist and have the form given by equation 5.138.

Example 5.22

Consider the causal square wave shown in Figure 5.26.
The first cycle of this waveform can be expressed as

$$x_1(t) = A\gamma(t) - 2A\gamma\left(t - \frac{T}{2}\right) + A\gamma(t - T) \qquad (5.140)$$

Taking the Laplace transform we get

$$X_1(s) = \frac{A}{s}(1 - 2e^{-sT/2} + e^{-sT}) \qquad (5.141)$$

and

$$X(s) = \frac{X_1(s)}{1 - e^{-sT}} = \frac{A(1 - e^{-sT/2})}{s(1 + e^{-sT/2})} \qquad (5.142)$$

∎

5.6.1 RESPONSE TO CAUSAL REPEATING INPUTS

Now that we know how to obtain the Laplace transforms of causal functions that repeat every T seconds, we are ready to apply them for determining the response of linear systems to such inputs. In general, we can proceed as before and determine the Laplace transform of the output by multiplying the transfer function of the system with the Laplace transform of the input for the case of zero initial conditions. We have already seen how to take care of situations where the initial conditions are not zero. Thus, our main problem is now that of evaluating the inverse Laplace transform of a function that is no longer only a ratio of polynomials but also contains exponentials in s, since

$$Y(s) = H(s)X(s) = \frac{H(s)X(s)}{1 - e^{-sT}} \tag{5.143}$$

We cannot use our usual procedure for determining inverse Laplace transforms by finding residues at the poles, since the poles of $Y(s)$ are the roots of the denominator of the product $H(s)X_1(s)$ as well as the roots of the equation

$$1 - e^{-sT} = 0 \tag{5.144}$$

It is easily seen that equation 5.144 has an *infinite number of roots*, located at $s = j2\pi n/T$, where n is any positive or negative integer. All of these poles are located on the $j\omega$-axis, at the various harmonics of ω_0, the fundamental frequency given by $2\pi/T$. This should have been expected because the poles of a nonsinusoidal periodic function must be located at all the harmonics as well as the fundamental frequency. Thus, we have run into the same problem that we encountered with the Fourier series, which required adding the responses due to an infinite number of harmonics.

This difficulty can be overcome in another way. First we express $Y(s)$ in the following form:

$$Y(s) = H(s)X_1(s)[1 + e^{-sT} + e^{-2sT} + e^{-3sT} + \cdots] \tag{5.145}$$

In this form, we note that if we just obtain the inverse Laplace transform of $H(s)X_1(s)$, then the remaining terms are obtained by shifting in time. It is important to note that the right-hand side of equation 5.145 is not an infinite series because only the first term exists in the interval $0 < t < T$ and the other terms vanish. Similarly, in the interval $(n - 1)T < t < nT$, only the first n terms exist. If we define

$$y_1(t) = \mathcal{L}^{-1}[H(s)X_1(s)] \tag{5.146}$$

then during the interval $(n - 1)T < t < nT$, the output can be expressed as

$$y(t) = y_1(t)\gamma(t) + y_1(t - T)\gamma(t - T) + \cdots$$
$$+ y_1(t - nT + T)\gamma(t - nT + T) \tag{5.147}$$

In most practical cases, we shall be able to put this result in a closed form, as will be demonstrated in the following example.

Example 5.23

Let us consider the case when the square wave shown in Figure 5.26 is applied to the series R-C network shown in Figure 5.27. It will be assumed that the amplitude, A, of the waveform is 20 V and the period T is 2 s. Also the switch is closed at $t = 0$ and the initial voltage across the capacitor is 10.

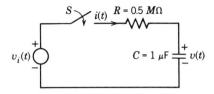

Figure 5.27   R-C network for Example 5.23.

The following differential equation is obtained by the application of Kirchhoff's voltage law to the circuit

$$v(t) + RC\frac{dv}{dt} = v_i(t) \tag{5.148}$$

Taking the Laplace transforms of both sides and recalling that the initial condition is not zero, we get

$$(1 + sCR)V(s) = V_i(s) + RCv(0) \tag{5.149}$$

With the given values, $RC = 0.5$, $v(0) = 10$, and

$$V_i(s) = \frac{20(1 - 2e^{-s} + e^{-2s})}{s(1 - e^{-2s})} \tag{5.150}$$

where the last equation has been obtained from Example 5.22, with the values $A = 20$ and $T = 2$.

Solving for $V(s)$, the Laplace transform of the voltage across the capacitor, we obtain

$$V(s) = \frac{10}{s + 2} + \frac{40(1 - 2e^{-s} + e^{-2s})}{s(s + 2)(1 - e^{-2s})} \tag{5.151}$$

The second term on the right-hand side can be simplified if we note that

$$\frac{1 - 2e^{-s} + e^{-2s}}{1 - e^{-2s}} = (1 - 2e^{-s} + e^{-2s})(1 + e^{-2s} + e^{-4s} + \cdots)$$

$$= 1 - 2e^{-s} + 2e^{-2s} - 2e^{-3s} + 2e^{-4s} - \cdots \tag{5.152}$$

This result can also be obtained by long division by the denominator term. In view of this relationship, we may write

$$V(s) = \frac{10}{s + 2} + \frac{40}{s(s + 2)}(1 - 2e^{-s} + 2e^{-2s} - 2e^{-3s} + 2e^{-4s} - \cdots) \tag{5.153}$$

The inverse transform of equation 5.153 is now easily obtained, using the property that shifting a time function by T will cause its Laplace transform to be multiplied by e^{-sT}. Thus, we obtain

$$
\begin{aligned}
v(t) = \; & 20 - 10e^{-2t} - 40[1 - e^{-2(t-1)}]\gamma(t-1) \\
& + 40[1 - e^{-2(t-2)}]\gamma(t-2) \\
& - 40[1 - e^{-2(t-3)}]\gamma(t-3) \\
& + \cdots
\end{aligned}
\tag{5.154}
$$

We can obtain an expression for the output voltage in the nth period, that is, for $2(n-1) < t < 2n$, by adding only those terms in the series that are nonzero for $t < 2n$. Consequently, for this period of time, we get

$$
\begin{aligned}
v(t) = \; & 20 - 10e^{-2t} - 40\gamma(t - 2n + 2) + 40\gamma(t - 2n + 1) \\
& + 40e^{-2t}[1 - e^2 + e^4 - \cdots - e^{2(n-1)}]
\end{aligned}
\tag{5.155}
$$

The last expression can be put in a more compact form by using the following algebraic identity:

$$
\frac{1 - x^n}{1 + x} = 1 - x + x^2 - x^3 + \cdots - x^{n-1}
\tag{5.156}
$$

With the help of this identity, we can express the response for the $(n - 1)$th period of the waveform as

$$
\begin{aligned}
v(t) = \; & 20 - 10e^{-2t} - 40\gamma(t - 2n + 2) + 40\gamma(t - 2n + 1) \\
& + 40\frac{1 - e^{2n}}{1 + e^2}e^{-2t}
\end{aligned}
\tag{5.157}
$$

∎

In the next section, we shall learn how to extract the steady-state component of the response from the complete response for a periodic nonsinusoidal input.

5.6.2 STEADY-STATE RESPONSE TO PERIODIC INPUTS

In the previous section, we described a procedure for obtaining the complete response of a stable linear· system to causal functions that repeat every T seconds, using Laplace transforms. In particular, the complete response of the system during the period $(n - 1)T < t < nT$ can usually be expressed in a compact form by using some algebraic properties of geometric series. From this expression, however, we cannot easily determine the steady-state component. The problem is caused by the fact that we cannot simply assume t to be very large and drop all terms multiplied by negative exponentials. For instance, if we did that in Example 5.22, then from equation 5.157 we would get a square wave for the output. We know intuitively that this is not the correct answer. In this section we derive a simple but elegant procedure for determining the steady-state response to a periodic input. We start by determining the steady-state response to a causal repetitive function that is identical to the periodic input for positive time. This is also the steady-state response to the periodic input, as follows from the definition of the steady-state response of a stable system for such inputs.

The idea behind this method is to use the complete response of the system to only the first cycle of the repetitive input, which is very easily calculated. Since the system does not know that the input will not be repeated in the following periods, this response will not be different from the response to the complete function (for $0 \le t \le \infty$) during $0 < t < T$. From this complete response, we then subtract the transient component of the response to the complete function to obtain the steady-state component of the response. The transient component is easily evaluated from the residues at the poles of the system transfer function. Note that these poles must lie strictly in the left half of the s-plane for the system to have a steady-state response. Also, the natural frequencies contributing to the transient component of the response are determined by these poles. The following equation describes this method:

$$y_{ss}(t) = \mathscr{L}^{-1}[H(s)X_1(s)] - \sum_{i=1}^{n} A_i e^{-p_i t} \qquad (5.158)$$

where $X_1(s)$ is the Laplace transform of the first cycle of $x(t)$, $p_i = 1, 2, \ldots, n$ are the poles of $H(s)$, and A_i are the residues of $Y(s)$ at these poles.

We now demonstrate this procedure by determining the steady-state response of the system in Example 5.23 for the same input.

Example 5.24

We recall from Example 5.23 that the Laplace transform of the first cycle of the input was given by

$$V_{i1}(s) = \frac{20(1 - 2e^{-s} + e^{-2s})}{s} \qquad (5.159)$$

The complete output during the first cycle is, accordingly, given by

$$\begin{aligned}
v_1(t) &= \mathscr{L}^{-1}[H(s)V_{i1}(s)] \\
&= \mathscr{L}^{-1}\left[\frac{40(1 - 2e^{-s} + e^{-2s})}{s(s + 2)}\right] \\
&= 20(1 - e^{-2t})\gamma(t) - 40[1 - e^{-2(t-1)}]\gamma(t - 1) \\
&\quad + 20[1 - e^{-2(t-2)}]\gamma(t - 2) \qquad (5.160)
\end{aligned}$$

To calculate the transient component of the complete response, we need only evaluate the residue at the pole at $s = -2$ from the Laplace transform of the output to the periodic input. This is given by

$$\begin{aligned}
A &= \left[\frac{40(1 - 2e^{-s} + e^{-2s})}{s(1 - e^{-2s})}\right]_{s = -2} \\
&= 15.232.
\end{aligned}$$

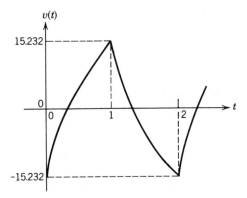

Figure 5.28 Steady-state output in Example 5.24.

Consequently, the steady-state output during the first cycle is given by

$$v_{ss}(t) = v_1(t) - Ae^{-2t}$$

$$= (20 - 35.232e^{-2t})\gamma(t) - 40[1 - e^{-2(t-1)}]\gamma(t - 1)$$

$$\text{(for } 0 < t < 2) \quad (5.161)$$

Note that the last term in equation 5.160 does not have any effect during the first cycle, $0 < t < 2$.

A plot of the steady-state output is shown in Figure 5.28.   ■

5.7 INVERSION OF BILATERAL LAPLACE TRANSFORMS

In our discussions thus far, we have considered only the inversion of unilateral or one-sided Laplace transforms obtained from causal functions. If $x(t)$ is noncausal, then its Laplace transform will be bilateral or two-sided. As shown in Section 5.3, in order to find $x(t)$ from $X(s)$ we must know the region of convergence in the s-plane. This is necessary so that we may know whether a particular pole is to be associated with a time function that will be nonzero for positive time or negative time.

Example 5.25

Consider

$$X(s) = \frac{20}{(s + 1)(s + 5)} \quad (5.162)$$

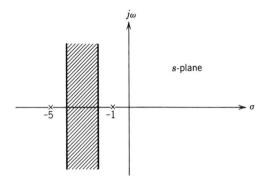

Figure 5.29   Region of convergence for $X(s)$ in equation 5.162.

where the region of convergence is given by

$$-4 < \sigma < -2 \tag{5.163}$$

as shown in Figure 5.29.

In this case, the pole at -5 lies to the left of the region of convergence and will, therefore, be associated with a time function that will be zero for $t < 0$. Similarly, the pole at $s = -1$ lies to the right of the region of convergence and will be associated with a function that will be zero for positive time. Consequently, we proceed by first obtaining the partial fraction expansion

$$X(s) = \frac{5}{s+1} - \frac{5}{s+5} \tag{5.164}$$

The inverse Laplace transform of the positive time function is evaluated as usual and we get

$$\mathscr{L}^{-1}\left[\frac{-5}{s+5}\right] = -5e^{-5t}\gamma(t) \tag{5.165}$$

We now see how to obtain the inverse Laplace transform of the negative time function. By definition, the Laplace transform for such a function is

$$\int_{-\infty}^{0} x(t)e^{-st}\,dt = \int_{0}^{\infty} x(-t)e^{st}\,dt = X(-s) \tag{5.166}$$

where $X(s)$ is the Laplace transform of the positive time function $x(t)$.

Thus we see that to obtain the Laplace transform of a negative time function, we first take the mirror image of the function about the vertical axis at $t = 0$ and find the Laplace transform of the resulting positive time function using the procedures and table developed for one-sided transforms. Finally, we replace s by $-s$ to get the Laplace transform of the negative time function. Similarly, to find the inverse Laplace transform of a function that has poles to the right of the region of convergence, we replace s by $-s$ and then obtain the inverse Laplace transform as we do for a one-sided transform. The final result is then obtained by replacing t by $-t$ and multiplying the resulting time function by $\gamma(-t)$ to emphasize that it is a negative-time or anti-causal function.

From the foregoing we may formulate the following simple rule for evaluating the inverse Laplace transform for a negative time function from the partial fraction expansion at poles to the right of the region of convergence (applicable for real or complex a):

$$\mathcal{L}^{-1}\left[\frac{A}{s+a}\right] = -Ae^{-at}\gamma(-t) \tag{5.167}$$

Accordingly, the inverse transform for equation 5.162 can be written as

$$x(t) = -5e^{-5t}\gamma(t) - 5e^{-t}\gamma(-t) \tag{5.168}$$

∎

This example demonstrates that the inversion of two-sided Laplace transforms does not present any problem if the region of convergence is specified. In this case, we simply identify the poles that will lead to positive time functions as those to the left of the region and obtain the inverse transform by using the procedure developed for one-sided Laplace transforms. The poles to the right of the region of convergence are identified as leading to negative time functions. The inverse transform for these poles is obtained, again, by using the rules for one-sided Laplace transforms after s has been replaced by $-s$ and finally we replace t by $-t$.

Two-sided Laplace transforms are necessary for the analysis of linear systems to which random signals are applied. In such cases, one has to use the autocorrelation and cross-correlation functions that exist for both positive and negative time.

5.8 RELATION BETWEEN FOURIER AND LAPLACE TRANSFORMS

It was shown in Section 5.2 that the defining equations for Fourier and Laplace transforms are quite similar. The only apparent difference is that the frequency variable ω in the former is replaced by the complex frequency variable s in the latter. The introduction of the convergence factor $e^{-\sigma t}$ in the Laplace transform makes it possible to obtain Laplace transforms of functions that are not absolutely integrable. Examples of functions for which Fourier transforms do not exist, but for which Laplace transforms do, are the ramp function and the increasing exponential.

Because of the similarity of the defining equations, one might try to obtain Fourier transforms from Laplace transforms by replacing s by $j\omega$. In some instances this does give correct results. For example, one may obtain the Fourier transform of the function $x(t) = e^{-\alpha t}\gamma(t)$ from its Laplace transform by using this method for the case when $\alpha > 0$. On the other hand, we know that we would not get the correct result using this approach when $x(t)$ is the unit step, since

$$\mathscr{L}[\gamma(t)] = \frac{1}{s}$$

whereas

$$\mathscr{F}[\gamma(t)] = \frac{1}{j\omega} + \pi\delta(\omega)$$

Consequently, in general, one cannot obtain the Fourier transform of a function from its Laplace transform by merely replacing s by $j\omega$. However, this will always work if $x(t)$ is causal and has a finite energy content.

5.9 SUMMARY

The introduction of a convergence factor to the Fourier transform leads to the two-sided Laplace transform, which exists for a larger class of functions. In this formulation the complex frequency variable s replaces the variable $j\omega$. The one-sided Laplace transform was studied in greater detail, since it has many applications in the theory of linear systems. It is specially suitable for the solution of linear differential equations with constant coefficients. A differential equation of this type is transformed into an algebraic equation in the Laplace domain, and the solution in the time domain is obtained by finding the inverse Laplace transform. Methods for inverting Laplace transforms were studied in detail and applied to the analysis of electrical networks. The concept of the transfer function of a linear system was reintroduced in terms of Laplace transforms and was seen to be very powerful in the study of linear systems, as it allows determination of the response to an arbitrary input more easily than is possible by using the integral. Poles and zeros of a transfer function have physical significance as the natural frequencies of the system and the frequencies that will be blocked by the system, respectively. It was learned that a linear system is stable if and only if the poles of the transfer function are located to the left of the $j\omega$-axis in the s-plane. The frequency response of such a system can be obtained by replacing s *in the transfer function* by $j\omega$. It is often more convenient to use this approach for determining the steady-state response of a system to a sinusoidal input. The Laplace transform method can also be used for determining the steady-state response to periodic nonsinusoidal inputs. Usually this method is less tedious than using the Fourier series with an infinite number of components. We also briefly studied a procedure for determining the inverse of bilateral Laplace transforms and noted that a unique solution cannot be obtained unless the region of convergence in the s-plane is specified. Finally, it was pointed out that we can always obtain Fourier transforms from Laplace transforms by replacing s by $j\omega$ for time functions that are causal and have finite energy content.

5.10 PROBLEMS

5.1 Determine the Laplace transform of each the following causal functions:

(a) $x(t) = t^3 e^{-2t} \gamma(t)$

(b) $x(t) = (1 - \cos 3t) \gamma(t)$

(c) $x(t) = \gamma(t) - \gamma(t - 1)$

(d) $x(t) = t\gamma(t) - 2(t - 1)\gamma(t - 1)$

(e) $x(t) = t^2 e^{-2t} \cos 3t \, \gamma(t)$

(f) $x(t) = \dfrac{d}{dt}(5e^{-2t} \cos 3t)$

(g) $x(t) = \begin{cases} \sin t & 0 < t < \pi \\ 0 & t > \pi \end{cases}$

5.2 Determine the inverse Laplace transform of each of the following functions assuming that they are causal:

(a) $X(s) = \dfrac{20(s^2 + 2s + 10)}{(s + 1)(s^2 + 6s + 25)}$

(b) $X(s) = \dfrac{40(s + 1)(s^2 + 2s + 5)}{(s + 3)(s + 4)(s^2 + 6s + 25)}$

(c) $X(s) = \dfrac{80(s + 1)}{s(s + 3)^2(s^2 + 16)}$

(d) $X(s) = \dfrac{8}{s(s^2 + 4)^2}$

(e) $X(s) = \dfrac{32(s + 4)}{s^2(s^2 + 4s + 8)^2}$

5.3 Obtain the complete solution of each of the differential equations given below with initial conditions as specified.

(a) $\dfrac{d^2y}{dt^2} + 8\dfrac{dy}{dt} + 12y = 6, \qquad y(0) = 2, \qquad \dfrac{dy}{dt}(0) = 5$

(b) $\dfrac{d^2y}{dt^2} + 8\dfrac{dy}{dt} + 16y = 6e^{-2t}, \qquad y(0) = 1, \qquad \dfrac{dy}{dt}(0) = 0$

(c) $\dfrac{d^2y}{dt^2} + 8\dfrac{dy}{dt} + 25y = 6\sin 2t, \qquad y(0) = 1, \qquad \dfrac{dy}{dt}(0) = 0$

(d) $\dfrac{d^3y}{dt^3} + 8\dfrac{d^2y}{dt^2} + 37\dfrac{dy}{dt} + 50y = 4e^{-3t}, \qquad y(0) = 2,$

$\dfrac{dy}{dt}(0) = 3, \qquad \dfrac{d^2y}{dt^2}(0) = 1$

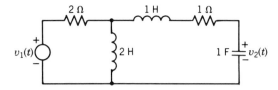

Figure 5.30 R-L-C network

5.4 Determine the transfer function for the electrical network shown in Figure 5.30, where $v_1(t)$ is the applied voltage and the output is the voltage $v_2(t)$ across the capacitor.

5.5 Determine the complete output of the network in the previous problem if the input is a unit step function.

5.6 Repeat Problem 5.4 if the input is given by $v_1(t) = 5e^{-2t}$.

5.7 Determine the steady-state component of the output of the network shown in Figure 5.30 if the input is given by

$$v_1(t) = 10 + 5\cos\left(2t - \frac{\pi}{3}\right) + 4\sin\left(3t + \frac{\pi}{4}\right)$$

5.8 Determine the transfer function $V_2(s)/V_1(s)$ of the lead network shown in Figure 5.31 and show its pole–zero plot. Also determine the gain and the phase shift of the network for sinusoidal inputs of frequency $\omega = 0, 1, 2, 5,$ and 10 rad/s.

5.9 Determine the output $v_2(t)$ of the network shown in Figure 5.31 if
(a) $v_1(t) = \gamma(t)$
(b) $v_1(t) = \gamma(t) - \gamma(t - 1)$
(c) $v_1(t) = 10\cos 2t\, \gamma(t)$

5.10 Determine the steady-state output of the network shown in Figure 5.31 if the input is given by $v_1(t) = 10 + 5\cos(2t - \pi/3)$.

5.11 Determine the transfer function $V_2(s)/V_1(s)$ of the R-C network shown in Figure 5.32. Also determine the gain and the phase shift of the network at $\omega = 0, 1, 2,$ and 5 rad/s.

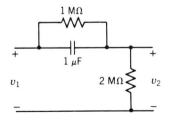

Figure 5.31 Lead network.

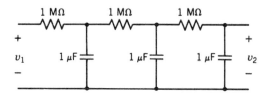

Figure 5.32 R-C ladder network.

5.12 Determine the output $v_2(t)$ of the network shown in Figure 5.30 if
  (a) $v_1(t) = \gamma(t)$
  (b) $v_1(t) = \gamma(t) - \gamma(t - 1)$
  (c) $v_1(t) = 10 \cos 2t\, \gamma(t)$

5.13 Determine the steady-state output of the network shown in Figure 5.30 if the input is given by

$$v_1(t) = 10 + 5\cos\left(2t - \frac{\pi}{3}\right) + 4\sin\left(5t + \frac{\pi}{4}\right)$$

5.14 Determine the Laplace transform of a causal repetitive waveform that is generated by applying the following sinusoidal input to a half-wave rectifier

$$v(t) = 100 \sin 377t$$

Assume that the rectifier is ideal so that while the negative half-cycle of the voltage is removed, the positive half-cycle remains unchanged.

5.15 Determine the Laplace transform of the causal repetitive sawtoothed waveform shown in Figure 5.33.

5.16 Determine the steady-state output of the lead network shown in Figure 5.16 if the input voltage has the sawtoothed waveform depicted in Figure 5.18.

5.17 Repeat Problem 5.16 if the input voltage has the half-wave rectified form described in Problem 5.14.

5.18 The R-C ladder network shown in Figure 5.34 is often used as a phase-shift network in an electronic oscillator. Determine the transfer

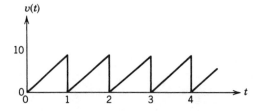

Figure 5.33 A sawtoothed waveform.

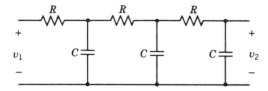

Figure 5.34 R-C ladder network.

function relating the output voltage v_2 to the input voltage v_1 and, hence, the frequency at which the input and the output differ in phase by 180°.

5.19 Determine the steady-state output of the R-C network shown in Figure 5.32 if the input voltage is of the sawtoothed waveform depicted in Figure 5.33.

5.20 Stochastic signals can often be represented by their autocorrelation functions, which are noncausal. A particular signal has the following auto correlation function. Determine its Laplace transform.

$$\phi(t) = 4e^{-2|t|}$$

5.21 Determine the inverse of the following bilateral Laplace transforms assuming the region of convergence is a narrow strip around the $j\omega$-axis in the s-plane. You can identify all poles in the left half of the s-plane with positive time functions and the poles in the right half of the s-plane with negative time functions.

(a) $X(s) = \dfrac{8}{16 - s^2}$

(b) $X(s) = \dfrac{192 - 38s^2}{(4 - s^2)(9 - s^2)}$

5.22 The signal $v(t)$ is a causal train of rectangular pulses of height A, duration τ, and period T as shown in Figure 5.35. Determine the Laplace transform of $v(t)$.

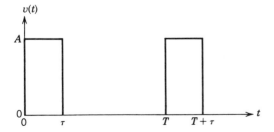

Figure 5.35 Causal train of rectangular pulses.

5.23 Determine the steady-state output of the lead network shown in Figure 5.31 if the input voltage is the periodic train shown in Figure 5.35.

5.24 The transfer function of the pitch control system of a supersonic airplane, flying at an altitude of 20,000 m, is given by

$$G(s) = \frac{80(s + 12)(s + 4)}{(s + 25)(s^2 + 2s + 26)}$$

(a) Determine the response to a unit step input.
(b) Determine the response if the input is a unit ramp function.
(c) Determine the steady-state response if the input is a square wave of amplitude 1 and period 0.2 s.

5.25 The transfer function of a network is given by

$$G(s) = \frac{s - 2}{s + 2}$$

(a) Calculate and sketch the impulse response of the network.
(b) Calculate the frequency response for $\omega = 0, 1, 2, 5, 10,$ and 100.

5.26 The following input is applied to the network in Problem 5.25. Determine the steady-state output.

$$u(t) = 10 + 30 \cos t + 20 \sin \left(2t + \frac{\pi}{3} \right) + 10 \cos \left(5t + \frac{\pi}{4} \right)$$

5.27 The transfer function of a filter network is given below

$$H(s) = \frac{1}{(s + 1)(s^2 + s + 1)}$$

(a) Calculate and sketch the impulse response of the network.
(b) Calculate the frequency response for $\omega = 0, 1, 2, 5,$ and 10.

5.28 Determine the steady-state output of the filter network of Problem 5.27 if the input is a square wave of amplitude 1 and frequency 0.5 rad/s.

5.29 Repeat the previous problem if the frequency of the square wave is 1 rad/s.

5.30 Determine and sketch the response of the filter network of Problem 5.27 to the noncausal input

$$u(t) = 4e^{-|t|}$$

5.31 A linear system is described by the transfer function given below.

$$H(s) = \frac{12(s + 1)}{s(s + 2)(s + 3)}$$

(a) Determine the impulse response of this system. Does this satisfy the conditions for BIBO stability?

(b) Determine the complete response of this system to a unit step input. Will the output be bounded? What conclusions would you draw about the stability of this system?

5.32 The transfer function of a linear system is given by

$$H(s) = \frac{10(s + 2)}{(s^2 + 4)(s + 1)}$$

(a) Determine the impulse response of this system. Does this satisfy the conditions for BIBO stability?

(b) Determine the complete response of this system for the input

$$u(t) = 4 \sin 2t$$

What conclusions would you draw about the stability of this system?

5.33 (a) Determine the output of the system described in Problem 5.31 to the input

$$u(t) = 4e^{-2t}$$

(b) Use the final value theorem to determine the output as $t \rightarrow \infty$ and verify by direct substitution in result obtained above.

(c) Could we apply the final value theorem to the solution obtained in part (b) of Problem 5.31? Explain you answer.

APPENDIX 5.1

Computation of Inverse Laplace Transforms

The calculation of inverse Laplace transform of a rational function of s is fairly straightforward if the residues at the different poles are evaluated. Therefore, given a rational function $X(s)$, the first step is to determine the locations of the poles of $X(s)$. Following that, the residue at each of the poles can be calculated using the procedure described in Section 5.4.3.

The computer program RESIDUE.EXE on the disk enclosed with the book requires the user to input the numerator and denominator polynomials, which may be either in the form of expanded polynomials or expressed as the product of linear and quadratic factors. It then calculates the roots of the denominator and displays the locations of the poles. If there are poles very near each other, the program asks the user if these are to be treated as multiple poles. The residue at any desired pole (including the case when the multiplicity is greater than one) is then calculated. If the pole is real, a real value of the residue is shown. For complex poles, a complex value of the residue is shown. The residues at conjugate poles are conjugates of each other. The user can then write the expression for the inverse Laplace transform using the locations of the poles and the values of the corresponding residues by using the following rules.

$$\frac{A}{s + \alpha} \to A e^{-\alpha t}$$

$$\frac{M + jN}{s + \alpha + j\beta} + \frac{M - jN}{s + \alpha - j\beta} \to e^{-\alpha t}(2M \cos \beta t + 2N \sin \beta t)$$

$$\frac{A}{(s + \alpha)^r} \to \frac{A t^{r-1} e^{-\alpha t}}{(r - 1)!}, \qquad \text{for } r > 1$$

$$\frac{M + jN}{(s + \alpha + j\beta)^2} + \frac{M - jN}{(s + \alpha - j\beta)^2} \to t e^{-\alpha t}(2M \cos \beta t + 2N \sin \beta t)$$

APPENDIX 5.2

Plot of the Response to a Unit Impulse or Step Function

The program RESPONSE.EXE on the disk enclosed with the book calculates and plots the response of a linear system to either a unit impulse or a unit step, as desired by the user. The system may be specified through either its transfer function or related state equations (see Chapter 8). The program first determines the locations of the poles of the transfer function and displays these to the user. If any pole has a positive real part, the system is unstable and the user is informed of this. No response is plotted in this case. On the other hand, if the system is stable, the response to the desired input is calculated by obtaining the inverse Laplace transform of the product of the transfer function and the Laplace transform of the input. This is done by evaluating the residues at all poles of the resulting rational function. The output is then plotted on the screen of the monitor. The time interval for the plot is taken from 0 to the settling time of the system (defined as five times the largest time constant of the system). The optimum scale for the vertical axis is selected by determining the maximum and minimum from 250 values of the response calculated at equal intervals between 0 and the settling time. The user can also have the plot redrawn between specified limits of t as well as for a different scale of the vertical axis. This feature enables the user to obtain a magnified plot of the response over a given range of t.

The program can also be used for calculating the response of the system to the causal inputs $\{\sin \beta t \gamma(t)\}$ and $\{\cos \beta t \gamma(t)\}$ for any given value of β. The plot of the steady-state response (if the system is stable) is obtained by selecting the initial and final values of t as $2\pi n/\beta$ and $2\pi(n + 1)\beta$, respectively, for some arbitrarily large n.

Z-Transforms

6.1 INTRODUCTION

In the preceeding chapter we noticed several advantages of using the Laplace transform method for the analysis of linear continuous-time systems. In particular, it was seen that differential equations in the time domain were changed to algebraic equations in terms of s in the transform domain. These equations were easily solved for the Laplace transform of the output variable, and the inverse Laplace transformation led to the answer in the time domain. An important advantage of this approach was that initial conditions could also be included in the expression for the Laplace transform of the output, with the result that the complete solution was obtained in one step. Similar advantages can be obtained in the analysis of discrete-time systems by the use of z-transforms, which change the system difference equations into algebraic equations in the transform domain.

As seen in Chapter 2, discrete-time signals have values only at discrete instants of time. Accordingly, such signals are represented by sequences of the form $x(n)$, where n is an integer that may assume any value between $-\infty$ and ∞. As we pointed out earlier, such signals can originate either from sampling a continuous-time signal or simply as a sequence of numbers that can be used for modeling signals internal to a digital computer. In the former case, the signal may be represented by a sequence of the form $x(nT)$, where T is the sampling interval, although it is often convenient to drop T in the notation. Regardless of its origin, the sequence may be expressed as

$$x = \{\ldots, x(-2), x(-1), x(0), x(1), x(2), \ldots\} \qquad (6.1)$$

In the following section, we shall define the z-transform of the sequence that would enable us to express it in a more compact form in most cases.

6.2 DEFINITION OF THE z-TRANSFORM

For a sequence of the type given in equation 6.1, we define a function $X(z)$ by the polynomial

$$X(z) = \sum_{n=-\infty}^{\infty} x(n) z^{-n} \qquad (6.2)$$

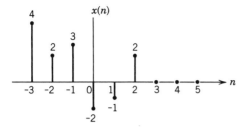

Figure 6.1   A finite sequence.

$X(z)$ is called the z-transform of the sequence $x(n)$. The following example will illustrate the purpose of this transformation.

Example 6.1

Consider the following discrete-time signal, shown in Figure 6.1, which has a finite number of elements

$$x(-3) = 4, \qquad x(-2) = 2, \qquad x(-1) = 3,$$
$$x(0) = -2, \qquad x(1) = -1, \qquad x(2) = 2$$

The z-transform of this sequence will be obtained as

$$X(z) = 4z^3 + 2z^2 + 3z^1 - 2z^0 - 1z^{-1} + 2z^{-2} \qquad (6.3)$$

An advantage of equation 6.3 is that the polynomial $X(z)$ gives us, in compact form, the values of $x(n)$ for each n in such a way that we can keep track of the position of the number in the sequence. For this reason, the variable z can be given the interpretation of a "position marker." Thus, the number multiplying the marker z^{-k} is identified as being the kth element of the sequence. Later in this chapter we shall see that in most instances it will be possible to write the expression for the polynomial in a closed form. At present let us examine the effect of multiplying $X(z)$ by z. It will be seen that in this case we get

$$zX(z) = 4z^4 + 2z^3 + 3z^2 - 2z^1 - 1z^0 + 2z^{-1} \qquad (6.4)$$

Thus, multiplication by z has given us another sequence, the elements of which have been obtained by moving those of the original sequence to the left by one, as depicted in Figure 6.2. Consequently, we may say that the result of multiplication by z has been to *advance* the sequence by one. Similarly, if we had multiplied $X(z)$ by z^{-1}, the result would have been to move the sequence backward in time by one unit. Thus, multiplication by z is observed to have the same effect on the sequence as would be produced by operating on it with the unit advance operator q that was introduced in Chapter 1 in connection with the representation of discrete-time systems. The similarity with Laplace and Fourier transforms, where multiplication by s (or $j\omega$) was seen as equivalent to operation by p, is evident.   ∎

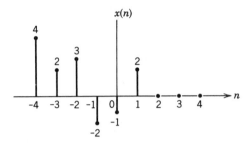

Figure 6.2 Effect of multiplication by z.

In view of the foregoing, it should not be surprising to find that the z-transform is related closely to Fourier and Laplace transforms. Although it is possible to study the theory of z-transforms without even mentioning Laplace or Fourier transforms, much better insight is gained by examining the interrelationships between these transforms. This will be described in the following section.

It may be pointed out that our definition of the z-transform, as given in equation 6.2, allows the sequence $x(n)$ to exist for positive as well as negative values of n. Thus, it leads to the *bilateral* or *two-sided* z-transform, in analogy with the bilateral Laplace transform. We later define the *single-sided* z-transform, which will be seen to be similar to the single-sided Laplace transform in many ways. Again, in most practical situations, it will be possible to make the sequence causal by a suitable choice of the origin, or the starting point. Therefore, in such cases, the single-sided z-transform will meet our requirements.

6.3 RELATIONSHIP WITH LAPLACE AND FOURIER TRANSFORMS

In Chapter 5 we studied several important relationships between the Laplace transform and the Fourier transform of continuous-time signals. Here we examine relationships between the z-transform, the discrete-time Fourier transform, and the Laplace transform. First we study the relationship between the z-transform and the discrete-time Fourier transform.

We begin by expressing the complex variable z in the polar form, as

$$z = re^{j\Omega} \tag{6.5}$$

Substituting this expression in the defining equation 6.2 gives us

$$X(re^{j\Omega}) = \sum_{n=-\infty}^{\infty} x(n)(re^{j\Omega})^{-n}$$

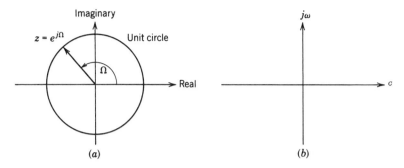

Figure 6.3 Relationships between the transforms. (*a*) *z*-plane. (*b*) *s*-plane.

which may also be written as

$$X(re^{j\Omega}) = \sum_{n=-\infty}^{\infty} [x(n)r^{-n}]e^{j\Omega n} \tag{6.6}$$

Comparing equation 6.6 with the defining equation for the discrete-time Fourier transform (see equation 4.34 in Chapter 4), it is evident that $X(re^{j\Omega})$ is the Fourier transform of the sequence $x(n)r^{-n}$, that is, of the sequence $x(n)$ multiplied by the real exponential weighting factor r^{-n}. This is reminiscent of the observation in Chapter 5 that the Laplace transform of $x(t)$ was the Fourier transform of $x(t)$ multiplied by the convergence factor $e^{-\sigma t}$. Consequently, the summation expressed by equation 6.2 or 6.6 will converge, with a proper choice of r, for a larger class of functions than is possible with the discrete-time Fourier transform, which requires that the sequence $x(n)$ be absolutely convergent. Furthermore, setting r equal to one makes the bilateral z-transform identical to the discrete-time Fourier transform, just as setting s equal to $j\omega$ makes the bilateral Laplace transform identical to the Fourier transform provided that certain conditions for convergence are satisfied. The relationship between the two transforms is depicted in Figure 6.3, which shows that the z-transform reduces to the discrete-time Fourier transform on the unit circle in the z-plane, just as the Laplace transform reduces to the Fourier transform if the path of integration in the s-plane is restricted to the $j\omega$-axis.

Further understanding is obtained by relating the z-transform to the Laplace transform. Let $x(t)$ be a continuous-time signal that is sampled at intervals of T s, as shown in Figure 6.4, to obtain the signal $x^*(t)$.

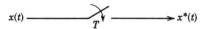

Figure 6.4 A sampled signal.

Figure 6.5 Sampling the signal $x(t)$.

Assuming ideal sampling, as discussed in Chapter 4, the sampled signal, denoted as $x^*(t)$, can be represented as a sequence of impulses of strength $x(nT)$, occurring at $t = nT$, as shown in Figure 6.5. Consequently, the sampled signal may be expressed as the impulse sequence

$$x^*(t) = \sum_{n=-\infty}^{\infty} x(nT)\delta(t - nT) \qquad (6.7)$$

Since $x^*(t)$ is a noncausal function, we take its bilateral Laplace transform. Following the usual rule for taking the Laplace transform of an impulse [i.e., the Laplace transform of the impulse $\delta(t - \tau)$ is $e^{-s\tau}$], we get the following sum as the Laplace transform of $x^*(t)$:

$$X^*(s) = \sum_{n=-\infty}^{\infty} x(nT)e^{-snT} \qquad (6.8)$$

The right-hand side of equation 6.8 will take the same form as equation 6.2 if we make the substitution

$$z = e^{sT} \qquad (6.9)$$

so that we may write

$$X^*(s)\big|_{z=e^{sT}} = \sum_{n=-\infty}^{\infty} x(nT)z^{-n} = X(z) \qquad (6.10)$$

Thus, the z-transform $X(z)$ of the sequence $x(nT)$ is nothing but the Laplace transform of the sampled signal $x^*(t)$, with the variable z substituted for e^{sT}. Furthermore, if we recall the theorem relating shifting of a function in the time domain to multiplication of the Laplace transform by e^{sT}, it is evident that multiplication by z or e^{sT} will cause the time function $x(t)$ and the sequence $x(n)$ to be advanced by one sampling interval T. This agrees with our earlier observation regarding the multiplication of $X(z)$ by z.

Equation 6.9 relates the two complex variables z and s. This is called a *mapping* in the complex plane and is shown in Figure 6.6.

A little examination reveals that both Figure 6.3 and Figure 6.6 are illustrating the same relationship between the complex variables s and z, although the former was derived through the discrete-time Fourier transform, whereas the latter was derived from the Laplace transform of the sampled signal that led to equation 6.9.

Under the mapping shown in Figure 6.6 and in accordance with equation 6.9, the imaginary axis of the s-plane maps onto the unit circle in the

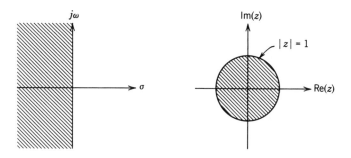

Figure 6.6 Mapping between s-plane and z-plane.

z-plane, and the entire left half of the s-plane maps into the region inside the unit circle in the z-plane. It also follows from equation 6.9 that as we move from 0 to $2\pi/T$ along the $j\omega$-axis of the s-plane, we go around the unit circle once. Thus, going around the unit circle once corresponds to increasing the angular frequency by $\omega_s = 2\pi/T$, which may be defined as the angular sampling frequency. This is also consistent with our observation in Chapter 4 that the frequency spectrum of the sampled signal repeats itself as ω is increased. The significance of this mapping will be more evident when we study the frequency response of discrete-time systems.

6.4 THE SINGLE-SIDED z-TRANSFORM

Just as for bilateral Laplace transforms, the region of convergence of a bilateral z-transform in the z-plane must be specified in order that a unique inverse transform can be obtained. In most practical cases, however, when it is possible to select the origin in the time axis (or the numbering of the elements in a sequence), it is often more convenient to use the *unilateral* or *single-sided* z-transform. Accordingly, we shall start with the theory of the unilateral z-transform and return later to the bilateral transform so that we can handle those situations where it is not possible to avoid noncausal signals.

The one-sided z-transform of a sequence $x(n)$ is defined as

$$X(z) = \sum_{n=0}^{\infty} x(n)z^{-n} \tag{6.11}$$

Note that equation 6.11 is identical to equation 6.2, which defined the two-sided or bilateral z-transform, except that the lower limit has been changed from $-\infty$ to 0. Consequently, for a causal sequence the two-sided and one-sided z-transforms will be identical.

To simplify our notation, the one-sided z-transform of a sequence will be denoted as

$$\mathscr{Z}[x(n)] = X(z) \tag{6.12}$$

In the next section we obtain the z-transforms of some simple but commonly encountered sequences. In all these cases, we shall see that it is possible to put the infinite sum denoted by equation 6.12 into a closed form by writing it as a rational function of z. Consequently, we shall be able to show $X(z)$ through its poles and zeros in the z-plane.

6.4.1 SOME SIMPLE z-TRANSFORM PAIRS

6.4.1.1 The Constant Sequence

Consider the constant sequence shown in Figure 6.7a. This would be obtained by sampling a step function. This sequence can be written as

$$x(n) = A, \qquad n = 0, 1, 2, \ldots, \infty \qquad (6.13)$$

If we use the defining equation 6.11, the z-transform of this sequence will be given by

$$X(z) = \sum_{n=0}^{\infty} Az^{-n} = A(1 + z^{-1} + z^{-2} + z^{-3} + \cdots)$$

$$= \frac{A}{1 - z^{-1}} = \frac{Az}{z - 1} \qquad (6.14)$$

In this derivation we have used the following property of a geometric series

$$1 + r + r^2 + \cdots + r^n = \frac{1 - r^{n+1}}{1 - r} \qquad (6.15)$$

In the particular case, where $|r| < 1$, the sum of the series will converge for $n = \infty$. Therefore, for this case we may write

$$\sum_{n=0}^{\infty} r^n = \frac{1}{1 - r}, \qquad |r| < 1 \qquad (6.16)$$

A comparison between equations 6.14 and 6.16 reveals that the z-transform of the constant sequence will converge if $|z^{-1}| < 1$, or $|z| > 1$. Thus, the region of convergence for this case will be outside the unit circle in the z-plane. This corresponds to the fact that the region of convergence of the Laplace transform of the step function is the right half of the s-plane, which

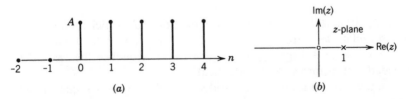

Figure 6.7 The constant sequence and its z-transform. (a) $x(n)$. (b) Pole–zero plot of $X(z)$.

is the map of the region outside the unit circle in the z-plane, as indicated by Figure 6.6 in Section 6.3. The smallest value of $|z|$ for which the z-transform converges is often called the *radius of convergence*. Thus, we may say that the radius of convergence for the constant sequence is 1.

Another interesting point to observe is that the z-transform of the constant sequence has a pole at $z = 1$, whereas the Laplace transform of the step function has a pole at $s = 0$. If we examine equation 6.9, which describes the mapping between the s-plane and the z-plane, we note that the origin of the s-plane maps into the point $z = 1$ in the z-plane. In other words, for this case, the pole of Laplace transform of the continuous-time signal in the s-plane maps into the pole of the z-transform of the constant sequence (the corresponding discrete-time signal) in the z-plane. We shall learn later that this is true for other cases as well.

6.4.1.2 The Exponential Sequence

Consider the sequence

$$x(n) = Ar^n \qquad (6.17)$$

Such a sequence would be generated by sampling an exponential function of time, of the form

$$x(t) = Ae^{\alpha t} \qquad (6.18)$$

where

$$r = e^{\alpha T} \qquad (6.19)$$

From the definition given by equation 6.11, the z-transform of this sequence is given by

$$X(z) = \sum_{n=0}^{\infty} Ar^n z^{-n} = \sum_{n=0}^{\infty} A(rz^{-1})^n$$

$$= \frac{A}{1 - rz^{-1}} = \frac{Az}{z - r}, \qquad |z| > |r| \qquad (6.20)$$

The exponential sequence and the pole–zero plot of its z-transform are shown in Figure 6.8 for $r > 1$.

For this sequence, the region of convergence is outside a circle of radius $|r|$ in the z-plane. It should, again, be noted from equation 6.19 that the pole of the z-transform of this sequence, located at $z = r$, is the map of the pole at $s = \alpha$ in the s-plane of the Laplace transform of the corresponding continuous-time exponential signal, according to the mapping represented by equation 6.9. Furthermore, a pole outside the unit circle in the z-plane will represent the z-transform of a sequence that increases as n is increased, just as a pole in the right half of the s-plane represents the Laplace transform of

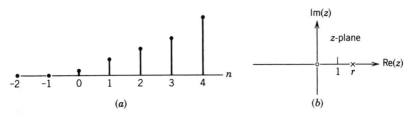

Figure 6.8 The exponential sequence and its z-transform. (a) $x(n) = Ar^n$. (b) Pole–zero plot of $X(z)$.

a continuous-time function that increases with time and eventually approaches infinity.

6.4.1.3 The Unit Impulse

We can recall from Chapter 3 that the discrete-time unit impulse is given by

$$x(k) = \begin{cases} 1 & k = 0 \\ 0 & \text{otherwise} \end{cases} \tag{6.21}$$

The z-transform of this sequence is obtained by direct substitution in equation 6.11, giving us

$$X(z) = 1 \tag{6.22}$$

6.4.1.4 Sinusoidal Sequences

The z-transforms of sequences of the form

$$x(n) = A \cos \beta n \tag{6.23}$$

and

$$x(n) = A \sin \beta n \tag{6.24}$$

can be obtained from the result of the previous section. The derivations are shown as follows.

$$\mathscr{Z}[A \cos \beta n] = \mathscr{Z}\left[\frac{A(e^{j\beta n} + e^{-j\beta n})}{2}\right]$$

$$= \frac{A}{2}\left[\frac{z}{z - e^{j\beta}} + \frac{z}{z - e^{-j\beta}}\right]$$

$$= \frac{Az(z - \cos \beta)}{z^2 - 2z \cos \beta + 1}, \quad |z| > 1 \tag{6.25}$$

The cosine sequence and the pole–zero plot for its z-transform are shown in Figure 6.9.

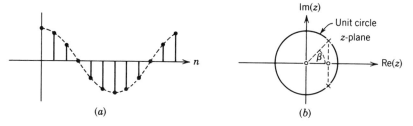

Figure 6.9 The cosine sequence and its z-transform. (a) $x(n) = A \cos \beta n$. (b) Pole–zero plot of $X(z)$.

Similarly, the z-transform of the sine sequence is evaluated as

$$\mathscr{Z}[A \sin \beta n] = \mathscr{Z}\left[\frac{A(e^{j\beta n} - e^{-j\beta n})}{2j}\right]$$

$$= \frac{A}{(2j)}\left[\frac{z}{z - e^{j\beta}} - \frac{z}{z - e^{-j\beta}}\right]$$

$$= \frac{Az \sin \beta}{z^2 - 2z \cos \beta + 1}, \qquad |z| > 1 \qquad (6.26)$$

The sine sequence and the pole–zero plot for its z-transform are shown in Figure 6.10.

The poles of the z-transforms of these functions lie on the unit circle of the z-planes, which maps into the $j\omega$-axis of the s-plane. It is again seen that the poles of the Laplace transform of a continuous-time signal map, according to equation 6.9, into the poles of the z-transform of the discrete-time sequence obtained by sampling the continuous-time signal.

Although we can obtain the z-transforms of other familiar sequences from the definition, as shown above, it will be much easier to derive them by utilizing some properties of the z-transform that will be presented in the following section.

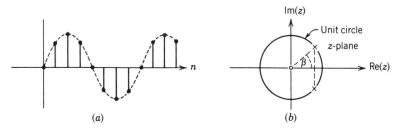

Figure 6.10 The sine sequence and its z-transform. (a) $x(n) = A \sin \beta n$. (b) Pole–zero plot of $X(z)$.

Drill Problem 6.1

Determine the z-transform of the sequence $x(n) = Ae^{-\alpha n} \cos \beta n$. (*Hint:* Express $x(n)$ in the form of complex exponentials.)

Answer: $X(z) = \dfrac{Az(z - e^{-\alpha} \cos \beta)}{z^2 - 2ze^{-\alpha} \cos \beta + e^{-2\alpha}}$

Drill Problem 6.2

Repeat Drill Problem 6.1 for the sequence $x(n) = Ae^{-\alpha n} \sin \beta n$.

Answer: $X(z) = \dfrac{Az \sin \beta}{z^2 - 2ze^{-\alpha} \cos \beta + e^{-2\alpha}}$

6.4.2 SOME PROPERTIES OF THE z-TRANSFORM

The z-transform has many properties that are similar to those of the Fourier and Laplace transforms. These will be very helpful in obtaining the z-transforms of many other sequences as well as in solving the inverse problem of determining a sequence from its z-transform.

6.4.2.1 Linearity

If $X_1(z) = \mathscr{Z}[x_1(n)]$ and $X_2(z) = \mathscr{Z}[x_2(n)]$ then

$$\mathscr{Z}[\alpha x_1(n) + \beta x_2(n)] = \alpha X_1(z) + \beta X_2(z) \tag{6.27}$$

This property follows directly from the linearity of the summation operation in the defining equation for the z-transform. In fact, we used this property while deriving the z-transforms of the sinusoidal sequences in the previous section. It is easily proved as follows:

$$\mathscr{Z}[\alpha x_1(n) + \beta n_2(n)] = \sum_{n=0}^{\infty} [\alpha x_1(n)z^{-n} + \beta x_2(n)z^{-n}]$$

$$= \alpha \sum_{n=0}^{\infty} x_1(n)z^{-n} + \beta \sum_{n=0}^{\infty} x_2(n)z^{-n}$$

$$= \alpha X_1(z) + \beta X_2(z)$$

The region of convergence of the resulting z-transform, given by equation 6.27, is at least as large as the region given by the intersection of the regions of convergence of $X_1(z)$ and $X_2(z)$.

6.4.2.2 Shifting

If $X(z) = \mathscr{Z}[x(n)]$ then

$$\mathscr{Z}[x(n + 1)] = zX(z) - zx(0) \tag{6.28}$$

This is very useful for solving linear difference equations and is similar to the corresponding property regarding the Laplace transform of the derivative of a continuous-time function. The proof is given as follows:

$$\mathscr{Z}[x(n+1)] = \sum_{n=0}^{\infty} x(n+1)z^{-n} = \sum_{m=1}^{\infty} x(m)z^{-(m-1)}$$

$$= z \sum_{m=1}^{\infty} x(m)z^{-m} = z \left[\sum_{m=0}^{\infty} x(m)z^{-m} - x(0) \right]$$

$$= zX(z) - x(0)$$

Repeated application of equation 6.28 leads to

$$\mathscr{Z}[x(n+k)] = z^k X(z) - z^k x(0) - z^{k-1} x(1) - \cdots - zx(k-1) \quad (6.29)$$

Note that equation 6.28 refers to shifting toward the left, that is, advancing the sequence. Shifting toward the right (backward shift) delays the sequence and does not involve initial conditions. Consequently, we obtain

$$\mathscr{Z}[x(n-k)] = z^{-k} X(z)$$

as the counterpart of equation 6.29 for the backward shift.

The following example will demonstrate how this property can be used for solving a difference equation.

Example 6.2

Consider the following second-order difference equation:

$$y(k+2) + 4y(k+1) + 3y(k) = u(k) \quad (6.30)$$

with the initial conditions

$$y(0) = 4, \qquad y(1) = 2 \quad (6.31)$$

Taking the z-transform of both sides of equation 6.30 and using the shifting property given by equation 6.29 we obtain

$$(z^2 + 4z + 3)Y(z) = U(z) + z^2 y(0) + zy(1) + 4zy(0)$$

$$= U(z) + 4z^2 + 6z \quad (6.32)$$

Equation 6.32 can now be solved for $Y(z)$ and evaluation of the inverse z-transform will yield $y(n)$. ∎

6.4.2.3 Multiplication by n

If $X(z) = \mathscr{Z}[x(n)]$ then

$$\mathscr{Z}[nx(n)] = -z \frac{d}{dz} X(z) \quad (6.33)$$

and in general

$$\mathscr{Z}[n^m x(n)] = (-z)^m \frac{d^m X(z)}{dz^m} \quad (6.34)$$

The proof of equation 6.33 is given below. Repeated application leads to equation 6.34.

$$\mathscr{Z}[nx(n)] = \sum_{n=0}^{\infty} nx(n)z^{-n} = z \sum_{n=0}^{\infty} nx(n)z^{-n-1}$$

$$= z \sum_{n=0}^{\infty} x(n)(nz^{-n-1}) = z \sum_{n=0}^{\infty} x(n)\left[-\frac{d}{dz}z^{-n}\right]$$

$$= -z\frac{d}{dz}\left[\sum_{n=0}^{\infty} x(n)z^{-n}\right] = -z\frac{d}{dz}X(z)$$

In the above, the interchange of the order of summation and differentiation is justified because one can always integrate or differentiate a power series term by term to obtain the integral or derivative.

The following examples will demonstrate the use of this property.

Example 6.3

The z-transform of the ramp sequence $x(n) = An$ will be obtained from that of the constant sequence $x(n) = A$, derived in equation 6.14.

$$\mathscr{Z}[An] = -z\frac{d}{dz}\left[\frac{Az}{z-1}\right] = \frac{Az}{(z-1)^2} \tag{6.35}$$

∎

Example 6.4

The z-transform of the sequence $x(n) = Anr^n$ will be obtained from the z-transform of the sequence $x(n) = Ar^n$, derived in equation 6.20.

$$\mathscr{Z}[Anr^n] = -z\frac{d}{dz}\left[\frac{Az}{z-r}\right] = \frac{Arz}{(z-r)^2} \tag{6.36}$$

∎

Drill Problem 6.3

Determine the z-transform of the sequence $x(n) = An\cos\beta n$.

Answer: $X(z) = \dfrac{Az(z^2\cos\beta - 2z + \cos\beta)}{(z^2 - 2z\cos\beta + 1)^2}$

6.4.2.4 Multiplication by r^n

If $\quad X(z) = \mathscr{Z}[x(n)] \quad$ then $\quad \mathscr{Z}[r^n x(n)] = X\left(\dfrac{z}{r}\right) \tag{6.37}$

The proof is given below.

$$\mathscr{Z}[r^n x(n)] = \sum_{n=0}^{\infty} r^n x(n)z^{-n} = \sum_{n=0}^{\infty} x(n)\left(\frac{z}{r}\right)^{-n} = X\left(\frac{z}{r}\right)$$

The following examples will demonstrate the use of this property for obtaining the z-transforms of other sequences.

Example 6.5

The z-transform of the sequence $x(n) = Ar^n \cos \beta n$ will be derived from that of $x(n) = A \cos \beta n$ obtained in equation 6.25.

$$\mathscr{Z}[Ar^n \cos \beta n] = \frac{A(z/r)[(z/r) - \cos \beta]}{(z/r)^2 - 2(z/r)\cos \beta + 1}$$

$$= \frac{A(z - r \cos \beta)}{z^2 - 2zr \cos \beta + r^2}, \quad |z| > |r| \qquad (6.38)$$

■

Example 6.6

As in the preceding example, we shall derive the z-transform of the sequence $x(n) = Ar^n \sin \beta n$ from that of $x(n) = A \sin \beta n$ obtained in equation 6.26.

$$\mathscr{Z}[Ar^n \cos \beta n] = \frac{A(z/r) \sin \beta}{(z/r)^2 - 2(z/r)\cos \beta + 1}$$

$$= \frac{Azr \sin \beta}{z^2 - 2zr \cos \beta + r^2}, \quad |z| > |r| \qquad (6.39)$$

■

Drill Problem 6.4

Determine the z-transform of the sequence $x(n) = Anr^n$, starting from the z-transform of An (see Example 6.3).

Answer: $X(z) = \dfrac{Arz}{(z - r)^2}$

6.4.2.5 Convolution

If $X_1(z) = \mathscr{Z}[x_1(n)]$ and $X_2(z) = \mathscr{Z}[x_2(n)]$ then

$$X_1(z) X_2(z) = \mathscr{Z}\left[\sum_{k=0}^{\infty} x_1(k) x_2(n - k)\right] \qquad (6.40)$$

As seen in the earlier chapters, convolution plays an important role in finding the response of a discrete-time system to an arbitrary input. The use of the convolution property of z-transforms, as given in equation 6.36, makes it possible to avoid having to calculate the convolution sum for each value of n. We simply multiply the z-transforms of the two sequences and obtain the inverse z-transform, which gives the result in a closed form. This property will, again, be recognized as similar to that encountered with Fourier and Laplace transforms.

PROOF

$$\mathscr{Z}\left[\sum_{k=0}^{\infty} x_1(k)x_2(n-k)\right] = \sum_{n=0}^{\infty}\left[\sum_{k=0}^{\infty} x_1(k)x_2(n-k)\right]$$

$$= \sum_{k=0}^{\infty} x_1(k)\sum_{n=0}^{\infty} x_2(m)z^{-m-k}, \qquad m = n - k$$

$$= \left[\sum_{k=0}^{\infty} x_1(k)z^{-k}\right]\left[\sum_{m=0}^{\infty} x_2(m)z^{-m}\right]$$

$$= X_1(z)X_2(z)$$

In this derivation, interchanging the order of summations is justified for all z for which the power series is uniformly convergent.

The convolution property is most useful in finding the response of a discrete-time system to an arbitrary input. If $h(n)$ represents the impulse response sequence of such a system and the input sequence is given by $u(k)$, then in view of equation 6.36 the z-transform of the output sequence $y(k)$ is obtained as

$$Y(z) = H(z)X(z) \tag{6.41}$$

Thus, a convenient way to determine the output sequence is to use equation 6.41 to determine $Y(z)$ and then to obtain the inverse z-transform. The procedure for evaluation of the inverse z-transform will be discussed in Section 6.4.3.

$H(z)$, which is the z-transform of the impulse response sequence, is also called the transfer function of the discrete-time system. It is similar to the transfer function of continuous-time systems and can be obtained from the difference equation of the system. This will be described in detail in Section 6.5.

6.4.2.6 Initial Value

If $X(z) = \mathscr{Z}[x(n)]$ then $x(0) = \lim_{z \to \infty} X(z)$ (6.42)

The main application of this property is for the determination of the initial value $x(0)$ directly from $X(z)$, without having to evaluate the inverse z-transform. The proof is given below.

From the defining equation for the one-sided z-transform,

$$X(z) = x(0) + x(1)z^{-1} + x(2) + \cdots$$

Hence, as $z \to \infty$, all the terms except the first vanish in the limit. This proves equation 6.42.

6.4.2.7 Final Value

If $X(z) = \mathscr{Z}[x(n)]$ then $\lim_{n \to \infty} x(n) = \lim_{z \to 1}\left[(z-1)X(z)\right]$ (6.43)

This property can be used for finding the final value of $x(n)$ from its z-transform $X(z)$ provided that all the poles of $X(z)$ are inside the unit circle in the z-plane, with the possible exception of a simple pole at $z = 1$.

PROOF Consider the z-transform of $[x(n + 1) - x(n)]$. From the shifting property shown in equation 6.28, we may write

$$\mathscr{Z}[x(n + 1) - x(n)] = [zX(z) - zx(0)] - X(z)$$

$$= \lim_{k \to \infty} \sum_{n=0}^{k} [x(n + 1) - x(n)]z^{-n}$$

This may be rearranged as

$$(z - 1)X(z) - x(0) = \lim_{k \to \infty} \sum_{n=0}^{k} [x(n + 1) - x(n)]z^{-n}$$

Taking the limit as $z \to 1$ on both sides, we obtain

$$\lim_{z \to 1} (z - 1)X(z) = x(0) + [x(1) - x(0)] + [x(2) - x(1)]$$

$$+ \cdots + [x(k) - x(k - 1)] + \cdots$$

$$= \lim_{k \to \infty} x(k)$$

As with the final value theorem in Laplace transform theory, the usefulness of this theorem is limited. The final value will be zero if all poles of $X(z)$ are inside the unit circle, whereas it will be infinite if any pole is outside the unit circle. It will be indeterminate if poles are located on the unit circle with the exception of a simple pole at $z = 1$, when the final value will be a constant. As we shall see in Section 6.4.3, this may also be calculated as the residue at the pole at $z = 1$. Still, this theorem is used extensively in the analysis of discrete-time control systems.

Drill Problem 6.5

Determine the initial and final value of $x(n)$ if

$$X(z) = \frac{2(z - 0.5)}{z(z - 1)(z - 0.9)}$$

Answer: $x(0) = 0$; $x(\infty) = 10$

Drill Problem 6.6

Repeat Drill Problem 6.5 if

$$X(z) = \frac{20z(z - 0.2)(z - 0.5)}{(z - 1)(z^2 - 0.6z + 0.4)}$$

Answer: $x(0) = 20$; $x(\infty) = 10$.

TABLE 6.1 Properties of z-Transforms

1. Linearity	$\mathscr{Z}[a_1 x_1(n) + a_2 x_2(n)] = a_1 X_1(z) + a_2 X_2(z)$
2. Shift in time	$\mathscr{Z}[x(n + 1)] = z[X(z) - x(0)]$
3. Multiplication by n	$\mathscr{Z}[nx(n)] = -z \dfrac{d}{dz} X(z)$
4. Multiplication by r^n	$\mathscr{Z}[r^n x(n)] = X\left(\dfrac{z}{r}\right)$
5. Convolution	$\mathscr{Z}\left[\displaystyle\sum_{k=0}^{\infty} x_1(k) x_2(n - k)\right] = X_1(z) X_2(z)$
6. Initial value	$x(0) = \lim\limits_{z \to \infty} X(z)$
7. Final value	$\lim\limits_{n \to \infty} x(n) = \lim\limits_{z \to 1} [(z - 1) X(z)]$

6.4.2.8 A Short Table of Properties of z-Transforms

We now present a short table (Table 6.1) of the important properties of the z-transform, derived in this section.

6.4.2.9 A Short Table of z-Transforms

A short table of z-transforms, derived mainly from the properties described above, is given in Table 6.2.

6.4.3 INVERSION OF THE z-TRANSFORM

Effective use of z-transform theory in the analysis of discrete-time systems requires inversion of z-transforms to obtain the corresponding sequence. This can be done in several ways. The three most common methods will be discussed in the following sections.

6.4.3.1 The Method of Long Division

Since the z-transform is in the form of a rational function, we can divide the numerator polynomial by the denominator to obtain an expansion in the form of an infinite series, with negative powers of z in the case of a causal sequence. The form of the resulting power series is

$$X(z) = \sum_{n=0}^{\infty} a_n z^{-n} \tag{6.44}$$

This series gives the values of the sequence $x(n)$ immediately, if we recall that the various powers of z act as position markers. Therefore, we obtain

$$x(n) = a_n, \qquad n = 0, 1, 2, \ldots \tag{6.45}$$

The following example will demonstrate the procedure.

TABLE 6.2 z-Transform Pairs

$x(n)$	$X(z)$	Comments
1. $\delta(n)$	1	Unit impulse
2. A (step)	$\dfrac{Az}{z-1}$	Pole at $z = 1$
3. Ar^n (exponential)	$\dfrac{Az}{z-r}$	Pole at $z = r$
4. An (ramp)	$\dfrac{Az}{(z-1)^2}$	2 poles at $z = 1$
5. $A\cos\beta n$	$\dfrac{Az(z - \cos\beta)}{z^2 - 2z\cos\beta + 1}$	Complex poles on unit circle
6. $A\sin\beta n$	$\dfrac{Az\sin\beta}{z^2 - 2z\cos\beta + 1}$	Complex poles on unit circle
7. $Ar^n\cos\beta n$	$\dfrac{Az(z - r\cos\beta)}{z^2 - 2zr\cos\beta + r^2}$	Complex poles on circle of radius r
8. $Ar^n\sin\beta n$	$\dfrac{Azr\sin\beta}{z^2 - 2zr\cos\beta + r^2}$	Complex poles on circle of radius r
9. Anr^n	$\dfrac{Arz}{(z-r)^2}$	
10. An^2	$\dfrac{Az(z+1)}{(z-1)^3}$	

Example 6.7

Consider the following z-transform:

$$X(z) = \frac{3z^2 - 5z}{z^3 - 4z^2 + 6z - 4} \tag{6.46}$$

Performing long division of the numerator by the denominator, we get

$$X(z) = 3z^{-1} + 7z^{-2} + 10z^{-3} + 10z^{-4} + 8z^{-5} + \cdots \tag{6.47}$$

It follows by comparing equation 6.47 with equation 6.44 that

$$x(0) = 0, \qquad x(1) = 3, \qquad x(2) = 7,$$
$$x(3) = 10, \qquad x(4) = 10, \qquad x(5) = 8,\ldots \qquad \blacksquare$$

This method is quite suitable for use on either a programmable pocket calculator or a computer. However, since it does not give the inverse transform in a closed form, it is not very convenient if the value of $x(n)$ is desired for large n. It also does not give us a clear idea of the nature of the

TABLE 6.3 Partial Fraction Equivalents for Causal Sequences

$X(z)$	$x(n)$
$\dfrac{Az}{z-r}$	$Ar^n, \quad n \geq 0$
$\dfrac{(C+jD)z}{z-re^{j\phi}} + \dfrac{(c-jD)z}{z-re^{-j\phi}}$	$2r^n(C\cos n\phi - D\sin n\phi), \quad n \geq 0$
$\dfrac{Az}{(z-r)^m}$	$\dfrac{An(n-1)\cdots(n-m+2)}{(m-1)!r^{m-1}}r^n, \quad n \geq m-1$

sequence $x(n)$. The method of partial fraction expansion, described in the following section, overcomes these problems.

6.4.3.2 Partial Fraction Expansion

The idea behind this method is similar to that used for obtaining the inverse Laplace transform. We start by locating the poles of $X(z)$ by determining the roots of the denominator polynomial. Since the coefficients of this polynomial are all real, these poles will either be real or occur in conjugate pairs if complex. The next step is to perform the partial fraction expansion of $X(z)$ and to identify the sequence for each term in the expansion. Looking at Table 6.2, which gives us the most common z-transform pairs, we notice that z occurs as a multiplier in the numerator in each case. It will, therefore, be more desirable to expand $X(z)/z$, rather than $X(z)$, into partial fractions. The procedure that was described in Section 5.4.3.1 for partial fraction expansion in connection with inverse Laplace transformation can then be used directly, whether the poles are real, complex, distinct, or multiple. As before, the residues at complex conjugate poles will be conjugates of each other. After the residues at the various poles have been evaluated, we can multiply them with z to conform with the standard forms shown in Table 6.2. The inverse transform of each term can then be obtained with the help of the table. In most instances it will be adequate to use the basic set of transform pairs shown in Table 6.3, where the terms due to pairs of complex conjugate poles have been combined to provide the inverse z-transform for each case of partial fraction expansion.

The following examples will demonstrate the procedure.

Example 6.8

We use this method to obtain the inverse z-transform of the function considered in Example 6.7.

$$X(z) = \frac{3z^2 - 5z}{z^3 - 4z^2 + 6z - 4}$$

$$= \frac{3z^2 - 5z}{(z-2)(z^2 - 2z + 2)} \tag{6.48}$$

We now obtain the partial fraction expansion of $X(z)/z$. Hence, we get

$$\frac{1}{z}X(z) = \frac{3z - 5}{(z - 2)(z^2 - 2z + 2)}$$

$$= \frac{0.5}{z - 2} + \frac{-0.25 - j1.25}{z - \sqrt{2}\,e^{j\pi/4}} + \frac{-0.25 + j1.25}{z - \sqrt{2}\,e^{-j\pi/4}} \qquad (6.49)$$

The inverse transform is now obtained as

$$x(n) = 0.5(2)^n - (\sqrt{2})^n\left(0.5\cos\frac{n\pi}{4} - 2.5\sin\frac{n\pi}{4}\right) \qquad (6.50)$$

It can be verified that this agrees with the results in Example 6.7.

Example 6.9

Consider the following:

$$X(z) = \frac{5z^4 - 29z^3 + 56z^2 - 34z}{(z - 1)(z - 2)^3} \qquad (6.51)$$

$$\frac{1}{z}X(z) = \frac{5z^3 - 29z^2 + 56z - 34}{(z - 1)(z - 2)^3}$$

$$= \frac{2}{z - 1} + \frac{3}{z - 2} + \frac{-2}{(z - 2)^2} + \frac{2}{(z - 2)^3}$$

Therefore, the inverse transform is obtained as

$$x(n) = 2 + 3(2)^n - n(2)^n + 0.25n(n - 1)(2)^n \qquad (6.52)$$

Drill Problem 6.7

Find the inverse transform of

$$X(z) = \frac{3z^4 - 10z^3 - 5.75z^2}{(z - 1)(z - 0.5)(z^2 + 0.25)}$$

Answer: $x(n) = 0.5^n\left(3.4\cos\frac{n\pi}{2} + 9.8\sin\frac{\pi}{2}\right) - 20.4 + 20(0.5)^n$

Drill Problem 6.8

Repeat Drill Problem 6.7 for

$$X(z) = \frac{5z^5 - 2.5z^4 + 2.5z^3 + 0.75z^2 - 0.25z}{(z - 0.2)(z - 1)^2(z^2 - z + 0.5)}$$

Answer: $x(n) = 13.75n + 0.9375 - 0.05515(0.2)^n$
$$+ 0.5^n\left(4.1177\cos\frac{n\pi}{4} - 6.4706\sin\frac{n\pi}{4}\right)$$

6.4.3.3 Use of the Inversion Integral

It was pointed out in Section 5.4.3 that the inverse Laplace transform can be obtained directly by using the defining equation. This method requires contour integration in the s-plane. It is seldom used because, in the most common case when the Laplace transform is the ratio of two polynomials, it is much easier to use the method of partial fractions. Nevertheless, the method is important, especially when the Laplace transform is not the ratio of two polynomial in s. A similar situation exists in the case of z-transforms. In this section, we briefly discuss the inversion integral for z-transform, which can be derived quite easily.

We start by recalling that the z-transform $X(z)$ of the sequence $x(n)$ is given by

$$X(z) = \sum_{n=0}^{\infty} x(n) z^{-n} \tag{6.53}$$

If we multiply both sides of equation 6.50 by z^{m-1} and integrate along a closed path C which lies entirely within the region of convergence of $X(z)$, then we get

$$\oint_C X(z) z^{m-1}\, dz = \oint_C \sum_{n=0}^{\infty} x(n) z^{-n+m-1}\, dz \tag{6.54}$$

If the sequence $x(n)$ is absolutely summable, that is,

$$\sum_{n=0}^{\infty} |x(n)| < \infty$$

then we can change the order of integration and summation in equation 6.54. This leads to

$$\oint_C X(z) z^{m-1}\, dz = \sum_{n=0}^{\infty} x(n) \oint_C z^{-n+m-1}\, dz \tag{6.55}$$

The integral on the right-hand side of equation 6.55 can be easily evaluated by using the residue theorem, described in Appendix D. For $n = m$, the integrand is simply $1/z$, that is, we have a first-order pole at the origin of the s-plane; therefore, the residue is equal to 1. On the other hand, when $n \neq m$, there is no first-order pole and the residue is zero. We may therefore write

$$\oint_C z^{-n+m-1}\, dz = \begin{cases} 2\pi j & \text{for } n = m \\ 0 & \text{for } n \neq m \end{cases}$$

Substituting this result in equation 6.55 gives us

$$\oint_C X(z) z^{m-1}\, dz = 2\pi j x(m)$$

or

$$x(n) = \frac{1}{2\pi j} \oint_C X(z) z^{n-1} \, dz \qquad (6.56)$$

The following example will illustrate the use of this integral for the evaluation of the inverse z-transform.

Example 6.10

Consider

$$X(z) = \frac{4 \cos z}{z - 0.5} \qquad (6.57)$$

Using the inversion formula given in equation 6.56

$$\begin{aligned}
x(n) &= \frac{1}{2\pi j} \oint_C \frac{4 z^{n-1} \cos z}{z - 0.5} \, dz \\
&= 4(0.5)^{n-1} \cos 0.5 \qquad (6.58)
\end{aligned}$$

where the residue theorem has been used for evaluating the contour integral. ∎

In the next section, we shall get further practice in the use of inverse z-transformation for solving linear difference equations.

6.4.4 SOLUTION OF DIFFERENCE EQUATIONS

The relationship between z-transforms and difference equations is similar to that between Laplace transforms and differential equations. Just as Laplace transformation converts linear differential equations with constant coefficients into algebraic equations in terms of the complex variable s, we shall see that z-transformation will change linear difference equations with constant coefficients into algebraic equations in terms of z. This is possible because of the shifting property discussed in Section 6.4.2.2, that is, multiplication by z is equivalent to a forward shift. The complete solution will then be obtained by finding the inverse transform. This is demonstrated through the following examples.

Example 6.11

Consider the second-order difference equation

$$y(n + 2) - 0.8y(n + 1) + 0.25y(n) = u(n) \qquad (6.59)$$

with the initial conditions

$$y(0) = 4, \qquad y(1) = 2 \qquad (6.60)$$

It is desired to determine the output sequence if the input sequence is given by

$$u(n) = 10(0.5)^n \tag{6.61}$$

Taking the z-transform of both sides of equation 6.59, we obtain

$$(z^2 - 0.8z + 0.25)Y(z) = U(z) + z^2 y(0) + zy(1) - 0.8zy(0)$$
$$= U(z) + 4z^2 - 1.2z \tag{6.62}$$

The z-transform of the input is given by

$$U(z) = \frac{10z}{z - 0.5} \tag{6.63}$$

Substituting this into equation 6.62 and solving for $Y(z)$, we get

$$Y(z) = \frac{4z^3 - 3.2z^2 + 10.6z}{(z - 0.5)(z^2 - 0.8z + 0.25)} \tag{6.64}$$

We now obtain the partial fraction expansion of $Y(z)/z$. This is given below

$$\frac{1}{z}Y(z) = \frac{4z^2 - 3.2z + 10.6}{(z - 0.5)(z^2 - 0.8z + 0.25)}$$
$$= \frac{100}{z - 0.5} + \frac{-48 + j16}{z - 0.5e^{j0.6435}} + \frac{-48 + j16}{z - 0.5e^{-j0.6435}} \tag{6.65}$$

Taking the inverse transform, we obtain

$$y(n) = 100(0.5)^n - (0.5)^n(96\cos 0.6435n + 32\sin 0.6435n) \tag{6.66}$$

∎

Example 6.12

We shall repeat the problem in Example 6.11, with the input changed to

$$u(n) = 10\sin 0.2n \tag{6.67}$$

The z-transform of the input is given by

$$U(z) = \frac{10z\sin 0.2}{z^2 - 2z\cos 0.2 + 1} \tag{6.68}$$

Substituting this into equation 6.62 and solving for $Y(z)$, we get

$$Y(z) = \frac{4z^4 - 9.0405z^3 - 6.3522z^2 + 0.7867z}{(z^2 - 0.8z + 0.25)(z^2 - 2z\cos 0.2 + 1)} \tag{6.69}$$

The partial fraction expansion of $Y(z)/z$ is given below

$$\frac{1}{z}Y(z) = \frac{7.681 - j5.333}{z - 0.5e^{j0.6435}} + \frac{7.681 + j5.333}{z - 0.5e^{-j0.6435}}$$

$$+ \frac{-5.681 - j9.54}{z - e^{j0.2}} + \frac{-5.681 + j9.54}{z - e^{-j0.2}} \tag{6.70}$$

Finally, taking the inverse transform, we get the output sequence

$$y(n) = (0.5)^n(15.362 \cos 0.6435n + 10.666 \sin 0.6435n)$$

$$-(11.362 \cos 0.2n - 19.08 \sin 0.2n) \tag{6.71}$$

∎

Drill Problem 6.9

Solve the following difference equations using z-transforms, if the initial conditions are $y(0) = 2$ and $y(1) = 5$.

(a) $y(n) + 0.6y(n - 1) + 0.08y(n - 2) = 4$

(b) $y(n) + 0.6y(n - 1) + 0.25y(n - 2) = 4(0.4)^n$

(c) $y(n) + 0.6y(n - 1) + 0.09y(n - 2) = 4\cos\left(\frac{n}{3}\right)$

Answer: (a) $\dfrac{50}{21} + \dfrac{259}{21}(-0.2)^n - \dfrac{267}{21}(-0.4)^n$

(b) $\dfrac{64}{65}(0.4)^n + \dfrac{699}{65}(0.5)^n \sin(2.2143n) + \dfrac{66}{65}(0.5)^n \cos(2.2143n)$

(c) $2.387 \cos\left(\dfrac{n}{3}\right) - 0.367 \sin\left(\dfrac{n}{3}\right) - (0.387 + 9.161n)(-0.3)^n$

6.5 TRANSFER FUNCTIONS OF LINEAR DISCRETE-TIME SYSTEMS

The concept of the operational transfer function of discrete-time systems was introduced in Chapter 1, in terms of the operator q. We are now ready to formalize the concept in terms of z-transforms. It will be shown that replacing q with z in the operational transfer function gives us the transfer function in terms of z-transforms, just as replacing p by s in the operational transfer function of a continuous-time system leads us to the transfer function defined in terms of Laplace transforms. It will also be seen that the transfer function obtained in this manner can be used in the same way as explained in Section 5.5 for continuous-time systems.

6.5.1 DEFINITION OF TRANSFER FUNCTIONS

As in Section 5.5, we begin with a formal definition of the transfer function of a discrete-time system. The following are equivalent.

Definition 1: The transfer function of a linear time-invariant discrete-time system is the z-transform of its impulse response sequence.

Definition 2: The transfer function of a linear time-invariant discrete-time system is the ratio of the z-transforms of the output and the input under zero initial conditions.

Both of these definitions are quite useful, as was seen for continuous-time systems. The former is of value in those cases where the impulse response of the system is known, whereas the latter is more useful for determining the transfer function from the difference equation for the system. In fact, all that we have to do in the latter case is to replace the operator q with z while taking the z-transforms and then solve for the ratio of the transforms of the output and the input.

The following example will demonstrate the procedure for derivation of the transfer function from the difference equation of a system.

Example 6.13

Consider a discrete-time system defined by the following difference equation:

$$y(n + 2) - 0.8y(n + 1) + 0.25y(n) = 3u(n + 1) + 2u(n) \quad (6.72)$$

Taking the z-transforms of both sides of equation 6.72 and assuming zero initial conditions, we get

$$(z^2 - 0.8z + 0.25)Y(z) = (3z + 2)U(z) \quad (6.73)$$

Therefore, the transfer function is obtained as

$$H(z) = \frac{Y(z)}{U(z)} = \frac{3z + 2}{z^2 - 0.8z + 0.25} \quad (6.74)$$

∎

As in the case of continuous-time systems, an important application of the transfer function is in determining the output of the system to any arbitrary input. Although it is possible to use convolution for this purpose, it is much more convenient to utilize the transfer function. In addition, the transfer function can be used for determining the frequency response as well as for investigating the stability of the system. It contains a great deal of information about the system in terms of its poles and zeros. This topic will be discussed in the following section.

Drill Problem 6.10

Determine the impulse response sequence for a discrete-time system described by following transfer function:

$$H(z) = \frac{8z}{(z - 0.5)(z - 0.7)}$$

Answer: $h(n) = 40(0.7)^n - 40(0.5)^n$

Drill Problem 6.11

Determine the transfer function corresponding to the following impulse response sequence:

$$h(n) = 100(0.5)^n - (0.5)^n(96\cos 0.6435n + 8\sin 0.6435n)$$

Answer: $H(z) = \dfrac{4z^3 + 4z^2 + 7z}{(z - 0.5)(z^2 - 0.8z + 0.25)}$

6.5.2 POLES AND ZEROS

The concept of poles and zeros of transfer functions has already been introduced in Chapter 5, during the study of continuous-time systems. The same ideas are carried over for transfer functions of discrete-time systems. The main difference is that in this case we have the poles and zeros in the z-plane instead of the s-plane for continuous-time systems. The poles of the transfer function again represent the "natural frequencies" of the system and, in general, if the z-transfer function of a discrete-time system has a pole at $z = r_i$, there will be a component of the form $A(r_i)^n$ in the natural response of the system. As for the case of continuous-time systems, a zero of the transfer function represents a mode that will be blocked by the system. Thus, as before, poles and zeros of the transfer function contain all the information about the behavior of the system, except for a constant or scale factor.

There is one important difference between continuous-time and discrete-time systems as far as the relationship between stability and the location of the poles of the transfer function is concerned. It is directly related to equation 6.9, which describes the mapping between the s-plane and the z-plane with the result that the left half of the s-plane maps into the region inside the unit circle in the z-plane. This will be discussed in the following section.

6.5.3 STABILITY OF LINEAR DISCRETE-TIME SYSTEMS

The concept of stability was introduced in Section 1.9, where a linear system was defined as being stable if and only if its output remains bounded for all possible bounded inputs. It was shown there that a discrete-time system will

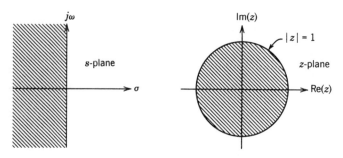

Figure 6.11 Mapping between s-plane and z-plane.

be stable in the BIBO sense if and only if all roots of the characteristic polynomial have magnitude less than one. We now present an interpretation in terms of the transfer function and the transformation between the s-plane and the z-plane. The mapping between the two planes was discussed in Section 6.3 and is depicted again in Figure 6.11.

We saw in Chapter 5 that a continuous-time system is stable if and only if all the poles of its transfer function are located in the left half of the s-plane. This follows from the fact that for this case all the components of the complete response of the system will either decay with time or remain bounded for all possible bounded inputs. Similarly, a discrete-time system will be stable if and only if all the poles of its transfer function are strictly inside the unit circle in the z-plane, since only in this case will all the components of the complete response either decay with time or remain bounded for all possible bounded input sequences. This is consistent with our earlier observation, as noted in Section 6.3, that the imaginary axis of the s-plane mapped onto the unit circle of the z-plane and the left half of the s-plane mapped into the region inside the unit circle of the z-plane, as shown in Figure 6.11.

In view of this discussion, the following statements regarding the stability of discrete-time systems are equivalent.

1. A discrete-time system is stable if and only if all the poles of its transfer function lie strictly inside the unit circle of the z-plane.

2. A discrete-time system is stable if and only if its impulse response sequence $h(n)$ satisfies the following property:

$$\lim_{n \to \infty} |h(n)| = 0$$

3. A discrete-time system is stable if and only if its impulse response sequence $h(n)$ satisfies the following property:

$$\sum_{n=0}^{\infty} |h(n)|^p < \infty, \quad \text{for any} \quad p \geq 1$$

4. A discrete-time system is stable if and only if the magnitude of every root of its characteristic polynomial is less than 1.

The similarity of these statements with those in Section 5.5.3, concerning the stability of continuous-time systems, should be noted.

The natural response of a stable system is therefore also called its *transient* response. Consequently, if a periodic forcing function is applied to a stable system, the steady-state output will also be periodic, with the same period as that of the input. As with continuous-time systems, the steady-state response of a discrete-time system to sinusoidal input sequences can be calculated more conveniently from the frequency response of the system, obtained simply by replacing z by $e^{j\Omega}$ in the transfer function and evaluating the resulting complex number for a given value of Ω. This will be discussed in the following section.

6.5.4 FREQUENCY RESPONSE FROM THE TRANSFER FUNCTION

As seen in Chapter 4, a sinusoidal discrete-time signal with period N can be represented by the following equation:

$$x(n) = A\left[\exp\left(\frac{j2\pi n}{N}\right)\right] + \left[\exp\left(\frac{-j2\pi n}{N}\right)\right] = 2A\cos\frac{2\pi n}{N} \quad (6.75)$$

To simplify the notation, we define the angular frequency as

$$\Omega = \frac{2\pi}{N} \quad (6.76)$$

Consequently, equation 6.74 can be written as

$$x(n) = A(e^{j\Omega n} + e^{-j\Omega n}) = 2A\cos\Omega n \quad (6.77)$$

We now determine the steady-state response of a discrete-time system to the input $Ae^{j\Omega n}$ if the transfer function $H(z)$ of the system is known. It will be assumed that the system is stable, that is, all the poles of $H(z)$ are strictly inside the unit circle in the z-plane, since, otherwise, the system cannot have a "steady state response." First we note that the z-transform of the complete output $y(n)$ is given by

$$Y(z) = H(z)X(z) = H(z)\frac{A}{z - e^{j\Omega}} \quad (6.78)$$

Since the poles of $H(z)$ give rise to only transient components, the steady-state component of the response to the input $Ae^{j\Omega n}$ is obtained by evaluating the residue of $Y(z)$ at the pole $z = e^{j\Omega}$. Thus we get

$$y_{ss}(n) = H(e^{j\Omega})Ae^{j\Omega n} \quad (6.79)$$

Let us denote the complex number $H(e^{j\Omega})$ in the polar form, that is,

$$H(e^{j\Omega}) = Me^{j\phi} \quad (6.80)$$

Then it follows that

$$H(e^{-j\Omega}) = Me^{-j\phi} \quad (6.81)$$

and the response to the complete sinusoid denoted by equation 6.77 will be given by

$$y_{ss}(n) = 2MA \cos(n\Omega + \phi) \qquad (6.82)$$

Thus, we have established that the steady-state response of a discrete-time system to a sinusoidal input sequence is obtained by simply multiplying the amplitude of the input by M and advancing the phase of the input by ϕ, where $Me^{j\phi}$ is the value of the transfer function $H(z)$, calculated for $z = e^{j\Omega}$. In other words, $H(e^{j\Omega})$ gives the frequency response of the system. This will be demonstrated by the following example.

Example 6.14

Consider a discrete-time system described by the following difference equation:

$$y(n) - 1.2y(n-1) + 0.61y(n-2) - 0.15y(n-3)$$
$$= 3u(n) + 2u(n-1) \qquad (6.83)$$

We would like to determine the steady-state response of this system if the input sequence is given by the following equation:

$$u(n) = 3 + 4\cos 0.2\pi n + 7\sin 0.3\pi n \qquad (6.84)$$

Taking the z-transform of both sides of equation 6.83 and assuming that the initial conditions are zero (note that the initial conditions do not affect the steady-state response), we get

$$(1 - 1.2z^{-1} + 0.61z^{-2} - 0.15z^{-3})Y(z) = (3 + 2z^{-1})U(z) \qquad (6.85)$$

From equation 6.85, the transfer function of the system is obtained as

$$H(z) = \frac{Y(z)}{U(z)} = \frac{3z^3 + 2z^2}{z^3 - 1.2z^2 + 0.61z - 0.15} \qquad (6.86)$$

First we verify that this is a stable system. This is done by finding the roots of the denominator polynomial. They are located at 0.6, $0.3 + j0.4$, and $0.3 - j0.4$. Since the magnitude of each roots is less than one, we have a stable system and we are justified in expecting that there will be a steady-state response, which will have the same frequencies as those of the input sequence.

Next, we note that our input sequence contains three frequency components, at $\Omega = 0$, 0.2π, and 0.3π. Therefore, we shall calculate $H(z)$ for the complex variable $z = e^{j0}$, $e^{j0.2\pi}$, and $e^{j0.3\pi}$, respectively, and use these values to determine the steady-state response due to each component. The results of these calculation are given below.

$$H(e^{j0}) = \frac{3 + 2}{1 - 1.2 + 0.61 - 0.15} = 19.23$$

$$H(e^{j0.2\pi}) = \frac{3e^{j0.6\pi} + 2e^{j0.4\pi}}{e^{j0.6\pi} - 1.2e^{j0.4\pi} + 0.61e^{j0.2\pi} - 0.15} = 12.67e^{j1.042}$$

$$H(e^{j0.3\pi}) = \frac{3e^{j0.9} + 2e^{j0.6\pi}}{e^{j0.9\pi} - 1.2e^{j0.6\pi} + 0.61e^{j0.3\pi} - 0.15} = 8.905e^{-j1.423}$$

We can now multiply these values of the frequency response with the amplitudes of the various components of the input as in equation 6.82 and add the respective phase shifts to obtain the steady-state output. The final result is given by

$$y_{ss}(n) = 57.69 + 50.68\cos(0.2\pi n - 2.123)$$

$$+ 62.335\sin(0.3\pi n - 1.423) \qquad (6.87)$$

∎

A graphical interpretation for the calculation of the frequency response from the transfer function can be given in the same way as was done for continuous-time systems in Section 5.4.5.1. There is one important difference. In the s-plane the value of the frequency is taken along the imaginary or $j\omega$-axis, whereas in the z-plane it is taken along the unit circle, since we evaluate $H(e^{j\Omega})$, and the magnitude of $e^{j\Omega}$ is one for every value of Ω. Therefore, in this instance, vectors will be drawn from the poles and zeros of the transfer function to a particular point on the unit circle of the z-plane, corresponding to the value of Ω for which the frequency response is to be evaluated. This is shown in Figure 6.12, illustrating the evaluation of the

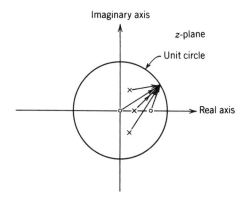

Figure 6.12 Graphical interpretation of frequency response.

frequency response for $\Omega = 0.3\pi$ for the transfer function given in equation 6.86.

Another interesting feature of the frequency response of discrete-time systems is that starting with $\Omega = 0$, which maps into the point $1 + j0$ or e^{j0} in the z-plane, we move along the unit circle in the z-plane in the counterclockwise direction as Ω increases and return to the starting point when $\Omega = 2\pi$. After that we again go around the unit circle as Ω is increased from 2π to 4π, and so on. This is to be expected, in view of the mapping between the s-plane and the z-plane and the definition of Ω given in equation 6.75. This leads to some interesting properties of the frequency response of discrete-time systems. We shall return to this topic in Chapter 7, when we study frequency response plots for discrete-time systems. Here we just observe that the frequency response repeats itself after we have gone once around the unit circle of the z-plane. This is due to the fact that the spectrum of a sampled signal is periodic, as observed in Chapter 4.

Drill Problem 6.12

The transfer function of a discrete-time system is given below.

$$H(z) = \frac{10(z - 0.3)}{(z - 0.4)(z^2 - 0.4z + 0.25)}$$

Determine its steady-state response to the input sequence

$$u(n) = 1 + 2\cos 0.3\pi n + 3\sin 0.6\pi n$$

Answer: $13.7255 + 29.84\cos(0.3\pi n - 2.12) + 26.903\sin(0.6\pi n - 4.36)$

6.6 INVERSION OF BILATERAL *z*-TRANSFORMS

In our discussion thus far, we have considered only the inversion of unilateral or one-sided z-transforms, which are obtained from sequences that are causal. If $x(n)$ is a noncausal sequence, then we obtain a two-sided or bilateral z-transform defined by equation 6.2. In such cases the inverse transform cannot be determined uniquely unless the region of convergence in the z-plane is specified. This is necessary in order to separate the causal and anticausal portions of the sequence. In particular, if $X(z)$ converges for $|z| > |r_i|$, then poles at $|z| \leq |r_i|$ will give rise to power series expansions in negative powers of z and the resulting sequence will exist for $n \geq 0$. On the other hand, if $X(z)$ converges for $|z| < |r_i|$, then these poles will give rise to a sequence that will exist for negative values of n. It is evident that unless the region of convergence is known, it is not possible to find the inverse transform uniquely.

The following example will demonstrate this.

Example 6.15

Consider the following z-transform, which has already been expanded into partial functions.

$$X(z) = \frac{3z}{z - 0.6} - \frac{2z}{z - 0.9} \tag{6.88}$$

If the region of convergence is known to be outside the unit circle of the z-plane, then the inverse transform will give us a causal sequence and

$$x(n) = \begin{cases} 3(0.6)^n - 2(0.9)^n & \text{for } n \geq 0 \\ 0 & \text{for } n < 0 \end{cases} \tag{6.89}$$

On the other hand, if the region of convergence is $0.7 < |z| < 0.8$, then we obtain

$$x(n) = \begin{cases} 3(0.6)^n & \text{for } n \geq 0 \\ 2(0.9)^n & \text{for } n < 0 \end{cases} \tag{6.90}$$

Finally, if the region of convergence is $|z| < 0.6$, then we have an anticausal sequence and

$$x(n) = \begin{cases} 0 & \text{for } n \geq 0 \\ -3(0.6)^n + 2(0.9)^n & \text{for } n < 0 \end{cases} \tag{6.91}$$

The inversion of bilateral transforms, therefore, first requires partial fraction expansion of $X(z)/z$. This can be carried out by using the procedure discussed in Section 6.4.3.2. We must then decide for each pole whether it will give rise to a causal or an anticausal sequence on the basis of the specified region of convergence. Table 6.4, which is the counterpart of Table 6.3. in Section 6.4.3.2, will be helpful in obtaining the time sequence for *anticausal* functions, while Table 6.3 can be used for the time sequences for causal functions.

Bilateral z-transforms normally occur in the analysis of discrete-time systems subject to random inputs. In this case one has to obtain the

TABLE 6.4 Partial Fraction Equivalents for Anticausal Sequences

$X(z)$	$x(n)$
$\dfrac{Az}{z - r}$	$-Ar^n, \quad n \leq -1$
$\dfrac{(C + jD)z}{z - r^{j\phi}} + \dfrac{(C - jD)z}{z - r^{-j\phi}}$	$-2r^n(C \cos n\phi - D \sin n\phi), \quad n \leq -1$
$\dfrac{Az}{(z - r)^m}$	$-\dfrac{An(n + 1) \cdots (n + m - 1)}{(m - 1)! r^{m-1}} r^n, \quad n \leq -m$

z-transform of the autocorrelation sequence that has symmetry around $n = 0$, so that the poles of the z-transform of the anticausal part of the sequence are the reciprocals of the poles of the z-transform of the causal part. In such cases, the region of convergence is an annular ring around the unit circle in the z-plane. Hence, all poles inside the unit circle identify with the causal part, and all poles outside the unit circle identify with the anticausal part. The following examples will illustrate the procedure.

Example 6.16

The autocorrelation sequence of a random signal is given below.

$$x(n) = 3(0.8)^{|n|}, \qquad -\infty < n < \infty \qquad (6.92)$$

We shall determine the z-transform of this noncausal sequence. First consider the causal part. The z-transform of this part is obtained immediately as

$$X_1(z) = \frac{3z}{z - 0.8}, \qquad |z| > 0.8 \qquad (6.93)$$

To obtain the z-transform of the anticausal part, we first note that it can be expressed as

$$x(n) = 3(1.25)^n, \qquad n \le 1 \qquad (6.94)$$

Hence, using Table 6.4 the z-transform of this part is given by

$$X_2(z) = \frac{-3z}{z - 1.25}, \qquad |z| < 1.25 \qquad (6.95)$$

This is easily verified from the power series expansion of equation 6.95, which gives us

$$X_2(z) = 3\left[(0.8z) + (0.8z)^2 + (0.8z)^3 + \cdots\right] \qquad (6.96)$$

Finally, combining the two parts, we get

$$X(z) = X_1(z) + X_2(z) = \frac{-1.35z}{(z - 0.8)(z - 1.25)},$$

$$0.8 < |z| < 1.25 \quad (6.97)$$

∎

Example 6.17

The z-transform of an autocorrelation sequence is given by

$$X(z) = \frac{-18z^3 + 50.25z^2 - 18z}{(z - 0.5)(z - 0.25)(z - 2)(z - 4)}, \qquad 0.5 < |z| < 2 \quad (6.98)$$

It is desired to obtain the inverse z-transform.

The partial fraction expansion of $X(z)$ can be carried out in the usual manner giving the following result:

$$\frac{1}{z}X(z) = \frac{2}{(z - 0.5)} + \frac{4}{(z - 0.25)} + \frac{-2}{(z - 2)} + \frac{-4}{(z - 4)} \quad (6.99)$$

From the specified region of convergence, we can identify the poles at 0.5 and 0.25 with sequences that exist for $n \geq 0$, and the poles at 2 and 4 with sequences that exist for $n < 0$. Consequently, we obtain

$$x(n) = \begin{cases} 2(0.5)^n + 4(0.25)^n & \text{for } n \geq 0 \\ 2(2)^n + 4(4)^n & \text{for } n \leq -1 \end{cases} \quad (6.100)$$

Due to the symmetry, the expression for $x(n)$ may be written in the following form, which is more compact:

$$x(n) = 2.(0.5)^{|n|} + 4(0.25)^{|n|} \quad (6.101)$$

∎

It is seen from these examples that the procedure for inverting bilateral z-transforms is only slightly more complicated than that for unilateral z-transforms. A unique inverse can be obtained only if the region of convergence in the z-plane is specified so that we may identify each pole with either a causal or an anticausal sequence. It may be recalled that the inversion of bilateral Laplace transforms requires the same information. In fact, the procedures for the inversion of bilateral z-transforms and bilateral Laplace transforms are almost identical.

6.7 TRANSFORMATION BETWEEN CONTINUOUS-TIME AND DISCRETE-TIME SYSTEMS

Often it is desirable to obtain the model for a discrete-time system that will mimic the behavior of a given continuous-time system. For example, one may like to simulate a continuous-time system on a digital computer to study the effect of applying certain inputs, as often required in the design of control systems. Alternatively, one may like to design a digital (discrete-time) filter that will approximate closely the response of a given analog (continuous-time) filter. In fact, an important motivation for obtaining such a transformation is that one can then utilize the wealth of information gathered over several decades in the design of continuous-time filter networks. This topic will be considered in greater detail in Chapter 9, where the reader will be introduced to the theory of filters.

Three basic approaches to transformation between continuous-time and discrete-time systems will be presented in this section. The first is called the *impulse-invariant* transformation; the object here is that the impulse response sequence of the discrete-time system should match the samples of the impulse response of the continuous-time system. The second method is based on obtaining a *numerical* solution to the differential equation for the continuous-time system by replacing the derivative with a finite difference. In other words, the system differential equation is replaced by an appropriate difference equation. The third method is based on a *bilinear transformation* from the s-plane and the z-plane, which gives the transfer function of a discrete-time system that approximates certain properties of the given continuous-time system. All of these methods are used extensively in the design of digital filters as well as digital control systems.

6.7.1   IMPULSE-INVARIANT TRANSFORMATION

As stated earlier, the aim is to design a discrete-time system, the impulse response of which is the sampled version of the impulse response of the given continuous-time system. Let $G(s)$ denote the transfer function of the continuous time system. Its impulse response is then given by

$$h(t) = \sum_{i=1}^{n} A_i e^{p_i t} \tag{6.102}$$

where it is assumed that $G(s)$ has the following partial fraction expansion:

$$G(s) = \sum_{i=1}^{N} \frac{A_i}{s - p_i} \tag{6.103}$$

Let the transfer function of the corresponding discrete-time system be denoted by $H(z)$. In order that the impulse response sequence $h(nT)$ of the $H(z)$ may be identical to $h(t)$ at the sampling instants, its transfer function must be the z-transform of $G(s)$. Therefore, $H(z)$ is given by

$$H(z) = \sum_{i=1}^{N} \frac{A_i z}{z - e^{-p_i T}} \tag{6.104}$$

It is important to examine the relationship between the frequency response of $G(s)$ and that of $H(z)$, as determined above. First we recall the following relationship between $H(z)$ and $G(s)$ from the theory of z-transforms:

$$H(z)\big|_{z=e^{sT}} = \frac{1}{T} \sum_{k=-\infty}^{\infty} G\left(s + j\frac{2\pi k}{T}\right) \tag{6.105}$$

This relationship is the consequence of the fact that when a continuous-time signal is sampled at intervals of T seconds, the spectrum of the sampled signal is the periodic repetition of the spectrum of the continuous-time signal, with period $f_s = 1/T$, but scaled by the factor f_s, as discussed in detail in Section 4.4. Aliasing occurs when the sampling frequency is less than twice the highest frequency contained in the continuous-time signal.

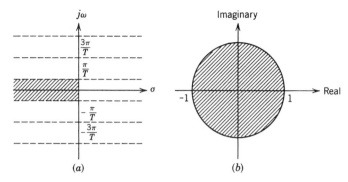

Figure 6.13 Mapping in impulse invariant transformation. (a) s-plane. (b) z-plane.

In view of equation 6.105, it follows that the frequency response of $H(z)$ and $G(s)$ are related as below.

$$H(e^{j\omega}) = \frac{1}{T} \sum_{k=-\infty}^{\infty} G\left(j\frac{\omega}{T} + j\frac{2\pi k}{T}\right) \qquad (6.106)$$

Equation 1.106 tells us that the frequency response of the discrete-time system with transfer function $H(z)$ will match exactly that of the continuous-time system with transfer function $G(s)$ provided that $G(j\omega)$ is zero for $\omega > \omega_s$, where $\omega_s = 2\pi/T$. In other words, the matching will not be perfect unless the sampling frequency is selected in such a way as to avoid aliasing. Unfortunately, this condition cannot be satisfied completely in a practical situation because it requires that the magnitude of the frequency response of the continuous-time system be zero at all frequencies above ω_s. A good approximation is obtained only if ω_s is selected so that the magnitude of the frequency response is negligible for all $\omega > \omega_s$.

It is interesting to examine the mapping from the s-plane into the z-plane in the case of impulse invariant transformation. From the relationship $z = e^{sT}$, it follows that strips of width $2\pi/T$, or ω_s, in the s-plane map into the entire z-plane, as shown in Figure 6.13.

It is seen that the left half of each strip in the s-plane maps into the interior of the *unit circle* in the z-plane. Similarly, the right half of each strip in the s-plane maps into the exterior of the unit circle. Also, the imaginary axis of the s-plane maps onto the unit circle in the z-plane in such a way that each segment of length ω_s is mapped once around the unit circle. Furthermore, it is evident from equation 6.105 that each horizontal strip of the s-plane is overlaid into the z-plane to form the transfer function of the digital filter from the transfer function of the analog filter. This explains why the impulse-invariant transformation is not a simple algebraic mapping from the s-plane to the z-plane and also explains aliasing. The relationship between frequency ω and the digital frequency Ω is, however, linear. The shape of the frequency response is therefore preserved. This will not be the case with the procedure to be discussed next.

6.7.2 NUMERICAL SOLUTION OF THE DIFFERENTIAL EQUATION

Another approach for obtaining a discrete-time approximation to a continuous-time system is to approximate the differential equation for the latter with a difference equation. The main idea is that for a sufficiently small sampling interval a derivative may be replaced by a finite difference. This may be written as

$$\frac{dx(t)}{dt} \approx \frac{x(n) - x(n-1)}{T} \tag{6.107}$$

Using the operator notation, equation 6.107 may be interpreted as

$$p \approx \frac{1 - q^{-1}}{T} \tag{6.108}$$

It has been seen that Laplace transformation of a differential equation has the effect of replacing the operator p with s and the operator q with z (recall that the z-transform is in fact the Laplace transform, with $z = e^{sT}$). Thus, the approximate transfer function of the discrete-time model can be obtained from that of the continuous-time model by simply making the substitution

$$s = \frac{1 - z^{-1}}{T} \tag{6.109}$$

For a better understanding of this transformation, let us examine the mapping represented by equation 6.109. Replacing s by $j\omega$ and solving for z, we obtain

$$z = \frac{1}{1 - j\omega T} = \frac{1}{2}\left[1 + \frac{1 + j\omega T}{1 - j\omega T}\right] = 0.5\left[1 + \exp\left(j2\tan^{-1}\omega T\right)\right] \tag{6.110}$$

The mapping represented by equation 6.110 is shown in Figure 6.14. It will be observed that the $j\omega$-axis of the s-plane maps into a circle of radius 0.5, with the center at $z = -0.5 + j0$. The left half of the s-plane maps inside this circle and the right half maps outside the circle. Thus, although this transformation does not satisfy the criterion of mapping the $j\omega$-axis into the unit circle in the z-plane, it does preserve stability. It does not, however, provide a linear relationship between ω and Ω.

This procedure usually requires a very high sampling rate to obtain an accurate conversion from analog to digital filters. As a result, it leads to a rather inefficient representation of the digital filter as well as the input signal. Therefore, it is unsatisfactory for most applications except for low-pass filters. As we shall learn in the next section, there is another mapping that

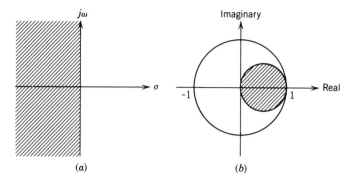

Figure 6.14 Mapping in discretization of differential equation.
(a) s-plane. (b) z-plane.

avoids the problem of aliasing encountered in the impulse invariant transformation and is also more efficient than the two discussed above. It also preserves the stability of the continuous-time system.

6.7.3 BILINEAR TRANSFORMATION

The previous method was based on the approximation of a derivative by a finite difference. We now consider an alternative approach in which the differential equation of the continuous-time system is integrated by using a popular method of numerical integration. This will lead us to the bilinear transformation, which is a conformal mapping that transforms the $j\omega$-axis of the s-plane into the unit circle in the z-plane only once and thus avoids the aliasing of frequency components.

Consider, for example, a continuous-time system described by the transfer function

$$G(s) = \frac{K}{s + a} \qquad (6.111)$$

The input $u(t)$ and the output $y(t)$ of this system are then related through the differential equation

$$\frac{dy}{dt} + ay(t) = Ku(t) \qquad (6.112)$$

If we integrate both sides of equation 6.112 with respect to t, between the limits $(n - 1)T$ and nT, we obtain

$$y_n - y_{n-1} + a\int_{(n-1)T}^{nT} y(t)\, dt = K\int_{(n-1)T}^{nT} u(t)\, dt \qquad (6.113)$$

where, for the sake of brevity, y_i represents $y(iT)$ for integer i.

The integrations indicated in equation 6.113 can be approximated by the trapezoidal rule of integration. This leads us to

$$y_n - y_{n-1} + a\frac{T}{2}(y_n + y_{n-1}) = K\frac{T}{2}(u_n + u_{n-1}) \qquad (6.114)$$

Taking the z-transforms of both sides of equation 6.114, we obtain

$$(1 - z^{-1})Y(z) + \left(\frac{aT}{2}\right)(1 + z^{-1})Y(z) = \left(\frac{KT}{2}\right)(1 + z^{-1})U(z) \quad (6.115)$$

Thus, the transfer function of the equivalent discrete-time system is given by

$$H(z) = \frac{Y(z)}{U(z)} = \frac{(KT/2)(1 + z^{-1})}{1 - z^{-1} + (aT/2)(1 + z^{-1})}$$

$$= \frac{K}{\dfrac{2}{T}\dfrac{1 - z^{-1}}{1 + z^{-1}} + a} \qquad (6.116)$$

Evidently, the mapping from $G(s)$ to $H(z)$ is the transformation

$$s = \frac{2}{T}\frac{1 - z^{-1}}{1 + z^{-1}} = \frac{2}{T}\frac{z - 1}{z + 1} \qquad (6.117)$$

This is called the *bilinear transformation*. Although we have shown this mapping to hold for a first-order transfer function, it applies to the general case as well. This follows from the fact that any transfer function of order n can be expressed as the sum of n first-order transfer functions by partial fraction expansion, which can then be integrated term by term. We shall now study some properties of this transformation. Let us define

$$z = re^{j\Omega} \qquad (6.118)$$

Then from equation 6.117 we get

$$s = \sigma + j\omega = \frac{2}{T}\frac{z - 1}{z + 1} = \frac{2}{T}\frac{re^{j\Omega} - 1}{re^{j\Omega} + 1}$$

$$= \frac{2}{T}\left[\frac{r^2 - 1}{1 + r^2 + 2r\cos\Omega} + j\frac{2r\sin\Omega}{1 + r^2 + 2r\cos\Omega}\right] \qquad (6.119)$$

Separating the real and imaginary parts, we obtain

$$\sigma = \frac{2}{T}\frac{r^2 - 1}{1 + r^2 + 2r\cos\Omega} \qquad (6.120)$$

$$\omega = \frac{2}{T}\frac{2r\sin\Omega}{1 + r^2 + 2r\cos\Omega} \qquad (6.121)$$

From equation 6.120 we observe that $\sigma > 0$ for $r > 1$ and $\sigma < 0$ for $r < 1$. This implies that the right half of the s-plane maps outside the unit

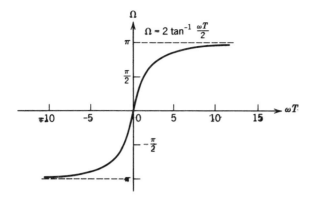

Figure 6.15 Mapping between Ω and ω due to bilinear transformation.

circle of the z-plane, and left half of the s-plane maps into the inside of the unit circle. Also, $\sigma = 0$ for $r = 1$, so that the $j\omega$-axis maps into the unit circle, with the relationship

$$\omega = \frac{2}{T} \frac{\sin \Omega}{1 + \cos \Omega} = \frac{2}{T} \tan \frac{\Omega}{2} \tag{6.122}$$

or

$$\Omega = 2 \tan^{-1} \frac{\omega T}{2} \tag{6.123}$$

Equation 6.123 gives us the relationship between the frequency variables in the s-plane and the z-plane, which is depicted in Figure 6.15.

It will be seen that the mapping between the frequencies in the two planes is one-to-one but also highly nonlinear. Thus, aliasing is avoided at the cost of distortion, or *warping*, in the frequency axis. Note that this distortion is more marked for $\Omega > \pi/2$. As pointed out earlier, this transformation preserves the stability of the system, since the left half of the s-plane maps inside the unit circle. Another feature of the bilinear transformation is that the point $s = 0$ maps into $z = 1$ and also that $G(0) = H(1)$. This implies that the dc gain of the system is preserved in the transformation. Similarly, the point $s = \infty$ maps into $z = -1$, with the result that a zero at ∞ in $G(s)$ will cause $H(z)$ to have a zero at $z = -1$.

The following example will demonstrate the use of these methods for obtaining a discrete-time equivalent model for a continuous-time system.

Example 6.18

The transfer function relating the applied voltage to the angular displacement in one of the joint axes of an industrial robot driven by a dc motor is given below.

$$G(s) = \frac{2.5}{s(s + 0.5)(s + 5)} \qquad (6.124)$$

To use a digital computer for controlling the robot, it is desired to obtain an equivalent discrete-model, with the sampling interval selected as $T = 0.1$ s. We shall use each of the three methods discussed in this section to derive such a model.

I. Model using impulse-invariant transformation

Here we start by obtaining the impulse response of the system, corresponding to the transfer function in equation 6.124. Partial fraction expansion of $G(s)$ yields

$$G(s) = \frac{1}{s} - \frac{10/9}{s + 0.5} + \frac{1/9}{s + 5}$$

Consequently, the impulse response is given by

$$h(t) = 1 - \frac{10}{9}e^{-0.5t} + \frac{1}{9}e^{-5t}$$

Taking the z-transform of $h(t)$, with $T = 0.1$, we obtain

$$H(z) = \frac{z}{z - 1} - \frac{(10/9)z}{z - e^{-0.5T}} + \frac{(1/9)z}{z - e^{-5T}}$$

$$= \frac{0.001471z(z + 0.832682)}{(z - 1)(z - 0.951229)(z - 0.606531)} \qquad (6.125)$$

II. Model using numerical solution of the differential equation

With the transformation shown in equation 6.109 here we replace s by $(1 - z^{-1})/T$ to obtain the discrete-time model. Since $T = 0.1$, we obtain

$$H(z) = \frac{2.5}{10(1 - z^{-1})\left[10(1 - z^{-1}) + 0.5\right]\left[10(1 - z^{-1}) + 5\right]}$$

$$= \frac{0.001587z^3}{(z - 1)(z - 0.952381)(z - 0.666667)} \qquad (6.126)$$

III. Model using bilinear transformation

Here, according to equation 6.117, we make the following substitution in $G(s)$ to obtain $H(z)$:

$$s = \frac{2}{T}\frac{z - 1}{z + 1} = \frac{20(z - 1)}{z + 1}$$

The resulting discrete-time transfer function is given by

$$H(z) = \frac{0.000244(z + 1)^3}{(z - 1)(z - 0.95122)(z - 0.6)} \qquad (6.127)$$

∎

It is instructive to compare the three equivalent discrete-time models obtained above. By looking at the denominators of equations 6.125, 6.126, and 6.127, we notice that all of these transfer functions have three poles, with one at $z = 1$, which corresponds to the pole at the origin of the s-plane in $G(s)$. The other two poles of the three transfer functions are close but not identical. Finally, the numerators of the three equivalent transfer functions are quite different. It may also be noted that the first method required a little more computation, since the residues at the poles of $G(s)$ had to be evaluated. Whereas, in general, the choice of the equivalent model depends on the application as well as the type of inputs to be applied to the system, in this case the impulse invariant transformation will be most suitable. This will be demonstrated in Chapter 7 by using the frequency response of the system considered in Example 6.18.

All of these transformations will be discussed further in Chapter 9, in connection with the design of digital filters.

6.8 SUMMARY

In this chapter we have studied the theory of z-transforms, which play the same role in the analysis of discrete-time systems as that played by Laplace transforms in the analysis of continuous-time systems. It was seen that the z-transform is closely related to both Fourier and Laplace transforms, and the mapping between the s-plane and the z-plane was studied. Although, in general, one can obtain z-transforms for sequences that are causal as well as noncausal, the former lead to single-sided or unilateral z-transforms. The theory of single-sided z-transforms was studied in detail, and it was seen that z-transforms can be applied to the solution of linear difference equations with constant coefficients with much less effort than is required with the classical method. Concepts of transfer functions, poles and zeros, stability, and frequency response with z-transforms were studied and found to be similar to those for Laplace transforms. The essential difference, that a discrete-time system is stable if and only if all of its poles are inside the unit circle of the z-plane, was seen to be a consequence of the relationship between the variables s and z, which caused the left half of the s-plane to be mapped into the region inside the unit circle of the z-plane. Furthermore, this led to the mapping of the $j\omega$-axis of the s-plane onto the unit circle of the z-plane, which caused the frequency response to repeat itself every time one went around the unit circle, with Ω increasing from $2k\pi$ to $2(k + 1)\pi$, where k is any integer.

In most engineering problems, it is possible to select the time origin in such a manner that one may deal with only causal functions. Consequently, the theory of single-sided z-transforms meets most of our needs. In some instances, however, it is necessary to use bilateral z-transforms. For example, for systems subject to random inputs, one must obtain z-transforms of the autocorrelation sequences of these inputs, which are noncausal. It was seen that the procedure for inverting bilateral z-transforms is only slightly more complicated than that for inverting unilateral z-transforms. The only important difference is that the region of convergence must be known in order to be able to determine whether a particular pole will give rise to a casual or anticausal sequence. This is essential so that the inverse z-transform can be determined uniquely.

The chapter concluded with a brief discussion of three most commonly used methods for transformation between continuous-time and discrete-time systems. These methods are particularly important in the areas of digital control as well as digital filtering, since it is often more convenient to implement a continuous-time system with an equivalent discrete-time system. The availability of inexpensive microprocessors and other digital hardware has made this approach quite attractive. These methods will be studied further in Chapter 9 in connection with the design of digital filters.

6.9   PROBLEMS

6.1   Determine the z-transforms of the following causal sequences. In each case, specify the region of convergence.
(a) $x(n) = n^3(0.5)^n$
(b) $x(n) = 6(0.6)^n - 3(1.5)^n \cos 0.5n$
(c) $x(n) = 10 \cos \left(\frac{n\pi}{4} + \frac{\pi}{4} \right)$
(d) $x(n) = 10(2)^n \cos \left(\frac{n\pi}{4} + \frac{\pi}{4} \right)$
(e) $x(n) = (n + 1)^2$
(f) $x(n) = n(n - 1)$

6.2   Determine the inverse of the following z-transforms. The resulting sequences are known to be causal.
(a) $X(z) = \dfrac{2z^2 + 3z}{(z - 1)(z - 0.5)}$
(b) $X(z) = \dfrac{z^3 + 7z^2 - 3z}{(z - 2)(z - 0.5)(z - 1)}$
(c) $X(z) = \dfrac{z^3 + 5z^2 - 7z}{(z - 1)(z^2 - 1.2z + 0.8)}$
(d) $X(z) = \dfrac{z^3 + 5z^2 - 7z}{(z - 1)(z^2 + 1)}$

(e) $X(z) = \dfrac{2z}{z^2 + 1} + \dfrac{2z}{z^2 - 1}$

(f) $X(z) = \dfrac{z^2}{z^2 + 1} + \dfrac{z}{z^2 - 1}$

6.3 Obtain the complete solution of each of the difference equations given below, with initial conditions as specified.

(a) $y(n) + 6y(n - 1) + 8y(n - 2) = 9,$ $y(0) = 2,$ $y(1) = 5$

(b) $y(n) + 6y(n - 1) + 9y(n - 2) = 3(2)^n,$ $y(0) = 0,$ $y(1) = 4$

(c) $y(n) + 6y(n - 1) + 13y(n - 2) = 4\sin(2n),$ $y(0) = 5,$
 $y(1) = 3$

(d) $y(n) - 1.3y(n - 1) + 0.65y(n - 2) - 0.5y(n - 3) =$
 $3(0.4)^n \sin 0.5n$ $y(0) = 1,$ $y(1) = 2,$ $y(2) = -2$

6.4 Obtain the complete solution for the difference equation

$$y(n) + 8y(n - 1) + 80y(n - 2) = u(n) + 3u(n - 1)$$

given the initial conditions $y(0) = 1$, $y(1) = 2$, for the following input sequences.

(a) $u(n) = 3\cos\left(\dfrac{n\pi}{3}\right)$

(b) $u(n) = 4e^{-2n}$

(c) $u(n) = 2ne^{-3n}$

6.5 Repeat Problem 6.4 for the following difference equation for the same inputs and initial conditions:

$$y(n) + 6y(n - 1) + 9y(n - 2) = u(n) + 3u(n - 1)$$

6.6 The z-transform of a causal sequence $x(n)$ is given below.

$$X(z) = \frac{3z}{4z^2 - 2z + 1}$$

Determine the z-transform of $y(n)$ if it is given by

(a) $y(n) = x(n - 1)\gamma(n - 1)$

(b) $y(n) = e^{-2n}x(n)$

(c) $y(n) = nx(n)$

(d) $y(n) = 2x(n) - 3x(n - 1) + 4x(n - 2)$

(e) $y(n) = x(n)\cos 0.5n$

(f) $y(n) = n^2 x(n)$

6.7 The impulse response sequence of a discrete-time system is given by

$$h(n) = 2(0.6)^n \cos(0.4n)$$

(a) Determine the transfer function of the system.

(b) Determine the response of the system to each of the following inputs:

(i) $u(n) = 1$

(ii) $u(n) = 3e^{-2n}$

6.8   Repeat Problem 6.7 for the following impulse response sequence:

$$h(n) = 3(0.8)^n \cos 0.5n + 2n(0.3)^n$$

6.9   The transfer function of a discrete-time systems is given below.

$$H(z) = \frac{2z^3 - 3z^2 + 4z}{z^3 - 1.5z^2 + 0.97z - 0.287}$$

(a)   Is this system stable?
(b)   Determine the steady-state response of this system to the input

$$u(n) = 3 + 4\cos 2n + 7\sin\left(3n + \frac{\pi}{3}\right)$$

6.10   Determine the complete response of the system described in the previous problem to the input sequence given below, assuming that the initial conditions are zero.

$$u(n) = 3 + 4(0.5)^n$$

6.11   Determine the initial value of each of the sequences corresponding to the z-transforms given in Problem 6.2. Use the initial value theorem.

6.12   Determine the initial and final values (where applicable) of each of the sequences corresponding to the z-transforms given below. Assume causality.

(a) $X(z) = \dfrac{30z^4 + 21z^3 + 13z^2 + 15z}{(z - 0.5)(z - 0.4)(z^2 - 1.4z + 0.65)}$

(b) $X(z) = \dfrac{2z^3 - 4z^2 + 5z}{(z - 1)(z^2 - 1.2z + 0.6)}$

(c) $X(z) = \dfrac{3z^2 + 5z + 7}{(z - 1)^2(z^2 - 1.2z + 0.8)}$

(d) $X(z) = \dfrac{4z^3 + 3z^2 + 2z}{(z^2 - 0.6z + 1)(z - 0.5)}$

(e) $X(z) = \dfrac{20z(z - 0.2)(z - 1.5)}{(z - 1)(z + 1)(z - 0.5)}$

6.13   Determine the z-transform of the convolution of the causal sequences $x(n)$ and $h(n)$ given below.

$$x(n) = 5 + 4\sin 0.5n, \qquad n \geq 0$$

$$h(n) = 10(0.5)^n \cos 2n, \qquad n \geq 0$$

6.14   Repeat Problem 6.13 if $x(n) = 2n + 4(2)^n$.

6.15   A linear discrete-time system is described by the following difference equation:

$$y(n) - y(n - 1) + 0.5y(n - 2) = 2u(n - 1) + 3u(n - 2)$$

(a)   Find the transfer function relating $Y(z)$ to $U(z)$.
(b)   Determine $y(n)$ if $u(n) = 1$.
(c)   Repeat part (b) if $u(n) = 4 \cos 0.2n$.

6.16   The transfer function of the discrete-time model of an attitude control system for a satellite is given by

$$H(z) = \frac{0.046872z + 0.043808}{z^2 - 1.771904z + 0.8625385}$$

Determine the response of this system if the input sequence $u(n) = 1$.

6.17   The transfer function of a digital filter is given by

$$H(z) = \frac{0.333(z^2 - 1.8z + 0.95)}{z^2 - 1.9z + 0.95}$$

Determine the gain and phase shift of this filter for sinusoidal input sequences of the form $e^{j\Omega n}$ for $\Omega = 0, 0.2, 0.5, 1$, and 2.

6.18   What will be the steady-state response of the digital filter described in Problem 6.17 if the input sequence is given by $u(n) = 1 + 2 \cos(0.2n) - 3.5 \sin(0.5n)$?

6.19   Repeat Problem 6.18 if the input sequence is given by $u(n) = n + 2 + 3 \cos n$.

6.20   The transfer functions of four discrete-time systems are given below. Determine which of these systems are causal.

(a) $\dfrac{12(z - 1)^2}{z(z - 0.5)}$ (b) $\dfrac{10(z - 1)^2}{z - 0.5}$

(c) $\dfrac{20(z - 0.25)^5}{(z - 0.6)^6}$ (d) $\dfrac{30(z - 0.25)^6}{(z - 0.6)^5}$

6.21   The transfer function of a causal discrete-time system is given by

$$H(z) = \frac{z - a^{-1}}{z - a}$$

(a)   Determine the range of values of a for which the system will be stable.
(b)   If $0 < a < 1$, show graphically, by using the pole–zero plot in the z-plane, that the transfer function $H(z)$ represents an "all-pass" system, that is, the magnitude of the frequency response is constant for all values of Ω.
(c)   What will be the magnitude of the frequency response for the case when $a = 0.5$?

6.22 The transfer function of a discrete-time control system is given by

$$G(z) = \frac{4z(z+1)(z-0.8)}{(z+0.6)(z^2 - 0.4z + 0.4)}$$

(a) Determine the complete response of the system when the input sequence is given by $u(n) = 1$, assuming zero initial conditions.
(b) Determine the frequency response of this system for Ω equal to 0, 0.5, $\pi/3$, and $\pi/2$.

6.23 Find the z-transform of the noncausal function

$$x(n) = 4e^{-0.2|n|} \cos 0.3n, \quad -\infty < n < \infty$$

6.24 The z-transform of the autocorrelation sequence of a random signal is

$$X(z) = \frac{-0.45z}{z^2 - 2.5z + 1}$$

Determine the autocorrelation sequence $x(n)$. The region of convergence is an annular ring around the unit circle in the z-plane.

6.25 Evaluate the inverse of the following z-transforms.

(a) $X(z) = \dfrac{2z^2}{(z-0.5)(z-0.2)}, \quad |z| < 0.2$

(b) $X(z) = \dfrac{2z^2}{(z-0.5)(z-0.2)}, \quad 0.2 < |z| < 0.5$

(c) $X(z) = \dfrac{2z^2}{(z-0.5)(z-0.2)}, \quad 0.5 < |z|$

6.26 A popular method for numerical integration is the trapezoidal rule, where the integral of a function is approximated as the area under trapezoids. Thus, if $y(t)$ represents the integral of $x(t)$, then we get the following difference equation:

$$y(k+1) - y(k) = \frac{T[x(k) + x(k+1)]}{2}$$

(a) Determine the transfer function relating $Y(z)$ to $X(z)$.
(b) Show how you would realize this transfer function using an ideal delay. (*Hint:* Refer to realization methods discussed in Chapter 1).

6.27 A discrete-time system will be stable if and only if all of its poles lie inside the unit circle in the z-plane.

(a) Determine the values of the parameters a and b so that all the roots of $(z^2 + az + b)$ will satisfy this condition.
(b) Show the region of stability in the parameter plane (i.e., the plane with a and b as the rectangular coordinates).

6.28 A person started with an initial deposit of $500 and after that makes regular deposits of $200 every month.

    (a) Assuming that the bank pays interest at the rate of 8 percent per annum, compounded every month, use z-transforms to determine an expression for the balance in the account at the end of the kth month, where k is a positive integer.

    (b) Determine the balance in the account at the end of 10 years.

6.29 Repeat the previous problem if the bank pays interest at the rate of 10 percent per annum, compounded monthly.

6.30 The transfer function of a continuous-time system is given below.

$$G(s) = \frac{4}{(s + 0.2)(s + 1)}$$

    (a) Determine an equivalent discrete-time model for the system using all three methods discussed in Section 6.7, assuming that the sampling interval is 0.5 s.

    (b) Determine the response of the continuous-time system to a unit step input and compare the values at the sampling instants with the responses of the three equivalent discrete-time models to a step sequence.

6.31 Repeat the previous problem, with the sampling interval reduced to 0.1 s.

6.32 The transfer function of a third-order continuous-time system is given below. Obtain the transfer functions of equivalent discrete-time systems using the three methods discussed in Section 6.7, assuming that the sampling interval $T = 0.1$ s.

$$G(s) = \frac{1}{(s + 1)(s^2 + s + 1)}$$

(This is called a Butterworth filter, as will be seen in Chapter 9.)

APPENDIX 6.1

Computation of Inverse z-Transforms

The calculation of inverse z-transforms is straightforward if the residues at the various poles are known. This computation proceeds along the same lines as in the case of inverse Laplace transformation. The program on the disk enclosed with the book is based on the same ideas as described in Appendix 5.1.

The program on the disk also allows the user to obtain the inverse z-transform using long division. Although this does not give the sequence in a closed form, the computer can quickly calculate and store the values of the response sequence for a large value of n. These stored values can then be utilized for obtaining an approximate plot of the response.

Frequency Response

7.1 INTRODUCTION

The concept of frequency response was first introduced in Chapter 3 during our study of the decomposition of a periodic function into a Fourier series. We started by noting that if a sinusoidal input is applied to a stable continuous-time system, the resulting steady-state output will be a sinusoid of the same frequency, but generally different from the input in amplitude and phase. Information about the amplitude and phase of the output was obtained by replacing the operator p in the system operator by $j\omega$ and evaluating the resulting complex number, which was then expressed in the polar form as $Me^{j\phi}$. The amplitude of the output sinusoid was M times that of the input, and the output led the input by ϕ rad in phase. This result was then extended to periodic but nonsinusoidal inputs by decomposing them into a Fourier series. The same concept was also found to be applicable to the case where the input was nonperiodic through the use of the Fourier transform, and it was observed that the Fourier transform of the output of the system was the product of the Fourier transform of the input and the "frequency response function" that was obtained by replacing the operator p with $j\omega$ in the system operator. Later, in Chapter 5, the concept of the transfer function was introduced. It was noted that the transfer function of a system could be obtained in three different ways: (1) as the ratio of the Laplace transforms of the output and the input with zero initial conditions, (2) by simply replacing the operator p by the complex frequency variable s in the system operator, and (3) as the Laplace transform of the impulse response of the system. Similar relationships were also observed for discrete-time systems, where the transfer function can be obtained (1) as the ratio of the z-transforms of the output and the input with zero initial conditions, (2) by replacing the operator q by the complex variable z in the system function, and (3) as the z-transform of the impulse response sequence of the system.

In this chapter we shall be concerned mainly with the frequency response aspect of the transfer function. As will be described, the transfer function and the frequency response of a system are uniquely related. In many practical situations, however, we do not know the transfer function of a system, but the frequency response can normally be measured experimen-

309

tally. Although it is theoretically possible to estimate the transfer function from the measurement of the frequency response, sufficient information about the important properties of a system can usually be obtained directly by studying its frequency response. For continuous-time systems, this would require the measurement of both the gain M and the phase-shift ϕ for the entire range of frequencies, that is, for ω varying from 0 to ∞. For discrete-time systems, on the other hand, the frequency response needs to be considered for the digital frequency Ω ranging only between 0 and 2π, as observed in Chapter 6. Since we are concerned with the variation of both M and ϕ with the frequency (ω for continuous-time systems and Ω for discrete-time systems), it is most convenient to present this information in a graphical form.

In the next section we study several different types of frequency response plots that are utilized for the study of continuous-time systems. This will be followed by the study of frequency response plots of discrete-time systems in Section 7.3.

7.2   FREQUENCY RESPONSE OF CONTINUOUS-TIME SYSTEMS

As stated previously, the frequency response of a stable continuous-time system is calculated by replacing s by $j\omega$ in the transfer function and evaluating the resulting expression for different values of ω. Since, in general, $G(j\omega)$ will be a complex number for any given ω, it is expressed in the polar form as $Me^{j\phi}$, where M represents the *gain* or the ratio of the magnitudes of the output and the input, whereas ϕ is the phase shift between them. Thus, we have two dependent variables, M and ϕ, with ω as the independent variable. The frequency response of a continuous-time system is therefore fully specified by the values of M and ϕ over the entire range of frequencies, that is, for ω varying from 0 to ∞. In fact, there is a one-to-one relationship between the transfer function of the system and the corresponding frequency response. In other words, there cannot be two transfer functions with the same frequency response (both M and ϕ) for the entire range of frequencies from 0 to ∞. However, it is possible for two transfer functions to have the same magnitude response for all ω but different phase shifts, since there exists a class of transfer functions that have a constant gain, $M = 1$, but varying ϕ for all ω. These are called *all-pass* functions. For example, consider the transfer function

$$G_a(s) = \frac{s - a}{s + a} \tag{7.1}$$

A pole–zero plot of this transfer function is shown in Figure 7.1. Using the graphical procedure for determining the frequency response from the pole–zero plot, we can see that the gain M will be one for all values of ω.

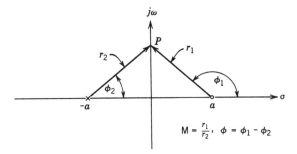

Figure 7.1 Pole–zero plot of transfer function given by equation 7.1.

This follows from the fact that M is equal to the ratio of the length of the vector from the zero to that from the pole, drawn to any point on the $j\omega$-axis, but these lengths are equal owing to the symmetry of the pole–zero plot about the $j\omega$-axis. Evidently, this will hold true for any rational transfer function having a pole–zero plot with this type of symmetry, that is, all the zeros are in the right half of the s-plane and are the mirror images about the $j\omega$-axis of the corresponding poles in the left half of the s-plane.

It may be observed that all the zeros of an all-pass transfer function must be in the right half of the s-plane. Furthermore, the phase shift produced by the transfer function of the type shown in equation 7.1 will vary with ω, but will be positive for all ω. This will hold true for any other all-pass function owing to the property that all its zeros are the mirror images of its poles about the $j\omega$-axis and every such pole–zero pair will produce a positive phase shift. It is also evident that if we multiply an all-pass transfer function, denoted by $G_a(s)$, with any other transfer function $G(s)$, the resulting transfer function, which will be given by $G_a(s)G(s)$, will have exactly the same gain as $G(s)$ for all values of ω, but the phase shifts for the two transfer functions will be different. Thus, we have shown that the transfer function of a system cannot be defined uniquely only from the knowledge of how the gain M varies with the frequency, unless we are certain that it does not include an all-pass transfer function. Since all-pass transfer functions must contain zeros in the right half of the s-plane, the relationship between the gain and the transfer function will be unique if the transfer function is rational and does not contain any zero in the right half of the s-plane. Such transfer functions are said to be of the *minimum-phase* type, since the presence of an all-pass function will increase the phase shift.

Note that thus far we have considered only those transfer functions that are ratios of polynomials of s, that is, rational functions of s. In practice, many physical systems cannot be modeled without an *ideal delay* or *transport lag*, represented by the transfer function $e^{-\beta s}$, where β is the time delay produced in the system. Since the magnitude of $e^{-j\beta\omega}$ will be one for all ω, it follows that an ideal delay will not affect the gain for any frequency, but will increase the phase lag (or reduce the phase shift) with frequency.

It follows from this discussion that both the gain and the phase shift should be considered together in relating the frequency response and the corresponding transfer function. Often, a convenient way to convey all the information contained in the frequency response is to show it graphically. This has led to the development of several different types of frequency response plots. These are discussed in the next section.

7.2.1   TYPES OF FREQUENCY-RESPONSE PLOTS

As pointed out previously, the frequency response of a system contains two dependent variables, the gain M and the phase shift ϕ, with ω as the independent variable. Therefore, it is necessary to represent all of these quantities in any plot. This can be done in several ways. The simplest approach is to have separate plots of M and ϕ versus ω.

The first step in obtaining any frequency response plot is to calculate the values of M and ϕ for different values of ω ranging from 0 to ∞. This is usually rather tedious, unless performed with the help of a computer. Nevertheless, the procedure will be illustrated through the example of a second-order system transfer function.

Example 7.1

Consider the following transfer function:

$$G(s) = \frac{10}{s^2 + 2s + 10} \tag{7.2}$$

Replacing s by $j\omega$, we obtain the frequency response function

$$G(j\omega) = \frac{10}{(j\omega)^2 + 2j\omega + 10} = \frac{10}{(10 - \omega^2) + j2\omega} \tag{7.3}$$

From equation 7.3 the following expressions are obtained for the gain M and the phase shift ϕ.

$$M = \frac{10}{\left[(10 - \omega^2)^2 + 4\omega^2\right]^{0.5}} \tag{7.4}$$

$$\phi = -\tan^{-1}\frac{2\omega}{10 - \omega^2} \tag{7.5}$$

We may now utilize equations 7.4 and 7.5 to calculate M and ϕ for different values of ω. These are shown in Table 7.1, for ω varying in the range 0 to 20. The values of the phase-shift have been converted from radians to degrees.   ∎

It will be seen that the gain increases until ω reaches the value of about 3 and then starts falling rapidly. On the other hand, the phase shift is decreasing for all ω and approaches 180° for large ω.

The reader should be cautioned about the calculation of phase shift using equation 7.5. With most electronic pocket calculators and with comput-

TABLE 7.1 Frequency Response of the Transfer Function in Equation 7.2

ω	0.0	1.0	1.5	2.0	2.5	3.0	3.5	4.0	4.5
M	1.0	1.09	1.2	1.39	1.6	1.64	1.36	1.00	0.73
ϕ	0.0	-12.5	-21.2	-33.7	-53.1	-80.54	-107.82	-126.87	-138.72

ω	5.0	6.0	7.0	8.0	10.0	15.0	20.0
M	0.56	0.35	0.24	0.18	0.11	0.05	0.028
ϕ	-146.31	-155.22	-160.25	-163.50	-167.47	-172.06	-174.14

ers, the value of ϕ will not come out as shown in Table 7.1. The problem is caused by the way the arc tangent is determined in most common calculators. In particular, if we are calculating the value of $\tan^{-1}(y/x)$, where y is the imaginary part of a complex number and x its real part, then for positive y and negative x, the angle ϕ should be in the second quadrant, whereas for negative y and positive x, the angle ϕ should be in the fourth quadrant. A calculator, however, uses the value of the ratio y/x to determine ϕ and, hence, does not differentiate between these two situations. In the same way, when both y and x are negative, the correct value of the angle ϕ should be in the third quadrant, but a calculator will usually put ϕ in the first quadrant in this instance, since the ratio y/x is positive. One way to overcome this difficulty is to use the rectangular-to-polar coordinate conversion function in calculators, as this will ensure the correct value of ϕ. In general, the latter procedure will be more efficient, since M and ϕ can be determined simultaneously by first converting both the numerator and denominator of $G(j\omega)$ into the polar form. The calculation will get very tedious, however, when the transfer function has several poles and zeros.

The frequency response plots for M and ϕ for this example are shown in Figure 7.2.

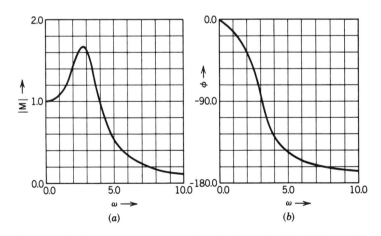

Figure 7.2 Frequency response plots for Example 7.1. (a) Plot of M against ω. (b) Plot of ϕ against ω.

TABLE 7.2 Some Common Decibel Equivalents

M	0.1	0.5	$1/\sqrt{2}$	1	$\sqrt{2}$	2	5	10	20	50	100
$20 \log M$	-20	-6	-3	0	3	6	14	20	26	34	40

It is possible to avoid the drudgery involved in the computation of the frequency response required by the procedure described above. A great deal of simplification is introduced when logarithmic coordinates are used for the gain as well as the frequency. The plots obtained in this manner are called *Bode* plots, honoring H. W. Bode, who used them in the study of feedback amplifiers. These are discussed in the next section.

7.2.2 BODE PLOTS

The reader is perhaps aware that logarithms were introduced by John Napier, a Scottish mathematician, in 1614, as an efficient means of computation for his pursuits in astronomy. The main advantage of logarithms is to replace the multiplication of two numbers by the addition of their logarithms, followed by looking up the antilogarithm of this sum to obtain the desired product. Similarly, division of one number by another is replaced by the process of subtracting the logarithm of the divisor by the dividend, followed by obtaining the antilogarithm. In Bode plots, the same idea is exploited in determining the frequency response of a transfer function that has many factors in the numerator and the denominator by using $20 \log M$ instead of M in the plot. The quantity $20 \log M$ is usually called the gain in decibels, denoted by the symbol dB. It is evident that the overall gain in dB will be the algebraic sum of the gain in dB due to the various factors. Table 7.2 gives some of the most common decibel equivalents for different values of M.

It will be observed that the logarithmic scale is highly nonlinear. This makes it possible to cover a much larger range of gains with greater clarity. As will be seen later, some additional advantages are obtained from the use of the logarithmic scale for the frequency as well.

Bode plots require the use of semilogarithmic graph paper, having a logarithmic scale along the horizontal or x-axis and a linear scale along the vertical or y-axis. Some interesting properties of the logarithmic scale should be noted. First, the scale is nonlinear, as will be seen from the fact that the distance between 1 and 2 is greater than that between 2 and 3. Furthermore, the distance between 1 and 2 is equal to that between 2 and 4 or between 4 and 8. This distance is called an *octave*, which means doubling the frequency. In general, the distance between k and $2k$ will be equal to this value for any k that is positive and nonzero. This follows from the fact that

$$\log 2k - \log k = \log 2 \qquad (7.6)$$

which is a constant. Another important feature is that semilog graph paper comes in one or more cycles. This indicates the range of coverage along the

x-axis. For instance, a three-cycle semilog paper will cover the range in three powers of 10, for example, from 1 to 1000, or 0.1 to 100. Again, it is easily observed that the distance between k and $10k$ is a constant and equal to $\log 10$ for any $k > 0$. This distance is called a *decade* and implies multiplication by a factor of 10. The x-axis of a three-cycle semilog paper will have a length of three decades. It should also be noted that the value zero cannot be located on the x-axis of the semilog graph paper. This follows from the fact that $\log 0 = -\infty$.

One important reason for the popularity of Bode plots is that by using them it is possible to obtain a good approximation to the gain curve without actually calculating the frequency response. As will be shown now, due to the use of logarithmic coordinates, the gain curve (with the gain expressed in decibels) can be approximated by straight-line segments with slopes given by $6n$ dB per octave (or, equivalently, $20n$ dB per decade), where n is an integer.

7.2.2.1 Gain Curves for Linear Factors

Consider the simple first-order transfer function given by

$$G(s) = 1 + \frac{s}{a} \tag{7.7}$$

In this case we have just one zero of the transfer function located at $s = a$. Replacing s by $j\omega$ in equation 7.7, the following expression is obtained for the gain M; which is the magnitude of the complex quantity $[1 + (j\omega/a)]$.

$$M = \sqrt{\left[1 + \frac{\omega^2}{a^2}\right]}$$

Taking the logarithm of both sides and multiplying by 20, we get

$$20 \log M = 10 \log \left[1 + \frac{\omega^2}{a^2}\right] \tag{7.8}$$

Let us now investigate the value of the right-hand side of equation 7.8 for frequencies far away from $\omega = a$. We first consider the case when $\omega \ll a$. For such values of ω, the expression within the parentheses can be considered nearly equal to one, with the result that the right-hand side of equation 7.8 may approximated as

$$20 \log M \approx 10 \log 1 = 0 \tag{7.9}$$

On the other hand, if $\omega \gg a$, we get the approximation

$$20 \log M \approx 20 \log \frac{\omega}{a} \tag{7.10}$$

Note that in the last expression we have used the relationship that the logarithm of the square of a number is two times the logarithm of that number.

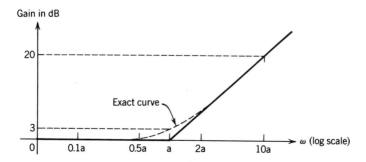

Figure 7.3 Gain curve for $G(s) = 1 + (s/a)$.

Note that both equations 7.9 and 7.10 represent straight lines on a semilog graph paper, where the gain in decibels is plotted along the vertical axis (which is linear) and the frequency is along the horizontal axis (which uses the logarithmic scale). It is evident that equation 7.9 defines a straight line of zero slope coinciding with the 0 dB line on the graph. Equation 7.10 represents a straight line of slope 6 dB per octave, or 20 dB per decade. This follows easily by noting that for $\omega = a$, the right-hand side of equation 7.10 will be 0, whereas for $\omega = 2a$, it will be equal to $20 \log 2$, or 6 dB. Similarly, for $\omega = 10a$, the right-hand side of equation 7.10 will be $20 \log 10$, or 20 dB. Therefore, we see that the plot of the gain in decibels against frequency on logarithmic scale is asymptotic to the two straight lines, one coinciding with the 0 dB line and the other with slope equal to 6 dB per octave or, equivalently, 20 db per decade. The two straight lines will intersect at the point where the gain is 0 dB and $\omega = a$. Accordingly, it is customary to call a the *corner* or *break* frequency.

We are now ready to investigate the value of the right-hand side of equation 7.8 for cases where ω is near a. First let us consider the case when ω is equal to a. Substituting this value in equation 7.8, it is seen that $20 \log M$ will now be equal to $20 \log \sqrt{2}$, or 3 dB. Similarly, if we set $\omega = 0.5a$, the gain will be approximately 1 dB, whereas for $\omega = 2a$ the gain will be about 7 dB, as can be easily verified by substituting these values in equation 7.8. The straight-line approximation and the actual gain curve is shown in Figure 7.3. As will be seen, the maximum deviation between the two occurs at $\omega = a$ and is equal to 3 dB.

The concepts presented in the foregoing discussion can be easily extended to obtain the straight-line approximation to the gain curve of a transfer function that contains several linear terms both in the numerator and the denominator. First we consider the case when the transfer function is the reciprocal of that given in equation 7.2:

$$G(s) = \frac{1}{1 + (s/a)} \tag{7.11}$$

Replacing s by $j\omega$ and expressing the gain in dB, we easily obtain

$$20 \log M = -10 \log \left[1 + \frac{\omega^2}{a^2} \right] \tag{7.12}$$

which is seen to be the negative of the right-hand side of equation 7.8. Consequently, it can be approximated by two straight-line segments, similar to the approximation shown in Figure 7.3, with the exception that for $\omega > a$, the slope of the straight line asymptotic to the curve will be negative instead of positive, that is, it will be -6 dB per octave. This is the direct result of using the logarithmic gain in our plot. The extension to the more general case of several factors in the transfer function will be illustrated by the following examples.

Example 7.2

Consider the transfer function

$$G(s) = \frac{400(s + 15)}{(s + 2)(s + 50)} \tag{7.13}$$

Our first step will be to rearrange equation 7.13 so that the constant term in each factor is one. This gives us

$$G(s) = \frac{60[1 + (s/15)]}{[1 + (s/2)][1 + (s/50)]} \tag{7.14}$$

Replacing s by $j\omega$ and expressing the gain in decibels, we obtain

$$20 \log M = 20 \log 60 + 10 \log \left(1 + \left(\frac{\omega}{15} \right)^2 \right)$$

$$- 10 \log \left(1 + \left(\frac{\omega}{2} \right)^2 \right) - 10 \log \left(1 + \left(\frac{\omega}{50} \right)^2 \right) \tag{7.15}$$

It follows from equation 7.15 that the total gain in decibels can be obtained as an algebraic sum of the gains due to each factor of $G(s)$ in equation 7.14, where a negative sign is attached to each of the factors in the denominator. An asymptotic plot for each factor in equation 7.15 is shown in Figure 7.4. The overall gain, obtained by adding them graphically, is shown in figure 7.5.

The graphical summation can be carried out directly if we recognize that each factor of the form $[1 + (s/a)]$ affects the asymptotic plot of the gain only for $\omega > a$, since the approximate gain for $\omega < a$ is zero, as is evident

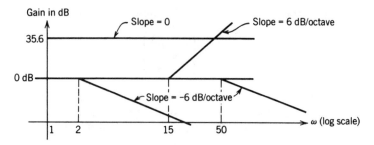

Figure 7.4 Gain curves for different factors in equation 7.15.

from Figure 7.3. Thus, for ω less than the lowest corner frequency, we need only consider the gain contributed by the constant term ($20 \log 60$, or 35.6 dB, in this instance). As ω is increased, we simply change the slope at each of the corner frequencies. If a corner frequency represents a pole, the slope is to be decreased by 6 dB per octave. On the other hand, if it represents a zero, the slope must be increased by 6 dB per octave.

To draw this plot, we start with a horizontal line (of slope 0) and height 35.6 dB, corresponding to the constant term. Proceeding toward the right, we meet the corner frequency at 2, which corresponds to a pole. The slope at this point is therefore reduced by 6 dB per octave, so that the resulting slope is -6 dB per octave. Proceeding toward the right, the next corner frequency occurs at 15, which corresponds to a zero. Accordingly, the slope must be increased by 6 dB per octave at $\omega = 15$, so that we now have a net slope of 0. The last corner frequency occurs at 50, which corresponds to another pole of the transfer function. The slope of the asymptote to the right of $\omega = 50$ is therefore reduced by 6 dB per octave, giving a net slope of -6 dB per octave. The asymptotic plot of the gain obtained in this manner is shown in Figure 7.5. For comparison, the actual gain is shown by a dotted curve. As expected, it almost coincides with the asymptotes, except near the break frequencies.

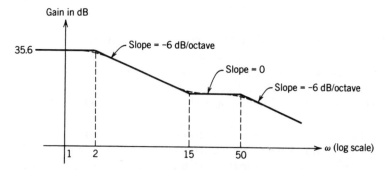

Figure 7.5 Gain curve for transfer function in equation 7.13.

Example 7.3

Consider the following transfer function:

$$G(s) = \frac{2000(s + 4)}{s(s + 10)(s + 100)} \qquad (7.16)$$

As in the previous example, we start by rearranging equation 7.16 so that the constant term in each factor is made equal to 1. This gives us

$$G(s) = \frac{8[1 + (s/4)]}{s[1 + (s/10)][1 + (s/100)]} \qquad (7.17)$$

This transfer function has corner frequencies at 0, 4, 10, and 100. Since the lowest corner frequency is at 0, which cannot be found on semilog graph paper, we start by drawing the straight line showing the gain for the term $8/\omega$. Evidently, the plot for this part of the transfer function will simply be a straight line of slope -6 dB per octave. To be able to draw the straight line, we need the coordinates of one point on it, since the slope is already known. This is done easily by replacing ω by any value less than or equal to 4, the next corner frequency, and calculating the gain, $20 \log(8/\omega)$, for this value of ω. Selecting the value of 4, we get the gain as 6 dB at this point. At $\omega = 4$, the slope will increase by 6 dB per octave, bringing the net slope to the value of 0 dB per octave, since we have a zero at this corner frequency. The other corner frequencies (at 10 and 100) correspond to poles. The slope at each of these will, therefore, decrease by 6 dB per octave. The resulting asymptotic plot for the gain is shown in Figure 7.6. The actual gain is also shown as a dotted curve. ■

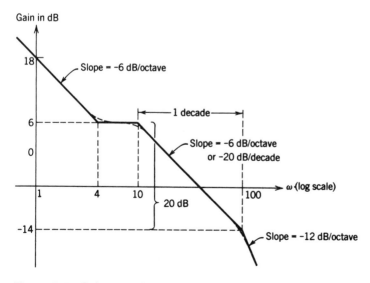

Figure 7.6   Gain curve for transfer function in equation 7.17.

7.2.2.2 Gain Curves for Quadratic Factors

The transfer functions that we have considered in Examples 7.2 and 7.3 have only real poles and zeros, with the result that each of the factors is a polynomial of the first degree. In the more general case, we may have some complex poles and zeros as well. Consequently, we may have both linear and quadratic factors in the numerator and the denominator of the transfer function. The latter can be expressed in the form $(s^2 + 2\zeta\omega_n s + \omega_n^2)$, where $0 < \zeta < 1$, for complex roots. The term ζ is called the damping ratio of the factor, and ω_n is called the undamped natural frequency. Note that for $\zeta \geq 1$, the quadratic has real roots. Let us consider (for $\zeta < 1$)

$$G(s) = 1 + 2\zeta\frac{s}{\omega_n} + \frac{s^2}{\omega_n^2} \qquad (7.18)$$

Note that the transfer function has been normalized to obtain the constant term equal to 1. If we now replace s by $j\omega$, the gain in decibels may be written as

$$20\log M = 10\log\left[\left(1 - \frac{\omega^2}{\omega_n^2}\right)^2 + \left(2\zeta\frac{\omega}{\omega_n}\right)^2\right] \qquad (7.19)$$

We again study the asymptotic behavior of the right-hand side of equation 7.19 for the two cases, $\omega/\omega_n \ll 1$ and $\omega/\omega_n \gg 1$. For the former, we get

$$20\log M \approx 0 \qquad (7.20)$$

while for the latter we get

$$20\log M \approx 40\log\left(\frac{\omega}{\omega_n}\right) \qquad (7.21)$$

It will be seen that equation 7.20 represents a straight line of zero slope, coinciding with the 0 dB line. On the other hand, equation 7.21 represents a straight line with slope 12 db per octave or 40 dB per decade. As for the case of linear factors, these two straight lines will intersect at the point where the gain is 0 dB and $\omega = \omega_n$.

We now investigate the behavior near $\omega = \omega_n$. Setting $\omega = \omega_n$ in equation 7.19, we obtain

$$20\log M = 20\log 2\zeta \qquad (7.22)$$

Thus, the difference between the asymptotes and the exact curve at the break frequency ω_n for the quadratic factor will depend on the value of ζ, the damping ratio of the pair of complex roots of equation 7.18. This is illustrated in Figure 7.7, which shows the straight-line asymptotes as well as the exact gain curve for the transfer function of equation 7.18 for different values of ζ. In particular, it should be noted that the right-hand side of

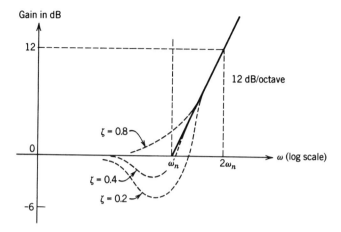

Figure 7.7 Gain plot for quadratic factor in equation 7.18.

equation 7.22 will be negative for $\zeta < 0.5$. Recall that $0 < \zeta < 1$, for the quadratic to have complex roots; otherwise, it has two real roots.

By differentiating equation 7.19 with respect to ω and setting the result to zero, it can be shown that the exact curve has a minimum for

$$\omega = \omega_n \sqrt{(1 - 2\zeta^2)} \qquad (7.23)$$

It follows from equation 7.23 that the minimum can occur only if $\zeta < 1/\sqrt{2}$. Substituting the value of ω from equation 7.23 into equation 7.19, the minimum value of the gain (for $\zeta < 1/\sqrt{2}$), is found to be

$$20 \log M = 20 \log 2\zeta \sqrt{(1 - \zeta^2)} \qquad (7.24)$$

We shall now show some examples of transfer functions containing both real and complex poles and zeros.

Example 7.4

Consider the transfer function

$$G(s) = \frac{500(s + 4)}{s(s^2 + 8s + 100)} \qquad (7.25)$$

Our first step is to rearrange the transfer function to bring it to the standard form with the constant term in each factor made equal to one. This gives us

$$G(s) = \frac{20[1 + (s/4)]}{s\left[1 + (2 \times 0.4)(s/10) + (s/10)^2\right]} \qquad (7.26)$$

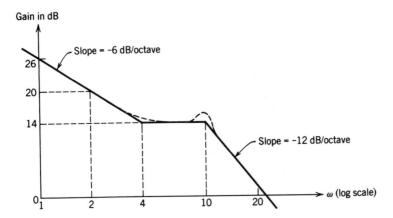

Figure 7.8 Gain curve for transfer function in equation 7.26.

From equation 7.26 we observe that the quadratic term does have complex roots with $\zeta = 0.4$ and undamped natural frequency $\omega_n = 10$. Thus, the corner frequencies are located at $\omega = 0$, 4, and 10. The asymptotic plot will, therefore, have an initial slope of -6 dB per octave, corresponding to the factor $20/\omega$. One point on this line can be obtained by evaluating the dB gain $20 \log(20/\omega)$ for any value of ω below the lowest corner frequency located at 4. For example, if we set $\omega = 2$, this value is obtained as 20 dB. Proceeding to the right, the zero at $s = -4$ will cause the slope to become zero at $\omega = 4$. Finally, the effect of the quadratic factor will be to make the slope -12 dB per octave for $\omega > 10$. The asymptotic plot of the gain, along with the actual curve, is shown in Figure 7.8. ∎

Example 7.5

Consider the following transfer function

$$G(s) = \frac{40s(s^2 + 4s + 25)}{(s + 0.5)(s^2 + 10s + 400)} \tag{7.27}$$

which can be rearranged as

$$G(s) = \frac{5s\left[1 + (2 \times 0.4)(s/5) + (s/5)^2\right]}{\left[1 + (s/0.5)\right]\left[1 + (2 \times 0.25)(s/20) + (s/20)^2\right]} \tag{7.28}$$

From equation 7.28 we see that we have one quadratic in the numerator with complex roots and damping ratio 0.4 and another quadratic in the denominator with complex roots having the damping ratio 0.25. Since there is a zero at the origin of the s-plane, the initial part of the asymptotic plot will be a straight line of slope 6 dB per octave. The various corner frequencies are located at 0.5, 5, and 20. The plot of the gain is shown in Figure 7.9. ∎

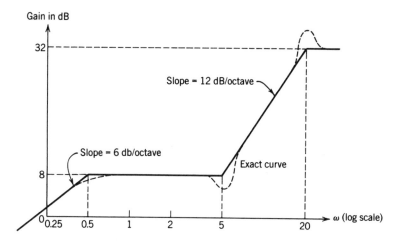

Figure 7.9   Gain curve for transfer function in equation 7.28.

These examples show that the asymptotic plots for the gain of any transfer function can be conveniently obtained if it is expressed in the factored form. The actual plots differ from the asymptotic plots slightly near the corner frequencies, but in most instances (especially for linear factors) it is possible to introduce corrections at these points to obtain a reasonable approximation. We now study similar approximations to the plot of the phase shift with frequency.

7.2.2.3   Phase Plots

For a transfer function expressed in a factored form, the phase shift at any frequency can be expressed as the algebraic sum of the phase shifts produced by the various factors, in a manner similar to that used for obtaining the plot of the gain curve. To illustrate the procedure in detail, we consider the following transfer function, which contains both linear and quadratic factors.

$$G(s) = \frac{K(s + a)}{s(s + b)(s^2 + 2\zeta\omega_n s + \omega_n^2)} \qquad (7.29)$$

The phase shift produced at any frequency ω is obtained by adding the arguments of the various factors in the numerator and subtracting from this sum the arguments of the various factors in the denominator. Hence,

$$\phi = \arg G(j\omega)$$

$$= \arg(K) + \arg(j\omega + a) - \arg(j\omega) - \arg(j\omega + b)$$

$$\quad - \arg(-\omega^2 + j2\zeta\omega_n\omega + \omega_n^2)$$

$$= 0 + \tan^{-1}\frac{\omega}{a} - \frac{\pi}{2} - \tan^{-1}\frac{\omega}{b} - \tan^{-1}\frac{2\zeta\omega_n\omega}{\omega_n^2 - \omega^2} \qquad (7.30)$$

As was seen when we discussed the logarithmic gain, it is possible to obtain straight-line approximations to the phase shifts produced by linear as well as quadratic factors, if a logarithmic scale is used for the frequency and a linear scale is used for the phase shift. Let us first examine the linear factor for which the phase shift is given by

$$\phi = \tan^{-1} \frac{\omega}{a} \qquad (7.31)$$

For asymptotic approximation, we consider the two cases when $\omega/a \ll 1$ and $\omega/a \gg 1$. It is easily seen that for the former

$$\phi \approx 0 \qquad (7.32)$$

whereas for the latter

$$\phi \approx \frac{\pi}{2}, \qquad \text{or } 90° \qquad (7.33)$$

For $\omega = a$, the phase shift is given by

$$\phi = \frac{\pi}{4}, \qquad \text{or } 45° \qquad (7.34)$$

These three equations suggest that the phase shift for this linear factor can be approximated by three straight-line segments, as illustrated in Figure 7.10, where the actual curve is shown dotted. The maximum deviation between the straight-line approximation and the actual curve occurs at the two corners, $0.1a$ and $10a$ (one decade above and below the break frequency), and is equal to $\tan^{-1} 0.1$, or about 5.7°. Furthermore, the straight-line approximation between the frequencies $0.1a$ and $10a$ has a slope of 45° per decade.

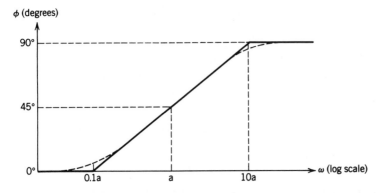

Figure 7.10 Plot of $\arg(j\omega + a)$.

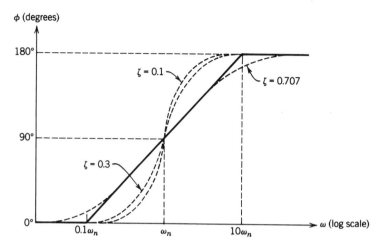

Figure 7.11   Plot of $\arg(-\omega + j2\zeta\omega_n\omega + \omega_n^2)$.

We now look at the quadratic term in equation 7.29. The phase shift produced by this term is given by

$$\phi = \tan^{-1}\frac{2\zeta\omega_n\omega}{\omega_n^2 - \omega^2} = \tan^{-1}\frac{2\zeta(\omega/\omega_n)}{1 - (\omega/\omega_n)^2} \qquad (7.35)$$

It is evident from equation 7.35 that for $\omega \ll \omega_n$,

$$\phi \approx 0 \qquad (7.36)$$

and for $\omega \gg \omega_n$,

$$\phi \approx \pi, \quad \text{or } 180° \qquad (7.37)$$

At $\omega = \omega_n$ the denominator of equation 7.35 becomes zero with the result that for this case $\tan \phi = \infty$, or

$$\phi = \frac{\pi}{2}, \quad \text{or } 90° \qquad (7.38)$$

The plot for the asymptotic approximation of the phase shift for a quadratic factor is shown in Figure 7.11. For comparison, the exact curves for different values of ζ are also shown. The straight-line approximation between $0.1\omega_n$ and $10\omega_n$ has a slope of 90° per decade. The deviation between the actual curves and the straight-line approximation depends on the value of ζ. At the two corners, $0.1\omega_n$ and $10\omega_n$, the maximum error will be 11.4° for the case when $\zeta = 1$. Note that for small ζ, the error in the portion between $0.1\omega_n$, and $10\omega_n$ may be larger. Also, the phase shift changes very rapidly near $\omega = \omega_n$ for small values of ζ.

The total phase shift for a given transfer function can therefore be approximated as the algebraic sum of the straight-line approximations due to each of the factors of the transfer function. This addition, however, is not as simple as in the case of the gain plot since these approximations consist of *three straight-line segments over two decades of frequency*, centered around the undamped natural frequency ω_n. An exception is the circumstance when the various poles and zeros are more than two decades apart. For the general case it may often be easier to make a table of phase shift against frequency for each of the factors and then obtain the total phase shift as the algebraic sum. Better accuracy can be obtained, especially with quadratic factors, by using exact values in the table instead of those obtained from the straight-line approximations. The procedure will be illustrated through some examples.

Example 7.6

Consider the transfer function given below.

$$G(s) = \frac{50s}{s + 10} \tag{7.39}$$

Here, we have one zero at the origin of the s-plane and a pole at $s = -10$. Since these are more than two decades apart, their effects are easily added to obtain the total phase shift. In particular, the zero at the origin produces a phase lead of 90° at all frequencies, whereas the pole at $s = -10$ will cause a phase lag that can be represented approximately by three straight-line segments as shown in Figure 7.10, where we have $a = 10$. The resulting plot of the phase shift, obtained from the algebraic sum of the phase shifts due to each of the two factors, is shown in Figure 7.12. For comparison, the exact curve is also shown by a dashed line. In this case, the maximum error between the exact and approximate plots will be 5.7°, as pointed out earlier in this section. ∎

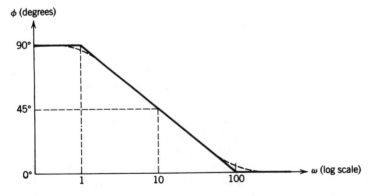

Figure 7.12 Phase shift for transfer function in equation 7.37.

Example 7.7

Consider the following transfer function.

$$G(s) = \frac{400(s + 4)}{s(s^2 + 4s + 25)} \qquad (7.40)$$

This transfer function has a pole at the origin, a zero at $s = -4$, and complex conjugate poles with undamped natural frequency 5 and damping ratio 0.4. Since the zero is rather close to the complex poles and the damping ratio of the latter is smaller than 0.5, it will be preferable to add the phase shifts produced by the different factors of the transfer function to obtain the total phase shift. Let the phase shift produced by the pole at the origin be denoted by ϕ_1, that by the zero at $s = -4$ by ϕ_2, and that by the pair of complex conjugate poles by ϕ_3. Then for each of these, we obtain the following equations:

$$\phi_1 = -90° \qquad (7.41)$$

$$\phi_2 = \tan^{-1}\left(\frac{\omega}{4}\right) \qquad (7.42)$$

and

$$\phi_3 = -\tan^{-1}\frac{4\omega}{25 - \omega^2} \qquad (7.43)$$

The total phase shift ϕ for the complete transfer function is obtained as

$$\phi = \phi_1 + \phi_2 + \phi_3 \qquad (7.44)$$

The phase shifts produced by each of these terms and the total phase shift for different values of ω are shown in Table 7.3.

A plot of the total phase shift, against ω on logarithmic scale, is shown in Figure 7.13. ■

It would appear from the foregoing example that the Bode plot of the phase shift requires much more effort than that of the gain. Note, however, that the straight-line approximation can still be used at very low frequencies as well as at very high frequencies. These are fairly accurate if they are, at

TABLE 7.3 Phase Shift Due to Different Factors

ω	0.1	0.2	0.5	1.0	2.0	3.0	5.0	10.0	20.0
$\phi_1(°)$	−90.0	−90.0	−90.0	−90.0	−90.0	−90.0	−90.0	−90.0	−90.0
$\phi_2(°)$	1.4	2.9	7.1	14.0	26.6	36.9	51.3	68.2	78.7
$\phi_3(°)$	−0.9	−1.8	−4.6	−9.5	−20.9	−36.9	−90.0	−151.9	−168.0
$\phi(°)$	−89.5	−88.9	−87.5	−85.5	−84.3	−90.0	−128.7	−173.7	−179.3

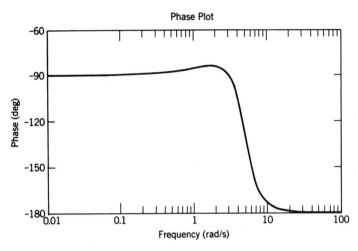

Figure 7.13 Plot of phase shift for transfer function in equation 7.40.

least, one decade away from all the break frequencies. The particular case of poles or zeros at the origin of the s-plane does not cause any problem, since these introduce a constant phase shift that is equal to 90° times the multiplicity of the pole or the zero.

Keep in mind that Bode plots were developed in the 1930s, long before the advent of the inexpensive digital computer. The main objective was to determine the frequency response for a specified transfer function without having to go through a great deal of computation. It is fair to say that this was achieved to very large extent. In the present age, when most engineers have ready access to a computer, it is often a lot easier to use a computer program to calculate the frequency response for any given transfer function. Such a program is included with this book and is described in Appendix 7.1. It is also possible to use the computer for a graphical display of the frequency response plot and to obtain a hard copy of this plot. The use of such a program is described in Appendix 7.3.

7.2.2.4 Estimation of Transfer Function from Bode Plots

Bode plots can be utilized for estimating the transfer function. This is often of great value in many practical situations, when the transfer function of a system is not known but it is possible to determine the frequency response experimentally by applying sine wave inputs at different frequencies and measuring the gain and phase shift in the steady state. From these measurements, the Bode plots are readily obtained. The first step in obtaining an estimate of the transfer function is to approximate the gain plot with a set of straight-line segments, taking care that the slope of each segment is $6n$ dB per octave, where n is an integer. The points of intersection of these straight-line segments are the various corner or break frequencies. If the *change in the slope* at any corner frequency is positive and equal to 6 dB per octave, then it corresponds to a simple zero of the transfer function. Similarly, if the change in slope is 6 dB per octave and negative, then it corresponds to a pole. On the other hand, if the change in slope is 12 dB per octave, the corner represents the undamped natural frequency corresponding to a pair of complex conjugate poles of zeros with damping ratio $0 < \zeta \leq 1$.* For the latter case, the value of the damping ratio ζ of these complex poles can be estimated by looking at the actual gain near the break frequency, especially the peak value of the gain. It is possible to use equations 7.20 and 7.21 to estimate the value of ζ.

As pointed out previously, the transfer function can be determined uniquely from the plot of the gain only if it is of the minimum-phase type. Therefore, it is always desirable to use the plot of the phase shift to verify that the estimated minimum phase transfer function is valid. If there is a significant difference between the actual plot of the phase shift and the one obtained from the estimated transfer function, probably we need an additional all-pass transfer function or an ideal delay for a better fit. In the latter instance, the phase shift will not approach a constant for very large values of ω. Accordingly, the value of the delay can be estimated from the actual phase shift at some frequencies at least one decade above the highest corner frequency and the corresponding values obtained from the estimated transfer function.

The following example illustrates the procedure for a simple case.

Example 7.8

The Bode plots of the frequency response of an R-C network are shown in Figure 7.14*a* and 7.14*b*. It is desired to estimate the transfer function.

The straight-line approximation of the gain plot is shown in Figure 7.14*a* by a dashed line. We observe that there are two corner frequencies, at $\omega = 2$ and 20. Since the slope is reduced from 0 to -6 dB per octave at $\omega = 2$, we must have a pole at $s = -2$. Similarly, since the slope increases from -6 dB per octave to zero at $\omega = 20$, we must have a zero at $s = -20$. Also, from the low-frequency asymptote, we conclude that the dc gain is 0 dB, or one. The estimated transfer function is, therefore, given by

$$G(s) = \frac{1 + (s/20)}{1 + (s/2)} = \frac{0.1(s + 20)}{s + 2} \qquad (7.45)$$

This also agrees with the plot of the phase shift. ∎

In general, the procedure gets involved if there are several poles and zeros close to each other so that it may not be possible to use this method to

---

*Note that $\zeta = 1$ implies two equal real roots.

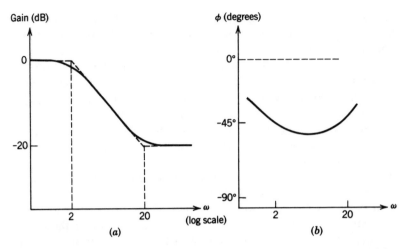

Figure 7.14 Bode plots of the frequency response of an R-C network. (*a*) Gain. (*b*) Phase shift.

get a good estimate of the poles and zeros of the transfer function from the frequency response in such cases.

7.2.3 POLAR PLOTS

Although Bode plots have many advantages, they have the serious drawback that one must look at two separate curves showing the variation of the gain and phase shift with frequency. It is possible to combine the information contained in the two plots into one curve in two ways. One of these will be discussed in this subsection, the other in the next. If we express the frequency response function $G(j\omega)$ in the polar form $Me^{j\phi}$, and plot the tip of the vector $Me^{j\phi}$ in the G-plane as ω varies from zero to infinity, we obtain the *polar* plot. The value of ω is labeled at selected points on the plot. Mathematically, the polar plot can be regarded as the mapping of the positive part of the $j\omega$-axis of the s-plane into the G-plane. The Nyquist criterion of stability utilizes this concept for determining the stability of a closed-loop system from its open-loop frequency response.

Example 7.9

Consider the transfer function

$$G(s) = \frac{20s}{(s+1)(s+10)} \qquad (7.46)$$

The values of M and ϕ for this function are given in Table 7.4.

TABLE 7.4 Frequency Response for Transfer Function in Equation 7.46

ω	0	0.2	0.5	1.0	2.0	3.16	5.0	10.0	50.0	100.0	∞
M	0	0.4	0.9	1.4	1.75	1.82	1.75	1.4	0.9	0.2	0
$\phi(°)$	90	77.5	60.6	39.3	15.3	0.0	-15.3	-39.3	-77.5	-39.3	-90

The polar plot is shown in Figure 7.15. It is seen that the gain is low for both low and high frequencies, whereas the phase shift decreases from 90° to $-90°$ as ω increases from 0 to ∞. ∎

Example 7.10

Consider the transfer function that was studied in Example 7.1. We had

$$G(s) = \frac{10}{s^2 + 2s + 10} \tag{7.47}$$

The values of the gain and phase shift for this transfer function are given in Table 7.1. Figure 7.16 shows the polar plot obtained by using these values. ∎

7.2.4 GAIN – PHASE PLOTS

Although the polar plot presents complete information about the frequency response in one curve, it requires much more computation than the Bode

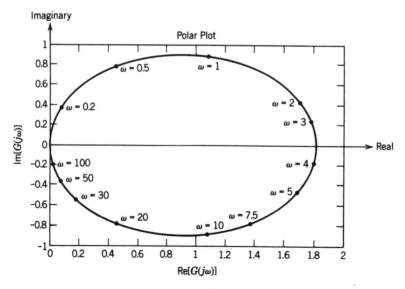

Figure 7.15 Polar plot for transfer function in equation 7.46.

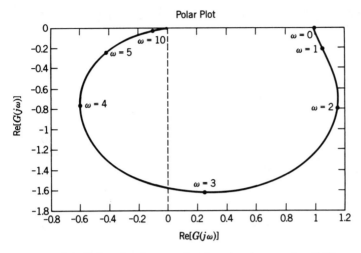

Figure 7.16 Polar plot for transfer function in equation 7.47.

plots. An alternative approach that retains the advantage of providing information about the gain and the phase shift in one curve, but does not require as much computation, will now be presented. The idea here is to use rectangular coordinates for plotting the gain in decibels against the phase shift in degrees, with ω as a parameter along the curve. The points along the curve can be obtained from the Bode plots for the gain and phase shift for different values of ω. Like polar plots, an important application of the gain–phase plot is in the determination of the stability of a closed-loop system from its open-loop frequency response.

Example 7.11

Consider the transfer function of the system that was used in Example 7.7 for illustration of phase plots.

$$G(s) = \frac{400(s + 4)}{s(s^2 + 4s + 25)} \qquad (7.48)$$

The values of the gain and phase shift for different values of ω are shown in Table 7.5. The corresponding gain-phase plot is shown in Figure 7.17. ∎

TABLE 7.5 Gain and Phase Shift for Transfer Function in Equation 7.48

ω	0.1	0.2	0.5	1.0	2.0	3.0	5.0	10.0	20.0
M (dB)	56.1	50.1	42.3	36.6	32.0	30.5	28.2	14.1	0.5
ϕ	−89.5	−88.9	−87.5	−85.5	−84.3	−90.0	−128.7	−173.7	−179.3

Gain-Phase Plot

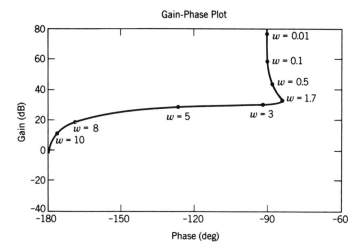

Figure 7.17 Gain–phase plot for transfer function in equation 7.80.

7.3 FREQUENCY RESPONSE OF DISCRETE-TIME SYSTEMS

As shown in Chapter 6, the frequency response of a discrete-time system is obtained by replacing z by $e^{j\Omega}$ in the transfer function and evaluating the resulting expression for different values of Ω. An important feature of the frequency response of discrete-time systems is evident. Here we evaluate $G(z)$ along the unit circle of the z-plane, whereas for continuous-time systems, the function $G(s)$ was evaluated along the $j\omega$-axis of the s-plane. A graphical interpretation was shown in Figure 6.12 and is repeated in Figure 7.18 for the calculation of the frequency response of a transfer function having two poles and a zero.

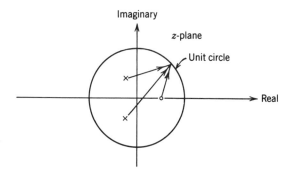

Figure 7.18 Frequency response from pole–zero plot.

Although this is consistent with the mapping between the two planes, it also implies that for discrete-time systems the frequency response repeats itself as the value of Ω increases beyond 2π, since

$$G(e^{j\Omega}) = G(e^{j(\Omega + 2n\pi)}) \tag{7.49}$$

where n is any integer.

Furthermore, it follows from the symmetry in Figure 7.18 that

$$G(e^{j\Omega}) = G^*(e^{-j\Omega}) = G^*(e^{j(2\pi - \Omega)}) \tag{7.50}$$

for discrete-time systems where G^* is the complex conjugate of G. Therefore, we need only calculate the frequency response within the range of Ω varying from 0 to π, instead of from 0 to ∞, as required for continuous-time systems.

The frequency response will, again, be a complex number, which can be expressed in the polar form as $Me^{j\phi}$, where M is the gain and ϕ is the phase shift between the output and the input. Note that the phase shift ϕ will be in radians but may be converted into degrees, if desired. An example of the calculation of the frequency response of a discrete-time system from its transfer function follows.

Example 7.12

Consider the transfer function

$$G(z) = \frac{0.144(z^2 + 1.14z + 1)}{z^2 - 0.96z + 0.45} \tag{7.51}$$

Replacing z by $e^{j\Omega}$, we obtain

$$G(e^{j\Omega}) = \frac{0.144(e^{j2\Omega} + 1.14e^{j\Omega} + 1)}{e^{j2\Omega} - 0.96e^{j\Omega} + 0.45} = Me^{j\phi} \tag{7.52}$$

To calculate the frequency response for a given Ω, we replace the exponential $e^{jn\Omega}$ by $(\cos n\Omega + j \sin n\Omega)$ and evaluate both the numerator and denominator of equation 7.52 as complex numbers. The ratio, expressed in the polar form gives, M and ϕ. The computational procedure for evaluating the above expression for different values of Ω is described in Appendix 7.2. A computer program for this purpose is included with the book. Table 7.6 shows the values of M and ϕ, calculated for this case, where the phase shift is given in radians.

TABLE 7.6 Gain and Phase Shift for Transfer Function in Equation 7.51

Ω	0.0	0.1π	0.2π	0.3π	0.4π	0.5π	0.6π	0.7π	0.8π	0.9π	π
M	0.92	0.97	1.02	0.73	0.35	0.15	0.05	0.02	0.03	0.05	0.05
ϕ	0.0	−0.39	−0.99	−1.81	−2.35	−2.62	−2.79	0.24	0.15	0.07	0.00

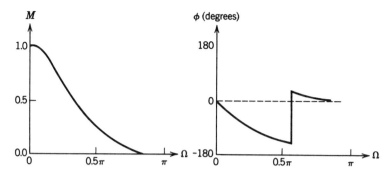

Figure 7.19 Pole–zero plot for transfer function in equation 7.51.

The plots of the gain and phase shift from Table 7.6 are shown in Figure 7.19a and 7.19b, respectively.

Often a better insight into the frequency response is obtained from the pole–zero plot of the transfer function. We start with expressing the transfer function in the factored form, showing the poles and zeros. The transfer function given in equation 7.51 can then be written as

$$G(z) = \frac{0.144(z - e^{j2.1773})(z - e^{-j2.1773})}{(z - 0.6708e^{j0.7734})(z - 0.6708e^{-j0.7734})} \quad (7.53)$$

The pole–zero plot is shown in Figure 7.20. The frequency response for any value of ω is determined by drawing vectors from the poles and zeros to the corresponding point on the unit circle, as shown in the figure.

The transfer function is seen to have a pair of complex zeros on the unit circle, located at $\Omega = 2.1773$. This explains why the value of M is close to zero for $\Omega = 0.6\pi \approx 2.2$. This also explains the discontinuity in the value of ϕ at that point, caused by the reversal in the direction of the vector drawn from that zero.

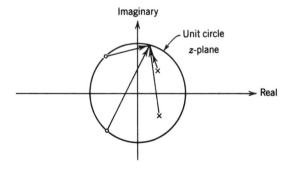

Figure 7.20 Frequency response plot of transfer function in equation 7.51.

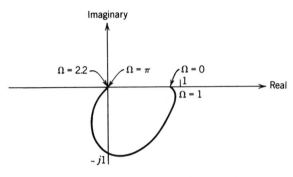

Figure 7.21 Polar plot of transfer function in equation 7.51.

The frequency response given in Table 7.6 can be plotted exactly as in the case of continuous-time systems. All the different types of plots can be used, keeping in mind that only the frequency range 0 to π is of interest. In view of this, it is not necessary to use logarithmic coordinates for the frequency, unless it is desired to expand the scale for low frequencies. As a result, the plots that are most commonly used with discrete-time systems are those with gain (either M or $20 \log M$) and the phase shift plotted against frequency on the linear scale. Polar and gain–phase plots can also be used without any modification.

The values of M and ϕ, in Table 7.6, can be utilized for obtaining the polar plot of the frequency response. If desired, the polar plot of Ω in the range π to 2π can also be plotted, as it is the mirror image about the real axis of the G-plane of the plot for Ω in the range 0 to π, in accordance with equation 7.50. This complete polar plot is the map of the unit circle of the z-plane into the G-plane. It would correspond to the map of entire $j\omega$-axis of the s-plane, which is the case if the polar plot of the frequency response for a continuous-time system is obtained for ω varying from $-\infty$ to ∞. The polar plot for the transfer function given in equation 2.51 is shown in Figure 7.21 for Ω varying from 0 to π. ∎

Frequency response of discrete-time systems is of great importance in the design of filters for discrete-time signal processing. This topic will be discussed in Chapter 9.

7.4 SOME APPLICATIONS OF FREQUENCY RESPONSE PLOTS

In the previous sections we presented several types of plots of frequency response of continuous-time as well as discrete-time systems. These plots are very useful, since they present a great deal of information about the system.

This is especially important in view of the fact that in many practical situations we do not know the transfer function of the system, but are able to measure the frequency response experimentally. As shown in Section 7.2.2.4, it is possible to estimate the transfer function of a system from the frequency response plot.

In the design of feedback control systems, the frequency response of the system with the loop open is used extensively for determining the stability of the system after the loop is closed. Frequency response plots allow the designer to determine not only if the system is stable but also how far it is from instability by using certain quantitative measures like the gain margin and the phase margin. For example, the polar plot is used with the celebrated Nyquist criterion of stability. The interested reader is referred to any textbook on control systems to learn more about the use of these plots in the analysis and design of feedback systems. We present here another application of frequency response plots.

In Chapter 6 three methods for obtaining approximate discrete-time models for continuous-time systems are discussed. An important problem there was the choice of the sampling interval. For a discrete-time model to be a good approximation to the corresponding continuous-time model, it is necessary to ensure that the sampling theorem is satisfied, but this requires that the signals be band-limited, as shown in Chapter 4. In practice, most control systems are of the low-pass nature, that is, the magnitude of their frequency response decreases rapidly above a certain frequency. Therefore, in such situations it is possible to select a suitable value for the sampling frequency ω_s such that aliasing is negligible. This can be done easily by looking at the plot of the frequency response of the system. The following example will demonstrate the main idea.

Example 7.13

In Example 6.18 we obtained discrete-time equivalent models for the following transfer function of an industrial robot:

$$G(s) = \frac{2.5}{s(s + 0.5)(s + 5)} \tag{7.54}$$

with the sampling interval arbitrarily taken as 0.1 s. We are now able to make a more rational choice of the sampling frequency by examining the frequency response of the system described by equation 7.54. Since the transfer function has three poles and no zeros, the system is of the low-pass type, with the magnitude of the response decreasing at -18 dB per decade for $\omega > 5$. The Bode plot of the magnitude is shown in Figure 7.22.

It can be seen from the plot that at low frequencies, the gain is about 20 dB, but falls off rapidly for ω above 5. For $\omega = 13.5$, the gain is less than -60 dB, which can therefore be regarded as the bandwidth in this case for all practical purposes. Consequently, we can select the sampling frequency ω_s as 27 without any loss of information due to aliasing. Thus a sampling

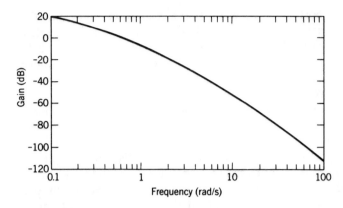

Figure 7.22 Gain curve for the transfer function in equation 7.40.

interval given by

$$T = \frac{2\pi}{\omega_s} = 0.2327$$

will be adequate. Hence, our choice of 0.1 s as the sampling interval was reasonable although even a sampling interval of 0.2 s would have been satisfactory. ∎

Frequency response plots are used extensively in the design of filters. This will be discussed in Chapter 9.

7.5 SUMMARY

In this chapter we have studied various aspects of the frequency response of linear systems. Although the frequency response can be readily calculated from the transfer function, in many practical situations we do not know the transfer function. In such cases the frequency response can be determined experimentally by measuring the gain and phase shift of the system for sinusoidal inputs at different frequencies provided that the system is stable. Often this provides sufficient knowledge of the important properties of the system. In fact, it is possible to estimate the transfer function from the frequency response. Since there are two dependent variables, the gain and the phase shift, we need the plots of two curves to obtain complete information about their variation with frequency. Several types of frequency response curves are used, especially for continuous-time systems.

In particular, Bode plots, which use logarithmic coordinates, have been very popular for continuous-time systems. Their main advantage is that the need for computing the frequency response is considerably reduced and approximate plots can be obtained with very little computation. This was a significant advantage in the age when computers were not as readily available as at the present time. However, they suffer from the disadvantage that two separate curves have to be plotted to present complete information about the frequency response. Polar plots do present the entire information in one curve, but they require much more computation. An alternative is the gain-phase plot using rectangular coordinates, with the gain in decibels and the phase shift in degrees plotted with frequency as a variable parameter along the curve. The information for this plot can be obtained from the Bode plots for the same system; hence, it does not require as much computation as for the polar plot. Polar and gain–phase plots are used extensively for determining the stability of feedback systems from the frequency response with the loop open.

Although all these plots can also be utilized for discrete-time systems, the use of logarithmic coordinates for the frequency is not necessary. This is because the frequency range of interest is between only 0 and π. Logarithmic coordinates may be used for expanding the frequency scale for small values of Ω, if desired. Polar plots and gain–phase plots can be used in the same way as in the case of continuous-time systems.

An important application of frequency response is in the design of filters. A brief introduction to the design of analog as well as digital filters will be presented in Chapter 9.

PROBLEMS

7.1 Plot the frequency response curves for each of the following transfer functions using linear coordinates.

(a) $G(s) = \dfrac{100(s + 2)}{s(s + 4)}$

(b) $G(s) = \dfrac{20(s + 10)}{(s + 1)(s^2 + 4s + 25)}$

(c) $G(s) = \dfrac{100(s - 2)}{s(s + 4)}$

(d) $G(s) = \dfrac{20(s - 10)}{(s + 1)(s^2 + 4s + 25)}$

(e) $G(s) = \dfrac{100(s + 4)e^{-0.2s}}{s(s^2 + 10s + 100)}$

(f) $G(s) = \dfrac{100,000s}{(s + 0.01)(s + 500)}$

7.2 Draw the Bode plots of the frequency response for each of the transfer functions given in Problem 7.1. The plots for the gain as well as the phase shift are required.

7.3 Draw the polar plot of the frequency response for each of the transfer functions given in Problem 7.1.

7.4 Sketch the gain–phase plot for the frequency response of each of the transfer functions given in Problem 7.1.

7.5 The simplified transfer function of the pitch control of a supersonic aircraft flying at 20,000 m above sea level is given below. Draw the

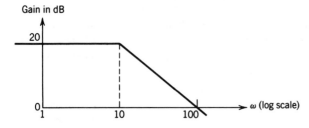

Figure 7.23 Asymptotic Bode plot for Problem 7.7.

polar plot of the frequency response.

$$G(s) = \frac{10(s + 3)e^{0.1s}}{s^2 + 2s + 26}$$

7.6 The transfer function for a chemical reactor can be approximated as

$$G(s) = \frac{300e^{-0.04}}{s(s + 5)(s + 12)}$$

Draw the Bode plots of the frequency response of the system and use these to draw the gain–phase plot of the frequency response.

7.7 The asymptotic Bode plot of the magnitude of a minimum-phase system is shown in Figure 7.23. Determine the transfer function.

7.8 Repeat Problem 7.7 for the plot shown in Figure 7.24.

7.9 A dc servomotor is commonly used as the "muscle arm" in automatic control systems. The transfer function relating the angular velocity of the armature of the motor to the applied voltage can be represented approximately by

$$G(s) = \frac{K}{1 + s\tau}$$

The values of K and τ can be determined from the Bode plots of the frequency response obtained experimentally.

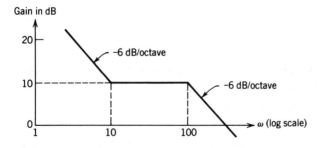

Figure 7.24 Asymptotic Bode plot for Problem 7.8.

The frequency response of a particular servomotor is given in the following table. Draw the Bode plots and use them to estimate the transfer function.

ω	0.1	0.2	0.3	0.5	0.7	1.0	1.5
Gain (dB)	20.0	19.8	19.6	19.0	18.2	17.0	14.9
ϕ (deg.)	-5.70	-11.3	-16.7	-26.6	-34.5	-45.0	-56.3

ω	2.0	3.0	4.0	5.0	6.0	8.0	10.0
Gain (dB)	13.0	10.0	7.7	5.8	4.3	1.9	0.0
ϕ (deg.)	-63.4	-71.6	-76.0	-78.7	-80.5	-82.9	-84.3

7.10   The transfer function of a third-order Butterworth normalized low-pass filter is given below. Calculate and plot the frequency response for ω varying from 0 to 3 rad/s.

$$G(s) = \frac{1}{s^3 + 2s^2 + 2s + 1}$$

7.11   The transfer function of a third-order normalized low-pass Chebyshev filter is given below. Calculate and plot the frequency response for ω varying from 0 to 3 rad/s.

$$G(s) = \frac{0.374226}{s^3 + 0.9027s^2 + 1.032934s + 0.374226}$$

7.12   The following table gives the frequency response of a minimum-phase system. The data were obtained experimentally. Draw the Bode plots and, hence, estimate the transfer function of the system.

ω	0.1	0.2	0.3	0.5	0.7	1.0	2.0
Gain (dB)	34.0	28.9	24.3	19.7	16.6	13.0	4.95
ϕ (deg.)	-93.0	-96.0	-98.5	-104.0	-109.3	-116.6	-135.0

ω	3.0	5.0	7.0	10.0	15.0	20.0	50.0
Gain (dB)	-3.0	-8.6	-14.1	-20.1	-27.1	-32.0	-48.0
ϕ (deg.)	-158.2	-158.2	-164.0	-168.7	-172.0	-176.6	-177.7

7.13   Repeat Problem 7.12 for the frequency response given below.

ω	0.1	0.5	1.0	1.5	2.0	2.5	3.0	3.5
Gain (dB)	0.0	0.04	0.17	0.2	0.0	-0.57	-1.6	-3.0
ϕ (deg.)	-2.3	-11.6	-24.0	-37.8	-53.1	-69.4	-85.2	-99.0

ω	4.0	4.5	5.0	6.0	8.0	10.0	20.0
Gain (dB)	-4.7	-6.3	-8.0	-12.3	-16.8	-19.9	-32.0
ϕ (deg.)	-110.6	-120.0	-127.0	-141.0	-149.6	-156.0	-168.4

7.14 The transfer functions of some discrete-time systems are given below. Plot the frequency response of each for Ω varying from 0 to π.

(a) $G(z) = \dfrac{(z - 0.3)(z - 0.7)}{(z - 0.4)(z - 0.6)}$

(b) $G(z) = \dfrac{z^2 + 2z + 1}{z^2 - z + 0.5}$

(c) $G(z) = \dfrac{1 - 0.8z^{-1} + 0.15z^{-2}}{1 + 0.1z^{-1} - 0.72z^{-2}}$

(d) $G(z) = \dfrac{z^2 - 4.5z + 5.0}{z^2 - 0.9z + 0.2}$

7.15 The transfer function of a digital filter is given below. Calculate and plot its frequency response for Ω varying between 0 and π rad. Plot gain in decibels and phase shift in degrees against Ω. Use linear scale for Ω.

$$H(z) = \frac{z^3 + 3z^2 + 3z + 1}{105z^3 - 213z^2 + 155z - 39}$$

7.16 The transfer function of a sixth-order low-pass digital filter is given below. Calculate and plot its frequency response for Ω varying between 0 and π. Use linear plots for showing gain and phase against frequency.

$$H(z) = \frac{0.0119(z + 1)^6}{(z^2 - 1.432z + 0.573)(z^2 - 1.115z + 0.706)(z^2 - 0.867z + 0.895)}$$

7.17 Draw the polar and gain–phase plots for the filter transfer function given in the previous problem.

7.18 A digital filter is said to be of the finite impulse response (FIR) form if its transfer function is a polynomial in negative powers of z, instead of being a ratio of two polynomials. The typical transfer function of such a filter is of the form

$$H(z) = \sum_{n=0}^{M-1} h(n)z^{-n}$$

(a) Determine the impulse response sequence for this filter.
(b) It can be shown that the phase shift of this filter will vary linearly with the frequency Ω if the following symmetry condition is satisfied:

$$h(n) = h(M - 1 - n)$$

Verify this by determining the phase shift for the case when $M = 7$ and the above condition is satisfied.

(d) Plot the gain and phase shift for such a filter of 17th order, with the coefficients given below, for Ω between 0 and π.

$$h(0) = h(16) = -0.0254$$
$$h(1) = h(15) = -0.0276$$
$$h(2) = h(14) = 0.0276$$
$$h(3) = h(13) = 0.0394$$
$$h(4) = h(12) = -0.0551$$
$$h(5) = h(11) = -0.0689$$
$$h(6) = h(10) = 0.1378$$
$$h(7) = h(9) = 0.2757$$
$$h(8) = 0.3333$$

7.19 The simplified transfer function for one axis of an industrial robot is given by

$$G(s) = \frac{10}{(s + 1)(s^2 + 4s + 5)}$$

(a) Draw the Bode plots of the frequency response of the system and determine the "cutoff frequency," which will be defined as the frequency where the gain is at least 60 dB below its dc value.

(b) Selecting the sampling frequency as twice the "cutoff frequency" determined above, determine an equivalent discrete-time model for the robot using the method of impulse-invariant transformation described in Chapter 6.

(c) Plot the frequency response of the discrete-time model determined in part (b) and compare that with the frequency response obtained in part (a).

7.20 Repeat parts (b) and (c) of the previous problem, using the bilinear transformation for obtaining the equivalent discrete-time model. Also calculate the impulse response sequence for this model and compare it with the values of the impulse response of the continuous-time system model at the sampling instants.

APPENDIX 7.1

Calculation of Frequency Response of Continuous-Time Systems

The calculation of the frequency response of continuous-time systems from a given transfer function $G(s)$ requires the computation of $G(j\omega)$ for many values of ω. Since $G(s)$ is a rational function of s, we must evaluate the polynomials in the numerator and the denominator for the imaginary argument $j\omega$. Arithmetic with complex numbers can be avoided by dividing each of the polynomials by the factor $(s^2 + \omega^2)$. The remainder is then a polynomial of the first degree of the form $(as + b)$, where a and b are real numbers. Thus, the value of the polynomial for that ω is simply the complex number $(b + ja\omega)$. The values of M and ϕ are then obtained from the two complex numbers representing the numerator and the denominator.

The computer program enclosed with this book can be utilized to obtain points on the frequency response curve for a given transfer function. The program requires the input of the coefficients of the numerator and denominator polynomials and the value of the transport lag, that is, a term of the form of $e^{-s\tau}$ (this may be given as zero if there is no transport lag). Note that only a positive value for τ need be entered, since it is a lag and the program automatically assumes the negative sign. The program than asks the user to input the lowest value of ω, the frequency step, and number of steps desired. The user has the choice of obtaining either the gain M or its value in decibels, that is, $20 \log M$. The data obtained will first be displayed on the monitor. The user is also given the choice to print the data or store it in a disk file. The data thus stored may then be used, along with any graph-plotting program, for obtaining different types of frequency response plots.

APPENDIX 7.2

Calculation of Frequency Response of Discrete-Time Systems

The calculation of the frequency response of a discrete-time system from a given transfer function $G(z)$ requires the computation of $G(e^{j\Omega})$ for different values of Ω. Since $G(z)$ is a rational function of z, we must evaluate the polynomials in the numerator and the denominator for the complex argument, $z = \cos \Omega + j \sin \Omega$. Complex arithmetic can, again, be avoided by dividing each of the polynomials by the quadratic $(z^2 + 2z \cos \Omega + 1)$ and utilizing the remainder. For example, consider the case when

$$P(z) = z^3 + 5z^2 + 7z + 10$$

is to be evaluated for $\Omega = \pi/3$. Since $\cos \pi/3 = 0.5$, we divide $P(z)$ by the quadratic $(z^2 + z + 1)$. This leads to the following equation:

$$P(z) = (z^2 + z + 1)(z + 4) + 2z + 6$$

so that

$$P(e^{j\pi/3}) = 2e^{j\pi/3} + 6 = 7 + j\sqrt{3}$$

The computer program included with this book uses this approach for efficient evaluation of the frequency response. Since only the values of Ω between 0 and π need be considered, the program calculates values of M and ϕ at the desired number of equally spaced points (maximum 250) within this range of frequencies.

As usual, the program requires the input of the coefficients of the numerator and denominator polynomials, which may be printed or stored in a disk file. The gain M can be calculated in decibels, if desired. The values of the gain and the phase shift for different values of Ω can be printed or stored in a disk file, if so desired. They can also be used, together with any graph-plotting program, to obtain different types of frequency response plots.

APPENDIX 7.3

Computer Program for Obtaining Frequency Response Plots

A program enclosed with this book can be utilized for computer generation of different types of frequency response plots. It is assumed that the computer is IBM compatible and has one of the standard graphics cards supported by Turbo Pascal version 5.5. The program calculates the frequency response after obtaining the transfer function and the desired frequency range from the user. The user may also specify whether a linear or logarithmic scale should be used for the frequency as well as whether the gain should be in decibels. It is also possible to plot the phase shift in radians instead of degrees.

In all situations, the scales are automatically selected from the given data to use as much of the screen as possible.

The plots thus obtained on the screen of the computer can also be printed by using a suitable screen-dump program.

State Equations

8.1 INTRODUCTION

In the preceding chapters of the book, we studied the use of transfer function models for linear continuous-time as well as discrete-time systems. Some applications of these models were discussed in Chapters 5 and 6, whereas in Chapter 7 we studied their application to analysis and design by using frequency response. Transfer function models have also been called frequency-domain models due mainly to the interpretation of the Laplace transform variable s as complex frequency. A similar interpretation may be given to the variable z in z-transform theory, where the frequency response is obtained by replacing z with $e^{j\Omega}$.

In this chapter we shall return to a particular class of time-domain models that are especially suitable for use with computers. We learned in Chapter 1 that linear continuous-time systems can be modeled by linear differential equations, whereas linear discrete-time systems can be modeled by linear difference equations. Some methods for solving these equations were presented, and it was observed that a unique solution for a differential or difference equation of order n requires the knowledge of n boundary conditions. In the simplest case, these can be the initial values of the output and its first $n - 1$ derivatives. This is often called the *initial value problem*. Here we shall start by defining a set of n variables called the *state variables*. This will enable us to replace the nth-order differential (or difference) equation for the system by a set of n first-order differential (or difference) equations in terms of these variables. The concept of state is introduced in the next section. This is followed by a study of the formulation and solution of state equations for continuous-time and discrete-time systems in Sections 8.3 and 8.4. The relationships between state equations and transfer functions is discussed in Sections 8.5 and 8.6. Finally, we study the effects of linear transformation of the state vector and the resulting variety of canonical forms of state–space models.

An important advantage of the state variable representation is that it allows us to study systems with several inputs and outputs without the need for changing the notational framework used with single-input single-output systems. Another advantage is that state variables give us information about

346

the internal behavior of the system, as well as its input–output behavior. This may be contrasted with the transfer function model, which tells us only about the input–output behavior of the system.

The state variables for a system of order n can be represented by a vector of dimension n, and the set of n first-order differential equations can be written in the form of a vector differential equation. At any given instant the tip of this vector represents the state of the system, and the movement of this tip in the state space defines a *trajectory*. Thus, we obtain compactness in notation as well as a geometric interpretation of the changes in the state.

To fully understand the subject matter of this chapter, the reader should be familiar with certain basic concepts of matrix algebra. These are reviewed briefly in Appendix A.

8.2 THE CONCEPT OF STATE

The state of a system is defined as *the smallest set of variables that must be known at any given instant in order that the future response of the system to any specified input may be calculated from the given dynamic equation.* Thus, the state can be regarded as a compact representation of the past history of the system, which can be utilized for predicting its future behavior in response to any external stimulus. This concept applies equally well to continuous-time as well as discrete-time systems. The only difference is that time is the independent variable for the former, whereas the independent variable for the latter is the index k of the sequence.

The number of state variables for any system will be precisely equal to the order of the differential (or difference) equation required to model it. For example, in an electrical network, knowledge of voltages across all capacitors and currents through all inductors is necessary to predict the future values of all voltages and currents for any set of given inputs. As expected, the number of independent state variables in an electrical network will *normally* be equal to the number of energy storage elements in the system. However, there will be fewer state variables if there are loops containing only capacitors and voltage sources or cut-sets containing only inductors and current sources. Usually, the choice of state variables for a system is not unique. In fact, the number of possible choices of the state variables can be infinite. In practice, it may often be desirable to select physical variables as the states, especially for control systems, so that it may be possible to measure them and to use them in feedback loops. The following example of a simple electrical network will illustrate the point about the choice of state variables.

Example 8.1

Consider the RLC network shown in Figure 8.1.

Application of Kirchhoff's voltage law to this circuit leads to the following integro-differential equation:

$$L\frac{di}{dt} + Ri + \int_{-\infty}^{t} \frac{1}{C}i\,dt = v(t) \tag{8.1}$$

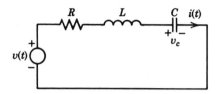

Figure 8.1 A simple RLC network.

Differentiating the above equation with respect to t, we obtain the following second-order differential equation:

$$L\frac{d^2i}{dt^2} + R\frac{di}{dt} + \frac{1}{C}i = \frac{dv}{dt} \tag{8.2}$$

One approach is to select i and di/dt as the state variables. Let

$$x_1 = i$$
$$x_2 = \frac{di}{dt} \tag{8.3}$$

We can now write equation 8.2 as

$$L\dot{x}_2 + Rx_2 + \frac{1}{C}x_1 = \dot{v} \tag{8.4}$$

where, to simplify the notation, the dot over a function of time indicates its derivative with respect to time.

Combining equation 8.4 with equation 8.3 and rearranging, we obtain the following set of two first-order differential equations:

$$\dot{x}_1 = x_2$$
$$\dot{x}_2 = -\frac{R}{L}x_2 - \frac{1}{LC}x_1 + \frac{1}{L}\dot{v} \tag{8.5}$$

Equations 8.5 constitute one set of state equations for this network, with the two state variables defined as in equation 8.3, but the presence of the derivative of the input is undesirable. Another set of state equations, which do not contain this derivative, may be obtained by the choice of i and v_c as the state variables. In this case, letting

$$x_1 = i$$
$$x_2 = v_c \tag{8.6}$$

we obtain, the following from equation 8.1:

$$\dot{x}_1 = -\frac{R}{L}x_1 - \frac{1}{L}x_2 + \frac{1}{L}v(t)$$
$$\dot{x}_2 = \frac{1}{C}x_1 \tag{8.7}$$

∎

Thus, we have obtained two sets of state equations for our network. Although both of them are equally valid, equations 8.7 utilize the physical variables i and v_c and do not require differentiation of the applied voltage. The solution of these equations can be obtained more directly if the initial conditions are given as $i(0)$ and $v_c(0)$. Furthermore, equations 8.7 are derived more easily by a direct application of Kirchhoff's laws. In fact, it is possible to write the state equations for electrical networks directly by using some basic concepts of network topology. For details, see Chapter 12 of the book by Desoer and Kuh, which is listed in Appendix E.

8.3 STATE EQUATIONS FOR CONTINUOUS-TIME SYSTEMS

The state equations for a continuous-time system with m inputs can be written more compactly as

$$\dot{x} = Ax + Bu \tag{8.8}$$

where

$$x = \begin{bmatrix} x_1 \\ x_2 \\ \cdots \\ \cdots \\ x_n \end{bmatrix} \tag{8.9}$$

is the n-dimensional *state vector*, A is an $n \times n$ matrix, B is an $n \times m$ matrix, and

$$u = \begin{bmatrix} u_1 \\ u_2 \\ \cdots \\ \cdots \\ u_m \end{bmatrix} \tag{8.10}$$

is the m-dimensional *input vector*. The components of $u(t)$ are the various inputs to the system. Equation 8.8 is also called the *vector differential equation* for the system. For a system with only one input, the dimension m of the input vector u will be one. The elements of the matrices A and B will all be real numbers and constant for linear time-invariant physical systems.

The output of the system can be expressed as a linear combination of the states and the inputs. Hence, the following equation is obtained:

$$y = Cx + Du \tag{8.11}$$

where

$$y = \begin{bmatrix} y_1 \\ y_2 \\ \cdots \\ y_r \end{bmatrix} \tag{8.12}$$

is the r-dimensional output vector for the general case of a multivariable system, C is an $r \times n$ matrix, and D is an $r \times m$ matrix. For a system with only one output, r will be equal to one. The elements of the matrices C and D will be real and constant for linear time-invariant physical systems.

Equations 8.8 and 8.11 constitute the *state-space description* of a linear time-invariant system. These equations can also be used with time-varying systems if we allow the elements of the matrices A, B, C, and D to be functions of time. We shall now discuss how to solve these equations for the time-invariant case.

8.3.1 THE SOLUTION OF STATE EQUATIONS

Given the vector differential equation 8.8, we can solve it for a given input $u(t)$ and specified initial conditions $x(t_0)$ in a manner similar to the procedure developed in Section 1.5.1 for solving a scalar differential equation of the first order. It was shown there that the solution of the differential equation

$$\frac{dx}{dt} + ax = u(t) \tag{8.13}$$

is given by

$$x(t) = e^{-a(t-t_0)}x(t_0) + e^{-at}\int_{t_0}^{t} e^{a\tau} u(\tau)\, d\tau \tag{8.14}$$

where the notation has been slightly modified to agree with the present case.

A comparison between equations 8.8 and 8.13 suggests that the solution of equation 8.8 should be given by

$$\mathbf{x}(t) = e^{\mathbf{A}(t-t_0)}\mathbf{x}(t_0) + e^{\mathbf{A}t}\int_{t_0}^{t} e^{-\mathbf{A}\tau} \mathbf{B}\mathbf{u}(\tau)\, d\tau \tag{8.15}$$

The main differences between equations 8.14 and 8.15 are the replacement of the scalar $-a$ with the matrix A and the occurrence of the multiplier B in the latter. These are easily seen as due to the differences between equations 8.8 and 8.13. In particular, if we had changed the sign of a in equation 8.13 to correspond with the sign of A and had included the multiplier b, then the two solutions would have exactly the same form, except for the fact that the scalars a and b would be replaced with the matrices A and B, respectively. We should also note that equation 8.15 contains the matrix exponential $e^{\mathbf{A}t}$. This can be expressed in the form of a power series, similar to the scalar exponential, that is,

$$e^{\mathbf{A}t} = \mathbf{I} + \mathbf{A}t + \frac{\mathbf{A}^2 t^2}{2!} + \frac{\mathbf{A}^3 t^3}{3!} + \frac{\mathbf{A}^4 t^4}{4!} + \cdots \tag{8.16}$$

Alternatively, by taking Laplace transforms of both sides of equation 8.8 we obtain

$$s\mathbf{X}(s) - \mathbf{x}(0) = \mathbf{A}\mathbf{X}(s) + \mathbf{B}\mathbf{U}(s) \tag{8.17}$$

which can be solved for $\mathbf{X}(s)$, so that

$$\mathbf{X}(s) = [s\mathbf{I} - \mathbf{A}]^{-1}[\mathbf{x}(0) + \mathbf{B}\mathbf{U}(s)] \tag{8.18}$$

Equation 8.18 is the Laplace transform of equation 8.15. Thus we recognize that

$$e^{\mathbf{A}t} = \mathscr{L}^{-1}\left[(s\mathbf{I} - \mathbf{A})^{-1}\right] \tag{8.19}$$

and the integral on the right-hand side of equation 8.15 is the convolution integral corresponding to the inverse Laplace transform of the product given by $[s\mathbf{I} - \mathbf{A}]^{-1}\mathbf{B}\mathbf{U}(s)$.

In view of the above, we have two alternative methods for solving the state equation. One of these is based on equation 8.18, where we first determine $\mathbf{X}(s)$ and then obtain its inverse Laplace transform. Not only does this require inversion of the matrix $(s\mathbf{I} - \mathbf{A})$, but after that the inverse Laplace transform of $\mathbf{X}(s)$ must also be obtained. On the other hand, equation 8.15 is ideally suited for numerical solution, provided that the matrix $e^{\mathbf{A}t}$ is known. This matrix is called the *state transition matrix* for the system. Some methods for evaluating this matrix will now be presented.

8.3.2 THE EVALUATION OF $e^{\mathbf{A}t}$

The state transition matrix $e^{\mathbf{A}t}$, also known as the *fundamental matrix* of the system and denoted by the symbol $\phi(t)$, can be calculated in several ways. Three of the most common methods will be described here.

8.3.2.1 Use of the Laplace Transform

Conceptually, the most straightforward approach is that given by equation 8.19. This involves first inverting the matrix $(s\mathbf{I} - \mathbf{A})$ and then taking the inverse Laplace transform of the resulting matrix. This latter step requires obtaining the inverse Laplace transform of each element of the matrix $(s\mathbf{I} - \mathbf{A})^{-1}$. The inversion of the matrix cannot be done on a computer, since each element of the inverse is a rational function in s instead of being a real number. The following example will illustrate the procedure.

Example 8.2

Consider the 2×2 matrix

$$\mathbf{A} = \begin{bmatrix} 0 & 1 \\ -3 & -4 \end{bmatrix} \tag{8.20}$$

Hence

$$(s\mathbf{I} - \mathbf{A}) = \begin{bmatrix} s & -1 \\ 3 & s + 4 \end{bmatrix} \tag{8.21}$$

The inverse of this matrix can be obtained by dividing its adjoint by its determinant. This leads us to

$$(s\mathbf{I} - \mathbf{A})^{-1} = \frac{\text{adj}\,(s\mathbf{I} - \mathbf{A})}{\det\,(s\mathbf{I} - \mathbf{A})} = \frac{\begin{bmatrix} s+4 & 1 \\ -3 & s \end{bmatrix}}{s^2 + 4s + 3}$$

$$= \begin{bmatrix} \dfrac{s+4}{(s+1)(s+3)} & \dfrac{1}{(s+1)(s+3)} \\[3mm] \dfrac{-3}{(s+1)(s+3)} & \dfrac{s}{(s+1)(s+3)} \end{bmatrix} \quad (8.22)$$

Taking the inverse Laplace transform of each element of the right-hand side of equation 8.22, we obtain the state transition matrix,

$$\boldsymbol{\phi}(t) = \begin{bmatrix} 1.5e^{-3t} - 0.5e^{-t} & 0.5(e^{-t} - e^{-3t}) \\ 2(e^{-3t} - e^{-t}) & 2.5e^{-3t} - 1.5e^{-t} \end{bmatrix} \quad (8.23)$$

It is evident that this matrix inversion, if done by hand, is rather cumbersome for matrices of dimension greater than 3×3. It can be avoided by using Leverrier's algorithm (also known as the Souriau–Frame algorithm) described below. Let

$$(s\mathbf{I} - \mathbf{A})^{-1} = \frac{\text{adj}\,(s\mathbf{I} - \mathbf{A})}{\det\,(s\mathbf{I} - \mathbf{A})}$$

$$= \frac{\mathbf{P}_{n-1}s^{n-1} + \mathbf{P}_{n-2}s^{n-2} + \cdots + \mathbf{P}_1 s + \mathbf{P}_0}{s^n + a_{n-1}s^{n-1} + \cdots + a_1 s + a_0} \quad (8.24)$$

where $\mathbf{P}_i$ are $n \times n$ matrices and a_i are scalars. The elements of $\mathbf{P}_i$ are real numbers and so are a_i if the elements of $\mathbf{A}$ are real, as is true of all physical systems. Leverrier's algorithm allows us to calculate $\mathbf{P}_i$ and a_i in a recursive manner as described below. It is also easily programmed for use on a digital computer.

$$\mathbf{P}_{n-1} = \mathbf{I}$$
$$a_{n-1} = -tr\,(\mathbf{A})$$
$$\mathbf{P}_{n-2} = \mathbf{P}_{n-1}\mathbf{A} + a_{n-1}\mathbf{I}$$
$$a_{n-2} = -\frac{1}{2}tr(\mathbf{P}_{n-2}\mathbf{A})$$
$$\cdots\cdots\cdots\cdots\cdots\cdots\cdots$$
$$\mathbf{P}_k = \mathbf{P}_{k+1}\mathbf{A} + a_{k+1}\mathbf{I}$$
$$a_k = -\frac{1}{n-k}tr(\mathbf{P}_k\mathbf{A}) \quad (8.25)$$

where $tr(\mathbf{A})$ represents the *trace* of the matrix $\mathbf{A}$, defined as the sum of the elements on the main diagonal of the matrix.

The result of the calculations in equation 8.25 can be verified from the following relationship

$$\mathbf{P}_0 \mathbf{A} + a_0 \mathbf{I} = 0 \qquad (8.26)$$

In general, it is desirable to utilize this relationship for verifying the results and detecting errors introduced by truncation in the computer. ∎

The following example will illustrate the procedure.

Example 8.3

Consider the 3 × 3 matrix given below.

$$\mathbf{A} = \begin{bmatrix} -2 & -5 & -5 \\ 1 & -1 & 0 \\ 0 & 1 & 0 \end{bmatrix} \qquad (8.27)$$

Following the procedure outlined above, we obtain (for $n = 3$)

$$\mathbf{P}_2 = \mathbf{I} = \begin{bmatrix} 1 & 0 & 0 \\ 0 & 1 & 0 \\ 0 & 0 & 1 \end{bmatrix} \qquad (8.28)$$

$$a_2 = -tr(\mathbf{A}) = 3 \qquad (8.29)$$

$$\mathbf{P}_1 = \mathbf{P}_2 \mathbf{A} + a_2 \mathbf{I} = \mathbf{A} + 3\mathbf{I} = \begin{bmatrix} 1 & -5 & -5 \\ 1 & 2 & 0 \\ 0 & 1 & 3 \end{bmatrix} \qquad (8.30)$$

$$
\begin{aligned}
a_1 &= -\frac{1}{2} tr[\mathbf{P}_1 \mathbf{A}] \\
&= -\frac{1}{2} tr\left(\begin{bmatrix} 1 & -5 & -5 \\ 1 & 2 & 0 \\ 0 & 1 & 3 \end{bmatrix} \begin{bmatrix} -2 & -5 & -5 \\ 1 & -1 & 0 \\ 0 & 1 & 0 \end{bmatrix} \right) \\
&= -\frac{1}{2} tr \begin{bmatrix} -7 & -5 & -5 \\ 0 & -7 & -5 \\ 1 & 2 & 0 \end{bmatrix} = 7
\end{aligned}
\qquad (8.31)
$$

$$
\begin{aligned}
\mathbf{P}_0 &= \mathbf{P}_1 \mathbf{A} + a_1 \mathbf{I} = \begin{bmatrix} 7 & -5 & -5 \\ 0 & -7 & -5 \\ 1 & 2 & 0 \end{bmatrix} + 7\mathbf{I} \\
&= \begin{bmatrix} 0 & -5 & -5 \\ 0 & 0 & -5 \\ 1 & 2 & 7 \end{bmatrix}
\end{aligned}
\qquad (8.32)
$$

$$
\begin{aligned}
a_0 &= -\frac{1}{3} tr[\mathbf{P}_0 \mathbf{A}] \\
&= -\frac{1}{3} tr\left(\begin{bmatrix} 0 & -5 & -5 \\ 0 & 0 & -5 \\ 1 & 2 & 7 \end{bmatrix} \begin{bmatrix} -2 & -5 & -5 \\ 1 & -1 & 0 \\ 0 & 1 & 0 \end{bmatrix} \right) \\
&= -\frac{1}{3} tr \begin{bmatrix} -5 & 0 & 0 \\ 0 & -5 & 0 \\ 0 & 0 & -5 \end{bmatrix} = 5
\end{aligned}
\qquad (8.33)
$$

Finally, we verify that

$$\mathbf{P}_0\mathbf{A} + a_0\mathbf{I} = \begin{bmatrix} -5 & 0 & 0 \\ 0 & -5 & 0 \\ 0 & 0 & -5 \end{bmatrix} + 5\mathbf{I} = 0 \qquad (8.34)$$

Hence,

$$\text{adj}(s\mathbf{I} - \mathbf{A}) = \mathbf{P}_2 s^2 + \mathbf{P}_1 s + \mathbf{P}_0$$

$$= \begin{bmatrix} 1 & 0 & 0 \\ 0 & 1 & 0 \\ 0 & 0 & 1 \end{bmatrix} s^2 + \begin{bmatrix} 1 & -5 & -5 \\ 1 & 2 & 0 \\ 0 & 1 & 3 \end{bmatrix} s + \begin{bmatrix} 0 & -5 & -5 \\ 0 & 0 & -5 \\ 1 & 2 & 7 \end{bmatrix}$$

$$= \begin{bmatrix} s^2 + s & -5s - 5 & -5s - 5 \\ s & s^2 + 2s & -5 \\ 1 & s + 2 & s^2 + 3s + 7 \end{bmatrix} \qquad (8.35)$$

and

$$\det(s\mathbf{I} - \mathbf{A}) = s^3 + a_2 s^2 + a_1 s + a_0$$
$$= s^3 + 3s^2 + 7s + 5 = (s + 1)(s^2 + 2s + 5) \quad (8.36)$$

The inverse of the matrix is now obtained by dividing its adjoint by its determinant. Some simplification is obtained by canceling common factors between the numerators and denominators of various elements of the inverse. The following matrix is obtained after these steps.

$$(s\mathbf{I} - \mathbf{A})^{-1}$$

$$= \begin{bmatrix} \dfrac{s}{s^2 + 2s + 5} & \dfrac{-5}{s^2 + 2s + 5} & \dfrac{-5}{s^2 + 2s + 5} \\[3mm] \dfrac{s}{s^3 + 3s^2 + 7s + 5} & \dfrac{s^2 + 2s}{s^3 + 3s^2 + 7s + 5} & \dfrac{-5}{s^3 + 3s^2 + 7s + 5} \\[3mm] \dfrac{1}{s^3 + 3s^2 + 7s + 5} & \dfrac{s + 2}{s^3 + 3s^2 + 7s + 5} & \dfrac{s^2 + 3s + 7}{s^3 + 3s^2 + 7s + 5} \end{bmatrix}$$

$$(8.37)$$

Finally, taking the inverse Laplace transform of each element of this matrix, the transition matrix $\boldsymbol{\phi}(t)$ is obtained as

$$\begin{bmatrix} e^{-t}(\cos 2t - 0.5\sin 2t) & -2.5e^{-t}\sin 2t & -2.5e^{-t}\sin 2t \\ \frac{1}{4}e^{-t}(\cos 2t + 2\sin 2t - 1) & \frac{1}{4}e^{-t}(5\cos 2t - 1) & 1.25e^{-t}(\cos 2t - 1) \\ \frac{1}{4}e^{-t}(1 - \cos 2t) & \frac{1}{4}e^{-t}(1 - \cos 2t + 2\sin 2t) & \frac{1}{4}e^{-t}(5 - \cos 2t + 2\sin 2t) \end{bmatrix}$$

■

It will be seen that the method is rather tedious. Although it is possible to use a computer program for evaluating the adjoint as well as the determinant of $(s\mathbf{I} - \mathbf{A})$, based on Leverrier's algorithm, the evaluation of the inverse Laplace transform can still be quite time consuming. The main problem is that the entire procedure is hard to automate. Some other methods that are more suitable for use with computers will now be presented.

Drill Problem 8.1A

Determine $e^{\mathbf{A}t}$ for the A-matrix given below.

$$\mathbf{A} = \begin{bmatrix} 1 & 2 \\ -3 & -4 \end{bmatrix}$$

Answer: $\begin{bmatrix} 3e^{-t} - 2e^{-2t} & 2e^{-t} - 2e^{-2t} \\ -3e^{-t} + 3e^{-2t} & -2e^{-t} + 3e^{-2t} \end{bmatrix}$

Drill Problem 8.2

Determine $e^{\mathbf{A}t}$ for the A-matrix given below, using Leverrier's algorithm.

$$\mathbf{A} = \begin{bmatrix} -1 & 2 & -8 \\ 0 & -2 & 4 \\ 0 & 0 & -4 \end{bmatrix}$$

Answer: $\begin{bmatrix} e^{-t} & 2e^{-t} - 2e^{-2t} & -4e^{-2t} + 4e^{-4t} \\ 0 & e^{-2t} & 2e^{-2t} - 2e^{-4t} \\ 0 & 0 & e^{-4t} \end{bmatrix}$

8.3.2.2 Use of Sylvester's Interpolation Formula

Using this formula (for details refer to Chapter 6 of the book by Ogata listed in Appendix D), $e^{\mathbf{A}t}$ can be expressed in the form of the following power series, if the eigenvalues of $\mathbf{A}$ are distinct:

$$e^{\mathbf{A}t} = f_0 \mathbf{I} + f_1 \mathbf{A} + f_2 \mathbf{A}^2 + \cdots + f_{n-1} \mathbf{A}^{n-1} \tag{8.38}$$

where f_i are scalar functions of t that can be evaluated by solving the following set of linear simultaneous equations

$$\begin{bmatrix} 1 & \lambda_1 & \lambda_1^2 & \cdots & \lambda_1^{n-1} \\ 1 & \lambda_2 & \lambda_2^2 & \cdots & \lambda_2^{n-1} \\ \cdot & \cdot & \cdot & \cdots & \cdot \\ \cdot & \cdot & \cdot & \cdots & \cdot \\ 1 & \lambda_n & \lambda_n^2 & \cdots & \lambda_n^{n-1} \end{bmatrix} \begin{bmatrix} f_0 \\ f_1 \\ \cdot \\ \cdot \\ f_{n-1} \end{bmatrix} = \begin{bmatrix} e^{\lambda_1 t} \\ e^{\lambda_2 t} \\ \cdot \\ \cdot \\ e^{\lambda_n t} \end{bmatrix} \tag{8.39}$$

and λ_i are the eigenvalues of the matrix $\mathbf{A}$.

The following example will demonstrate the procedure.

Example 8.4

Consider again the matrix **A** for which we obtained the transition matrix in Example 8.2. We have the 2×2 matrix

$$\mathbf{A} = \begin{bmatrix} 0 & 1 \\ -3 & -4 \end{bmatrix} \tag{8.40}$$

The eigenvalues of the matrix are the roots of the determinant of $(\lambda \mathbf{I} - \mathbf{A})$. In Example 8.2, we evaluated the determinant of $(s\mathbf{I} - \mathbf{A})$ and found it to be $(s^2 + 4s + 3)$. Hence,

$$\det(\lambda \mathbf{I} - \mathbf{A}) = \lambda^2 + 4\lambda + 3 = (\lambda + 1)(\lambda + 3) \tag{8.41}$$

The two eigenvalues of **A** are, therefore, given by

$$\lambda_1 = -1$$

and

$$\lambda_2 = -3 \tag{8.42}$$

Using these in equation 8.39, we obtain

$$\begin{bmatrix} 1 & -1 \\ 1 & -3 \end{bmatrix}\begin{bmatrix} f_0 \\ f_1 \end{bmatrix} = \begin{bmatrix} e^{-t} \\ e^{-2t} \end{bmatrix} \tag{8.43}$$

and solving these,

$$f_0 = 1.5e^{-t} - 0.5e^{-3t}$$
$$f_1 = 0.5e^{-t} - 0.5e^{-3t} \tag{8.44}$$

Substitution of these values in equation 8.38 yields

$$\begin{aligned}
e^{\mathbf{A}t} &= f_0\mathbf{I} + f_1\mathbf{A} \\
&= (1.5e^{-t} - 0.5e^{-3t})\begin{bmatrix} 1 & 0 \\ 0 & 1 \end{bmatrix} \\
&\quad + (0.5e^{-t} - 0.5e^{-3t})\begin{bmatrix} 0 & 1 \\ -3 & -4 \end{bmatrix} \\
&= \begin{bmatrix} 1.5e^{-t} - 0.5e^{-3t} & 0.5e^{-t} - 0.5e^{-3t} \\ 2(e^{-3t} - e^{-t}) & 2.5e^{-3t} - 1.5e^{-t} \end{bmatrix} \tag{8.45}
\end{aligned}$$

which is identical to equation 8.23, the result obtained in Example 8.2. ∎

This procedure would appear to be a little simpler than the method that uses Laplace transforms and is more suitable for use with digital computers, especially since good computer programs are available for determining eigenvalues as well as for matrix inversion. It has to be modified slightly if the matrix **A** has multiple eigenvalues, since in that instance the matrix on the left-hand side of equation 8.39 will have two or more identical rows and will, therefore, be singular. If the multiplicity of a certain eigenvalue, say λ_r, is m, then the corresponding rows of equation 8.39 will need modification. With the first row of this group as in the above equation, the following $(m - 1)$ rows will be replaced by successive derivatives with respect to λ_r. For example, consider the case when the **A** matrix is of order 4, but the eigenvalue λ_1 is repeated three times. Here equation 8.38 will be replaced by the following:

$$
\begin{bmatrix}
1 & \lambda_1 & \lambda_1^2 & \lambda_1^3 \\
0 & 1 & 2\lambda_1 & 3\lambda_1^2 \\
0 & 0 & 2 & 6\lambda_1 \\
1 & \lambda_2 & \lambda_2^2 & \lambda_2^3
\end{bmatrix}
\begin{bmatrix}
f_0 \\
f_1 \\
f_2 \\
f_3
\end{bmatrix}
=
\begin{bmatrix}
e^{\lambda_1 t} \\
t e^{\lambda_1 t} \\
t^2 e^{\lambda_1 t} \\
e^{\lambda_2 t}
\end{bmatrix}
\tag{8.46}
$$

This can be easily extended to the more general case when a matrix has many sets of repeated eigenvalues. The following example will illustrate the procedure.

Example 8.5

Consider the 2×2 matrix shown below.

$$
\mathbf{A} = \begin{bmatrix} 0 & 1 \\ -4 & -4 \end{bmatrix}
\tag{8.47}
$$

It is easily seen that is has two equal eigenvalues $\lambda = -2$. Hence, following the procedure suggested in equation 8.46, we obtain

$$
\begin{bmatrix} 1 & -2 \\ 0 & 1 \end{bmatrix}
\begin{bmatrix} f_0 \\ f_1 \end{bmatrix}
=
\begin{bmatrix} e^{-2t} \\ t e^{-2t} \end{bmatrix}
\tag{8.48}
$$

Solving these, we get

$$
f_1 = t e^{-2t}
$$

$$
f_0 = (1 + 2t) e^{-2t}
\tag{8.49}
$$

Substituting these values in equation 8.38, we obtain

$$
\phi(t) = f_0 \mathbf{I} + f_1 \mathbf{A} =
\begin{bmatrix}
(1 + 2t) e^{-2t} & t e^{-2t} \\
-4t e^{-2t} & (1 - 2t) e^{-2t}
\end{bmatrix}
\tag{8.50}
$$

∎

The procedure described in this section gets a little involved if **A** has complex eigenvalues, because some elements of the matrix on the left-hand side of equation 8.39 will be complex. This would therefore require the inversion of a complex matrix. Computer programs for inverting such matrices are readily available.

Drill Problem 8.3

Repeat Drill Problem 8.1 by using Sylvester's interpolation formula.

8.3.2.3   Use of Diagonal or Jordan Forms

The computation of $e^{\mathbf{A}t}$ is quite straightforward for the special case when $\mathbf{A}$ is a diagonal matrix. For example, consider

$$\mathbf{\Lambda} = \begin{bmatrix} \lambda_1 & 0 & 0 & 0 \\ 0 & \lambda_2 & 0 & 0 \\ 0 & 0 & \lambda_3 & 0 \\ 0 & 0 & 0 & \lambda_4 \end{bmatrix} \tag{8.51}$$

Since $(s\mathbf{I} - \mathbf{\Lambda})$ is a diagonal matrix, it is evident that its inverse will also be diagonal with elements of the form $1/(s - \lambda_i)$. Taking the inverse Laplace transform, we obtain

$$e^{\mathbf{\Lambda}t} = \begin{bmatrix} e^{\lambda_1 t} & 0 & 0 & 0 \\ 0 & e^{\lambda_2 t} & 0 & 0 \\ 0 & 0 & \cdot e^{\lambda_3 t} & 0 \\ 0 & 0 & 0 & e^{\lambda_4 t} \end{bmatrix} \tag{8.52}$$

This is a very useful result because the diagonal matrix represents a set of *uncoupled* first-order differential equations, that is, every equation contains only one of the state variables on the right-hand side and its derivative on the left-hand side. Since this is not the usual case with state equations, we would like to find out if it is possible to diagonalize the A-matrix. We shall now show that this can always be done if all the eigenvalues of $\mathbf{A}$ are distinct. Let λ_i be an eigenvalue of $\mathbf{A}$ and let $\mathbf{v}_i$ be the corresponding eigenvector. Then we obtain the following set of equations from the definition of eigenvalues and eigenvectors:

$$\begin{aligned} \mathbf{A}\mathbf{v}_1 &= \lambda_1 \mathbf{v}_1 \\ \mathbf{A}\mathbf{v}_2 &= \lambda_2 \mathbf{v}_2 \\ &\cdots\cdots \\ &\cdots\cdots \\ \mathbf{A}\mathbf{v}_n &= \lambda_n \mathbf{v}_n \end{aligned} \tag{8.53}$$

These equations can be rearranged to obtain

$$\mathbf{A}\mathbf{M} = \mathbf{M}\mathbf{\Lambda} \tag{8.54}$$

where $\mathbf{\Lambda}$ is defined in equation 8.51 and the columns of the matrix $\mathbf{M}$ are the n eigenvectors of $\mathbf{A}$, that is,

$$\mathbf{M} = \begin{bmatrix} \mathbf{v}_1 & \mathbf{v}_2 & \cdots & \mathbf{v}_n \end{bmatrix} \tag{8.55}$$

If **M** is nonsingular (this will always be true if the matrix **A** has distinct eigenvalues), we may solve equation 8.54 for **Λ** to obtain

$$\Lambda = M^{-1}AM \tag{8.56}$$

It also follows that

$$sI - \Lambda = M^{-1}(sI - A)M \tag{8.57}$$

and

$$(sI - \Lambda)^{-1} = M^{-1}(sI - A)^{-1}M \tag{8.58}$$

so that

$$(sI - A)^{-1} = M(sI - \Lambda)^{-1}M^{-1} \tag{8.59}$$

Taking the inverse Laplace transform of equation 8.59, we now obtain

$$e^{At} = Me^{\Lambda t}M^{-1} \tag{8.60}$$

The following example will illustrate the procedure.

Example 8.6

Consider the **A**-matrix, which was also used in Example 8.4 with Sylvester's interpolation formula.

$$A = \begin{bmatrix} 0 & 1 \\ -3 & -4 \end{bmatrix}$$

As shown in Example 8.4, the eigenvalues of **A** are given by $\lambda_1 = -1$ and $\lambda_2 = -3$. The corresponding eigenvectors are easily obtained as

$$v_1 = \begin{bmatrix} 1 \\ -1 \end{bmatrix} \quad \text{and} \quad v_2 = \begin{bmatrix} 1 \\ -3 \end{bmatrix}$$

so that

$$M = \begin{bmatrix} 1 & 1 \\ -1 & -3 \end{bmatrix} \quad M^{-1} = \begin{bmatrix} 1.5 & 0.5 \\ -0.5 & -0.5 \end{bmatrix}$$

and

$$\Lambda = \begin{bmatrix} -1 & 0 \\ 0 & -3 \end{bmatrix}$$

The state transition matrix is now obtained as

$$
\begin{aligned}
e^{At} &= Me^{\Lambda t}M^{-1} \\
&= \begin{bmatrix} 1 & 1 \\ -1 & -3 \end{bmatrix}\begin{bmatrix} e^{-t} & 0 \\ 0 & e^{-3t} \end{bmatrix}\begin{bmatrix} 1.5 & 0.5 \\ -0.5 & -0.5 \end{bmatrix} \\
&= \begin{bmatrix} 1.5e^{-t} - 0.5e^{-3t} & 0.5e^{-t} - 0.5e^{-3t} \\ 1.5e^{-3t} - 1.5e^{-t} & 1.5e^{-3t} - 0.5^{-t} \end{bmatrix}
\end{aligned}
$$

which agrees with the result obtained in Example 8.4. ∎

Equation 8.60 provides us with a straightforward procedure that is especially suitable for calculating the transition matrix $e^{\mathbf{A}t}$, if $\mathbf{A}$ is diagonalizable, on a digital computer. Several standard routines for computing the eigenvalues and eigenvectors of a matrix with real elements can be used for this purpose. The most well-known is the Q-R algorithm. The corresponding computer program, EISPACK, is available in most computer libraries. It should be noted, however, that diagonalization is guaranteed only if all of the eigenvalues are distinct. For the general case of repeated eigenvalues, it may not be possible to diagonalize the matrix $\mathbf{A}$ through the procedure given here. In such cases, it will be possible to obtain the *Jordan* form by using generalized eigenvectors for the matrix. We will not go into details here, but a discussion of these eigenvectors can be found in books on control systems that are listed in Appendix E. (Also see Problem 8.7 at the end of this chapter.)

Drill Problem 8.4

Repeat Drill Problem 8.2 by diagonalizing the A-matrix.

8.3.3 THE CHARACTERISTIC POLYNOMIAL AND STABILITY

The determinant of the matrix $(s\mathbf{I} - \mathbf{A})$ is called the characteristic polynomial of $\mathbf{A}$. The roots of this polynomial are the eigenvalues of $\mathbf{A}$. As will be shown in Section 8.5, the characteristic polynomial is identical to the denominator of the transfer function of the system. Hence, it is evident that the eigenvalues are also the poles of the system transfer function.

From our study of stability of linear continuous-time systems, it follows that *such a system will be stable if and only if all the eigenvalues of the matrix* $\mathbf{A}$ *have negative real parts.*

If we are given the state equations of a system, we can determine whether it is stable by finding the eigenvalues of the $\mathbf{A}$ matrix. This is particularly useful for a system of high order, where one can use a numerically robust method for calculating the eigenvalues. This usually gives more accurate results than would normally be obtained when the roots are evaluated after first determining the characteristic polynomial.

It is not necessary to determine all of the roots of a polynomial to find out if any of them have positive real parts. This information can be obtained more easily by using the Routh–Hurwitz criterion, which is described in any book on control systems.

8.4 STATE EQUATIONS FOR DISCRETE-TIME SYSTEMS

A difference equation of order n can be decomposed into n first-order difference equations just as in the case of differential equations. The resulting state equations will, in general, have the form shown below.

$$x(k + 1) = \mathbf{A}x(k) + \mathbf{B}u(k) \tag{8.61}$$

$$y(k) = \mathbf{C}x(k) + \mathbf{D}u(k) \tag{8.62}$$

where, as before, $\mathbf{x}$ is the n-dimensional state vector, $\mathbf{u}$ is the m-dimensional input vector, and $\mathbf{y}$ is the r-dimensional output vector. It will be seen that equations 8.8 and 8.61 are very similar in form. The following example will illustrate the main idea.

Example 8.7

Consider the discrete-time system described by the difference equation

$$y(k) + a_1 y(k - 1) + \cdots + a_n y(k - n) = u(k) \tag{8.63}$$

To express this in the form of state equations, let us define the following state variables

$$\begin{aligned} x_1(k) &= y(k - 1) \\ x_2(k) &= y(k - 2) \\ &\phantom{={}} \cdots \\ x_n(k) &= y(k - n) \end{aligned} \tag{8.64}$$

We can now combine equations 8.63 and 8.64 to obtain the following:

$$\begin{aligned} x_1(k + 1) &= u(k) - a_1 x_1(k) - a_2 x_2(k) - \cdots - a_n x_n(k) \\ x_2(k + 1) &= x_1(k) \\ &\phantom{={}} \cdots \\ x_n(k + 1) &= x_{n-1}(k) \end{aligned} \tag{8.65}$$

These can be rearranged in the form of a matrix as shown below.

$$x(k + 1) = \mathbf{A}x(k) + \mathbf{B}u(k) \tag{8.66}$$

where

$$\mathbf{x}(k) = \begin{bmatrix} x_1(k) \\ x_2(k) \\ \cdots \\ \cdots \\ x_n(k) \end{bmatrix} \tag{8.67}$$

$$\mathbf{A} = \begin{bmatrix} -a_1 & -a_2 & \cdots & -a_n \\ 1 & 0 & \cdots & 0 \\ 0 & 1 & \cdots & 0 \\ 0 & 0 & \cdots & 1 \end{bmatrix} \tag{8.68}$$

and

$$
\mathbf{B} = \begin{bmatrix} 1 \\ 0 \\ 0 \\ \cdot \\ \cdot \\ 0 \end{bmatrix}
\tag{8.69}
$$

Also, the output of the system is given by

$$
y(k) = x_1(k + 1) = \mathbf{C}\mathbf{x}(k) + \mathbf{D}\mathbf{u}(k)
\tag{8.70}
$$

where

$$
\mathbf{C} = [\, -a_1 \quad -a_2 \quad \cdots \quad -a_n \,]
\tag{8.71}
$$

and

$$
\mathbf{D} = 1
\tag{8.72}
$$

∎

The general case of difference equations, where the right-hand side contains past values of the input as well, will be discussed in detail in Section 8.6. We shall now see how to solve equation 8.61.

8.4.1 THE STATE TRANSITION EQUATION

Let us consider the problem of determining the state vector $\mathbf{x}(k)$, given the initial state $\mathbf{x}(0)$ and the input sequence, $\mathbf{u}(0), \mathbf{u}(1), \ldots, \mathbf{u}(k)$. Repeated application of equation 8.61, starting with $k = 0$, gives

$$
\mathbf{x}(1) = \mathbf{A}\mathbf{x}(0) + \mathbf{B}\mathbf{u}(0)
\tag{8.73}
$$

$$
\mathbf{x}(2) = \mathbf{A}\mathbf{x}(1) + \mathbf{B}\mathbf{u}(1)
$$

$$
= \mathbf{A}^2\mathbf{x}(0) + \mathbf{A}\mathbf{B}\mathbf{u}(0) + \mathbf{B}\mathbf{u}(1)
\tag{8.74}
$$

Proceeding in this way, it is seen that

$$
\mathbf{x}(k) = \mathbf{A}^k\mathbf{x}(0) + \sum_{i=0}^{k-1} \mathbf{A}^{k-1-i}\mathbf{B}\mathbf{u}(i)
\tag{8.75}
$$

Equation 8.75 is the counterpart of the state transition equation for continuous-time systems, derived in Section 8.3.1. It will be of some interest to compare equations 8.75 and 8.15. First, we note that the natural response of the discrete-time system depends on the matrix $\mathbf{A}^k$, which replaces the matrix $e^{\mathbf{A}t}$ for the continuous-time system. It is, therefore, usual to call $\mathbf{A}^k$ the *transition* or *fundamental* matrix for the discrete-time system. Note also that the convolution integral in equation 8.15 has been replaced by a convolution sum in equation 8.75, as expected.

The solution of the state equations can also be obtained by taking z-transforms of both sides of equation 8.61. This gives us

$$
z\mathbf{X}(z) - z\mathbf{x}(0) = \mathbf{A}\mathbf{X}(z) + \mathbf{B}\mathbf{U}(z)
\tag{8.76}
$$

which can be solved for $\mathbf{X}(z)$ to obtain

$$\mathbf{X}(z) = (z\mathbf{I} - \mathbf{A})^{-1}z\mathbf{x}(0) + (z\mathbf{I} - \mathbf{A})^{-1}\mathbf{B}U(z) \qquad (8.77)$$

It is interesting to observe the similarity between equation 8.77 and equation 8.18, which was derived for the solution of the state equations for continuous-time systems. Taking the inverse z-transform of both sides of equation 8.77 yields the state transition equation 8.75. It also tells us that

$$\mathbf{A}^k = \mathscr{Z}^{-1}\left[(z\mathbf{I} - \mathbf{A})^{-1}\right] \qquad (8.78)$$

Equation 8.78 provides us with another approach to computing the transition matrix, which will be discussed in the next section. It also gives us some insight into the stability of discrete-time systems that are described by using the state–space formulation.

8.4.2 EVALUATION OF STATE TRANSITION MATRICES

It would appear from the state transition equation 8.75 that, unlike the case of continuous-time systems, we do not have the problem of the evaluation of the transition matrix for the discrete-time case. Although it is possible to calculate the matrix $\mathbf{A}^k$ by repeated multiplications, it is not desirable for many reasons. The first is the mere inconvenience of the required computation, especially if k is a large integer. The second reason is the problem of numerical inaccuracy that would be introduced because any digital computer can carry only a finite number of digits, with the result that all numbers must be truncated. This effect is more marked when the eigenvalues of the matrix $\mathbf{A}$ have magnitude close to or greater than one. Finally, we need a closed-form solution, since just raising the matrix $\mathbf{A}$ to the power k does not provide us with any insight into the structure of the solution. In view of these considerations, we now present three other methods for evaluating $\mathbf{A}^k$ in this section.

8.4.2.1 Use of Cayley – Hamilton Theorem

This method is based on the Cayley–Hamilton theorem, which states that every $n \times n$ matrix satisfies its own characteristic equation. Thus if

$$f(\lambda) \triangleq \det(\lambda\mathbf{I} - \mathbf{A})$$

$$= \lambda^n + a_1\lambda^{n-1} + a_2\lambda^{n-2} + \cdots + a_{n-1}\lambda + a_n \qquad (8.79)$$

is the characteristic polynomial of $\mathbf{A}$ then according to this theorem, we have

$$\mathbf{A}^n + a_1\mathbf{A}^{n-1} + a_2\mathbf{A}^{n-2} + \cdots + a_{n-1}\mathbf{A} + a_n\mathbf{I} = \mathbf{0} \qquad (8.80)$$

In view of this relationship, it is possible to express any higher power of $\mathbf{A}$ as a linear combination of various powers of $\mathbf{A}$ from 0 to $n - 1$. For instance, we may rewrite equation 8.80 in the form

$$\mathbf{A}^n = -a_1\mathbf{A}^{n-1} - a_2\mathbf{A}^{n-2} - \cdots - a_{n-1}\mathbf{A} - a_n\mathbf{I} \qquad (8.81)$$

To determine $\mathbf{A}^{n+1}$, we multiply both sides of equation 8.81 by $\mathbf{A}$ to obtain

$$\mathbf{A}^{n+1} = -a_1\mathbf{A}^n - a_2\mathbf{A}^{n-1} - \cdots - a_{n-1}\mathbf{A}^2 - a_n\mathbf{A} \qquad (8.82)$$

We can now substitute for $\mathbf{A}^n$ from equation 8.80 and obtain an expression for $\mathbf{A}^{n+1}$ in terms of the powers of $\mathbf{A}$ from 0 to $n - 1$. This is shown below.

$$\mathbf{A}^{n+1} = \left(a_1^2 - a_2\right)\mathbf{A}^{n-1} + \left(a_1a_2 - a_3\right)\mathbf{A}^{n-2} + \cdots + a_1a_n\mathbf{I} \qquad (8.83)$$

We can proceed in this manner for higher powers of $\mathbf{A}$. Although it looks straightforward, this process can get tedious. A simpler approach is to perform long division of the polynomial λ^k by $f(\lambda)$. The remainder will be a polynomial of degree less than n, that is, we may write

$$\lambda^k = g(\lambda)f(\lambda) + h(\lambda) \qquad (8.84)$$

where

$$h(\lambda) = \alpha_1\lambda^{n-1} + \alpha_2\lambda^{n-2} + \cdots + \alpha_{n-1}\lambda + \alpha_n \qquad (8.85)$$

In view of the Cayley–Hamilton theorem, it follows that

$$\mathbf{A}^k = \alpha_1\mathbf{A}^{n-1} + \alpha_2\mathbf{A}^{n-2} + \cdots + \alpha_{n-1}\mathbf{A} + \alpha_n\mathbf{I} \qquad (8.86)$$

The following example will illustrate this procedure.

Example 8.8

Consider the matrix $\mathbf{A}$ shown below. We use the procedure described above to calculate $\mathbf{A}^6$.

$$\mathbf{A} = \begin{bmatrix} -2 & 0 & 1 \\ 1 & -2 & 0 \\ 1 & 1 & -1 \end{bmatrix} \qquad (8.87)$$

The first step is to evaluate the characteristic polynomial. By using Leverrier's method, this was found to be

$$f(\lambda) = \lambda^3 + 5\lambda^2 + 7\lambda + 1 \qquad (8.88)$$

We now perform the long division of λ^6 by $f(\lambda)$. The result is given below.

$$\lambda^6 = (\lambda^3 + 5\lambda^2 + 7\lambda + 1)(\lambda^3 - 5\lambda^2 + 18\lambda - 56) + 159\lambda^2 + 374\lambda + 56$$

It follows that

$$\begin{aligned}
\mathbf{A}^6 &= 159\mathbf{A}^2 + 374\mathbf{A} + 56\mathbf{I} \\
&= 159\begin{bmatrix} 5 & 1 & -3 \\ -2 & 4 & 1 \\ -3 & -3 & 2 \end{bmatrix} + 374\begin{bmatrix} -2 & 0 & 1 \\ 1 & -2 & 0 \\ 1 & 1 & -1 \end{bmatrix} + 56\begin{bmatrix} 1 & 0 & 0 \\ 0 & 1 & 0 \\ 0 & 0 & 1 \end{bmatrix} \\
&= \begin{bmatrix} 103 & 159 & -103 \\ 56 & -56 & 159 \\ -103 & -159 & 0 \end{bmatrix}
\end{aligned} \qquad (8.89)$$

∎

8.4.2.2 Use of Sylvester's Interpolation Formula

It is easier to evaluate the coefficients α_i in equation 8.86 by using Sylvester's interpolation formula. We first describe the method for the case when the eigenvalues of $\mathbf{A}$ are distinct. Let these be denoted by $\lambda_1, \lambda_2, \ldots, \lambda_n$. Then we obtain the simultaneous equations,

$$
\begin{bmatrix}
1 & \lambda_1 & \lambda_1^2 & \cdots & \lambda_1^{n-1} \\
1 & \lambda_2 & \lambda_2^2 & \cdots & \lambda_2^{n-1} \\
\cdot & \cdot & \cdot & \cdots & \cdot \\
\cdot & \cdot & \cdot & \cdots & \cdot \\
\cdot & \cdot & \cdot & \cdots & \cdot \\
1 & \lambda_n & \lambda_n^2 & \cdots & \lambda_n^{n-1}
\end{bmatrix}
\begin{bmatrix}
\alpha_n \\
\alpha_{n-1} \\
\cdot \\
\cdot \\
\cdot \\
\alpha_1
\end{bmatrix}
=
\begin{bmatrix}
\lambda_1^k \\
\lambda_2^k \\
\cdot \\
\cdot \\
\cdot \\
\lambda_n^k
\end{bmatrix}
\tag{8.90}
$$

The coefficients α_i are now obtained by solving these equations. The following example illustrates the procedure.

Example 8.9

Consider the following matrix, which was also used in Example 8.6:

$$
\mathbf{A} = \begin{bmatrix} 0 & 1 \\ -3 & -4 \end{bmatrix}
$$

We use Sylvester's interpolation formula to determine $\mathbf{A}^{10}$.

As shown in Example 8.6, the eigenvalues of this matrix are located at -1 and -3. Since $n = 2$, we get the following equation:

$$
\mathbf{A}^{10} = \alpha_1 \mathbf{A} + \alpha_2 \mathbf{I} \tag{8.91}
$$

where the constants α_1 and α_2 can be evaluated from the following equations:

$$
\begin{bmatrix} 1 & -1 \\ 1 & -3 \end{bmatrix}
\begin{bmatrix} \alpha_2 \\ \alpha_1 \end{bmatrix}
=
\begin{bmatrix} (-1)^{10} \\ (-3)^{10} \end{bmatrix}
$$

Solving the above equation, we obtain

$$
\alpha_1 = -29524 \quad \text{and} \quad \alpha_2 = -29523
$$

Using these values in equation 8.91, we obtain

$$
\mathbf{A}^{10} = -29524 \begin{bmatrix} 0 & 1 \\ -3 & -4 \end{bmatrix} - 29523 \begin{bmatrix} 1 & 0 \\ 0 & 1 \end{bmatrix}
$$

$$
= \begin{bmatrix} -29523 & -29524 \\ 88572 & 88573 \end{bmatrix} \tag{8.92}
$$
∎

This approach is easily extended to the case when the matrix $\mathbf{A}$ has some repeated eigenvalues by using a procedure similar to that in Section 8.3.2.2. If the multiplicity of a certain eigenvalue, say λ_r, is m, then the corresponding rows of equation 8.90 will have to be modified. With the first row of this group as in the above equation, the following $(m - 1)$ rows will be replaced by successive derivatives with respect to λ_r. For example, consider the case when the **A** matrix is of order 4, but the eigenvalue λ_1 is repeated three times. Equation 8.90 will now be replaced by the following:

$$\begin{bmatrix} 1 & \lambda_1 & \lambda_1^2 & \lambda_1^3 \\ 0 & 1 & 2\lambda_1 & 3\lambda_1^2 \\ 0 & 0 & 2 & 6\lambda_1 \\ 1 & \lambda_2 & \lambda_2^2 & \lambda_2^3 \end{bmatrix} \begin{bmatrix} \alpha_4 \\ \alpha_3 \\ \alpha_2 \\ \alpha_1 \end{bmatrix} = \begin{bmatrix} \lambda_1^k \\ k\lambda_1^{k-1} \\ k(k-1)\lambda_1^{k-2} \\ \lambda_2^k \end{bmatrix} \tag{8.93}$$

The following example will illustrate the procedure for the case of two repeated eigenvalues.

Example 8.10

Consider the following matrix, which was used in Example 8.5:

$$\mathbf{A} = \begin{bmatrix} 0 & 1 \\ -4 & -4 \end{bmatrix}$$

We use the procedure described above to determine $\mathbf{A}^{10}$.

This matrix has two equal eigenvalues located at $\lambda = -2$. Hence,

$$\begin{bmatrix} 1 & -2 \\ 0 & 1 \end{bmatrix} \begin{bmatrix} \alpha_2 \\ \alpha_1 \end{bmatrix} = \begin{bmatrix} (-2)^{10} \\ 10(-2)^9 \end{bmatrix}$$

Solving the above equation, we obtain

$$\alpha_1 = -5120 \quad \text{and} \quad \alpha_2 = -9216$$

Using these values in equation 8.91, we get

$$\mathbf{A}^{10} = -5120 \begin{bmatrix} 0 & 1 \\ -3 & -4 \end{bmatrix} - 9216 \begin{bmatrix} 1 & 0 \\ 0 & 1 \end{bmatrix}$$

$$= \begin{bmatrix} -9216 & -5120 \\ 15360 & 11264 \end{bmatrix} \tag{8.94}$$

∎

8.4.2.3 Use of Diagonal or Jordan Forms

As seen in Section 8.3.2.3, it is quite straightforward to raise a diagonal matrix to the power k, as this simply requires raising each of the diagonal elements of the matrix to the power k. Consequently, if the matrix **A** has distinct eigenvalues, we can easily demonstrate that

$$\mathbf{A}^k = \mathbf{M}\mathbf{\Lambda}^k\mathbf{M}^{-1} \tag{8.95}$$

where the columns of **M** are the eigenvectors of **A**, and $\mathbf{\Lambda}$ is a diagonal matrix containing the eigenvalues of **A** and satisfying the equation

$$\mathbf{\Lambda} = \mathbf{M}^{-1}\mathbf{A}\mathbf{M}$$

For illustration, we repeat Example 8.9 using this method.

Example 8.11

Consider again the following matrix:

$$A = \begin{bmatrix} 0 & 1 \\ -3 & -4 \end{bmatrix}$$

We shall evaluate A^{10} using equation 8.95.

The eigenvalues of this matrix are located at -1 and -3. The matrices M, M^{-1}, and Λ for this case were calculated in Example 8.6 and are given below.

$$M = \begin{bmatrix} 1 & 1 \\ -1 & -3 \end{bmatrix} \quad M^{-1} = \begin{bmatrix} 1.5 & 0.5 \\ -0.5 & -0.5 \end{bmatrix}$$

and

$$\Lambda = \begin{bmatrix} -1 & 0 \\ 0 & -3 \end{bmatrix}$$

Thus, we obtain

$$A^{10} = \begin{bmatrix} 1 & 1 \\ -1 & -3 \end{bmatrix} \begin{bmatrix} -1 & 0 \\ 0 & -3 \end{bmatrix}^{10} \begin{bmatrix} 1.5 & 0.5 \\ -0.5 & -0.5 \end{bmatrix}$$

$$= \begin{bmatrix} -29523 & -29524 \\ 88572 & 88573 \end{bmatrix} \qquad ■$$

Drill Problem 8.5

For the A-matrix given below, determine A^{10} by each of the methods described in this section.

$$A = \begin{bmatrix} 4 & 2 \\ -3 & -1 \end{bmatrix}$$

Answer: $\begin{bmatrix} 3070 & 2046 \\ -3069 & -2045 \end{bmatrix}$

8.4.3 THE CHARACTERISTIC POLYNOMIAL AND STABILITY

The determinant of the matrix $(zI - A)$ is called the characteristic polynomial of the matrix A in the state equation 8.61 for the discrete-time system. The roots of this polynomial are the eigenvalues of A. As will be shown in Section 8.5, the characteristic polynomial is identical to the denominator of the transfer function of the system. Consequently, the eigenvalues are also the poles of the system transfer function.

From our study of stability of linear discrete-time systems in Chapter 6, it follows that a *system will be stable if and only if all the eigenvalues of the matrix* **A** *have magnitude less than one.* This is also obvious from our discussions in the previous section, since A^k will increase indefinitely for large values of k, unless all of the eigenvalues of A lie inside the unit circle.

If we are given the state equations of a system, we can determine whether it is stable by finding the eigenvalues of the **A** matrix. This is particularly useful for a system of high order, where one can use a numerically robust method for calculating the eigenvalues. This usually gives more accurate results than would normally be obtained when the roots are evaluated after first determining the characteristic polynomial.

It is not necessary to determine all the roots of a polynomial to find out if the magnitude of any of them is greater than one. Several methods have been developed for this purpose. The interested reader is referred to any of the books on control systems, listed in Appendix E.

8.5 TRANSFER FUNCTION FROM STATE EQUATIONS

As pointed out earlier, state equations represent the complete internal description of the system, whereas the transfer function is only the input–output representation. As a result, given the state equations of any system, its transfer function can be obtained uniquely.

We start with continuous-time systems. From the definition of the transfer function as given in Chapter 5, it is the ratio of the Laplace transforms of the output and the input under zero initial conditions. Consequently, given the state equations

$$\dot{\mathbf{x}} = \mathbf{Ax} + \mathbf{Bu} \tag{8.96}$$

$$\mathbf{y} = \mathbf{Cx} + \mathbf{Du} \tag{8.97}$$

we first take the Laplace transform of both sides of equation 8.96 with the assumption that

$$\mathbf{x}(0) = \mathbf{0} \tag{8.98}$$

and solve for $\mathbf{X}(s)$. This gives us

$$\mathbf{X}(s) = (s\mathbf{I} - \mathbf{A})^{-1}\mathbf{BU}(s) \tag{8.99}$$

If we now take the Laplace transform of both sides of equation 8.97 and substitute for $\mathbf{X}(s)$ from equation 8.99, we obtain

$$\mathbf{Y}(s) = \left[\mathbf{C}(s\mathbf{I} - \mathbf{A})^{-1}\mathbf{B} + \mathbf{D}\right]\mathbf{U}(s) \tag{8.100}$$

It is customary to define

$$\mathbf{G}(s) = \mathbf{C}(s\mathbf{I} - \mathbf{A})^{-1}\mathbf{B} + \mathbf{D} \tag{8.101}$$

as the transfer function matrix for the system.

For the special case of single-input single-output systems, $Y(s)$ and $U(s)$ are scalars, and the transfer function matrix in this case is reduced to a scalar that is the ratio $Y(s)/U(s)$.

Note that in this instance **C** is a matrix with one row and n columns (also called a *row* vector), whereas **B** is a matrix with one column and n rows, and thus is a *column* vector. Also **D** is a matrix with one row and one column, that is, a scalar.

Recalling that the inverse of a matrix can be obtained by dividing its adjoint by its determinant, we may rewrite equation 8.101 as

$$G(s) = \frac{\mathbf{C} \, \text{adj} \, (s\mathbf{I} - \mathbf{A})\mathbf{B}}{\det (s\mathbf{I} - \mathbf{A})} + D = \frac{P(s)}{Q(s)} \tag{8.102}$$

It follows from equation 8.102 that the transfer function $G(s)$ is the ratio of two polynomials in s. The denominator polynomial $Q(s)$ is the determinant of $(s\mathbf{I} - \mathbf{A})$ and, thus, a polynomial of degree n if **A** is an $n \times n$ matrix. This implies that the denominator of the transfer function is the characteristic polynomial of **A**. Furthermore, since the poles of the transfer function are the roots of $Q(s)$ and the eigenvalues of **A** are the roots of its characteristic polynomial, it follows that the poles must be the eigenvalues of **A**. This explains why the condition for stability of the system is the same either in terms of the eigenvalues of **A** or the poles of $G(s)$.

The numerator of the transfer function is given by

$$P(s) = \mathbf{C} \, \text{adj} \, (s\mathbf{I} - \mathbf{A})\mathbf{B} + DQ(s) \tag{8.103}$$

The degree of the first term on the right-hand side of equation 8.103 will be less than or equal to $(n - 1)$, whereas that of the second term will be n, since D is a scalar. Therefore, the degree of the numerator of the transfer function obtained from equation 8.102 will always be less than or equal to that of the denominator, that is, the transfer function will be a *proper* rational function. In the particular case when $D = 0$, the degree of the numerator will always be less than n, with the result that the transfer function will be *strictly proper*.

Proceeding in the same manner with state equations for discrete-time systems, but taking z-transforms instead of Laplace transforms, it is easily shown that the transfer function is given by

$$G(z) = \frac{Y(z)}{U(z)} = \mathbf{C}(z\mathbf{I} - \mathbf{A})^{-1}\mathbf{B} + D \tag{8.104}$$

Since equation 8.104 is identical to equation 8.101, except that s replaces by z, all of the statements made about $G(s)$ also apply to $G(z)$.

In both cases, determination of the transfer function from state equations requires the inversion of either matrix $(s\mathbf{I} - \mathbf{A})$ or $(z\mathbf{I} - \mathbf{A})$. This is done conveniently by using Leverrier's algorithm, described in Section 8.3.2.1. A computer program for evaluating the transfer function from state equations, which uses this algorithm, is described in Appendix 8.1 and is on the disk enclosed with this book.

The following example will illustrate the procedure for obtaining the transfer function from the state equations for a continuous-time system. For convenience, the matrix **A** will be identical to that in Example 8.3.

Example 8.12

Consider a continuous time system described by the standard state equations 8.96 and 8.97, with the following matrices:

$$\mathbf{A} = \begin{bmatrix} -2 & -5 & -5 \\ 1 & -1 & 0 \\ 0 & 1 & 0 \end{bmatrix} \quad \mathbf{B} = \begin{bmatrix} 1 \\ 0 \\ 1 \end{bmatrix} \quad \mathbf{C} = \begin{bmatrix} 2 & 0 & 1 \end{bmatrix} \quad D = 0$$

Both the adjoint and the determinant of the matrix $(s\mathbf{I} - \mathbf{A})$ were obtained in Example 8.3 and are given below.

$$\text{adj}\,(s\mathbf{I} - \mathbf{A}) = \begin{bmatrix} s^2 + s & -5s - 5 & -5s - 5 \\ s & s^2 + 2s & -5 \\ 1 & s + 2 & s^2 + 3s + 7 \end{bmatrix}$$

$$\det\,(s\mathbf{I} - \mathbf{A}) = s^3 + 3s^2 + 7s + 5$$

The numerator of the transfer function is evaluated by premultiplying the adjoint by $\mathbf{C}$ and postmultiplying by $\mathbf{B}$. Also, the denominator of the transfer function is the determinant. The resulting transfer function is

$$G(s) = \frac{3s^2 - 5s - 2}{s^3 + 3s^2 + 7s + 5} \tag{8.105}$$

∎

Drill Problem 8.6

Determine the transfer function corresponding to the standard state equations with the following matrices:

$$\mathbf{A} = \begin{bmatrix} -2 & -5 & -4 \\ 1 & -1 & 0 \\ 0 & 1 & 0 \end{bmatrix} \quad \mathbf{B} = \begin{bmatrix} 0 \\ 1 \\ 2 \end{bmatrix} \quad \mathbf{C} = \begin{bmatrix} 3 & 1 & 0 \end{bmatrix} \quad D = 0$$

Answer: $\dfrac{s^2 - 37s - 44}{s^3 + 3s^2 + 7s + 4}$

8.6   STATE EQUATIONS FROM TRANSFER FUNCTIONS

We now study the inverse problem of determining the state equations of a system from its transfer function. State equations represent the complete description of the system, whereas transfer functions represent only the input–output description. Therefore, as expected, state equations for a given transfer function are not unique. There is a considerable amount of similarity between state–space descriptions for given transfer functions and their simulation on analog or digital computers, which was discussed in the first chapter of this book. There, several methods of realization were discussed, and it was pointed out that the only essential difference between the

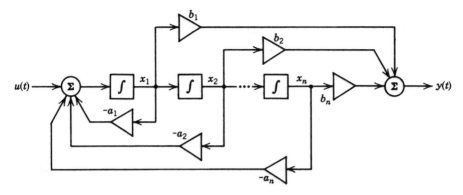

Figure 8.2 Direct realization of system described by equation 8.106.

simulation of continuous-time and discrete-time systems was the replacement of integrators with delays. In fact, all of the methods for realization that were discussed in Chapter 1 can be utilized for obtaining state equations of either type of system. We start with direct realization.

8.6.1 DIRECT REALIZATION

In Section 1.7.1 it was shown that a continuous-time system described by the differential equation

$$\frac{d^n y}{dt^n} + a_1 \frac{d^{n-1} y}{dt^{n-1}} + \cdots + a_n y(t) = b_1 \frac{d^{n-1} u}{dt^{n-1}} + \cdots + b_n u(t) \quad (8.106)$$

can be realized as in Figure 8.2.

From this realization diagram, a set of state equations is easily obtained by labeling the output of each integrator as a state variable. For the selection shown above, we obtain the following set of equations:

$$\dot{x}_1 = u(t) - a_1 x_1 - a_2 x_2 - \cdots - a_n x_n$$

$$\dot{x}_2 = x_1$$

$$\dot{x}_3 = x_2 \qquad\qquad (8.107)$$

$$\cdots\cdots\cdots\cdots$$
$$\cdots\cdots\cdots\cdots$$

$$\dot{x}_n = x_{n-1}$$

and

$$y(t) = b_1 x_1 + b_2 x_2 + \cdots + b_n x_n \qquad (8.108)$$

We can now write the state equations in the matrix form, using our standard notation. The various matrices are given below.

$$A = \begin{bmatrix} -a_1 & -a_2 & \cdots & -a_n \\ 1 & 0 & \cdots & 0 \\ 0 & 1 & \cdots & 0 \\ \cdots\cdots\cdots\cdots\cdots\cdots\cdots \\ 0 & 0 & \cdots & 1 & 0 \end{bmatrix} \qquad B = \begin{bmatrix} 1 \\ 0 \\ 0 \\ 0 \\ 0 \end{bmatrix}$$

$$C = \begin{bmatrix} b_1 & b_2 & \cdots & b_n \end{bmatrix} \qquad D = 0 \qquad (8.109)$$

From equation 8.106 the transfer function of the system may be written as

$$G(s) = \frac{b_1 s^{n-1} + \cdots + b_{n-1} s + b_n}{s^n + a_1 s^{n-1} + \cdots + a_{n-1} s + a_n} \qquad (8.110)$$

A comparison between equations 8.109 and 8.110 tells us that it is possible to write the state equations in this particular form for a given transfer function by inspection. The state equations in equation 8.109 are said to be in the *controller canonical form*, as these are useful for the design of a controller based on state variable feedback (see the book by Kailath listed in Appendix E). Note, however, that the transfer function is strictly proper. For a proper (but not strictly proper) transfer function, it is necessary to first divide the numerator by the denominator to obtain the constant *D*. Since the transfer function is now the sum of *D* and a strictly proper transfer function, we can use this procedure. The following examples will illustrate the procedure.

Example 8.13

Consider the following transfer function:

$$G(s) = \frac{2s^3 + 9s^2 + 14s + 30}{s^3 + 4s^2 + 6s + 12} \qquad (8.111)$$

To obtain the state equations in this case, we must first express the transfer function as

$$G(s) = 2 + \frac{s^2 + 2s + 6}{s^3 + 4s^2 + 6s + 12} \qquad (8.112)$$

Hence, we get the following matrices for the state equations:

$$\left. \begin{array}{c} A = \begin{bmatrix} -4 & -6 & -12 \\ 1 & 0 & 0 \\ 0 & 1 & 0 \end{bmatrix} \qquad B = \begin{bmatrix} 1 \\ 0 \\ 0 \end{bmatrix} \\ C = \begin{bmatrix} 1 & 2 & 6 \end{bmatrix} \qquad D = 2 \end{array} \right\} \qquad (8.113)$$

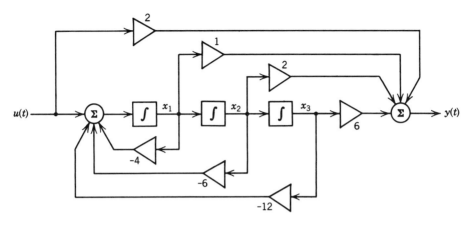

Figure 8.3 Direct realization of system described by equation 8.113.

Figure 8.3 shows the direct realization of these equations. Note that there is a direct path from $u(t)$ to $y(t)$, corresponding to the value of the parameter D. ∎

Example 8.14

We now consider a discrete-time system that has the following transfer function:

$$G(z) = \frac{z^3}{z^3 - 2.2z^2 + 1.57z - 0.36} \qquad (8.114)$$

This will first have to be expressed as the sum of a strictly proper transfer function and a constant, as shown below.

$$G(z) = 1 + \frac{2.2z^2 - 1.57z + 0.36}{z^3 - 2.2z^2 + 1.57z - 0.36} \qquad (8.115)$$

The state equations in this instance will be of the standard form given by equations 8.61 and 8.62 with the various matrices given below.

$$A = \begin{bmatrix} 2.2 & -1.57 & 0.36 \\ 1 & 0 & 0 \\ 0 & 1 & 0 \end{bmatrix} \qquad B = \begin{bmatrix} 1 \\ 0 \\ 0 \end{bmatrix}$$

$$C = \begin{bmatrix} 2.2 & -1.57 & 0.36 \end{bmatrix} \qquad D = 1 \qquad (8.116)$$

Direct realization of these equations is shown in Figure 8.4.

It is possible to obtain another canonical form of state equations by direct realization if the outputs of the integrators are labeled in the reverse order. For example, consider the diagram in Figure 8.5, which is obtained from Figure 8.4.

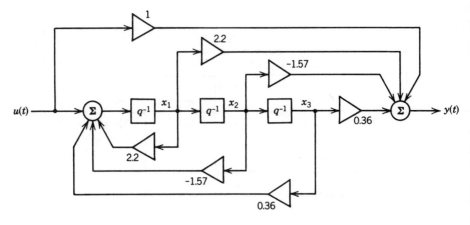

Figure 8.4 Direct realization of system described by equation 8.116.

The state equations for this case will again be in the standard form given by equations 8.61 and 8.62, but the various matrices will be different. The following equations are obtained from Figure 8.5.

$$x_1(k + 1) = x_2(k)$$

$$x_2(k + 1) = x_3(k)$$

$$x_3(k + 1) = 0.36x_1(k) - 1.57x_2(k) + 2.2x_3(k) + u(k)$$

$$y(k) = 0.36x_1(k) - 1.57x_2(k) + 2.2x_3(k) + u(k)$$

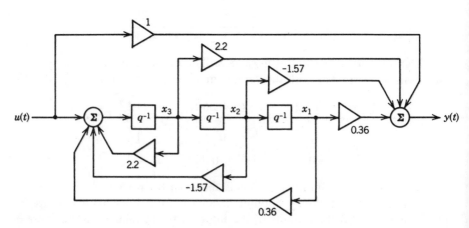

Figure 8.5 Another realization of system described by equation 8.116.

The resulting matrices are as follows:

$$A = \begin{bmatrix} 0 & 1 & 0 \\ 0 & 0 & 1 \\ 0.36 & -1.57 & 2.2 \end{bmatrix} \quad B = \begin{bmatrix} 0 \\ 0 \\ 1 \end{bmatrix}$$

$$C = \begin{bmatrix} 0.36 & -1.57 & 2.2 \end{bmatrix} \quad D = 1 \qquad \blacksquare$$

These equations are said to be in the *controllable canonical form* and have been used extensively in the literature on control theory for the design of state feedback controllers. As we shall learn later, one can obtain the state equations in this form through a simple linear transformation of the state equations for the controller canonical form, which was discussed earlier.

8.6.2 CASCADE REALIZATION

Another approach that was discussed in Section 1.7.2 is cascade programming. The basic idea here is to represent the transfer function of the system as a product of several elementary transfer functions of order one or two. The latter are required for pairs of complex conjugate poles in order to avoid complex numbers. Each of these elementary transfer functions can be simulated separately and connected in cascade to obtain the overall transfer function. State equations are easily obtained by selecting the output of each integrator (or delay element in the case of discrete-time systems) as a state variable and writing one equation for the input to each integrator.

The following example will illustrate the procedure for obtaining the state equations through cascade realization.

Example 8.15

Consider the transfer function

$$G(s) = \frac{3s + 5}{s^3 + 8s^2 + 37s + 50} \tag{8.118}$$

Simulation of this transfer function through cascade realization was studied in Example 1.16 in Chapter 1. The first step is to factorize the denominator of the transfer function. Since it has one real and a pair of complex conjugate roots, it will be desirable to express $G(s)$ as the product of two transfer functions, one of first order and the other of second order. This is shown as follows:

$$G(s) = \frac{1}{s + 2} \cdot \frac{3s + 5}{s^2 + 6s + 25} \tag{8.119}$$

The realization diagram for this case is shown in Figure 8.6.

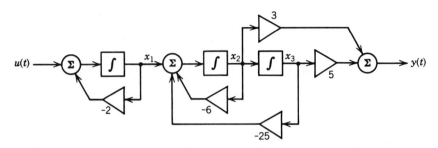

Figure 8.6 Cascade realization of system described by equation 8.119.

Selecting the state variables as shown in the simulation diagram, we obtain the following differential equations:

$$\dot{x}_1 = -2x_1 + u(t)$$
$$\dot{x}_2 = x_1 - 6x_2 - 25x_3$$
$$\dot{x}_3 = x_2 \qquad (8.120)$$

and the output is given by

$$y(t) = 3x_2 + 5x_3 \qquad (8.121)$$

Note that, as in the previous case, these equations are already in a form suitable for writing as state equations. They are easily arranged in the form of the standard vector differential equation. The corresponding matrices are given below.

$$\mathbf{A} = \begin{bmatrix} -2 & 0 & 0 \\ 1 & -6 & -25 \\ 0 & 1 & 0 \end{bmatrix} \quad \mathbf{B} = \begin{bmatrix} 1 \\ 0 \\ 0 \end{bmatrix}$$
$$\mathbf{C} = \begin{bmatrix} 0 & 3 & 5 \end{bmatrix} \quad D = 0 \qquad (8.122)$$

∎

8.6.3 PARALLEL REALIZATION

In parallel realization, which was discussed in Section 1.7.3, the main idea is to expand a proper transfer function into partial fractions. To avoid complex numbers, the denominators in this expansion are polynomials of either first degree, corresponding to real poles, or of second degree, corresponding to a pair of complex conjugate poles. State equations can be written for each of these transfer functions and the output obtained as the sum. The main advantage of this formulation is that the **A** matrix is either diagonal (or block diagonal with 2×2 diagonal blocks for complex eigenvalues) in the case of distinct eigenvalues. If there are repeated eigenvalues, the size of the corresponding diagonal block will be equal to the multiplicity for real poles

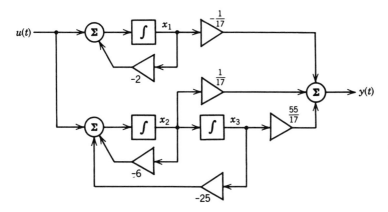

Figure 8.7 Parallel realization of system described by equation 8.123.

and twice the multiplicity for complex poles. The following examples will illustrate the formulation of state equations from the partial fraction expansion of the transfer function.

Example 8.16

Partial fraction expansion of the transfer function considered in example 8.15 gives us

$$G(s) = \frac{-\frac{1}{17}}{s+2} + \frac{\frac{1}{17}s + \frac{55}{17}}{s^2 + 6s + 25} \tag{8.123}$$

The diagram for parallel realization, given in Section 1.7.3, is shown in Figure 8.7, where the outputs of the three integrators are again labeled state variables.

With the state variables as labeled in the simulation diagram, the following differential equations are obtained:

$$\dot{x}_1 = -2x_1 + u(t)$$

$$\dot{x}_2 = -6x_2 - 25x_3 + u(t)$$

$$\dot{x}_3 = x_2 \tag{8.124}$$

and the output of the system is given by

$$y(t) = -\frac{1}{17}x_1 + \frac{1}{17}x_2 + \frac{55}{17}x_3 \tag{8.125}$$

The resulting system matrices are given below.

$$A = \begin{bmatrix} -2 & \vdots & 0 & 0 \\ \cdots & \cdots & \cdots & \cdots \\ 0 & \vdots & -6 & -25 \\ 0 & \vdots & 1 & 0 \end{bmatrix} \quad B = \begin{bmatrix} 1 \\ 1 \\ 0 \end{bmatrix}$$

$$C = \begin{bmatrix} -\dfrac{1}{17} & \dfrac{1}{17} & \dfrac{55}{17} \end{bmatrix} \quad D = 0 \tag{8.126}$$

The block diagonal form of the matrix **A** should be noted. As a result, the transition matrix can be evaluated separately for each of the diagonal blocks and then put together in the same order as in **A**. It can be easily verified that for this example, the transition matrix is given by

$$e^{At} = \begin{bmatrix} e^{-2t} & \vdots & 0 & 0 \\ \cdots & \cdots & \cdots & \cdots \\ 0 & \vdots & e^{-3t}(\cos 4t - 0.75 \sin 4t) & -6.25 e^{-3t} \sin 4t \\ 0 & \vdots & 0.25 e^{-3t} \sin 4t & e^{-3t}(\cos 4t + 0.75 \sin 4t) \end{bmatrix} \quad \blacksquare$$

Example 8.17

The partial fraction expansion of a transfer function of order three, with one pole of multiplicity two, is shown below.

$$G(s) = \frac{3}{s+2} + \frac{4}{(s+2)^2} + \frac{7}{s+3}$$

$$= \frac{7}{s+3} + \frac{1}{s+2}\left[3 + \frac{4}{s+2}\right] \tag{8.127}$$

From equation 8.127, it is evident that $G(s)$ can be realized as the sum of two transfer functions, where the second part takes the multiple poles into account by having two first-order terms in cascade. The diagram for parallel realization is shown in Figure 8.8.

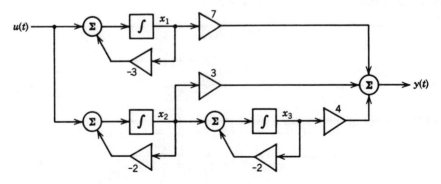

Figure 8.8 Parallel realization of transfer function in equation 8.127.

With the states as labeled, the following equations are obtained:

$$\dot{x}_1 = -3x_1 + u(t)$$
$$\dot{x}_2 = -2x_2 + u(t)$$
$$\dot{x}_3 = x_2 - 2x_3$$

and

$$y(t) = 7x_1 + 3x_2 + 4x_3 \tag{8.128}$$

The corresponding system matrices are given below.

$$\left. \mathbf{A} = \begin{bmatrix} -3 & \vdots & 0 & 0 \\ 0 & \vdots & -2 & 0 \\ 0 & \vdots & 1 & -2 \end{bmatrix} \quad \mathbf{B} = \begin{bmatrix} 1 \\ 1 \\ 0 \end{bmatrix} \\ \mathbf{C} = \begin{bmatrix} 7 & 3 & 4 \end{bmatrix} \qquad D = 0 \right\} \tag{8.129}$$

The block diagonal structure of **A**, together with the Jordan block, makes it possible to write the state transition matrix by inspection in this case. It is given below.

$$\boldsymbol{\phi}(t) = \begin{bmatrix} e^{-3t} & \vdots & 0 & 0 \\ 0 & \vdots & e^{-2t} & 0 \\ 0 & \vdots & te^{-2t} & e^{-2t} \end{bmatrix} \tag{8.130}$$

∎

In addition to the methods described in this section, there are several other procedures for obtaining a set of state equations for a specified transfer function. The nonuniqueness of the state–variable representation for a given transfer function will be discussed further in the next section. We conclude this section by studying another canonical realization that may be considered the dual of direct realization and leads to the *observer canonical form* of state equations.

8.6.4 ANOTHER CANONICAL REALIZATION

To explain this procedure, we start with a third-order system for simplicity, rather than the general case. Extension to the general case will be straight-forward. Consider the following system equation:

$$\frac{d^3y}{dt^n} + a_1\frac{d^2y}{dt^2} + a_2\frac{dy}{dt} + a_3y(t) = b_1\frac{d^2u}{dt^2} + b_2\frac{du}{dt} + 3u(t) \tag{8.131}$$

Using the operator notation, the above may be written more concisely as

$$\left(p^3 + a_1p^2 + a_2p + a_3\right)y(t) = \left(b_1p^2 + b_2p + b_3\right)u(t)$$

Multiplying both sides of the above equation with p^{-3} and rearranging, we

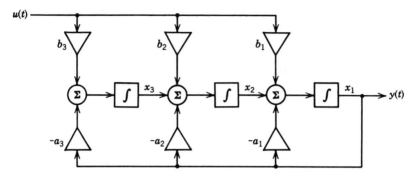

Figure 8.9 Observer form realization.

obtain

$$y(t) = p^{-1}(b_1 u(t) - a_1 y(t)$$
$$+ p^{-1}\{b_2 u(t) - a_2 y(t) + p^{-1}[b_3 y(t) - a_3 y(t)]\}) \quad (8.132)$$

Recalling that the operator p^{-1} implies integration, it follows that we can realize the system represented by equation 8.132 by using three integrators as shown in Figure 8.9.

With the outputs of the integrators labeled as states as shown in Figure 8.9, the following equations are obtained:

$$\dot{x}_1 = -a_1 x_1 + x_2 + b_1 u$$
$$\dot{x}_2 = -a_2 x_1 + x_3 + b_2 u$$
$$\dot{x}_3 = -a_3 x_1 + b_3 u$$

and

$$y = x_1$$

These equations can be arranged in the matrix form giving us

$$\mathbf{A} = \begin{bmatrix} -a_1 & 1 & 0 \\ -a_2 & 0 & 1 \\ -a_3 & 0 & 0 \end{bmatrix} \quad \mathbf{B} = \begin{bmatrix} b_1 \\ b_2 \\ b_3 \end{bmatrix} \quad \mathbf{C} = \begin{bmatrix} 1 & 0 & 0 \end{bmatrix} \quad \mathbf{D} = 0 \quad (8.133)$$

A comparison of equation 8.133 with 8.109 shows that like the controller canonical form, the coefficients of the transfer function appear directly in the state equations. Furthermore, the matrix $\mathbf{A}$ in equation 8.133 is the transpose of $\mathbf{A}$ in equation 8.109, whereas $\mathbf{B}$ and $\mathbf{C}$ have been interchanged. Thus, we observe a duality between these canonical forms. Note that one can write the transfer function from these forms by inspection. We shall be learning more about the applications of these forms in Section 8.8. The procedure described above is easily generalized to a system of order n. This will be left as an exercise.

8.7   LINEAR TRANSFORMATIONS AND CANONICAL FORMS

One reason for the nonuniqueness of state equations is that the input–output description of a system is invariant under linear transformation of the state. Consider such a transformation, given by

$$\tilde{\mathbf{x}} = \mathbf{P}\mathbf{x} \tag{8.134}$$

where $\mathbf{P}$ is an $n \times n$ nonsingular constant matrix. Substituting equation 8.134 into equations 8.8 and 8.11, we obtain a new set of equations in terms of the transformed state vector $\tilde{\mathbf{x}}$. These are of the same form as equations 8.8 and 8.11 and are given below.

$$\dot{\tilde{\mathbf{x}}} = \tilde{\mathbf{A}}\tilde{\mathbf{x}} + \tilde{\mathbf{B}}u \tag{8.135}$$

$$y(t) = \tilde{\mathbf{C}}\tilde{\mathbf{x}} + Du \tag{8.136}$$

where

$$\tilde{\mathbf{A}} = \mathbf{P}^{-1}\mathbf{A}\mathbf{P}$$
$$\tilde{\mathbf{B}} = \mathbf{P}^{-1}\mathbf{B}$$
$$\tilde{\mathbf{C}} = \mathbf{C}\mathbf{P} \tag{8.137}$$

It is evident that with different choices of $\mathbf{P}$, numerous sets of state equations can be derived from any given set of state equations. We now show that the transfer function will remain unchanged for all such transformations with any nonsingular $\mathbf{P}$. From equation 8.101, the transfer function is given by

$$\begin{aligned} G(s) &= \tilde{\mathbf{C}}(s\mathbf{I} - \tilde{\mathbf{A}})^{-1}\tilde{\mathbf{B}} + D = \mathbf{C}\mathbf{P}(s\mathbf{I} - \mathbf{P}^{-1}\mathbf{A}\mathbf{P})^{-1}\mathbf{P}^{-1}\mathbf{B} + D \\ &= \mathbf{C}\mathbf{P}(s\mathbf{P}^{-1}\mathbf{P} - \mathbf{P}^{-1}\mathbf{A}\mathbf{P})^{-1}\mathbf{P}^{-1}\mathbf{B} + D \\ &= \mathbf{C}\mathbf{P}\mathbf{P}^{-1}(s\mathbf{I} - \mathbf{A})^{-1}\mathbf{P}\mathbf{P}^{-1}\mathbf{B} + D \\ &= \mathbf{C}(s\mathbf{I} - \mathbf{A})^{-1}\mathbf{B} + D \end{aligned} \tag{8.138}$$

The last equality follows from the matrix identity

$$(\mathbf{P}\mathbf{Q})^{-1} = \mathbf{Q}^{-1}\mathbf{P}^{-1} \tag{8.139}$$

An important application of linear transformations is in obtaining state equations in certain *canonical* forms from any noncanonical form. For example, if the matrix

$$\mathbf{P} = \mathbf{M} \tag{8.140}$$

where the columns of $\mathbf{M}$ are the eigenvectors of $\mathbf{A}$ and are linearly independent, it transforms the state equations into the diagonal form. On the other hand, if the eigenvalues of $\mathbf{A}$ is not distinct, we can transform the state equations into the *Jordan canonical form* by making the columns of $\mathbf{M}$ the generalized eigenvectors of $\mathbf{A}$. This topic is discussed further in Appendix A, as well as in Problem 8.7 at the end of this chapter. Similarly, it is possible to transform the state equations into the *controller canonical form* provided that they satisfy certain properties, known as state controllability. Because of these and several other applications, linear transformations of the state equations are of great importance in the study of feedback control systems. Some books on control theory that carry these ideas further are listed in Appendix E.

8.8 DISCRETIZATION OF STATE EQUATIONS OF CONTINUOUS-TIME SYSTEMS

As mentioned previously, discrete-time systems may also be obtained by sampling continuous-time systems. This is necessary with computer control systems, where a microprocessor is used as a controller. In such systems, the microprocessor generates a sequence of numbers, denoted by $u(n)$, which represent the input sequence that should be applied to the system to produce the desired output. These numbers are then processed by a digital-to-analog converter and changed into a continuous-time staircase function, which has the value $u(k)$ during the kth sampling interval, that is,

$$u(t) = u(k), kT < t \leq (k + 1)T \qquad (8.141)$$

where T is the sampling interval. Such a signal is shown in Figure 8.10.

The output of a continuous-time system to such an input is readily calculated following our discussion in Section 8.3.1. Consider a system, described by equation 8.8, which is repeated here for convenience.

$$\dot{\mathbf{x}} = \mathbf{Ax} + \mathbf{Bu} \qquad (8.142)$$

It was pointed out in Section 8.3.1 that the solution to the above equation may be written as

$$\mathbf{x}(t) = e^{\mathbf{A}(t-t_0)}\mathbf{x}(t_0) + e^{\mathbf{A}t}\int_{t_0}^{t} e^{-\mathbf{A}\tau}\mathbf{Bu}(\tau)\, d\tau \qquad (8.143)$$

where t_0 is any arbitrary initial time. Replacing t_0 with kT and t with

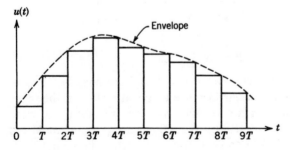

Figure 8.10 Staircase signal for computer control.

$(k + 1)T$, in equation 8.143, where k is an integer, we obtain

$$\mathbf{x}(kT + T) = e^{\mathbf{A}T}\mathbf{x}(kT) + e^{\mathbf{A}kT+T} \int_{kT}^{(k+1)T} e^{-\mathbf{A}\tau}\mathbf{B}u(\tau)\, d\tau \quad (8.144)$$

As noted in equation 8.141, $u(t)$ is held constant at the value $u(kT)$ during this interval. Therefore, equation 8.144 may be rewritten as

$$\mathbf{x}(kT + T) = \mathbf{F}(T)\mathbf{x}(kT) + \mathbf{G}(T)\mathbf{u}(kT) \quad (8.145)$$

where the matrices $\mathbf{F}$ and $\mathbf{G}$ are given by

$$\mathbf{F}(T) = e^{\mathbf{A}T}$$

$$\mathbf{G}(T) = \int_0^T e^{\mathbf{A}t}\, dt\ \mathbf{B} \quad (8.146)$$

The last result is obtained as follows. From equations 8.144 and 8.145,

$$\mathbf{G}(T) = \int_{kT}^{(k+1)T} e^{\mathbf{A}(kT+T-\tau)}\mathbf{B}\, d\tau$$

$$= -\int_T^0 e^{\mathbf{A}\zeta}\mathbf{B}\, d\zeta \quad \text{where } \zeta = kT + T - \tau$$

$$= \int_0^T e^{\mathbf{A}\zeta}\, d\zeta\ \mathbf{B}$$

Both $\mathbf{F}(T)$ and $\mathbf{G}(T)$ can be calculated easily on a computer by using the power series expansions given below.

$$\mathbf{F}(T) = \mathbf{I} + \mathbf{A}T + \frac{1}{2!}(\mathbf{A}T)^2 + \frac{1}{3!}(\mathbf{A}T)^3 + \cdots \quad (8.147)$$

$$\mathbf{G}(T) = \left[\mathbf{I} + \frac{1}{2!}\mathbf{A}T + \frac{1}{3!}(\mathbf{A}T)^2 + \frac{1}{4!}(\mathbf{A}T)^3 + \cdots\right] \quad (8.148)$$

where the series are truncated after a certain number of terms to obtain a specified accuracy. It can be shown that if the sampling interval T is selected so that $|\lambda_m|T < 0.5$, where λ_m is the eigenvalue of $\mathbf{A}$ that has the largest magnitude (this is often called the *spectral radius* of $\mathbf{A}$), one can truncate the series after 12 terms with an error of less than 10^{-9} in each component of $\mathbf{F}$ and $\mathbf{G}$. The disk enclosed with this book includes a computer program for calculating $\mathbf{F}$ and $\mathbf{G}$ for given $\mathbf{A}$, $\mathbf{B}$, and T.

Equation 8.145 is called the state transition equation for the system. The reader may want to compare it with equation 8.61, describing the state equation for a discrete-time system. It will be seen that they are of the same form, except that $\mathbf{A}$ and $\mathbf{B}$ in equation 8.61 have been replaced with $\mathbf{F}$ and $\mathbf{G}$ in equation 8.145. This difference occurs because the latter has been obtained by discretizing the corresponding continuous-time system by holding the input constant between sampling instants.

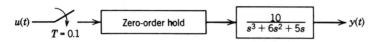

Figure 8.11 A discretized system.

Example 8.18

Consider the continuous-time system shown in Figure 8.11, where the input is sampled and passed through a zero-order hold so that it is in the form of a staircase function. We shall determine the state transition matrix of the resulting discrete-time system.

The state equations for the given continuous-time system are easily written in the controller canonical form. The resulting matrices are

$$A = \begin{bmatrix} -6 & -5 & 0 \\ 1 & 0 & 0 \\ 0 & 1 & 0 \end{bmatrix} \quad B = \begin{bmatrix} 1 \\ 0 \\ 0 \end{bmatrix} \quad C = [\,0 \quad 0 \quad 10\,] \quad D = 0$$

Using equations 8.147 and 8.148, the state transition matrices are obtained as

$$F = \begin{bmatrix} 0.531954 & -0.372883 & 0 \\ 0.074577 & 0.979414 & 0 \\ 0.004117 & 0.099280 & 1 \end{bmatrix} \quad G = \begin{bmatrix} 0.074577 \\ 0.004177 \\ 0.000144 \end{bmatrix}$$ ∎

8.9 SUMMARY

In this chapter we studied the state–space formulation of system equations. The most interesting feature is that these apply equally well to continuous-time and to discrete-time systems; the only difference is that the vector differential equation for the continuous-time case has to be replaced with a vector difference equation. State equations provide us with the complete internal description of the system. Therefore, they contain more information than transfer functions, which provide us only with the input–output description.

An important aspect of state–space models is the ease with which they can be simulated on computers. It was seen in this chapter that all of the methods of simulation lend themselves easily to the formulation of state equations for systems from their transfer functions. Another important feature was their applicability to multivariable systems without any change in notation, in contrast with the transfer function formulation, which becomes cumbersome in the multivariable case.

The geometric interpretation of the state vector has led to the use of important concepts of linear algebra in the solution of state equations. In particular, linear transformations of state equations transforming the matrix

A to a diagonal or Jordan form have the effect of *decoupling* the state equations so that they are replaced by a set of n uncoupled first-order differential equations that can be solved easily. This idea was also found useful in the evaluation of the state transition matrix $e^{\mathbf{A}t}$ with the help of a computer.

State equations for linear systems have been applied to many areas of control and communication systems. An attempt has been made in this chapter to lay a good foundation to prepare the interested reader for these applications. Some challenging problems and the computer programs described in the appendices to this chapter should provide further motivation.

PROBLEMS

8.1   The state equations for a dc servomotor are given below. Obtain a complete solution of these equations if $x_1(0) = 1$, $x_2(0) = 0$, and the input $u(t)$ is a unit step.

$$\dot{\mathbf{x}} = \begin{bmatrix} 0 & 1 \\ 0 & -0.2 \end{bmatrix} \mathbf{x} + \begin{bmatrix} 0 \\ 4 \end{bmatrix} u$$

8.2   Determine $e^{\mathbf{A}t}$ for the following A-matrices.

(a) $\begin{bmatrix} 0 & 2 \\ -1 & -3 \end{bmatrix}$ (b) $\begin{bmatrix} -1 & 1 \\ 0 & 1 \end{bmatrix}$ (c) $\begin{bmatrix} -1 & 1 & 0 \\ 0 & -4 & 2 \\ 0 & 0 & -10 \end{bmatrix}$

8.3   Determine $\mathbf{A}^k$ for each of the following A-matrices

(a) $\begin{bmatrix} 0.5 & 0.2 \\ 0.1 & 0.4 \end{bmatrix}$ (b) $\begin{bmatrix} 0.25 & 0.5 \\ -0.75 & -1.0 \end{bmatrix}$ (c) $\begin{bmatrix} 1 & 0.2 \\ 5 & 1 \end{bmatrix}$

8.4   Write a set of state equations for the electrical networks shown in Figure 8.12.

8.5   The diagonalized matrix, $\mathbf{\Lambda}$, discussed in Sections 8.3.2.3 and 8.4.2.3, would have complex elements if the matrix $\mathbf{A}$ has complex eigenvalues. A simple transformation leads to a block diagonal structure for $\mathbf{\Lambda}$, with each pair of complex conjugate eigenvalues replaced by 2×2 blocks of

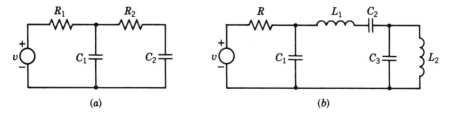

Figure 8.12   Networks for Problem 8.4.

real numbers. For example, consider the case when

$$\Lambda = \begin{bmatrix} -1 + j2 & 0 \\ 0 & -1 - j2 \end{bmatrix}$$

If we now apply the transformation

$$P = \begin{bmatrix} 1 & j \\ 1 & -j \end{bmatrix}$$

then we get

$$\tilde{\Lambda} = \mathbf{P}^{-1}\Lambda P = \begin{bmatrix} -1 & -2 \\ 2 & 1 \end{bmatrix}$$

Use the above procedure to find $e^{\mathbf{A}t}$ for the following **A**-matrices.

(a) $\begin{bmatrix} 0 & 1 \\ -8 & -4 \end{bmatrix}$ (b) $\begin{bmatrix} 0 & 1 & 0 \\ 0 & 0 & 1 \\ -8 & -12 & -5 \end{bmatrix}$

8.6 Determine the matrix $e^{\mathbf{A}t}$ for each of the following **A**-matrices given below. These are said to be in the Jordan canonical form. Use the method of Laplace transformation. Can you think of a simple rule for finding the transition matrix for such cases?

(a) $\begin{bmatrix} 2 & 1 \\ 0 & 2 \end{bmatrix}$ (b) $\begin{bmatrix} 2 & 1 & 0 \\ 0 & 2 & 1 \\ 0 & 0 & 2 \end{bmatrix}$ (c) $\begin{bmatrix} 2 & 1 & 0 \\ 0 & 2 & 0 \\ 0 & 0 & 2 \end{bmatrix}$

8.7 If the matrix **A** has an eigenvalue λ of multiplicity m, we cannot diagonalize it unless there are m linearly independent eigenvectors associated with the eigenvalue λ. If there are only q (less than m) linearly independent eigenvectors $\mathbf{v}_1, \mathbf{v}_2, \ldots, \mathbf{v}_q$ for this eigenvalue, then we can only transform **A** to the Jordan canonical form by using sets of generalized eigenvectors associated with λ. If we denote these as $\{\mathbf{x}_{i,1}, \mathbf{x}_{i,2}, \ldots, \mathbf{x}_{i,j_i}\}$, with $\mathbf{x}_{i,1} = \mathbf{v}_i$, $j_i \geq 1$, then we may use the following equations for finding the generalized eigenvectors:

$$\mathbf{A}\mathbf{x}_{i,1} = \lambda\mathbf{x}_{i,1}$$
$$\mathbf{A}\mathbf{x}_{i,2} = \lambda\mathbf{x}_{i,2} + \mathbf{x}_{i,1}$$
$$\mathbf{A}\mathbf{x}_{i,3} = \lambda\mathbf{x}_{i,3} + \mathbf{x}_{i,3}$$
$$\vdots \quad \vdots$$
$$\mathbf{A}\mathbf{x}_{i,j_i} = \lambda\mathbf{x}_{i,j_i} + \mathbf{x}_{i,j_{i-1}}$$

and the total number of such vectors will be equal to m.
Using these generalized eigenvectors in the matrix **M** will bring $\mathbf{M}^{-1}\mathbf{A}\mathbf{M}$ to the Jordan form. Apply this method to transform the following **A**-matrices to the Jordan form.

(a) $\begin{bmatrix} 0 & 1 \\ -4 & -4 \end{bmatrix}$ (b) $\begin{bmatrix} 0 & 1 & 0 \\ 0 & 0 & 1 \\ -8 & -12 & -6 \end{bmatrix}$

8.8 The state equations modeling the number of undergraduate students in an engineering school are given below. The components of $x(k)$ represent the number of students in each year of the four-year program and $u(k)$ is the input, or the enrollment into the freshman class. The output $y(k)$ represents the number of students graduating in a particular year.

Determine the transfer function relating the z-transform of the output $y(k)$ to the z-transform of the input $u(k)$.

$$\mathbf{x}(k+1) = \begin{bmatrix} 0.1 & 0 & 0 & 0 \\ 0.7 & 0.1 & 0 & 0 \\ 0 & 0.82 & 0.08 & 0 \\ 0 & 0 & 0.85 & 0.02 \end{bmatrix} \mathbf{x}(k) + \begin{bmatrix} 1 \\ 0 \\ 0 \\ 0 \end{bmatrix} u(k)$$

$$y(k) = \begin{bmatrix} 0 & 0 & 0 & 0.97 \end{bmatrix} \mathbf{x}(k)$$

8.9 The state equations of a helicopter near hover are given below.

$$\dot{\mathbf{x}} = \begin{bmatrix} -0.002 & -1.4 & 9.8 \\ -0.01 & -0.4 & 0 \\ 0 & 1 & 2 \end{bmatrix} \mathbf{x} + \begin{bmatrix} 9.8 \\ 6.3 \\ 0 \end{bmatrix} u$$

$$y = \begin{bmatrix} 0 & 0 & 1 \end{bmatrix} \mathbf{x}$$

(a) Determine the transfer function relating $Y(s)$ to $U(s)$.
(b) Is this system stable?

8.10 The linearized equations of a satellite in a circular equatorial orbit are given by $\dot{\mathbf{x}} = \mathbf{A}\mathbf{x} + \mathbf{B}\mathbf{u}$, where, after normalization,

$$\mathbf{A} = \begin{bmatrix} 0 & 1 & 0 & 0 \\ 3 & 0 & 0 & 2 \\ 0 & 0 & 0 & 1 \\ 0 & -2 & -3 & 0 \end{bmatrix} \qquad \mathbf{B} = \begin{bmatrix} 0 \\ 1 \\ 0 \\ 0 \end{bmatrix}$$

where the state variables are

x_1 = the distance from the center of the Earth

x_2 = the rate of change of x_1

x_3 = angular displacement in the equatorial plane

x_4 = the rate of change of x_3

The input $u(t)$ is the thrust produced by a rocket engine. Determine the transfer function relating $X_1(s)$ to $U(s)$.

8.11 The transfer function of the pitch control system of a supersonic aircraft is given by

$$\frac{Y(s)}{U(s)} = \frac{20(s+12)(s+4)}{(s+25)(s^2+2s+25)}$$

Determine a suitable state–space representation for the system.

8.12 The steady-state response of a stable system to a constant input can be determined directly from the state equations. This follows from the fact that for such a system the values of all the states must approach some constants as t approaches infinity. Hence, $\dot{x}$ must approach zero as $t \to \infty$, with the result that the steady-state value of x is obtained as $x_{ss} = -A^{-1}Bu$, where u is the constant input.

Use this approach to determine the steady-state output for a unit step input of the system described by the state equations given below and verify your answer by using the transfer function of the system.

$$\dot{x} = \begin{bmatrix} -1.2 & -5 & -20 \\ 10 & -8 & 0 \\ 0 & 1 & 0 \end{bmatrix} x + \begin{bmatrix} 1.5 \\ 0.5 \\ 2.5 \end{bmatrix} u$$

$$y = \begin{bmatrix} 2 & 0 & 3 \end{bmatrix} x$$

8.13 A continuous-time system can be discretized by allowing the input to change only at $t = kT$, where k is an integer and T is the sampling interval, with the input held constant between the sampling instants.

Show that if the continuous-time system is described by the equation

$$\dot{x} = Ax + Bu$$

then the state equation for the corresponding discrete-time system is given by

$$x(k+1) = Fx(k) + Gu(k)$$

where

$$F = e^{AT} \quad \text{and} \quad G = \int_0^T e^{At} B \, dt$$

[Note that $x(k)$ denotes $x(kT)$].

8.14 Using the notation of Problem 8.13, determine F and G for the following cases.

(a) $A = \begin{bmatrix} -1 & 1 \\ 0 & 1 \end{bmatrix}$ $B = \begin{bmatrix} 1.5 \\ 0 \end{bmatrix}$ $T = 0.2$

(b) $A = \begin{bmatrix} -2 & 0 & 1 \\ 1 & -3 & 0 \\ 1 & 1 & -1 \end{bmatrix}$ $B = \begin{bmatrix} 1 \\ 0 \\ 1 \end{bmatrix}$ $T = 0.25$

8.15 Determine F and G for the state equations for a helicopter near hover, given in Problem 8.9, with the sampling interval $T = 0.1$.

8.16 The transfer function of a discrete-time system is given below. Derive a set of state equations for this system.

$$G(z) = \frac{2z^2 + 5z}{z^3 - 1.2z^2 + 0.45z - 0.05}$$

8.17 Transform the state equations for a helicopter near hover, given in Problem 8.9, to the diagonal form, if possible. Hence, determine the state transition equation for the system.

8.18 The state equations for the discrete-time model for the mixing system of a rotary cement kiln are given below.

$$\mathbf{x}(k + 1) = \begin{bmatrix} 0 & 1 & 0 & 0 \\ 0.24 & 0 & 0 & 0.76 \\ 0 & 0.07 & 0.93 & 0 \\ 0 & 0 & 0 & 1 \end{bmatrix} \mathbf{x}(k) + \begin{bmatrix} 1 \\ 0.76 \\ 0 \\ 0 \end{bmatrix} u(k)$$

$$y(k) = \begin{bmatrix} 1 & 0 & 0 & 0 \end{bmatrix} \mathbf{x}(k)$$

(a) Determine the transfer function relating $Y(z)$ to $U(z)$.
(b) Transform the state equations to the diagonal form.

8.19 The linearized state equations for an automatic ship steering system can be written in the form $\dot{\mathbf{x}} = \mathbf{A}\mathbf{x} + \mathbf{B}u$, where

$$\mathbf{A} = \begin{bmatrix} -0.05 & -6.00 & 0 & 0 \\ -0.001 & -0.16 & 0 & 0 \\ 1 & 0 & 0 & 12 \\ 0 & 1 & 0 & 0 \end{bmatrix} \qquad \mathbf{B} = \begin{bmatrix} -0.5 \\ 0.9 \\ 0 \\ 0 \end{bmatrix}$$

(a) Transform $\mathbf{A}$ to the Jordan canonical form and determine $e^{\mathbf{A}t}$.
(b) Is this system stable? Explain the reasons for your answer.

8.20 The $\mathbf{A}$-matrix for a discrete-time system is given below. Determine $\mathbf{A}^k$ by transforming it to the diagonal form. Is this system stable? Give reasons for your answer.

$$\mathbf{A} = \begin{bmatrix} -0.096 & 0.088 & -3.223 & -11.974 \\ -0.011 & -0.038 & 15.763 & -1.255 \\ 0.002 & -0.011 & 0.498 & 0.018 \\ 0.025 & 0.004 & -0.057 & 0.081 \end{bmatrix}$$

8.21 The linearized state equations for a satellite are given in Problem 8.10. Determine a discrete-time version of these equations if the sampling interval T is 0.2. Is this system stable? Give reasons for your answer.

8.22 The simplified transfer function for the longitudinal motion of an airplane is given by

$$G(s) = \frac{60s + 4}{(s + 10)(s^2 + 0.2s + 7.5)}$$

(a) Use direct realization to obtain a set of state equations in the controller canonical form.
(b) Sketch the realization diagram for the corresponding observer canonical form for this system.
(*Hint:* The observer form is described in Section 8.6.4.)

8.23 A discrete-time system is described by the transfer function

$$G(z) = \frac{z^2 + 0.5z}{z^3 - 0.8z^2 - 0.21z + 0.01}$$

(a) Obtain a set of state equations in the controller canonical form and sketch the corresponding realization diagram.

(b) Derive the state equations in the diagonal form and sketch the corresponding realization diagram.

8.24 Repeat Problem 8.22 for the transfer function given below, which represents a robot force control system.

$$G(s) = \frac{20(s + 2)}{(s^2 + 2s + 5)(s^2 + 4s + 13)}$$

8.25 Determine the state transition equation for the system described in Problem 8.22, with the state equations in the controller canonical form.

APPENDIX 8.1

Calculation of Transfer Functions from State Equations

As described in Section 8.5, calculation of the transfer function from the state equations requires inverting the matrix $(s\mathbf{I} - \mathbf{A})$ for the case of continuous-time systems and the matrix $(z\mathbf{I} - \mathbf{A})$ for discrete-time systems. Use of Leverrier's algorithm makes it possible to perform this on a digital computer. The accompanying program, Transfer.EXE, utilizes this algorithm and determines the transfer function without actually inverting the matrix. This is possible because each of the coefficients of the numerator of the transfer function can be obtained by premultiplying the corresponding matrix of the adjoint of $\mathbf{A}$ by $\mathbf{C}$ and postmultiplying by $\mathbf{B}$. This procedure also makes it unnecessary to store the various terms of the adjoint. The user is required to input the matrices $\mathbf{A}$, $\mathbf{B}$, and $\mathbf{C}$. This may be done either from a disk file or from the keyboard. The user has the choice of getting these matrices printed. The program then displays the coefficients of the numerator and denominator polynomials. These may, again, be either printed or stored in a disk file for other uses.

Although the program has been written primarily for single-input single-output systems, it can also be used for multivariable systems by storing the $\mathbf{A}$-matrix and using columns of $\mathbf{B}$ and rows of $\mathbf{C}$ to obtain various elements of the resulting transfer function matrix.

The same program can be used for determining the transfer function of either a continuous-time or a discrete-time system.

APPENDIX 8.2

State Transition Matrices of a Discretized System

As described in Section 8.87, a continuous-time system is often discretized so that the input to the system is held constant between the sampling instants. The state transition matrices for the resulting system can be obtained by adding the power series in equations 8.147 and 8.148. This series converges rapidly if the sampling interval is selected to satisfy the condition $\lambda_m T < 0.5$, where λ_m is the spectral radius of $\mathbf{A}$.

The program TRANSITION.EXE on the disk enclosed with this book is based on the assumption that this condition is satisfied. It calculates $\mathbf{F}$ and $\mathbf{G}$ for given $\mathbf{A}$, $\mathbf{B}$, and T.

Introduction to Filters

9.1 INTRODUCTION

An electric filter can be defined as a network or system that transforms an input signal in some specified way to yield an output signal with desired characteristics. Although the input signal may be modified either in the time domain or in the frequency domain, in its most common usage, a filter is a frequency-selective device, and its frequency response has significant values only in certain bands along the frequency axis. Filters are used extensively in electronic devices. For instance, telephone, radio, telegraph, television, radar, sonar, and space vehicles utilize filters in one form or another.

Filters may be either *analog* or *digital*. The components of an analog filter may be passive circuit elements like resistors, capacitors, and inductors. Alternatively, analog filters may be of the *R-C* active type that have resistors, capacitors, and operational amplifiers as the basic circuit elements. In both cases, an analog filter can be represented by a transfer function of the continuous-time type. On the other hand, the transfer function of a digital filter is of the discrete-time type, and the basic building blocks are ideal delays, adders, and multipliers. Digital filters can also be implemented on microprocessors if they are represented in the form of difference equations. These have become very important owing to rapid advances in the area of digital signal processing.

In the next section we shall study analog filters. This will be followed by the study of digital filters in Section 9.3.

9.2 INTRODUCTION TO ANALOG FILTERS

The earliest work in filter theory was done by Campbell in the United States and Wagner in Germany in 1915. The theory has evolved extensively since then, culminating into the development of "modern filter theory" and the preparation of extensive design tables in the 1960s. By using the concepts of impedance and frequency transformations, it is now possible to use tables for

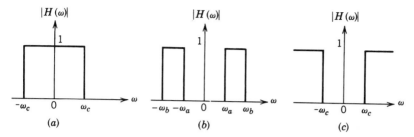

Figure 9.1 Frequency responses of different types of ideal filters. (a) Low-pass, (b) band-pass, (c) high-pass.

"normalized" filters for determining the values of the components of the most common types of analog filters.

Because of their importance, a large amount of work has been published on the design of analog filters. In earlier work analog filters consisted of passive circuit elements, primarily inductors and capacitors. Because of the large bulk of inductors and their lossy nature, especially for iron-cored inductors, the theory of R-C-active filters was developed. These filters use resistors, capacitors, and operational amplifiers so that they are much more compact with characteristics that are fairly close to those desired. In this section we introduce the reader to the basic principles in the design of analog filters without going into all of the details.

Filters can be classified on the basis of their frequency response. Some of the most common frequency-selective filters are the *low-pass, high-pass, band-pass, band-elimination*, and *all-pass* filters. There are other types of filters in addition to these, for example, those required to provide specified phase shift with frequency. The plots of the gain M versus frequency of ideal low-pass, band-pass, and high-pass filters are shown in Figure 9.1. Observe that the gain of each ideal filter is required to be one in the pass-band and zero in the stop-band. The pass-band, in each case, is specified by cutoff frequencies. For example, the low-pass filter will pass all complex exponentials with frequencies in the range $-\omega_c$ to ω_c, that is, its pass-band extends form $-\omega_c$ to ω_c. Note that the pass-band is centered around 0 for this case.

These ideal characteristics cannot be realized in practice. This follows immediately by recalling from Chapter 3 that the frequency response is also the Fourier transform of the impulse response of the system. It may also be recalled that the inverse transform of the rectangular pulse is the sinc function. Thus, the impulse response of the ideal low-pass filter will be the sinc function shown in Figure 9.2, which is noncausal and therefore physically unrealizable.

However, it is not really necessary to require the ideal frequency response characteristics shown in Figure 9.1. Generally, a certain amount of tolerance is permissible, both in the pass-band and the stop-band, so that the frequency response of a low-pass filter can be of the form shown in Figure

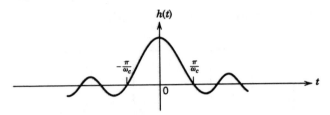

Figure 9.2   Impulse response of the ideal low-pass filter.

9.3, where the frequency response has been shown for only positive values of ω. As noted earlier, it will be symmetrical about $\omega = 0$.

It will be seen from Figure 9.3 that now we have a transition band between the pass-band and the stop-band. In the pass-band it is required that the gain be within the range $1 \pm \varepsilon$, where ε is a specified tolerance. In the stop-band the gain must not exceed another specified tolerance δ. The frequency range from ω_c to ω_p allows for the transition between the pass- and stop-bands. By reducing the values of the tolerances and the width of the transition region, we obtain a closer approximation to the ideal filter.

The modern approach to the design of analog filters consists of two main steps. First we determine a rational transfer function with a frequency response that is a close approximation to the one shown in Figure 9.3. This is called the *approximation problem*. The second step is to synthesize a network that will have this transfer function. This is the *network synthesis problem* that has attracted a lot of attention in the past. Although the synthesis of filters directly from transfer functions offers an elegant solution to the problem, it usually involves a great deal of computation. It is much simpler to use design curves and tables in handbooks (for example, see *Electronic Filter Design Handbook*, by Arthur B. Williams and Fred J. Taylor, McGraw-Hill, second edition, 1988). Design by synthesis can then be left to the advanced specialists. Our aim here is to introduce the reader to the basic concepts of approximation as well as those of impedance and frequency transformations.

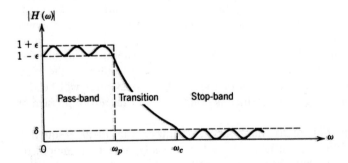

Figure 9.3   A practical approximation to the ideal low-pass filter.

The main reason for not going into all these details is that, it is possible to use the table of prototypes of different types of filters and to transform them to meet the specifications.

9.2.1 APPROXIMATION TO THE IDEAL LOW-PASS FILTER

The magnitude response of the ideal low-pass filter, with the cutoff frequency $\omega_c = 1$, can be approximated in several ways. A commonly used approximation is given by

$$|H(\omega)| = \frac{1}{\sqrt{(1 + \omega^{2n})}} \qquad (9.1)$$

where n is an integer. This is called the *Butterworth* or *"maximally flat"* approximation to the ideal low-pass filter, and n is called the order of the filter. The reason for the latter name (maximally flat) is that the first n derivatives of the magnitude part of the frequency response curve are zero for $\omega = 0$, that is, the curve has maximum flatness. Plots of this function for n equal to 2 and 10 are shown in Figure 9.4. In the pass-band the magnitude response decreases monotonically from 1 at $\omega = 0$ to $1/\sqrt{2}$ at $\omega = 1$ for all values of n. Thus, it will be seen that the response approaches the ideal as n is increased.

The transfer function $H(s)$, which corresponds to the magnitude response function given by equations 9.1, has all its poles on the unit circle of the s-plane. For a Butterworth filter of order n, these poles are obtained from the n roots in the left half of the s-plane of the equation

$$s^{2n} - 1 = 0 \qquad (9.2)$$

For example, the transfer function of the third-order Butterworth filter is

$$H(s) = \frac{1}{(s + 1)(s^2 + s + 1)} \qquad (9.3)$$

and it is easily verified that the poles of $H(s)$ are the three roots in the left half of the s-plane of equation 9.2 for $n = 3$. The pole–zero plot for this case is shown in Figure 9.5.

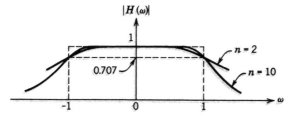

Figure 9.4 Magnitude response of a Butterworth filter.

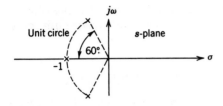

Figure 9.5 Pole–zero plot for the third-order Butterworth filter.

The frequency response of the Butterworth filter is flat near the frequency $\omega = 0$, but its cutoff rate is not high. A better cutoff rate is obtained by using *Chebyschev* filters with the magnitude response

$$|H(\omega)| = \frac{1}{\sqrt{1 + \varepsilon^2 C_n^2(\omega)}} \tag{9.4}$$

where ε is a constant and

$$C_n(\omega) = \cos\left(n \cos^{-1} \omega\right) \tag{9.5}$$

is the Chebyschev polynomial of order n.

Although from the definition in equation 9.5, $C_n(\omega)$ appears to be a transcendental function, in fact, it is a polynomial. To show this, first we note that

$$C_0(\omega) = \cos(0) = 1 \tag{9.6}$$

and

$$C_1(\omega) = \cos\left(\cos^{-1} \omega\right) = \omega \tag{9.7}$$

We now derive a recursion formula for obtaining higher order Chebyschev polynomials. Let us define

$$\omega = \cos \phi \tag{9.8}$$

so that

$$C_n(\omega) = \cos n\phi \tag{9.9}$$

By using the trigonometric identity

$$\cos\left(n + 1\right)\phi + \cos\left(n - 1\right)\phi = 2 \cos n\phi \cos \phi \tag{9.10}$$

and comparing with equation 9.9, we obtain the recursion formula

$$C_{n+1}(\omega) + C_{n-1}(\omega) = 2C_n(\omega)\omega$$

or

$$C_{n+1}(\omega) = 2\omega C_n(\omega) - C_{n-1}(\omega) \tag{9.11}$$

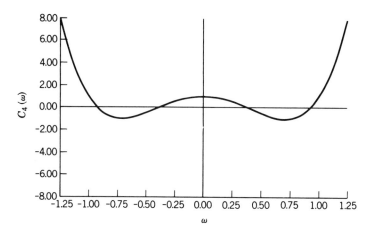

Figure 9.6 Chebyschev polynomial $C_4(\omega)$.

With the help of equations 9.6, 9.7, and 9.11, the following are easily established:

$$C_2(\omega) = 2\omega^2 - 1 \qquad (9.12)$$

$$C_3(\omega) = 4\omega^3 - 3\omega \qquad (9.13)$$

$$C_4(\omega) = 8\omega^4 - 8\omega^2 + 1 \qquad (9.14)$$

$$C_5(\omega) = 16\omega^5 - 20\omega^3 + 5\omega \qquad (9.15)$$

$$C_6(\omega) = 32\omega^6 - 48\omega^4 + 18\omega^2 - 1 \qquad (9.16)$$

and so on.

It follows from the definition in equation 9.5 and the nature of the polynomials that for $-1 \leq \omega \leq 1$, we must have $C_n(\omega)$ oscillating between the values of -1 and 1, whereas outside this range the magnitude of $C_n(\omega)$ increases monotonically. For example, the plot of $C_4(\omega)$ is shown in Figure 9.6 for ω between -1.25 and 1.25. Consequently, the function $|H(\omega)|$ defined in equation 9.4 will oscillate between 1 and $1/\sqrt{(1 + \varepsilon^2)}$. As a result, $|H(\omega)|$ is said to have the *equiripple* property in the pass-band. It can be shown mathematically that among all filters with constant numerator and having the same order and pass-band ripple, the Chebyschev filter has the maximum slope at $\omega = 1$ and, therefore, the largest cutoff rate. The response of a Chebyschev filter of order 4 is shown in Figure 9.7.

The transfer function $H(s)$ corresponding to the function $|H(\omega)|$ in equation 9.4 can be obtained by noting that

$$|H(\omega)|^2 = H(s)H(-s)|_{s=j\omega} \qquad (9.17)$$

It follows that the poles of $H(s)$ can be obtained from the roots in the left

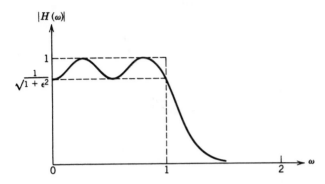

Figure 9.7 Response of Chebyschev filter of order 4.

half of the s-plane of the equation

$$1 + \varepsilon^2 C_n^2(\omega) = 0$$

or

$$1 + \varepsilon^2 C_n^2(-js) = 0 \tag{9.18}$$

where we have used the relationship $s = j\omega$ along the $j\omega$-axis of the s-plane.

Although it is possible to develop a procedure for solving for the roots of equation 9.18, we do not describe it here, since standard tables for the denominator of $H(s)$ for different orders of the Chebyschev filter are available in books on filter theory. Those readers who are interested may look up the derivation in one of the standard books listed in the reference.

Although the Chebyschev filter gives a faster cutoff than a similar Butterworth filter, a better approximation to the ideal filter is possible by allowing the transfer function to have finite zeros in addition to poles, in such a way that response is equiripple in both the pass-band and the stop-band. Such filters are called *elliptic*, and the typical magnitude ratio is shown in Figure 9.8.

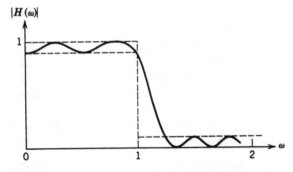

Figure 9.8 Response of elliptic function filter of order 4.

The transfer function $H(s)$ of an elliptic function filter can be obtained by using Chebyschev rational functions.

9.2.2 IMPEDANCE AND FREQUENCY TRANSFORMATIONS

One of the attractive features of filter theory is being able to obtain different types of filters from the tables for normalized low-pass filters, having a cutoff frequency of 1 rad/s while terminated into a 1-Ω load resistance. These tables are available for the various types of approximation discussed earlier and for different orders. In the general case, transformations of both impedance and frequency are required. The basic idea behind these transformations will now be presented.

In the simplest situation, we may consider the problem of obtaining a low-pass filter with cutoff frequency ω_c and design resistance R_0 from the normalized low-pass filter. It is evident that for changing the impedance level from 1 to R_0, it will be necessary to multiply the impedance of each component by this factor. This implies the following replacements:

1. Each resistor R with a resistor $R_0 R$
2. Each inductor L with an inductor $R_0 L$ $\qquad (9.19)$
3. Each capacitor C with a capacitor $\dfrac{C}{R_0}$

These changes will alter only the impedance level, without having any effect on the cutoff frequency. To change the cutoff frequency, let us first denote the normalized frequency by the symbol ν. Our objective is to retain the same gain-frequency characteristic for the normalized filter, with the difference that $\nu = 1$ should be replaced by ω_c. Therefore, it is evident that the following frequency transformation is needed

$$\omega = \nu \omega_c \qquad (9.20)$$

This implies that every element with frequency dependence in the normalized filter should now have the frequency dependency ω/ω_c. This can be achieved by making the following changes in the values of the various circuit elements of the normalized filter:

1. All resistors are left unchanged
2. Replace every inductor L with an inductor $\dfrac{L}{\omega_c}$ $\qquad (9.21)$
3. Replace every capacitor C with a capacitor $\dfrac{C}{\omega_c}$

The following example illustrates this.

Example 9.1

The normalized third-order low-pass Butterworth filter, with the transfer function given in equation 9.3, can be realized by the ladder network shown in Figure 9.9a. We first transform it to change the cutoff frequency to 1000 rads. This will be achieved by scaling down the inductors and capacitors by 1000, while keeping the resistor unchanged. The resulting network will be as shown in Figure 9.9b. Next, we transform it to raise the impedance level by 1000. This requires that we multiply the values of the two inductors and the resistor by 1000 and divide the value of the capacitor by 1000. The final network, with both of these transformations, is shown in Figure 9.9c.

By writing the loop equations of the network in Figure 9.9c, it can be easily verified that this network will have the frequency response as shown in Figure 9.2, but with $\omega_c = 1000$. ∎

The frequency transformation discussed above can be generalized to obtain other types of filters. Let the gain-frequency characteristic of the normalized low-pass filter be denoted by the function $|H(\nu)|$. This is an even function of ν, as seen from equations 9.1 or 9.4, that is,

$$|H(\nu)| = |H(-\nu)| \qquad (9.22)$$

The pass-band extends from $-1 \leq \nu \leq 1$, being centered around $\nu = 0$.

Let us now define a single-valued real function of ω, which we denote by $X(\omega)$. Our aim is to transform the normalized low-pass filter in such a way that the resulting filter has the gain-frequency characteristic given by $|H[X(\omega)]|$. It is evident that this can be achieved if every element in the normalized filter that has a frequency dependence on ν is changed so that now it has a frequency dependence on $X(\omega)$. This implies that an inductor of impedance $j\nu L$ should be replaced by an impedance $jX(\omega)L$. In the same way, a capacitor of admittance $j\nu C$ should be replaced by an admittance $jX(\omega)C$. We now apply this to various cases.

For the low-pass case, with cutoff frequency at ω_c, we obtain

$$X(\omega) = \frac{\omega}{\omega_c} \qquad (9.23)$$

This leads immediately to the result of equation 9.21.

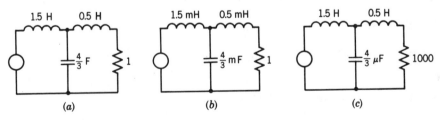

Figure 9.9 Frequency and amplitude scaling. (a) Normalized. (b) Frequency scaled. (c) Amplitude scaled.

We now consider transformation to a high-pass filter. In this case, since we are changing the pass-band to the stop-band and vice versa, the following relationship must be satisfied

$$X(\omega) = -\frac{\omega_c}{\omega} \tag{9.24}$$

This will create a high-pass filter with cutoff frequency ω_c. Note that the negative sign implies that a capacitor in the normalized low-pass filter must be replaced with an inductor in the high-pass filter and vice versa. It is also seen from the above that a low-pass filter with cutoff frequency ω_c can be transformed into a high-pass filter with the same cutoff frequency by replacing each inductor L_i of the low-pass filter with a capacitor C_i given by

$$C_i = \frac{1}{L_i\omega_c^2} \tag{9.25}$$

and every capacitor C_j of the low-pass filter with an inductor

$$L_j = \frac{1}{C_j\omega_c^2} \tag{9.26}$$

Example 9.2

We shall transform the low-pass filter with cutoff frequency 1000 rad/s and load resistance 1000 Ω that was obtained in Example 9.1 into a high-pass filter with the same cutoff frequency and load resistance. Following the procedure described above, we obtain the network shown in Figure 9.10. The reader can easily verify that this network will have the high-pass Butterworth response with the desired cut-off frequency. ■

Let us now consider the transformation given by

$$X(\omega) = \frac{\omega^2 - \omega_1\omega_2}{\omega(\omega_1 - \omega_2)} \tag{9.27}$$

The pass-band of the resulting filter, defined by $-1 \le X(\omega) \le 1$, is seen to be given by $\omega_1 \le \omega \le \omega_2$. Equation 9.25 can, therefore, be used for transforming the normalized low-pass filter to a band-pass filter. This implies that

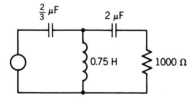

Figure 9.10 High-pass filter.

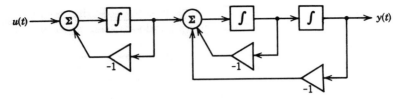

Figure 9.11 Cascade realization of filter described by equation 9.3.

each inductor should be replaced by a series L-C circuit with resonant frequency given by $\omega_0 = \sqrt{(\omega_1\omega_2)}$ and that each capacitor should be replaced by a parallel resonant circuit with the same resonant frequency.

After the desired transfer function of a filter has been determined, it is not necessary to use only passive elements like inductors and capacitors to realize the filter. In fact, in many applications, inductors are undesirable owing to their bulk and inherent losses. The availability of inexpensive operational amplifiers on silicon chips makes it possible to realize analog filters with resistors, capacitors, and operational amplifiers. For example, all of the techniques described in Section 1.7 for the simulation of continuous-time systems can be utilized for the realization of analog filters with specified transfer functions.

Example 9.3

Consider the third-order Butterworth filter, the transfer function for which is given in equation 9.3. A cascade realization, using the procedure described in Section 1.7.2, is shown in Figure 9.11.

It is important to note that the third-order filter considered in this example may be realized by using only one operational amplifier. For example, consider the network shown in Figure 9.12. Starting with the basic network equations, it is easily shown that the transfer function is given by

$$H(s) = \frac{V_2(s)}{V_1(s)} = \frac{1}{C_1C_2C_3s^3 + 2C_3(C_1 + C_2)s^2 + (C_2 + 3C_3)s + 1}$$

$$(9.28)$$

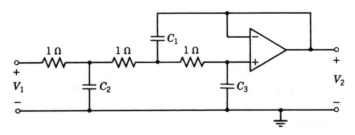

Figure 9.12 Realization of a third-order transfer function.

The transfer function in equation 9.3 can be realized by selecting the values of the three capacitors to match the coefficients in the denominator of equation 9.3.

As in the case of filters containing passive elements, frequency and impedance transformations can also be carried out for filters with operational amplifiers. ■

9.3 INTRODUCTION TO DIGITAL FILTERS

Digital filters play an important role in the processing of digital or discrete-time signals, similar to that of analog filters in the processing of continuous-time signals. The basic problem is the same: we have to design a filter that will have a specified response, in either the frequency or the time domain. The essential difference is the method of realization. For analog filters we use either inductors, capacitors, and resistors, or resistors, capacitors, and operational amplifiers. On the other hand, digital filters are mostly implemented as programs on a digital computer, which may be either a general-purpose computer or one that is specially designed for signal processing. One important limitation to be kept in mind while one designs digital filters is the finite precision inherent in all digital components, caused by the fact that all numbers can be represented by only a finite number of digits. This is analogous to the problem of tolerance in the values of components used in analog filters.

Digital filtering has acquired special importance because of the widespread use of digital computers and special-purpose digital hardware. It is currently being used in a wide variety of applications related to digital signal processing. These include processing of signals that arise in speech recognition, biomedical instrumentation, radar, sonar, image processing, and seismic applications. Owing to their great popularity, a great deal of work has been done on the design of digital filters, and a large number of papers as well as several books have been devoted to the subject. Our aim here is only to introduce the reader to this very interesting subject.

As for analog filters, the design of digital filters involves three basic steps: (1) the specification of the desired properties of the filter, (2) the approximation of these properties by the transfer function of a discrete-time system, and (3) the realization of this transfer function using finite-precision arithmetic. There is one important difference. To ensure physical realizability, transfer functions of analog devices are limited to being rational functions of s, with the result that the impulse response of such a system (the inverse Laplace transform of the transfer function) is of infinite duration in the time domain. In the case of digital filters, however, it is possible to use delays to construct a device with a transfer function that is simply a polynomial in z^{-1}. The impulse response of such devices will be nonzero for only a finite number of samples. Digital filters of this type are known as *finite-duration impulse response*, or *FIR*, filters. The other type, for which the transfer function is a rational function of z, is known as an *infinite-duration impulse response*, or *IIR*, filter. In general, the implementation of IIR filters involves fewer parameters, less memory requirement, and lower computational complexity. However, one has to ensure that they are stable, that is, all the poles of the transfer function of IIR filters must be inside the unit circle of the z-plane. In practice, FIR filters are used in applications requiring linear phase shift (i.e., phase shift varying linearly with frequency) within the pass-band. For example, the linear phase shift property is essential for filters used for processing video signals; otherwise the pictures will get distorted. It is not possible to obtain IIR filters that have linear phase shift as well as desired magnitude response. We begin with a brief discussion of the procedure for designing IIR filters and then introduce the reader to the design of FIR filters. Another reason for studying IIR filters first is that they can be obtained by converting an analog filter design.

9.3.1 DESIGN OF IIR FILTERS

The first step in the design of a filter is the determination of a transfer function that will provide the desired frequency response. This is the *approximation problem*. Since this problem has been thoroughly studied and solved for analog filters, we can take advantage of this highly advanced art by starting with a suitable analog transfer function that will satisfy the specifications and by determining the transfer function of a digital filter with matching frequency response. Several methods for obtaining discrete-time approximations of continuous-time systems were discussed in Chapter 6. In the next subsections we shall study the application some of those methods to the design of digital filters.

9.3.1.1 Impulse-Invariant Transformation

As described in Section 6.7, the aim here is to design a digital filter such that its impulse response is the sampled version of the impulse response of the corresponding analog filter. We review it briefly here. Let $G(s)$ denote the transfer function of the analog filter. It can be expanded into the partial fraction form to yield

$$G(s) = \sum_{i=1}^{N} \frac{A_i}{s - p_i} \qquad (9.29)$$

In order that the impulse response sequence of the corresponding digital filter be identical to $g(t)$ at the sampling instants, its transfer function must be the z-transform of $G(s)$. Therefore, $H(z)$ is given by

$$H(z) = \sum_{i=1}^{N} \frac{A_i z}{z - e^{-p_i T}} \qquad (9.30)$$

It was shown in Section 6.7 that the frequency response of $H(z)$ and $G(s)$ are related as below:

$$H(e^{j\Omega}) = \frac{1}{T} \sum_{k=-\infty}^{\infty} G\left(j\frac{\omega}{T} + j\frac{2\pi k}{T}\right) \qquad (9.31)$$

Equation 9.31 tells us that the frequency response of the digital filter $H(z)$ will match exactly with that of the analog filter $G(s)$, if $G(j\omega)$ is zero for $\omega > \omega_s$, where $\omega_s = 2\pi/T$. In other words, the matching will not be perfect unless the sampling frequency is selected in such a way as to avoid aliasing. Unfortunately, this condition cannot be satisfied completely by a practical analog filter. For example, if we are designing a digital filter from a low-pass analog filter, this condition requires the analog filter to have infinite attenuation at all frequencies above ω_s. A good approximation is obtained only if ω_s is selected so that the attenuation is quite large for all $\omega > \omega_s$. The following example will illustrate this.

Example 9.4

Consider the third-order normalized Butterworth filter. Its transfer function is given by

$$G(s) = \frac{1}{(s + 1)(s^2 + s + 1)} \qquad (9.32)$$

We determine the transfer function of the equivalent digital filter using the impulse-invariant transformation. This requires the partial fraction expansion of $G(s)$, shown below.

$$G(s) = \frac{1}{s + 1} - \frac{0.5 + j0.5/\sqrt{3}}{s + 0.5 - j\sqrt{3}/2} - \frac{0.5 - j0.5/\sqrt{3}}{s + 0.5 + j\sqrt{3}/2} \qquad (9.33)$$

Taking the z-transform of each term of $G(s)$ and combining the terms with the complex conjugate poles, we obtain

$$H(z) = \frac{z}{z - e^{-T}} - \frac{z\left(z - e^{-0.5T}\left(\cos\sqrt{3}\,T/2 + \left(1/\sqrt{3}\right)\sin\sqrt{3}\,T/2\right)\right)}{z^2 - 2ze^{-0.5T}\cos\sqrt{3}\,T/2 + e^{-T}}$$

$$(9.34)$$

As expected, the transfer function $H(z)$ depends on the choice of the sampling interval T. A plot of the magnitude curve of the frequency response of the digital filter $H(z)$ for Ω varying from 0 to π is shown in Figure 9.13 for $T = 0.5$ and 0.1. For comparison, the magnitude curve for the analog filter, $G(s)$, is also shown. It is seen that the digital filter with $T = 0.1$ has frequency response much closer to that of the analog filter.

The mapping from the s-plane into the z-plane in the case of impulse-invariant transformation was studied in Section 6.7. It was shown that strips

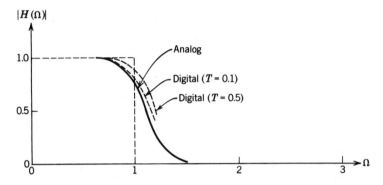

Figure 9.13 Magnitude response for analog and digital filters.

of width $2\pi/T$, or ω_s, in the s-plane map into the entire z-plane, as shown in Figure 9.14. It will be seen that the left half of each strip in the s-plane maps into the interior of the *unit circle* in the z-plane. Similarly, the right half of each strip in the s-plane maps into the exterior of the unit circle. Also, the imaginary axis of the s-plane maps onto the unit circle in the z-plane in such a way that each segment of length ω_s is mapped once around the unit circle. This explains aliasing. Although this transformation preserves stability (i.e., all poles in the left half of the s-plane are mapped in the interior of the unit circle in the z-plane), this is not a simple algebraic mapping between the s-plane and the z-plane. Furthermore, the relationship between the analog frequency ω and the digital frequency Ω is linear. Consequently, the shape of the frequency response is preserved. This will not be the case with bilinear transformation. ∎

9.3.1.2 Step-Invariant Transformation

Instead of matching the impulse response of the analog filter with that of the digital filter at the sampling instants, we can match their step responses. The

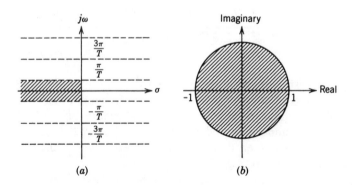

Figure 9.14 Mapping in impulse invariant transformation. (*a*) s-plane. (*b*) z-plane.

procedure is similar to that described above. Therefore, we simply illustrate it with an example.

Example 9.5

Consider the third-order normalized Butterworth filter that was used in Example 9.4. Its transfer function is given by

$$G(s) = \frac{1}{(s+1)(s^2+s+1)} \tag{9.35}$$

We determine the transfer function of the equivalent digital filter using the step-invariant transformation. This requires the partial fraction expansion of $G(s)/s$, shown below.

$$\frac{1}{s}G(s) = \frac{1}{s} - \frac{1}{s+1} + \frac{j1/\sqrt{3}}{s+0.5-j\sqrt{3}/2} - \frac{j1/\sqrt{3}}{s+0.5+j\sqrt{3}/2} \tag{9.36}$$

Taking the z-transform of each term of $G(s)/s$ and combining the terms with the complex conjugate poles, we obtain the z-transform of the step-response of the digital filter as

$$\frac{zH(z)}{z-1} = \frac{z}{z-1} - \frac{z}{z-e^{-T}} + \frac{2z/(\sqrt{3})\sin\sqrt{3}\,T/2}{z^2 - 2ze^{-0.5T}\cos\sqrt{3}\,T/2 + e^{-T}} \tag{9.37}$$

Equation 9.37 can be easily solved to obtain $H(z)$, which is the transfer function of the digital filter, the step response sequence of which is identical to the step response of the analog filter at the sampling instants. As in the previous case, it depends on the sampling interval, and a good approximation to the frequency response of the analog filter is obtained only if the sampling interval is selected such that aliasing is avoided. ∎

9.3.1.3   Bilinear Transformation

This method was also discussed in Section 6.7. It is based on approximating the process of integration with the popular trapezoidal rule and leads to the transformation

$$s = \frac{2}{T}\frac{1-z^{-1}}{1+z^{-1}} = \frac{2}{T}\frac{z-1}{z+1} \tag{9.38}$$

This is called the *bilinear transformation*. Evidently, it does not require as much effort to obtain the digital filter equivalent to a given analog filter with the transformations discussed earlier, since we only replace s in $G(s)$ with the right-hand side of equation 9.38 to obtain $H(z)$.

It was seen in Section 6.7 that the bilinear transformation avoids the aliasing problem at the cost of frequency warping so that the shape of the frequency response is not preserved. In particular, the relationship between

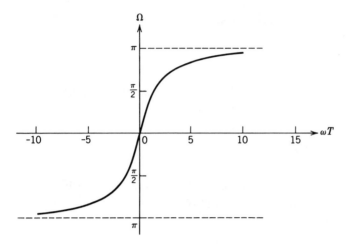

Figure 9.15 Mapping between Ω and ω due to bilinear transformation.

the analog and digital frequencies was shown to be

$$\Omega = 2\tan^{-1}\frac{\omega T}{2} \qquad (9.39)$$

which is depicted in Figure 9.15.

It will be observed that the mapping between the frequencies in the two planes is one to one but also highly nonlinear. Thus, aliasing is avoided at the cost of distortion, or *warping*, in the frequency axis. Note that this distortion is more marked for $\Omega > \pi/2$. It will, therefore, be desirable to keep the pass-band within $\Omega < \pi/2$. This transformation preserves the stability of the system, since the left half of the s-plane maps inside the unit circle. Another feature of the bilinear transformation is that the point $s = 0$ maps into $z = 1$ and also that $G(0) = H(1)$. This implies that the dc gain of the system is preserved in the transformation. Similarly, the point $s = \infty$ maps into $z = -1$, with the result that a zero at ∞ in $G(s)$ will cause $H(z)$ to have a zero at $z = -1$. This is an important reason for the fact that bilinear transformation is often used in the design of digital control systems.

Example 9.6

For example, we shall obtain an IIR filter corresponding to the third-order normalized Butterworth filter by using bilinear transformation. Here, we have

$$G(s) = \frac{1}{(s+1)(s^2+s+1)} = \frac{1}{s^3+2s^2+2s+1} \qquad (9.40)$$

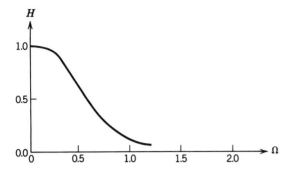

Figure 9.16 Magnitude response for filter given by equation 9.42.

If we select $T = 0.5$, then from equation 9.38

$$s = 4\frac{z-1}{z+1} \qquad (9.41)$$

Substituting this for s in equation 9.40, the transfer function of the corresponding digital filter is obtained as

$$H(z) = \frac{1}{64\dfrac{(z-1)^3}{(z+1)^3} + 32\dfrac{(z-1)^2}{(z+1)^2} + 8\dfrac{z-1}{z+1} + 1}$$

$$= \frac{z^3 + 3z^2 + 3z + 1}{105z^3 - 213z^2 + 155z - 39} \qquad (9.42)$$

As expected, $H(z)$ has three zeros at $z = -1$, since $G(s)$ has three zeros at infinity. The magnitude of the frequency response of the resulting digital filter $H(z)$ is shown in Figure 9.16.

It is seen from Figure 9.16 that the 3-dB bandwidth extends to $\Omega \approx 0.48$. This agrees with the value of the cutoff frequency obtained from equation 9.39. Since $T = 0.5$ and $\Omega_c = 1$, we obtain the cutoff frequency of the digital filter as

$$\Omega_c = 2\tan^{-1} 0.25 \approx 0.49 \qquad (9.43)$$
∎

Although, in general, bilinear transformation leads to a simple design and acceptable magnitude-frequency characteristics, the distortion in the frequency axis introduced by bilinear transformation influences the phase characteristic of the filter. In general, all IIR filters suffer from phase distortion. They are, therefore, not suitable for applications where it is important to have linear phase shift. This leads us to FIR filters, which can be easily designed to meet this requirement. In addition, they can take advantage of the computational speed of the FFT algorithm.

9.3.2 DESIGN OF FIR FILTERS

As stated earlier, unlike the case of IIR filters, in the design of FIR filters we cannot start with an analog filter. From its definition, it follows that the transfer function of a causal FIR filter will be of the form

$$H(z) = \sum_{n=0}^{M-1} h(n) z^{-n} \tag{9.44}$$

where M denotes the duration of the finite impulse response sequence of the filter. Since $H(z)$ is a polynomial in z^{-1} of degree $M - 1$, it will have exactly $M - 1$ zeros that can be located anywhere in the *finite part* of the z-plane. It will also have $M - 1$ poles, all of which are located at $z = 0$. As a result of this, FIR filters are always stable. The frequency response of the filter is obtained as

$$H(e^{j\Omega}) = \sum_{n=0}^{M-1} h(n) e^{-j\Omega n} \tag{9.45}$$

It will now be shown that the filter defined by equation 9.44 will have a linear phase characteristic if the following symmetry condition is satisfied:

$$h(n) = h(M - 1 - n) \tag{9.46}$$

First consider the case when M is an odd number, say 5. Then

$$H(e^{j\Omega}) = h(0) + h(1)e^{-j\Omega} + h(2)e^{-j2\Omega} + h(3)e^{-j3\Omega} + h(4)e^{-j4\Omega}$$

$$= h(0)(1 + e^{-j4\Omega}) + h(1)(e^{-j\Omega} + e^{-j3\Omega}) + h(2)e^{-j2\Omega}$$

$$= e^{-j2\Omega}[2h(0)\cos 2\Omega + 2h(1)\cos \Omega + h(2)] \tag{9.47}$$

It is evident from equation (9.47) that the phase-shift for this case is

$$\phi = -2\Omega \tag{9.48}$$

which is linear with Ω.

Let us now consider the case when M is even, say 6. Here we have

$$H(e^{j\Omega}) = h(0) + h(1)e^{-j\Omega} + h(2)e^{-j2\Omega}$$

$$+ h(3)e^{-j3\Omega} + h(4)e^{-j4\Omega} + h(5)e^{-j5\Omega}$$

$$= h(0)(1 + e^{-j5\Omega}) + h(1)(e^{-j\Omega} + e^{-j4\Omega}) + h(2)(e^{-j2\Omega} + e^{-j3\Omega})$$

$$= 2e^{-j2.5\Omega}[h(0)\cos 2.5\Omega + h(1)\cos 1.5\Omega + h(2)\cos 0.5\Omega] \tag{9.49}$$

so that the phase shift is now obtained as

$$\phi = -2.5\Omega \tag{9.50}$$

which is, again, linear.

For the general case, it can be shown that

$$
H(e^{j\Omega}) = \begin{cases} \exp\left(-j\Omega\dfrac{M-1}{2}\right)\left[h\left(\dfrac{M-1}{2}\right) + \displaystyle\sum_{n=0}^{(M-3)/2} 2h(n)\cos\left(\Omega\left(n - \dfrac{M-1}{2}\right)\right)\right] \\ \qquad\qquad\qquad\qquad\qquad\qquad\qquad\qquad\qquad\qquad\text{for odd } M \\[2ex] \exp\left(-j\Omega\dfrac{M-1}{2}\right)\left[\displaystyle\sum_{n=0}^{(M/2)-1} 2h(n)\cos\left(\Omega\left(n - \dfrac{M-1}{2}\right)\right)\right] \\ \qquad\qquad\qquad\qquad\qquad\qquad\qquad\qquad\qquad\qquad\text{for even } M \end{cases}
$$

$$(9.51)$$

so that in either case the phase shift is given by

$$\phi = -\frac{M-1}{2}\Omega \qquad (9.52)$$

Thus, we have established that we can obtain linear phase shift if we select the impulse response sequence of the digital filter to ensure the symmetry required by equation 9.46. A consequence of this symmetry will be to make the roots of $H(z)$ occur in reciprocal pairs. This follows from the fact that owing to the symmetry in the coefficients of $H(z)$, we may write

$$H(z^{-1}) = z^{-(M-1)}H(z) \qquad (9.53)$$

We present here a brief description of the *window* method, which is one of the many methods used for the design of FIR filters that would have linear phase and specified magnitude response. The object here is to determine the transfer function $H(z)$, which has the property of symmetry that is required by equation 9.46 and the magnitude response that is close to that of a desired function $H_d(e^{j\Omega})$ in some sense. Any given $H_d(e^{j\Omega})$ can be expressed as the discrete-time Fourier transform of some impulse response sequence $h_d(n)$ through the equation

$$H_d(e^{j\Omega}) = \sum_{n=-\infty}^{\infty} h_d(n)e^{-jn\Omega} \qquad (9.54)$$

and the coefficients $h_d(n)$ can be evaluated through the inversion integral

$$h_d(n) = \frac{1}{2\pi}\int_{-\pi}^{\pi} H_d(e^{j\Omega})e^{jn\Omega}\,d\Omega \qquad (9.55)$$

Since the sequence $h_d(n)$ is of infinite length, we must determine a sequence $h(n)$ of finite length M, which is a close approximation to $h_d(n)$. One approach is to simply truncate the sequence over a window of length M, that is,

$$h(n) = \begin{cases} h_d(n) & \text{for } -(M-1)/2 \le n \le (M-1)/2 \\ 0 & \text{otherwise} \end{cases} \qquad (9.56)$$

Note that here we have assumed that M is odd and that the sequence $h(n)$

possesses the symmetry required for linear phase characteristic. Since the transfer function is completely defined by $h(n)$, this completes our task.

The important question still to be answered is the value of M. As we make M larger, we expect our design to match the specified frequency response more closely. From the theory of the Fourier series, we know that for a given M, our approach will lead to the design that will be the best approximation in the least-squares sense. In fact, we can use Parseval's theorem to relate the error to the value of M. Let us define

$$E = \frac{1}{2\pi} \int_{-\pi}^{\pi} |H_d(e^{j\Omega}) - H(e^{j\Omega})|^2 \, d\Omega = \sum_{n=-\infty}^{\infty} |h_d(n) - h(n)|^2 \quad (9.57)$$

where the last equality follows from Parseval's theorem.

In view of equation 9.56 and assuming that for most common cases the function $H_d(e^{j\Omega})$ is real-valued, it follows that $h_d(n)$ will be symmetric about $n = 0$. Therefore, we obtain the error in approximation as

$$E = 2 \sum_{n=(M+1)/2}^{\infty} |h_d(n)|^2 \quad (9.58)$$

Thus equation 9.58 allows us to determine the truncation error for a given value of M and provides us with a means for selecting the length of the FIR filter.

The procedure described above uses a *rectangular window* for matching $h(n)$ and $h_d(n)$. Several other window functions have been proposed in the literature, which provide a better frequency response. Some of the most popular windows used for the design of FIR filters are the *Hamming* window, the *Kaiser* window, and the *Hahn* window. Several sophisticated computer-aided design procedures have also been developed. Interested readers are advised to look at some of the books listed in Appendix E.

9.3.3 FREQUENCY TRANSFORMATIONS

In Section 9.2.2 frequency transformation methods were described in connection with the design of analog filters. The main advantage is that one can use tables for the design of prototype normalized low-pass filters to obtain the parameters of other types of filters. It is possible to use the same methods for digital filters.

First let us consider the design of IIR filters. In this case, one may proceed in two ways. The first approach is to start with the prototype normalized analog filter and perform the necessary frequency transformation to obtain the analog filter with the desired characteristics. The last step is then to transform this analog filter into a digital filter. This approach works quite well only with the bilinear transformation method. As pointed out earlier, the impulse invariant transformation method as well as the method of approximate solution of the differential equation of the analog filter are not suitable for other than low-pass filters. The alternative approach is to first obtain the design of the prototype normalized low-pass digital filter and then to perform the transformation in the z-domain. This would avoid the aliasing problem encountered with filters designed by using the impulse invariant transformation or the method of approximate solution of differential equations.

The transformations can be derived in a manner similar to that used in Section 9.2.2. The main idea in all of these is to replace the variable z^{-1} with a rational function $f(z^{-1})$, which satisfies the following properties.

1. The transformation $z^{-1} \rightarrow f(z^{-1})$ must map all points inside the unit circle in the z-plane into itself.

2. The unit circle must also be mapped into itself.

The second condition implies that for $|z| = 1$, we must also have $|f(z^{-1})| = 1$. Consequently, the mapping must be of the all-pass nature, that is, for every pole p_i of $f(z^{-1})$ there must be a zero at $1/p_i$. This leads us to the form

$$f(z^{-1}) = \pm \prod_{i=1}^{n} \frac{z^{-1} - a_i}{1 - a_i z^{-1}} \tag{9.59}$$

where $|a_i| < 1$ so that the stability of the filter is preserved in the transformation.

Some of the most common transformations are given in Table 9.1. It is assumed in the table that the prototype low-pass digital filter has cutoff frequency Ω_c.

9.3.4 REALIZATION OF DIGITAL FILTERS

The realization problem is the construction of a system that will have a prescribed transfer function. Realization of analog filters requires resistors, capacitors, and inductors or operational amplifiers. A digital filter, on the other hand, can be realized as a software program on either a general-purpose digital computer or a special-purpose digital processor that is designed especially for signal processing. In Chapter 1, we discussed several methods for simulating discrete-time systems, using delays, multipliers, and adders as the basic building blocks. Each of those methods can be utilized for realization of digital filters, either through software or special hardware. One important consideration to be kept in mind is the finite word-length constraint in digital computers and devices. A realization procedure that is less prone to errors caused by truncation and quantization will, therefore, be most desirable. Such a design is said to be *robust*. The structure of the filter realization often has a profound effect on its sensitivity to finite-precision arithmetic. The related problems of choice of the filter structure and the direct design of filters that have quantized coefficients have been and still are important areas of research.

TABLE 9.1 Frequency Transformation for Digital Filters

Type of Transformation	Transformation	Parameters
Low-pass	$f(z^{-1}) = \dfrac{z^{-1} - a}{1 - az^{-1}}$	$a = \dfrac{\sin{(\Omega_c - \Omega'_c)/2}}{\sin{(\Omega_c + \Omega'_c)/2}}$ Ω'_c = new cutoff frequency
High-pass	$f(z^{-1}) = \dfrac{z^{-1} - a}{1 - az^{-1}}$	$a = \dfrac{\cos{(\Omega_c - \Omega'_c)/2}}{\cos{(\Omega_c + \Omega'_c)/2}}$ Ω'_c = new cutoff frequency
Band-pass	$f(z^{-1}) = -\dfrac{z^{-2} - a_1 z^{-1} + a_2}{1 - a_1 z^{-1} + a_2 z^{-2}}$	Ω_1 = lower cutoff frequency Ω_u = upper cutoff frequency $a_1 = -2bK/(K+1)$ $a_2 = (K-1)/(K+1)$ $b = \dfrac{\cos{(\Omega_u + \Omega_1)/2}}{\cos{(\Omega_u - \Omega_1)/2}}$ $K = \cot{\dfrac{\Omega_c - \Omega_1}{2}} \tan{\dfrac{\Omega_c}{2}}$
Band-stop	$f(z^{-1}) = -\dfrac{z^{-2} - a_1 z^{-1} + a_2}{1 - a_1 z^{-1} + a_2 z^{-2}}$	Ω_1 = lower cutoff frequency Ω_u = upper cutoff frequency $a_1 = -2bK/(K+1)$ $a_2 = (1-K)/(1+K)$ $b = \dfrac{\cos{(\Omega_u + \Omega_1)/2}}{\cos{(\Omega_u - \Omega_1)/2}}$ $K = \tan{\dfrac{\Omega_u - \Omega_1}{2}} \tan{\dfrac{\Omega_c}{2}}$

Present work in this field suggests that the cascade and parallel realization procedures, described in Chapter 1, are generally more robust to parameter quantization effects as compared with direct realization. This is especially true with linear-phase FIR filters, where the cascade form reduces the number of multiplications significantly.

We conclude this section with two simple examples of the cascade form realization of IIR and FIR filters.

Example 9.7

The transfer function of a three-stage low-pass Butterworth filter is derived in Example 9.6 by using the bilinear transformation method. It is given below. We shall obtain a cascade form realization.

$$H(z) = \frac{z^3 + 3z^2 + 3z + 1}{105z^3 - 213z^2 + 155z - 39} \tag{9.60}$$

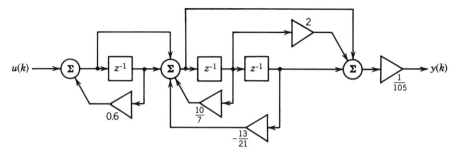

Figure 9.17 Cascade realization of low-pass IIR filter.

The first step is to factorize the numerator and denominator of the transfer function and rearrange as a product for cascade realization. This results in equation 9.61.

$$H(z) = \frac{(z+1)^3}{105(z - 0.6)\left(z^2 - \frac{10}{7}z + \frac{13}{21}\right)}$$

$$= \frac{1 + z^{-1}}{1 - 0.6z^{-1}} \frac{1 + 2z^{-1} + z^{-2}}{\left(1 - \frac{10}{7}z^{-1} + \frac{13}{21}z^{-2}\right)} \frac{1}{105} \qquad (9.61)$$

The transfer function can be realized as the cascade combination of a first-order transfer function and a second-order transfer function. The latter represents the combination of a pair of complex conjugate poles. The realization is shown in Figure 9.17. ∎

Example 9.8

Consider the fourth-order FIR filter given by the equation

$$y(k) = au(k) + bu(k - 1) + bu(k - 2) + au(k - 3) \qquad (9.62)$$

where the symmetry in the coefficients is due to the desired linear-phase characteristic. A direct form realization is shown in Figure 9.18.

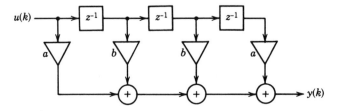

Figure 9.18 Direct form realization of FIR filter.

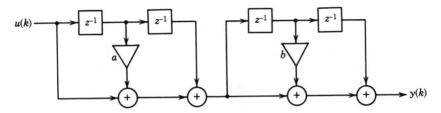

Figure 9.19   Cascade realization of FIR filter.

As seen in Figure 9.18, we need four multiplications in this form of realization. It is possible to reduce the number of multiplications by half if we realize the filter in the cascade form, utilizing the property that the zeros of a linear-phase FIR filter are reciprocals of each other. Therefore, we may write the transfer function of the filter in the following form

$$H(z) = (1 - z_1 z^{-1})\left(1 - \frac{z^{-1}}{z_1}\right)(1 - z_2 z^{-1})\left(1 - \frac{z^{-1}}{z_2}\right)$$

$$= (1 + az^{-1} + z^{-2})(1 + bz^{-1} + z^{-2}) \qquad (9.63)$$

where $a = -(z_1 + 1/z_1)$ and $b = -(z_2 + 1/z_2)$.

The cascade form realization, with only two multiplications, is shown in Figure 9.19. ∎

9.4 SUMMARY

An important application of frequency response is in the design of filters. A brief introduction to the design of analog as well as digital filters was presented. In both cases, the design consists of two main steps. First, a suitable transfer function must be determined (a rational function in the case of analog filters), which will be a close approximation to the desired frequency response. The second step is to synthesize a network that will have this transfer function. In the case of analog filters, standard tables for normalized prototype filters are available and can be utilized, together with some impedance and frequency transformations, for the design of different types of filters. The basic concepts were presented, along with some simple examples. The synthesis problem was not discussed for this case, but it was pointed out that if operational amplifiers are available, then these networks can be synthesized using all the methods for analog simulation discussed in Chapter 1. Digital filters can be of two types, those with finite impulse response (FIR) and those with an infinite impulse response (IIR). The transfer function of an FIR filter is simply a polynomial in z^{-1}, whereas that for an IIR filter is a rational function in z^{-1}. IIR filters are attractive, since it is possible to convert an analog filter into an equivalent digital filter. FIR filters, on the other hand, can have linear phase shift with frequency and are

important in applications where phase distortion is not acceptable. The basic
concepts for the design of both FIR and IIR filters were presented.

PROBLEMS

9.1 A realization of the normalized low-pass filter was shown in Figure
9.9a. This was then transformed into a normalized high-pass filter in
Example 9.2. Determine the transfer function of the realization shown
in Figure 9.10 and draw the Bode plots of the frequency response for
ω varying from 10 to 100,000 rad/s.

9.2 Transform the normalized low-pass filter shown in Figure 9.9a into a
high-pass filter with cut-off at 1000 rad/s and the impedance level
changed from 1 Ω to 10000 Ω.

9.3 Transform the normalized low-pass filter shown in Figure 9.9a into a
band-pass filter with a pass-band between 60,000 and 70,000 Hz and
the impedance level changed from 1 Ω to 10000 Ω.

9.4 The transfer function of a third-order normalized Chebyschev filter is
given below. Determine the transfer function of the corresponding
digital filter using the impulse invariant transformation and plot the
frequency response for Ω between 0 and π, if (a) $T = 0.1$, (b) $T = 0.5$.

$$G(s) = \frac{0.374226}{s^3 + 0.9027s^2 + 1.03294s + 0.374226}$$

9.5 Repeat Problem 9.4 using the bilinear transformation.

9.6 Use bilinear transformation to obtain, from the transfer function in
Problem 9.4, the transfer function of a high-pass digital filter that has
pass-band for Ω between $\pi/2$ and π. Plot the frequency response for
the resulting transfer function.

9.7 Determine the transfer function of an FIR filter of length $M = 9$, that
approximates the following frequency response:

$$H_d(e^{j\Omega}) = \begin{cases} 1 & 0 < \Omega < \dfrac{\pi}{3} \\ 0 & \dfrac{\pi}{3} < \Omega < \pi \end{cases}$$

Plot the frequency response of the resulting transfer function.

9.8 Repeat Problem 9.7 for $M = 7$.

9.9 The transfer function of an ideal differentiator is given by

$$H_d(e^{j\Omega}) = j\Omega, \quad \text{where } |\Omega| < \pi$$

Determine an FIR approximation of length (a) $M = 9$ and (b) $M = 17$.
Plot the resulting frequency response for each case.

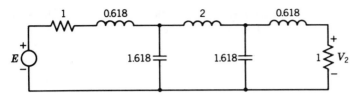

Figure 9.20 Realization of fifth-order normalized Butterworth filter.

9.10 Derive a procedure for the step-invariant transformation of an analog filter (i.e., the responses to a unit step will be identical at the sampling instants).

9.11 Determine the transfer function of a high-pass linear-phase FIR filter of length $M = 9$ and cutoff frequency at $\Omega = \pi/4$.

9.12 The transfer function of a normalized low-pass fifth-order Butterworth filter is given by

$$G(s) = \frac{1}{(s + 1)(s^2 + 1.618s + 1)(s^2 + 0.618s + 1)}$$

(a) Plot the frequency response for ω ranging from 0 to 5 rad/s.

(b) Show that the network shown in Figure 9.20 is a realization of this filter where both the source and the load have resistance of 1 Ω.

9.13 Transform the network in Figure 9.20 to obtain a low-pass filter with cutoff frequency at 4000 Hz if the load and source resistances are 1000 Ω.

9.14 Transform the network of Figure 9.20 to obtain a band-pass filter with pass-band between 10,000 and 12,000 Hz. The load and source impedances may be taken as 400 Ω.

9.15 The transfer function of a normalized low-pass third-order Chebyschev filter, with pass-band ripple of 1 dB, is given below.

$$G(s) = \frac{1}{(s + 0.4513)(s^2 + 0.4514s + 0.829)}$$

(a) Plot the frequency response for ω ranging from 0 to 5 rad/s.

(b) Show that the network shown Figure 9.21 is a realization of this filter where both the source and the load have resistance of 1 Ω.

9.16 Transform the network in Figure 9.21 to obtain a low-pass filter with cutoff frequency at 4000 Hz if the load and source resistance are 1000 Ω.

9.17 Transform the network of Figure 9.21 to obtain a band-pass filter with pass-band between 10,000 and 12,000 Hz. The load and source impedances may be taken as 400 Ω.

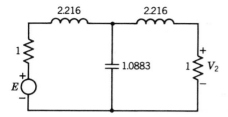

Figure 9.21 Realization of third-order normalized Chebyschev filter.

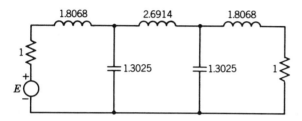

Figure 9.22 Realization of fifth-order normalized Chebyschev filter.

9.18 The transfer function of a normalized low-pass fifth-order Chebyschev filter, with pass-band ripple of 0.5 dB, is given below.

$$G(s) = \frac{1}{(s + 0.342)(s^2 + 0.5534s + 0.4249)(s^2 + 0.2104s + 0.9232)}$$

(a) Plot the frequency response for ω ranging from 0 to 5 rad/s.
(b) Show that the network shown Figure 9.22 is a realization of this filter where both the source and the load have resistance of 1 Ω.

9.19 Transform the network in Figure 9.22 to obtain a low-pass filter with cutoff frequency at 4000 Hz if the load and source resistance are 1000 Ω.

9.20 Transform the network of Figure 9.22 to obtain a band-pass filter with pass-band between 10,000 and 12,000 Hz. The load and source impedances may be taken as 400 Ω.

9.21 Determine the transfer function of an IIR digital filter equivalent to the fifth-order Butterworth filter for which the transfer function is given in Problem 9.12. Use the impulse-invariant transformation method with $T = 0.1$ and plot the frequency response of the resulting filter.

9.22 Repeat Problem 9.21 using the bilinear transformation.

9.23 Determine the transfer function of an IIR digital filter equivalent to the third-order Chebyschev filter for which the transfer function is given in Problem 9.15. Use the impulse-invariant transformation method with $T = 0.1$ and plot the frequency response of the resulting filter.

9.24 Repeat Problem 9.23 using the bilinear transformation.

9.25 Obtain a cascade realization for the transfer function of the digital filter obtained in Problem 9.23.

APPENDIX

A Brief Review of Linear Algebra

A.1 INTRODUCTION

It is expected that the reader has some familiarity with the basic concepts of linear algebra. The object of this appendix is to review these concepts briefly and put together the main ideas in a compact form. Starting with the definition of vectors, we shall proceed to matrices, some properties of their determinants, and finally to eigenvalues and eigenvectors. It is hoped that this appendix will provide sufficient background for the material in Chapter 9.

A.2 VECTORS

Let $\mathbf{x}$ denote the column array of numbers

$$\mathbf{x} = \begin{bmatrix} x_1 \\ x_2 \\ \vdots \\ x_n \end{bmatrix} \qquad (A.1)$$

If each x_i is a real number then $\mathbf{x}$ is a real vector; if one or more x_i are complex numbers then $\mathbf{x}$ is a complex vector. Let E denote the set of all vectors $\mathbf{x}$ of the form given by equation A.1. The ith component of the vector $(\mathbf{x} + \mathbf{y})$ is $(x_i + y_i)$, where x and y are in E. The vector $\alpha\mathbf{x}$, where α is a scalar, has αx_i as its ith component.

The set of vectors $\{\mathbf{x}_1, \mathbf{x}_2, \ldots, \mathbf{x}_k\}$ in E is said to be linearly independent if the only solution to the equation

$$\sum_{i=1}^{k} a_i \mathbf{x}_i = 0 \qquad (A.2)$$

is $a_i = 0$ for $i = 1, 2, \ldots, k$; otherwise, the set of vectors is said to be *linearly*

421

dependent. A linearly independent set of vectors

$$\{x_1, x_2, \ldots, x_n\}$$

in E is said to be a *basis* for E if any vector y in E can be written as a unique linear combination

$$y = \sum_{i=1}^{n} c_i x_i$$

This means that when $\{x_1, x_2, \ldots, x_n\}$ and y are given, the n numbers c_i are uniquely determined.

If all vectors in E are real, we can define a real inner product, denoted by $\langle . , . \rangle$ as a function that satisfies the conditions

(a) $\langle x, x \rangle > 0$ for all $x \neq 0$ in E
(b) $\langle x, y \rangle = \langle y, x \rangle$ for all x and y in E
(c) $\langle \alpha x, y \rangle = \alpha \langle x, y \rangle$ for all real numbers α and all x and y in E
(d) $\langle x + y, z \rangle = \langle x, z \rangle + \langle y, z \rangle$ for all x, y, and z in E

If $\langle x, y \rangle = 0$ then x and y are said to be *orthogonal*.

If $\{x_1, x_2, \ldots, x_k\}$ is a linearly independent set of vectors in E, we can construct a mutually orthogonal set of vectors $\{y_1, y_2, \ldots, y_k\}$ from the x-vectors by using the *Gram-Schmidt* process:

(a) Set $y_1 = x_1$
(b) For $j = 2, 3, \ldots, k$ we compute y_j as

$$y_j = x_j - \sum_{i=1}^{j-1} c_{ij} y_i$$

where $c_{ij} = \langle x_j, y_i \rangle / \langle y_i, y_i \rangle$ for $i = 1, 2, \ldots, j - 1$.

If $\{y_1, y_2, \ldots, y_k\}$ is a mutually orthogonal set of vectors with

$$\langle y_i, y_i \rangle = 1 \text{ for all } i$$

then $\{y_1, y_2, \ldots, y_k\}$ is an *orthonormal* set of vectors.

A.3 MATRICES

If n and m are positive integers, the $n \times m$ matrix $A = (a_{ij})$ is a rectangular array (if $n \neq m$) or square array (if $n = m$) of the nm numbers a_{ij}. If all a_{ij} are real numbers, then A is called a real matrix; if some of the a_{ij} are complex numbers, then A is a complex matrix. The entry in the ith row and jth column of A is a_{ij}. The transpose of the $n \times m$ matrix A, denoted by A^T, is the $m \times n$ array whose (i, j)th entry is a_{ji}. If $A = (a_{ij})$ and $B = (b_{ij})$ are $n \times m$ matrices then the (i, j)th entry of the matrix $(A + B)$ is $(a_{ij} + b_{ij})$. If $A = (a_{ij})$ is $n \times m$ and $C = (c_{jk})$ is $m \times p$ then the (i, k)th entry of the

$n \times p$ product matrix $\mathbf{B} = \mathbf{AC}$ is given by

$$b_{ik} = \sum_{j=1}^{m} a_{ij}c_{jk} \qquad (A.3)$$

The vector $\mathbf{x}$ with m components, can be considered as an $m \times 1$ matrix. Consequently, the product $\mathbf{Ax}$ is a vector with n components, if $\mathbf{A}$ is $n \times m$.

If $\mathbf{A} = (a_{ij})$ is an $n \times n$ matrix then the *main diagonal* of $\mathbf{A}$ consists of the entries a_{ii} for $i = 1, 2, \ldots, n$. The *subdiagonal* of $\mathbf{A}$ contains the entries $a_{i, i-1}$ for $i = 2, 3, \ldots, n$; this is the diagonal immediately below the main diagonal. The *superdiagonal* of $\mathbf{A}$ is made up of the entries $a_{i-1, i}$ for $i = 2, 3, \ldots, n$; this is the diagonal immediately above the main diagonal. An *upper triangular* matrix is one in which $a_{ij} = 0$ for all $j < i$; a *lower triangular* matrix is one in which $a_{ij} = 0$ for all $j > i$. A diagonal matrix has $a_{ij} = 0$ for all $j \neq i$. Because all the entries in a diagonal matrix off the main diagonal are zero, we need specify only those entries on the main diagonal, using the notation $\mathbf{D} = \text{diag}(d_1, d_2, \ldots, d_n)$. If the $n \times n$ matrix $\mathbf{A}$ has an inverse, we say that $\mathbf{A}$ is *nonsingular* and denote its inverse by $\mathbf{A}^{-1}$; if $\mathbf{A}$ does not have an inverse, then $\mathbf{A}$ is *singular*.

We often use an $n \times n$ *identity* matrix; $\mathbf{I}$ is an $n \times n$ identity matrix if

$$\mathbf{I} = \text{diag}(1, 1, \ldots, 1)$$

where there are n ones on the diagonal.

An $n \times n$ permutation *matrix* is obtained from the $n \times n$ identity matrix by interchanging its rows.

An $n \times n$ real matrix $\mathbf{P}$ is called *orthogonal* if $\mathbf{P}^T\mathbf{P} = \mathbf{I}$.

The $n \times n$ matrix $\mathbf{A}$ is *similar* to the $n \times n$ matrix $\mathbf{B}$ if there exists a nonsingular $n \times n$ matrix $\mathbf{S}$ such that $\mathbf{B} = \mathbf{S}^{-1}\mathbf{AS}$. The matrix $\mathbf{A}$ is said to be *diagonalizable* if $\mathbf{A}$ is similar to a diagonal matrix.

A.4 DETERMINANTS

Let $\mathbf{A} = (a_{ij})$ be an $n \times n$ matrix. The *determinant* of $\mathbf{A}$, denoted by $\det(\mathbf{A})$ or

$$\begin{vmatrix} a_{11} & a_{12} & \cdots & a_{1n} \\ a_{21} & a_{22} & \cdots & a_{2n} \\ \vdots & \vdots & & \vdots \\ a_{n1} & a_{n2} & \cdots & a_{nn} \end{vmatrix}$$

is defined by

$$\det(\mathbf{A}) = \sum (-1)^{\sigma(\Pi)} a_{1j_1} a_{2j_2} \cdots a_{nj_n} \qquad (A.4)$$

where $\Pi = \{j_1, j_1, \ldots, j_1\}$ is a permutation of the n numbers $\{1, 2, \ldots, n\}$,

$$\sigma(\Pi) = \begin{cases} 0 & \text{if } n \text{ is an } even \text{ permutation} \\ 1 & \text{if } n \text{ is an } odd \text{ permutation} \end{cases}$$

and the summation is taken over all possible combinations of the n numbers $\{1, 2, \ldots, n\}$.

If $\mathbf{A} = (a_{ij})$ and $\mathbf{B}$ are $n \times n$ matrices, the determinant function has the following properties:

1. $\det(\mathbf{A}) = \det(\mathbf{A}^T)$.

2. If $\mathbf{B}$ is obtained from $\mathbf{A}$ by interchanging two rows (or two columns) then $\det(\mathbf{B}) = -\det(\mathbf{A})$.

3. If $\mathbf{B}$ is obtained from $\mathbf{A}$ by multiplying a row (or a column) by the scalar s, then $\det(\mathbf{B}) = s \det(\mathbf{A})$.

4. If $\mathbf{B}$ is obtained from $\mathbf{A}$ by adding a scalar multiple of one row to another row (or by adding a scalar multiple of one column to another column), then $\det(\mathbf{B}) = \det(\mathbf{A})$.

5. If $\mathbf{A}$ is an upper triangular matrix, then $\det(\mathbf{A}) = a_{11}a_{22} \cdots a_{nn}$.

6. $\det(\mathbf{AB}) = \det(\mathbf{A})\det(\mathbf{B})$.

7. $\mathbf{A}$ is nonsingular if, and only if, $\det(\mathbf{A}) \neq 0$.

8. If $\mathbf{A}$ is nonsingular, then $\det(\mathbf{A}^{-1}) = [\det(\mathbf{A})]^{-1}$.

9. If $\mathbf{B}$ is nonsingular, then $\det(\mathbf{B}^{-1}\mathbf{AB}) = \det(\mathbf{A})$.

If $\mathbf{A} = (a_{ij})$ is an $n \times n$ matrix, we can define $\mathbf{A}_{pq}$ as the submatrix obtained from $\mathbf{A}$ by deleting the pth row and qth column of $\mathbf{A}$. The number $\det(\mathbf{A}_{pq})$ is called the *minor* associated with the element a_{pq} of $\mathbf{A}$. The signed minor, $(-1)^{p+q}\det(\mathbf{A}_{pq})$, is called the *cofactor* of a_{pq}.

The determinant of $\mathbf{A} = (a_{ij})$ can be calculated using the method of *expansion by minors* (or *cofactor expansion*) because, for fixed indices p and q, we have

$$\det(\mathbf{A}) = \sum_{j=1}^{n} a_{pj}(-1)^{p+j} \det(\mathbf{A}_{pj}) \qquad (\text{expansion by row } p)$$

$$= \sum_{j=1}^{n} a_{jq}(-1)^{j+q} \det(\mathbf{A}_{jq}) \qquad (\text{expansion by } column \ q)$$

The linear algebraic system

$$\mathbf{Ax} = \mathbf{b} \qquad\qquad (A.5)$$

is often solved using *Cramer's rule*, when the $n \times n$ matrix $\mathbf{A}$ is nonsingular. The solution is written as ratios of determinants. Let $\mathbf{A}_k$ denote the $n \times n$ matrix obtained from $\mathbf{A}$ by replacing the kth column of $\mathbf{A}$ by the vector $\mathbf{b}$. The kth component of the solution is

$$x_k = \frac{\det(\mathbf{A}_k)}{\det(\mathbf{A})} \qquad\qquad (A.6)$$

A.5   EIGENVALUES AND EIGENVECTORS

We earlier defined a matrix as an array of numbers. We can also look at it as a *transformation*. For example, consider the equation

$$\mathbf{Ax} = \mathbf{y} \qquad (A.7)$$

where $\mathbf{A}$ is an $n \times m$ matrix, $\mathbf{x}$ is a vector with m rows, and $\mathbf{y}$ is a vector with n rows. We can say that the matrix $\mathbf{A}$ has transformed the vector $\mathbf{x}$ into the vector $\mathbf{y}$. In general, the vectors $\mathbf{x}$ and $\mathbf{y}$ will be different, both in length and in direction.

Let us now consider the case when $\mathbf{A}$ is an $n \times n$ matrix. The vector $\mathbf{y}$ obtained from equation A.7 will also be of dimension n now. It is of great interest to find if there are vectors that will not be changed in direction by the transformation indicated by equation A.7. Such vectors do exist and are called *eigenvectors* of the matrix $\mathbf{A}$. In a geometric sense, they define the principal axes associated with the finite-dimensional space obtained from a linear combination of the vectors formed from the columns of the matrix $\mathbf{A}$. A formal definition is given below.

The number λ is an *eigenvalue* of $\mathbf{A}$ if there is a nonzero vector $\mathbf{x}$ such that

$$\mathbf{Ax} = \lambda \mathbf{x} \qquad (A.8)$$

which may also be written as

$$(\lambda \mathbf{I} - \mathbf{A})\mathbf{x} = 0 \qquad (A.9)$$

The nonzero vector $\mathbf{x}$ is called an *eigenvector* of $\mathbf{A}$ associated with the eigenvalue λ. A trivial solution for equation A.9 is obtained when $\mathbf{x}$ is the null or zero vector. A *nontrivial* solution will exist only if

$$\det (\lambda \mathbf{I} - \mathbf{A}) = 0 \qquad (A.10)$$

The roots of the above equation are called the eigenvalues of $\mathbf{A}$. In other words, the eigenvalues of $\mathbf{A}$ satisfy the *characteristic equation* of $\mathbf{A}$, which is given by

$$\det (s \mathbf{I} - \mathbf{A}) = 0 \qquad (A.11)$$

The left-hand side of equation A.11 is a polynomial of degree n in the variable s. It is called the *characteristic polynomial* of $\mathbf{A}$. Consequently, equation A.11 has n roots, which may be complex numbers even if the entries in $\mathbf{A}$ are all real numbers. However, if they are complex, they must occur in conjugate pairs for a real $\mathbf{A}$.

If λ is an eigenvalue of $\mathbf{A}$, then the eigenvector(s) associated with λ satisfy equation A.9. Equation A.9 has nonzero solutions $\mathbf{x}$ because the matrix $(\lambda \mathbf{I} - \mathbf{A})$ is singular.

If λ is a root of multiplicity k of the characteristic polynomial, then λ is said to have *algebraic multiplicity* k. If λ has associated with it a set of q linearly independent eigenvectors, where q is maximal, then the *geometric multiplicity* of λ is q. In general, $q \le k$. If $q < k$ then $\mathbf{A}$ is said to be *defective*. Let the q linearly independent eigenvectors associated with λ be $\mathbf{v}_1, \mathbf{v}_2, \ldots, \mathbf{v}_q$. We can always find sets of *generalized eigenvectors*, associated with λ,

$$\left\{\mathbf{x}_{i,1}, \mathbf{x}_{i,2}, \ldots, \mathbf{x}_{i,j_i}\right),$$

with $\mathbf{x}_{i,1} = \mathbf{v}_i$, $j_i \geq 1$, for $i = 1, 2, \ldots, q$. The integer j_i depends on the integer i. The generalized eigenvectors satisfy the equations

$$\mathbf{A}\mathbf{x}_{i,1} = \lambda \mathbf{x}_{i,1}$$
$$\mathbf{A}\mathbf{x}_{i,2} = \lambda \mathbf{x}_{i,2} + \mathbf{x}_{i,1}$$
$$\mathbf{A}\mathbf{x}_{i,3} = \lambda \mathbf{x}_{i,3} + \mathbf{x}_{i,3}$$
$$\vdots \quad \vdots$$
$$\mathbf{A}\mathbf{x}_{i,j_i} = \lambda \mathbf{x}_{i,j_i} + \mathbf{x}_{i,j_{i-1}}$$

for $i = 1, 2, \ldots, q$ and

$$\sum_{i=1}^{q} j_i = k - q$$

If the $n \times n$ matrix $\mathbf{A}$ has a linearly independent set of n eigenvectors, then $\mathbf{A}$ is similar to a diagonal matrix $\mathbf{D}$, which contains the eigenvalues along its main diagonal. Thus, $\mathbf{S}^{-1}\mathbf{A}\mathbf{S} = \mathbf{D}$, where the columns of $\mathbf{S}$ are the eigenvectors of $\mathbf{A}$. If the matrix $\mathbf{A}$ does not have n independent eigenvectors, then we form such a set with the generalized eigenvectors and obtain the matrix $\mathbf{P}$, the columns of which constitute of this set. In this case, the matrix $\mathbf{J} = \mathbf{P}^{-1}\mathbf{A}\mathbf{P}$ is called the Jordan form. The matrix $\mathbf{J}$ is similar in structure to the diagonal matrix $\mathbf{D}$, with the eigenvalues on its main diagonal, but it also has some 1s on its superdiagonal, corresponding to the repeated eigenvalues for which independent eigenvectors could not be found.

If $\mathbf{A}$ is an $n \times n$ real symmetric matrix, then $\mathbf{A}$ has only real eigenvalues. In addition, the eigenvectors of $\mathbf{A}$ are mutually orthogonal and so can be made into orthonormal vectors (orthogonal unit vectors). As a result, a real symmetric matrix $\mathbf{A}$ is orthogonally similar to a diagonal matrix $\mathbf{D}, \mathbf{S}^T\mathbf{A}\mathbf{S} = \mathbf{D}$ where $\mathbf{S}$ is an orthogonal matrix.

If its eigenvalues are all positive, $\mathbf{A}$ is called positive definite; if all the eigenvalues are negative, $\mathbf{A}$ is called negative definite. Since the determinant of a matrix is the product of its eigenvalues, it follows that a positive definite (or a negative definite) matrix will always be nonsingular.

The scalar $\mathbf{x}^T\mathbf{A}\mathbf{x}$ is called a quadratic form for a square matrix $\mathbf{A}$. For a positive definite matrix, the quadratic form is always positive for any nonzero vector $\mathbf{x}$. Similarly, the quadratic form for a negative definite matrix is always negative for any nonzero vector $\mathbf{x}$. The matrix $\mathbf{A}$ is said to be positive semi-definite if $\mathbf{x}^T\mathbf{A}\mathbf{x} \geq 0$ for all $\mathbf{x}$.

Tables of Fourier, Laplace, and z-Transforms

B.1 TABLE OF FOURIER TRANSFORMS

$x(t)$	$X(\omega)$	Comments
1. $A\delta(t - t_0)$	$Ae^{-j\omega t_0}$	Impulse at $t = t_0$
2. A	$2\pi A\delta(\omega)$	Constant
3. $A\gamma(t)$	$A\left[\dfrac{1}{j\omega} + \pi\delta(\omega)\right]$	Step function
4. $Ae^{-at}\gamma(t)$	$\dfrac{A}{j\omega + a}$	Valid only for $a > 0$
5. $Ae^{-a\lvert t\rvert}$	$\dfrac{2Aa}{a^2 + (j\omega)^2}$	Valid only for $a > 0$
6. $Ae^{-at}\cos\omega_0 t\,\gamma(t)$	$\dfrac{A(j\omega + a)}{(j\omega + a)^2 + \omega_0^2}$	Valid only for $a > 0$
7. $Ae^{-at}\sin\omega_0 t\,\gamma(t)$	$\dfrac{A\omega_0}{(j\omega + a)^2 + \omega_0^2}$	Valid only for $a > 0$
8. $Ate^{-at}\gamma(t)$	$\dfrac{A}{(j\omega + a)^2}$	Valid only for $a > 0$
9. $Ae^{j\omega_0 t}$	$2A\pi\delta(\omega - \omega_0)$	Complex sinusoid
10. $A\cos\omega_0 t$	$A\pi[\delta(\omega + \omega_0) + \delta(\omega - \omega_0)]$	Periodic cosine wave
11. $A\sin\omega_0 t$	$jA\pi[\delta(\omega + \omega_0) - \delta(\omega - \omega_0)]$	Periodic sine wave
12. $\displaystyle\sum_{n=-\infty}^{\infty}\delta(t - nT)$	$\left(\dfrac{2\pi}{T}\right)\displaystyle\sum_{n=-\infty}^{\infty}\delta\left(\omega - \dfrac{2\pi n}{T}\right)$	Periodic impulse train
13. $AP_T(t)$	$AT\,\mathrm{sinc}\left(\dfrac{\omega T}{2}\right)$	Rectangular pulse of height A for $-\dfrac{T}{2} < t < \dfrac{T}{2}$

$x(t)$	$X(\omega)$	Comments
14. $\dfrac{AW}{2\pi}\,\text{sinc}\left(\dfrac{Wt}{2}\right)$	$AP_w(\omega)$	Sinc function
15. $\text{sgn}(t)$	$\dfrac{2}{j\omega}$	Signum function
16. Ae^{-at^2}	$A\sqrt{\left(\dfrac{\pi}{a}\right)}\,e^{-\omega^2/4a}$	
17. $t\gamma(t)$	$\pi\delta'(\omega) - \dfrac{1}{\omega^2}$	Unit ramp function where δ' is the derivative of the impulse

B.2 TABLE OF UNILATERAL LAPLACE TRANSFORMS

$x(t)$	$X(s)$	Comments
1. $A\delta(t - \tau)$	$Ae^{-s\tau}$	Impulse occurring at $t = \tau$
2. A	$\dfrac{A}{s}$	Pole at the origin
3. $Ae^{-\alpha t}$	$\dfrac{A}{s + \alpha}$	Pole at $s = -\alpha$
4. $A\cos\beta t$	$\dfrac{A}{s^2 + \beta^2}$	Poles at $s = \pm j\beta$
5. $A\sin\beta t$	$\dfrac{A\beta}{s^2 + \beta^2}$	Poles at $s = \pm j\beta$
6. $Ae^{-\alpha t}\cos\beta t$	$\dfrac{A(s + \alpha)}{(s + \alpha)^2 + \beta^2}$	Poles at $s = -\alpha \pm j\beta$
7. $Ae^{-\alpha t}\sin\beta t$	$\dfrac{A\beta}{(s + \alpha)^2 + \beta^2}$	Poles at $s = -\alpha \pm j\beta$
8. t	$\dfrac{1}{s^2}$	Two poles at the origin
9. $t^n\ (n = 1, 2, 3, \ldots)$	$\dfrac{n!}{s^{n+1}}$	$(n + 1)$ poles at the origin
10. $t^n e^{-\alpha t}\ (n = 1, 2, \ldots)$	$\dfrac{n!}{(s + \alpha)^{n+1}}$	$(n + 1)$ poles at $s = -\alpha$
11. $P_T(t)$	$\dfrac{1}{s}(1 - e^{-sT})$	Rectangular pulse of unit height for $0 < t < T$
12. $\displaystyle\sum_{n=0}^{\infty} P_T(t - 2nT)$	$\dfrac{1}{s(1 + e^{sT})}$	Train of rectangular pulses

B.2 (Continued)

$x(t)$	$X(s)$	Comments
13. $\sinh at$	$\dfrac{a}{s^2 - a^2}$	
14. $\cosh at$	$\dfrac{s}{s^2 - a^2}$	
15. $t \sin \omega_0 t$	$\dfrac{2\omega_0 s}{\left(s^2 + \omega_0^2\right)^2}$	
16. $t \cos \omega_0 t$	$\dfrac{s^2 - \omega_0^2}{\left(s^2 + \omega_0^2\right)^2}$	
17. $\sin \omega_0 t - \omega_0 t \cos \omega_0 t$	$\dfrac{2\omega_0^3}{\left(s^2 + \omega_0^2\right)^2}$	
18. $\dfrac{e^{\alpha t} - e^{\beta t}}{\alpha - \beta}$	$\dfrac{1}{(s - \alpha)(s - \beta)}$	
19. $\dfrac{\alpha e^{\alpha t} - \beta e^{\beta t}}{\alpha - \beta}$	$\dfrac{s}{(s - \alpha)(s - \beta)}$	
20. e^{-bt^2}	$\dfrac{1}{2}\sqrt{\left(\dfrac{\pi}{b}\right)}\, e^{s^2/4b}\, \mathrm{erfc}\left(\dfrac{s}{2\sqrt{b}}\right) \quad b > 0$	

$$\text{where } \mathrm{erfc}\,(s) = \frac{2}{\sqrt{\pi}} \int_s^\infty e^{-z^2}\, dz,$$

the complementary error function

B.3 TABLE OF UNILATERAL z-TRANSFORMS

$x(k)$	$X(z)$	Comments
1. $\delta(k)$	1	Unit impulse
2. A	$\dfrac{Az}{z - 1}$	Pole at $z = 1$, $\quad |z| > 1$
3. Ar^k	$\dfrac{Az}{z - r}$	Pole at $z = r$, $\quad |z| > 2$
4. Ak	$\dfrac{Az}{(z - 1)^2}$	Two poles at $z = 1$, $\quad |z| > 1$
5. $A \cos \beta k$	$\dfrac{Az(z - \cos \beta)}{z^2 - 2z \cos \beta + 1}$	Complex poles on unit circle, $|z| > 1$
6. $A \sin \beta k$	$\dfrac{Az \sin \beta}{z^2 - 2z \cos \beta + 1}$	Complex poles on unit circle, $|z| > 1$
7. $Ar^k \cos \beta k$	$\dfrac{Az(z - r \cos \beta)}{z^2 - 2zr \cos \beta + r^2}$	Complex poles, $\quad |z| > r$

B.3 (*Continued*)

$x(k)$	$X(z)$	Comments
8. $Ar^k \sin \beta k$	$\dfrac{Azr \sin \beta}{z^2 - 2zr \cos \beta + r^2}$	Complex poles, $\|z\| > r$
9. Akr^k	$\dfrac{Arz}{(z-r)^2}$	$\|z\| > r$
10. Ak^2	$\dfrac{Az(z+1)}{(z-1)^3}$	$\|z\| > 1$
11. $Ak^n r^k$	$A\left(-z\dfrac{d}{dz}\right)^n (1 - rz^{-1})^{-1}$	
12. $\dfrac{1}{k}$	$-\ln(1 - z^{-1})$	$k > 0$

B.4 TABLE FOR INVERSION OF LAPLACE TRANSFORMS FROM THE PARTIAL FRACTION EXPANSION OF A RATIONAL FUNCTION $X(s)$

The following table will be useful for the inversion of one-sided Laplace transforms from the partial fraction expansion of $X(s)$. The program for evaluation of residues on the disk included with the book can be used for partial fraction expansion of $X(s)$, including the case when the poles are complex and of multiplicity greater than one.

$X(s)$	$x(t)$
$\dfrac{A}{s + \alpha}$	$Ae^{-\alpha t}$
$\dfrac{C + jD}{s + \alpha + j\beta} + \dfrac{C - jD}{s + \alpha - j\beta}$	$2e^{-\alpha t}(C \cos \beta t + D \sin \beta t)$
$\dfrac{A}{(s + \alpha)^{n+1}}$	$\dfrac{t^n e^{-\alpha t}}{n!}$
$\dfrac{C + jD}{(s + \alpha + j\beta)^{n+1}} + \dfrac{C - jD}{(s + \alpha - j\beta)^{n+1}}$	$\dfrac{2t^n e^{-\alpha t}}{n!}(C \cos \beta t + D \sin \beta t)$

B.5 TABLE FOR INVERSION OF UNILATERAL z-TRANSFORMS FROM PARTIAL FRACTION EXPANSION OF THE RATIONAL FUNCTION $X(z)/z$

The following table will be useful for the inversion of one-sided z-transforms from the partial fraction expansion of $X(z)/z$. In the case of complex poles, it is more convenient to express them in the polar form for use with the table, although the residues at these poles may still be left in the rectangular form.

$X(z)$	$x(n)$
$\dfrac{Az}{z - r}$	$Ar^n, \quad n \geq 0$
$\dfrac{(C + jD)z}{z - re^{j\phi}} + \dfrac{(C - jD)z}{z - re^{-j\phi}}$	$2r^n(C \cos n\phi - D \sin n\phi), \quad n \geq 0$
$\dfrac{Az}{(z - r)^m}$	$\dfrac{An(n - 1) \cdots (n - m + 2)}{(m - 1)!\, r^{m-1}} r^n, \quad n \geq m - 1$

Summation of Some Sequences

In Chapters 2 and 6, while studying sequences and z-transforms, we encountered the need for evaluating the sum of some sequences. In this appendix we present a short table of some of these. In each instance, the sum may be evaluated either by algebraic methods, or by using z-transforms.

1. $\quad 1 + r + r^2 + \cdots + r^n = \dfrac{1 - r^{n+1}}{1 - r}$

2. $\quad 1 + 2r + 3r^2 + 4r^3 + \cdots + nr^{n-1} = \dfrac{1 - r^n}{(1 - r)^2} - \dfrac{nr^n}{1 - r}$

3. $\quad 1 + 2 + 3 + \cdots + n = \dfrac{n(n + 1)}{2}$

4. $\quad 1 + 2^2 + 3^2 + \cdots + n^2 = \dfrac{n(n + 1)(2n + 1)}{6}$

5. $\quad 1 + 2^3 + 3^3 + \cdots + n^3 = \dfrac{n^2(n + 1)^2}{4}$

It would be a good exercise to prove these results. This can be done easily by using the relationship between the step response and impulse response of a discrete-time system that was derived in Section 2.11, that is,

$$g(n) = \sum_{k=0}^{n} h(k)$$

where $h(k)$ is the impulse response sequence and $g(k)$ is the corresponding step response sequence.

APPENDIX

D

Contour Integration and Cauchy's Residue Theorem

The inverse Laplace and z-transform integrals were defined in Chapters 5 and 6. These integrals are *complex line integrals*. In this appendix we shall study a method for evaluating such integrals. Although we shall be specifically talking about functions of the complex variable s, our discussions will also apply to functions of z.

The function $F(s)$ can be written as

$$F(s) = u(\sigma, j\omega) + jv(\sigma, j\omega) \qquad \text{(D.1)}$$

where

$$s = \sigma + j\omega \qquad \text{(D.2)}$$

Note that both u and v are real functions of σ and ω.

$F(s)$ is said to be *analytic* within a region $\Re$ of the complex plane if it is single-valued in that region and if the derivative of $F(s)$ exists at every point in the region and is independent of the direction, that is,

$$\frac{dF}{ds} = \lim_{\Delta s \to 0} \frac{\Delta F}{\Delta s} \qquad \text{(D.3)}$$

independent of the choice of Δs. The necessary and sufficient conditions for $F(s)$ to be analytic are called the *Cauchy–Riemann equations* and are given below.

$$\frac{\partial u}{\partial \sigma} = \frac{\partial v}{\partial \omega} \qquad \text{(D.4)}$$

$$\frac{\partial u}{\partial \omega} = -\frac{\partial v}{\partial \sigma} \qquad \text{(D.5)}$$

Let us now consider a closed curve C in the s-plane, as shown in Figure D.1.

The integral of $F(s)$, performed along this curve while going around it in the positive (counterclockwise) direction, is called a *contour* integral and is

433

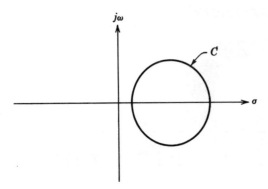

Figure D.1   Path of integration in the s-plane.

denoted by the symbol

$$\oint_c F(s)\, ds \tag{D.6}$$

Cauchy's integral formula states that if $F(s)$ is analytic on the path C (i.e., it does not have any pole on the path), then

$$\frac{1}{2\pi j} \oint_c F(s)\, ds = \text{Sum of the residues at all simple} \atop \qquad\qquad\qquad\text{poles of } F(s) \text{ within } C \tag{D.7}$$

Note that a multiple pole inside C does not contribute to the integral, nor do any poles of $F(s)$ outside C.

We now consider application of this theorem to the evaluation of inverse Laplace and z-transforms. It may be recalled that the defining integral for

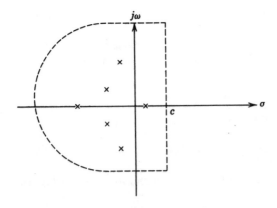

Figure D.2   Path of integration in the s-plane.

the former is

$$f(t) = \frac{1}{2\pi j} \int_{c-j\infty}^{c+j\infty} F(s) e^{st} \, dt \tag{D.8}$$

where the constant c is to be selected in such a way that for unilateral transforms, all poles of $F(s)$ are to the left of the path of integration. This is shown in Figure D.2.

Note that the path of integration is along a vertical line in the s-plane, extending from $c - j\infty$ to $c + j\infty$. However, if $F(s)$ vanishes for $|s| = \infty$, we can integrate along the closed path shown in Figure D.2 without affecting the integral. In that case, we can use the integral formula described above. The result leads directly to the method of partial fraction expansions that was discussed in Chapter 5.

For inverse z-transformation, the path of integration is the unit circle in the z-plane and the integral formula can be applied directly.

References

Because of the importance and popularity of the theory of linear systems and signals, numerous excellent books have been written on the subject and related topics. The following list is not exhaustive but merely names the books that were used as reference material in the preparation of this text.

BASIC CIRCUIT AND SYSTEMS THEORY

C. A. DESOER and E. S. KUH, *Basic Circuit Theory*, McGraw-Hill, New York, 1969.

ROBERT L. GABEL and RICHARD A. ROBERTS, *Signals and Linear Systems*, third edition, Wiley, New York, 1987.

W. H. HAYT and J. E. KEMMERLY, *Engineering Circuit Analysis*, third edition, McGraw-Hill, New York, 1977.

J. D. IRWIN, *Basic Engineering Circuit Analysis*, Macmillan, New York, 1984.

E. KAMEN, *Introduction to Signals and Systems*, Macmillan, New York, 1987.

R. J. MAYHAN, *Discrete-time and Continuous-time Linear Systems*, Addison-Wesley, Reading, MA, 1983.

A. PAPOULIS, *Circuits and Systems: A Modern Approach*, Holt, Rinehart & Winston, New York, 1980.

RODGER E. ZIEMER, WILLIAM H. TRANTER, and D. R. FANNIN, *Signals and Systems—Continuous and Discrete*, MacMillan, New York, 1983.

COMPUTATIONAL METHODS

G. E. FORSYTHE, M. A. MALCOLM, and C. B. MOLER, *Computer Methods for Mathematical Computations*, Prentice-Hall, Englewood Cliffs, NJ, 1977.

G. J. LASTMAN and N. K. SINHA, *Microcomputer-based Numerical Methods for Science and Engineering*, Holt, Rinehart & Winston, New York, 1989.

W. H. Press, B. P. Flannery, S. A. Teukkolsky, and W. T. Vettering, *Numerical Recipes: The Art of Scientific Computing*, Cambridge University Press, New York, 1986.

CONTROL SYSTEMS AND STATE VARIABLE METHODS

J. J. D'Azzo and C. H. Houpis, *Linear Control System Analysis & Design*, third edition, McGraw-Hill, New York, 1988.

P. M. deRusso, R. J. Roy, and C. M. Close, *State Variables for Engineers*, Wiley, New York, 1965.

R. C. Dorf, *Modern Control Systems*, fifth edition, Addison-Wesley, Reading, MA, 1988.

T. Kailath, *Linear Systems*, Prentice-Hall, Englewood Cliffs, NJ, 1980.

B. C. Kuo, *Automatic Control Systems*, fourth edition, Prentice-Hall, Englewood Cliffs, NJ, 1982.

K. Ogata, *State Space Analysis of Control Systems*, Prentice-Hall, Englewood Cliffs, NJ, 1967.

N. K. Sinha, *Control Systems*, Holt, Rinehart & Winston, New York, 1986.

CONVOLUTION TECHNIQUES

Robert L. Gabel and Richard A. Roberts, *Signals and Linear Systems*, third edition, Wiley, New York, 1987.

B. P. Lathi, *Signals, Systems and Controls*, Intext Educational Publishers, New York, 1974.

A. Papoulis, *Signal Analysis*, McGraw-Hill, New York, 1977.

DESIGN OF FILTERS

A. Antoniou, *Digital Filters: Analysis and Design*, McGraw-Hill, New York, 1979.

N. K. Bose, *Digital Filters—Theory and Applications*, North-Holland, New York, 1985.

David E. Johnson, *Introduction to Filter Theory*, Prentice-Hall, Englewood Cliffs, NJ, 1976.

R. A. Roberts and C. T. Mullis, *Digital Signal Processing*, Addison-Wesley, Reading, MA, 1987.

James E. Storer, *Passive Network Synthesis*, McGraw-Hill, New York, 1957.

M. E. Van Valkenberg, *Network Analysis*, Prentice-Hall, Englewood Cliffs, NJ, 1955.

LOUIS WEINBERG, *Network Analysis and Synthesis*, McGraw-Hill, New York, 1962.

ARTHUR B. WILLIAMS and FRED J. TAYLOR, *Electronic Filter Design Handbook*, second edition, McGraw-Hill, New York, 1988.

DIGITAL SIGNAL PROCESSING

A. ANTONIOU, *Digital Filters: Analysis and Design*, McGraw-Hill, New York, 1979.

N. K. BOSE, *Digital Filters—Theory and Applications*, North-Holland, New York, 1985.

L. C. LUDEMAN, *Fundamentals of Digital Signal Processing*, Harper & Rowe, New York, 1986.

ALAN V. OPPENHEIM and RONALD W. SHAFER, *Digital Signal Processing*, Prentice-Hall, Englewood Cliffs, NJ, 1975.

JOHN G. PROAKIS and G. M. DIMITRIS, *Introduction to Digital Signal Processing*, Macmillan, New York, 1988.

L. R. RABINER and B. GOLD, *Theory and Application of Digital Signal Processing*, Prentice-Hall, Englewood Cliffs, NJ, 1975.

W. M. STANLEY, *Digital Signal Processing*, Reston, NY, 1975.

Selected Papers in Digital Signal Processing II, IEEE Press, New York, 1976.

Programs for Digital Signal Processing, IEEE Press, New York, 1980.

FOURIER ANALYSIS

C. D. McGILLEM and G. R. COOPER, *Continuous and Discrete Signal and System Analysis*, Holt, Rinehart & Winston, New York, 1974.

A. PAPOULIS, *The Fourier Integral and Its Applications*, McGraw-Hill, New York, 1962.

M. SCHWARTZ, *Information Transmission, Modulation, and Noise*, third edition, McGraw-Hill, New York, 1980.

R. E. ZIEMER and W. H. TRANTER, *Principles of Communications*, Houghton Mifflin, Boston, MA, 1976.

LAPLACE TRANSFORMS

E. BOHN, *The Transform Analysis of Linear Systems*, Addison-Wesley, Reading, MA, 1963.

E. J. CRAIG, *Laplace and Fourier Transforms for Engineers*, Holt, Rinehart & Winston, New York, 1964.

S. KARNI and W. J. BYATT, *Mathematical Methods in Continuous and Discrete Systems*, Holt, Rinehart & Winston, New York, 1982.

M. E. VAN VALKENBERG, *Network Analysis*, Prentice-Hall, Englewood Cliffs, NJ, 1955.

LINEAR ALGEBRA

G. L. BRADLEY, *A Primer of Linear Algebra*, Prentice-Hall, Englewood Cliffs, NJ, 1975.

G. STRANG, *Linear Algebra and Its Applications*, Academic Press, New York, 1976.

z-TRANSFORMS

G. F. FRANKLIN and J. D. POWELL, *Digital Control of Dynamic Systems*, Addison-Wesley, Reading, MA, 1980.

H. FREEMAN, *Discrete-time Systems*, Wiley, New York, 1965.

C. H. HOUPIS and G. B. LAMONT, *Digital Control Systems, Theory, Hardware, Software*, McGraw-Hill, New York, 1985.

E. I. JURY, *Theory and Application of z-transforms*, Wiley, New York, 1964.

B. C. KUO, *Digital Control Systems*, Holt, Rinehart & Winston, New York, 1980.

C. L. PHILLIPS and H. T. NAGLE, *Digital Control Systems Analysis and Design*, Prentice-Hall, Englewood Cliffs, NJ, 1984.

H. F. VAN LANDINGHAM, *Introduction to Digital Control Systems*, Macmillan, New York, 1985.

Answers to Selected Problems

CHAPTER 1

1.1 (a) $0.5 + 3.5e^{-2t} - 2e^{-6t}$ (b) $1.5e^{-2t} - 0.5e^{-4t} + te^{-4t}$

    (c) $\dfrac{126}{697}\sin 2t - \dfrac{96}{697}\cos 2t + \dfrac{793}{697}e^{-4t}\cos 3t + \dfrac{2920}{2091}e^{-4t}\sin 3t$

1.2 $\dfrac{0.25}{p^3 + 1.25p^2 + 1.75p + 0.25}$

1.7 $y(k) = -9 + 9(3)^k - 9k(2)^k$

1.8 $y(k) = -20 + 13(2)^k + 5(3)^k - 9k(2)^k$

1.13 $y(k) = 1.17082034(1.618034)^k - 0.17080234(0.61834)^k$,
$y(10) = 144$

1.14 $y(k) = 2(3)^k$, $y(12) = 1{,}062{,}882$ pairs

1.15 (a) $y(k) = \dfrac{8}{15} + \dfrac{7}{10}(-2)^k + \dfrac{23}{30}(-4)^k$

    (b) $y(k) = \dfrac{12}{25} - \dfrac{12}{25}(-3)^k - \dfrac{8}{15}k(-3)^k$

1.16 (a) $(8.94427)^k(0.952865\cos 2.03444k + 0.74237\sin 2.03444k)$
       $+ 0.047135\cos(k\pi/3) - 0.120059\sin(k\pi/3)$

    (b) $(8.94427)^k(0.97907\cos 2.03444k + 2.41956\sin 2.03444k)$
       $+ 0.02093e^{-2k}$

    (c) $7.5315e^{-3k} + 0.0037771ke^{-3k}$
       $-(8.94427)^k(6.5315\cos 2.03444k + 60.2676\sin 2.03444k)$

1.17 (a) $0.807692\cos(k\pi/3) - 0.199852\sin(k\pi/3) + 0.192308(-3)^k$
       $-0.403846k(-3)^k$

    (b) $1.27578e^{-2k} - 0.27578(-3)^k - \dfrac{k}{3}(-3)^k$

    (c) $1.02893(-3)^k + 0.96343k(-3)^k - 0.02892e^{-3k} + 0.3625ke^{-3k}$

440

1.18 $\dfrac{10}{3} - 0.4465e^{-2.13712t} - e^{-0.93144t}(2.8868 \cos 2.48016t$
$+ 1.4698 \sin 2.48016t)$

1.19 $10e^{-2t} - 6.9567e^{-2.13712t} - e^{-.93144t}(3.03996 \cos 2.48016t$
$+ 0.2958 \sin 2.48016t)$

1.20 $e^{-0.93144t}(0.44247 \cos 2.48016t + 3.46467 \sin 2.4801t) -$
$0.01451e^{-2.13712t}$
$-e^{-2t}(0.42822 \cos 3t + 3.02268 \sin 3t)$

1.21 $2t - 1 + e^{-2t}$

1.22 $1 - 3.7988e^{-62.12214t} + 2.7988e^{-12.87786t}$

1.23 $1 - 2.7597e^{-62.12214t} + 11.7597e^{-12.87786t}$

1.24 Sam's fund = \$196,694.12,   Joseph's fund = \$343,136.37

1.25 Sam's fund = \$228,826.61,   Joseph's fund = \$480,473.01

1.26 (a) $L(p) = \dfrac{2p + 7}{p^3 + 9p^2 + 32p + 10}$

   (b) $\dfrac{2p + 3}{(p + 3)(p^2 + 4p + 12)}$

   (c) $\dfrac{5p^2 + 22p + 39}{(p + 3)(p^2 + 4p + 12)}$

1.27 (a) stable   (b) unstable

   (c) stable   (d) stable   (e) unstable

CHAPTER 2

2.1 (a) $8\gamma(t) - 3\gamma(t - 4) - 0.4r(t - 4) + 0.4r(t - 10)$

   (b) $1.6r(t) - 3.2r(t - 5) + 1.6r(t - 10)$

   (c) $10\gamma(t) + 10\gamma(t - 5) - 10\gamma(t - 10) - 10\gamma(t - 15)$

   (d) $2r(t) - 2r(t - 5) - 2(t - 15) + r(t - 20)$

2.3 (a) e^{50} (b) $2/13$

   (c) -0.1455 (d) 0.02798

2.4 $v(t) = 1000e^{-1000t}$

2.5 $v(t) = 1000.1(e^{-1000.05t} - e^{-19998999.95t})$

2.6 (a) $e^{-2t} - e^{-3t}$ (b) $3e^{-3t} - e^{-2t}$

   (c) $0.5e^{-2t} \sin 2t$ (d) $2e^{-2t} \cos 2t - 0.5e^{-2t} \sin 2t$

   (e) te^{-2t} (f) $2e^{-2t} - te^{-2t}$

   (g) $0.25e^{-2t}(1 - \cos 2t)$ (h) $0.25e^{-2t}(\cos 2t + \sin 2t - 1)$

2.8 (a) $4(0.8)^k - 3(0.6)^k$, $k \geq 2$ (b) $23(0.8)^k - 21(0.6)^k$, $k \geq 1$

(c) $\cos 0.9273(k - 2) + 0.75 \sin 0.9273(k - 2)$, $k \geq 2$

(d) $2 \cos 0.9273(k - 1) + 5.25 \sin 0.9273(k - 1)$, $k \geq 1$

(e) $k - 1$, $k \geq 2$ (f) $5k - 3$, $k \geq 1$

(g) $11.56(0.1127)^k - 46.57(0.6)^k + 37.01(0.8873)^k$, $k \geq 1$

2.9 (a) $\dfrac{1}{6} - \dfrac{1}{2}e^{-2t} + \dfrac{1}{3}e^{-6t}$ (b) $\dfrac{1}{2}(1 + e^{-2t}) - e^{-3t}$

(c) $\dfrac{1}{8} - \dfrac{1}{8}e^{-2t}(\cos 2t - - 2\sin 2t)$

(d) $\dfrac{3}{8} - \dfrac{1}{8}e^{-2t}(3\cos 2t - 5\sin 2t)$

(e) $\dfrac{1}{4}(1 - e^{-2t} + 2te^{-2t})$ (f) $\dfrac{1}{4}(3 - 3e^{-2t} + 2te^{-2t})$

(g) $\dfrac{1}{16}[1 - e^{-2t}(2 - \cos 2t + \sin 2t)]$

(h) $\dfrac{1}{16}[3 + e^{-2t}(2 - 5\cos 3t - 3\sin 2t)]$

2.10 (a) $\dfrac{1}{6}t - \dfrac{5}{36} + \dfrac{1}{4}e^{-2t} - \dfrac{1}{9}e^{-3t}$

(b) $\dfrac{1}{2}t - \dfrac{1}{12} - \dfrac{1}{4}e^{-2t} + \dfrac{1}{3}e^{-3t}$

(c) $\dfrac{1}{16}[2t - 1 + e^{-2t}(\cos 2t - 5\sin 2t)]$

(d) $\dfrac{1}{16}[6t + 1 + e^{-2t}(3\cos 2t - \sin 2t)]$

(e) $\dfrac{1}{4}[t - 1 + e^{-2t}(t + 1)]$ (f) $\dfrac{1}{4}[t - 1 - e^{-t}(t - 1)]$

(g) $\dfrac{1}{32}[2t - 2 + e^{-2t}(2 - \sin 2t)]$

(h) $\dfrac{1}{16}[3t - 1 - e^{-2t}(1 - 2\cos 2t + 6\sin 2t)]$

2.12 (a) $12.5 - 20(0.8)^{k-1} + 7.5(0.6)^{k-1}$

(b) $62.5 - 11.5(0.8)^k + 52.5(0.6)^k$

(c) $12.5[1 - \cos 0.9273(k - 1) - 0.5 \sin 0.9273(k - 1)]$

(d) $6.25(1 - \cos 0.9273k) - 4.625 \sin 0.9273k$

(e) $0.5k(k - 1)$ (f) $0.5k(5k - 1)$

(g) $225 + 116.43(0.6)^k - 13.03(0.1127)^k - 328.4(0.8873)^k$

2.13 (a) $12.5k - 93.75 + 100(0.8)^{k-1} - 18.75(0.6)^{k-1}$

(b) $62.5k - 506.25 + 575(0.8)^{k-1} - 131.25(0.6)^{k-1}$

(c) $1.25k - 1.5625 \sin 0.9273k$

(d) $6.25k - 7.75(1 - \cos 0.9273k) - 2.565 \sin 0.9273k$

(e) $k(k-1)(k-2)/6$ (f) $k(k-1)(5k-4)/6$

(g) $225k - 2647.54 - 291.07(0.6)^k - 14.685(0.1127)^k$
$+ 2913.93(0.8873)^k$

2.14 $2 - (0.5)^{k-1}$

2.15 $0.25t - 10 + 10e^{-0.25t}$

2.16 (a) $\dfrac{2}{13} - \dfrac{2}{13}e^{-2t}\cos 3t - \dfrac{8}{39}e^{-2t}\sin 3t$

(b) $\dfrac{2}{13}t - \dfrac{8}{169}(1 - e^{-2t}\cos 3t) + \dfrac{72}{169}e^{-2t}\sin 3t$

(c) $\left[\dfrac{6}{13}(1 - e^{-2t}\cos 3t) - \dfrac{8}{13}e^{-2t}\sin 3t\right]\gamma(t)$
$- \left[\dfrac{6}{13}\left(1 - e^{-2(t-1)}\cos 3(t-1)\right) - \dfrac{8}{13}e^{-2(t-1)}\sin 3(t-1)\right]\gamma(t-1)$

2.17 (a) $[1 - e^{-t}(\cos 3t + \dfrac{1}{3}\sin 3t)]\gamma(t) - [1 - e^{-(t-1)}(\cos 3(t-1)$
$+ \dfrac{1}{3}\sin 3(t-1))]\gamma(t-1)$

(b) $y_r(t)\gamma(t) - 2y_r(t-1)\gamma(t-1) + y_r(t-2)\gamma(t-2)$

2.19 (a) $10(0.5)^k - 8(0.8)^k$ (b) $20(0.5)^k - 160(0.8)^k - 20k + 140$

2.25 $7.5(2)^k - \dfrac{11}{6}(3)^k - \dfrac{19}{2}$

2.26 $15(2)^k - \dfrac{11}{8}(3)^k - \dfrac{19}{4}k^2 - \dfrac{23}{6}k - \dfrac{71}{4}$

2.27 $15(2)^k - \dfrac{11}{8}(3)^k - \dfrac{19}{4}k^2 - \dfrac{23}{6}k - \dfrac{71}{4}$

2.28 (a) $0.17647e^{-2t}\cos\sqrt{8}\,t - 0.51994e^{-2t}\sin\sqrt{8}\,t - 0.17647e^{-5t}$

(b) $0.33333e^{-2t}\cos\sqrt{8}\,t - 0.58926e^{-2t}\sin\sqrt{8}\,t - 0.33333e^{-3t}$

(c) $2e^{-3t} + 3e^{-2t}\cos\sqrt{3}\,t - \dfrac{1}{\sqrt{8}}e^{-2t}\sin\sqrt{3}\,t$

CHAPTER 3

3.1   (a) $10 - \sum_{n=1}^{\infty} \dfrac{20}{n\pi} \sin n\omega_0 t$

(b) $\dfrac{20}{\pi} + 10 \sin \dfrac{2\pi t}{T} - \sum_{n=1}^{\infty} \dfrac{40}{\pi(4n^2 - 1)} \cos \dfrac{4\pi nt}{T}$

(c) $\sum_{n=1}^{\infty} \dfrac{20}{n\pi} \sin 0.1 n\pi t$

(d) $5 + \sum_{n=1}^{\infty} \dfrac{25}{n\pi} \sin 1.6 n\pi \cos 0.08 n\pi t$

$+ \sum_{n=1}^{\infty} \dfrac{25}{n\pi}(1 - \cos 1.6 n\pi) \sin 0.08 n\pi t$

3.2   (a) $c_0 = 10, \qquad c_n = \dfrac{j10}{n\pi} \qquad$ for $n \neq 0$

(b) $c_n = \begin{cases} -j5 & \text{for } n = 1 \\ 0 & \text{for odd } n, \text{ except } n = 1 \\ \dfrac{-20}{\pi(n^2 - 1)} & \text{for even } n \end{cases}$

(c) $c_n = \begin{cases} 0 & \text{for } n = 0 \\ -j\dfrac{10}{n\pi} & \text{otherwise} \end{cases}$

(d) $c_0 = 5, \qquad c_n = 12.5 \dfrac{\sin 1.6 n\pi - j(1 - \cos 1.6 n\pi)}{n\pi}$

3.3 $c_0 = 0, \qquad c_n = j\dfrac{2AT}{\Delta n^2} \sin \dfrac{N\pi\Delta}{T}$

3.4 $\dfrac{200}{\pi} - \sum_{n=1}^{\infty} \dfrac{800}{\pi(n^2 - 1)} \cos 754nt$

3.5 $\dfrac{200}{\pi} - \sum_{n=1}^{\infty} \dfrac{800}{\pi(n^2 - 1)} \cos 754nt \cos n\pi$

3.6 $c_n = \begin{cases} 0 & \text{for even } n \\ \dfrac{2}{n\pi}(-1)^{(n-1)/2} & \text{for odd } n \end{cases}$

3.7 $c_n = \begin{cases} 0 & \text{for even } n \\ \dfrac{j2}{n\pi} e^{-j2n\pi/3} & \text{for odd } n \end{cases}$

3.8 $\dfrac{1 - e^{-(10+jn\pi)}}{2 + j0.2n\pi}$

3.9 $c_n = 0.4\left[\dfrac{e^{1-jn\pi} - 1}{0.2 - j0.2n\pi} + \dfrac{e^{0.2-jn\pi} - e^{-0.8-j2n\pi}}{0.2 + j0.2n\pi}\right]$

3.10 a_n

$= \dfrac{30}{\pi}\left[\dfrac{1 - \cos(n+1)\alpha}{n+1} - \dfrac{1 - \cos(n-1)\alpha}{n-1} + \dfrac{4}{3}\dfrac{\sin n\dfrac{\pi}{2} - /\sin n\alpha}{n}\right],$

$$n \neq 1, \qquad a_1 = \dfrac{280}{9\pi}$$

3.11 $a_n = \dfrac{30}{\pi}\left[\dfrac{1 - \cos(n+1)\dfrac{\pi}{3}}{n+1} - \dfrac{1 - \cos(n-1)\dfrac{\pi}{3}}{n-1}\right.$

$$\left. + \dfrac{4}{3}\dfrac{\sin\dfrac{n\pi}{2} - \sin\dfrac{n\pi}{3}}{n}\right], \qquad n \neq 1$$

3.12 (a) $9.78\cos(3t + 0.0768)$

(b) $0.76925 + 1.1242\cos(2t + 0.9046) + 3.962\cos(4t - 1.3569)$

3.13 (a) $1.9894\cos(0.5t - 1.0517)$ (b) $1.414\cos(t - 2.3562)$

(c) $0.682\cos(1.4t - 3.1227)$

(d) $\dfrac{40}{\pi}[0.707\sin(t - 2.356) + 0.0123\sin(3t - 4.03)$

$$+ 0.0016\sin(5t - 4.31)]$$

3.14 $4 + 1.491\cos(2t - 3.725)$

3.15 $10 + 2.1221\cos t - 0.1604\sin(3t - 3.986) - 0.045\sin(5t - 3.7)$

3.16 $\dfrac{2}{j\omega}$

3.17 (a) $\dfrac{A(1 - e^{-j\omega})}{j\omega}$ (b) $\dfrac{A(1 - e^{-a-j\omega})}{a + j\omega}$

3.18 (a) $\dfrac{20}{\omega}(\sin 5\omega + \sin 10\omega)$ (b) $\dfrac{200}{\omega^2}(\cos 5\omega - \cos 10\omega)$

3.19 (a) $j\dfrac{10}{\pi t}(\sin 5t + \sin 10t)$ (b) $\dfrac{100}{\pi t^2}(\cos 5t - \cos 10t)$

3.20 $-\dfrac{4A}{\omega^2\Delta}\sin^2\dfrac{\omega\Delta}{4}$

3.21 $\dfrac{2A}{\pi t^2 B}\sin^2\dfrac{Bt}{4}$

3.22 (a) $\dfrac{j10\omega}{j\omega + 4}$ (b) $\dfrac{10}{j\omega + 6}$

(c) $\dfrac{10(j\omega + 4)}{20 - \omega^2 + j8\omega}$ (d) $-\dfrac{10\omega^2}{j\omega + 4}$

(e) $\dfrac{10e^{-j3\omega}}{j\omega + 8}$ (f) $\dfrac{100}{j\omega + 8}$

(g) $\dfrac{100}{(j\omega + 8)^2}$

3.23 596.46 W

3.24 (a) $\dfrac{A^2(1 - e^{j\omega})(1 - e^{-j\omega})}{\omega^2}$

(b) $\dfrac{A^2(1 - e^{-a+j\omega})(1 - e^{-a-j\omega})}{a^2 + \omega^2}$

3.25 (a) $-\dfrac{400}{\omega^2}(\sin 5\omega + \sin 10\omega)$ (b) $\dfrac{40000}{\omega^4}(\cos 5\omega - \cos 10\omega)^2$

3.26 (d) (i) $0.5e^{-|\tau|}$ (ii) $0.5e^{-|\tau|}$

(iii) $\dfrac{16A^2}{\Delta^2\omega^4}\sin^4\dfrac{\Delta\omega}{4}$

CHAPTER 4

4.1 $a_0 = 0$, $a_1 = (1 - j - j\sqrt{2})/4$, $a_2 = 0$, $a_3 = (1 + j - j\sqrt{2})/4$
$a_4 = 0$, $a_5 = (1 - j + j\sqrt{2})/4$, $a_6 = 0$, $a_7 = (1 + j + j\sqrt{2})/4$

4.2 $a_0 = 0.375$, $a_1 = 0.05178 + j0.07322$, $a_2 = 0.375 - j0.5$,
$a_3 = 0.30178 + j0.42678$, $a_4 = 1.375$, $a_5 = 0.30178 - j0.42678$,
$a_6 = 0.375 + j0.5$, $a_7 = 0.05178 - j0.07322$

4.3 (a) $17.011\sin(0.2\pi k - 1.5555)$

(b) $17.011\sin(0.2\pi k - 1.5555) - 4.6715\sin(0.5\pi k - 0.5083)$

(c) $0.5522[e^{j(k\pi/2 - 3.0309)} + e^{j(3k\pi/2 + 3.0309)}]$

(d) $0.5556e^{jk\pi} - j0.315e^{j(k\pi/3 - 1.9013)} + j0.1848e^{j(2k\pi/3 - 2.5539)}$
$+ j0.1848e^{j(4k\pi/3 + 2.5539)} - j0.315e^{j(5k\pi/3 + 1.9013)}$

4.4 (a) $140.6896\sin(0.2k\pi - 2.0329)$

(b) $140.6896\sin(0.2k\pi - 2.0329) - 22.3125\sin(0.4k\pi + 4.024)$

(c) $3.8628[e^{j(k\pi/2 + 0.2324)} + e^{j(3k\pi/2 + 0.2324)}]$

(d) $0.3774 + 1.8707e^{j(k\pi/3 + 1.719)} - 0.3852e^{j(2k\pi/3 + 0.4327)}$
$+ 0.3852e^{j(4k\pi/3 - 0.4327)} - 1.8707e^{j(5k\pi/3 - 1.719)}$

4.5 $\dfrac{1}{N}\sum\limits_{n=0}^{N-1} A(n)w_N^{-kn}$, $k = 0, 1, \cdots, N - 1$

4.6 $1 + e^{-j\Omega} + e^{-j2\Omega} + e^{-j3\Omega} - e^{-j5\Omega} - e^{-j6\Omega} - e^{-j7\Omega}$

4.7 $1 + e^{-j\Omega} - 2e^{-j3\Omega} - 3e^{-j5\Omega} + 2e^{-j6\Omega} - 2e^{-j7\Omega}$

4.8   (a) $\dfrac{10}{(j\Omega + 4)^2}$ (b) $\dfrac{20e^{-j3\Omega}}{j\Omega + 8}$

    (c) $\dfrac{10}{4 - j\Omega}$ (d) $\dfrac{10(1 - j\Omega)}{j\Omega + 4}$

    (e) $\dfrac{10}{j\Omega + 3.3069}$ (f) $\dfrac{40 + j10\Omega}{20 - \Omega^2 + j8\Omega}$

4.9   (a) 0 if $|n| \neq 2$, and 5 if $n = \pm 2$

    (b) 0 if $|n| \neq 3$, and $j10$ if $n = \pm 3$

    (c) 10 if $n = 0$ or ± 2, 0 otherwise

    (d) $\dfrac{5}{\pi} \dfrac{4 - 4e^{-2\Omega}\cos n + 2ne^{-2\Omega}\sin n}{n^2 + 4}$

    (e) $\dfrac{2}{\pi} \dfrac{\sin n}{n}$ (f) $\dfrac{1}{\pi} \dfrac{\sin(n-1)}{n-1}$

4.11 $y(0) = 1$, $y(2) = 1.5$, $y(3) = -0.25$, $y(4) = 0.425$, $y(5) = 1.2$,

$y(6) = 0.625$,

$y(7) = 0.3185$, $y(8) = 1.1435$, $y(9) = 0.0565$, $y(10) = 0.0315$,

$y(11) = 0.0185$,

$y(12) = 0.006$, $y(13) = 0$, $y(14) = 0$, $y(15) = 0$, $y(16) = 0$, $y(17) = 0$.

4.12 $y = \{1, 1.5, -0.25, -1.125, 0.425, 1.2, 0.6125, 0.3185, 0.1435, 0.0565,$
$0.0315, 0.0315, 0.0185, 0.006, 0, 0\}$

4.13 $X(0) = 5.318229 + j0.0$ $X(1) = 2.887007 - j1.223852$
$X(2) = 2.229698 - j1.103594$ $X(3) = 1.860245 - j0.935265$
$X(4) = 1.620238 - j0.754268$ $X(5) = 1.458757 - j0.568226$
$X(6) = 1.353636 - j0.379784$ $X(7) = 1.293391 - j0.190146$
$X(8) = 1.274628 + j0.0$ $X(9) = 1.293391 + j0.190146$
$X(10) = 1.353636 + j0.379784$ $X(11) = 1.458757 + j0.568226$
$X(12) = 1.620238 + j0.754268$ $X(13) = 1.860245 + j0.935265$
$X(14) = 2.229696 + j1.103594$ $X(15) = 2.887007 + j1.223852$

4.14 $y = \{1, 1.4, -0.45, -1.45, 0.15, 1.4, 0.91, 0.011, -0.359,$
$-0.061, 0.059, 0.011, 0, 0, 0\}$

4.22   (a) 23,352 μs   (b) 19,968 μs

4.23   (a) 23,654.4 μs   (b) 21,964.8 μs

4.24   (a) 7168 μs   (b) 7680 μs

CHAPTER 5

5.1 (a) $\dfrac{18}{(s+2)^3}$ (b) $\dfrac{9}{s(s^2+9)}$

(c) $\dfrac{1-e^{-s}}{s}$ (d) $\dfrac{1-e^{-s}}{s^2}$

(e) $\dfrac{2s^3+24s^2-14s-144}{\left(s^2+4s+13\right)^2}$

(f) $\dfrac{10s+65}{s^2+4s+13}$

(g) $\dfrac{1+e^{-s\pi}}{s^2+1}$

5.2 (a) $9+e^{-3t}(11\cos 4t+15\sin 4t)$

(b) $\dfrac{1560}{17}e^{-4t}-40e^{-3t}+e^{-3t}\left(\dfrac{100}{17}\cos 4t+\dfrac{400}{17}\sin 4t\right)$

(c) $\dfrac{5}{9}-\dfrac{1477}{225}e^{-3t}+\dfrac{32}{15}te^{-3t}-0.712\cos 2t-0.4\sin 2t$

(d) $0.5(1-\cos 2t-t\sin 2t)$

(e) $2t-1.5-1.5e^{-2t}\cos 2t+te^{-2t}(\cos 2t+\sin 2t)$

5.3 (a) $0.5+3.5e^{-2t}-2e^{-6t}$ (b) $1.5-0.5e^{-4t}-7te^{-4t}$

(c) $0.1808\sin 2t-0.1377\cos 2t+e^{-4t}(1.1377\cos 2t-1.2703\sin 2t)$

(d) $\dfrac{73}{17}e^{-2t}+0.25e^{-3t}\left(\dfrac{139}{68}\cos 4t-\dfrac{5}{17}\sin 4t\right)$

5.4 $\dfrac{V_2(s)}{V_1(s)}=\dfrac{s}{s^3+4s^2+2s+1}$

5.5 $0.9017e^{-3.152t}-e^{-0.244t}(0.0918\cos 0.4745t-0.6318\sin 0.4745t)$

5.6 $1.0656e^{-3.152t}-2e^{-2t}+e^{-0.244t}(0.9358\cos 0.4745t$
$-0.0639\sin 0.4745t)$

5.7 $-0.645\cos(2t-0.7812)+0.292\sin(3t-1.3258)$

5.8 $G(j0)=0.667e^{j0}$, $G(j1)=0.784e^{j0.197}$, $G(j2)=0.894e^{j0.094}$
$G(j5)=0.977e^{j0.977}$, $G(j10)=0.994e^{j0.049}$

5.9 (a) $\dfrac{2}{3}-\dfrac{1}{3}e^{-1.5t}$

(b) $\dfrac{2}{3}-\dfrac{1}{3}e^{-1.5t}-\left[\dfrac{2}{3}-\dfrac{1}{3}e^{-1.5(t-10)}\right]\gamma(t-1)$

(c) $1.2e^{-1.5t}+8.8\cos 2t-1.6\sin 2t$

5.10 $4.47\cos(2t-0.8674)+20/3$

5.11 $G(s) = \dfrac{1}{s^3 + 5s^2 + 6s + 1}$

$G(j0) = 1,\ G(j1) = 0.1562e^{-j2.2455},\qquad G(j2) = 0.0064e^{-j3.7954}$

5.12 (a) $1 - 1.2204e^{-0.198t} + 0.2801e^{-1.555t} - 0.0597e^{-3.247t}$

(b) $1 - 1.2204e^{-0.198t} + 0.2801e^{-1.555t} - 0.0597e^{-3.247t}$
$\quad -(1 - 1.2204e^{-0.198(t-1)} + 0.2801e^{-1.555(t-1)}$
$\qquad\qquad - 0.0597e^{-3.247(t-1)})\gamma(t-1)$

5.13 $10 + 0.2575\cos(2t - 3.98) + 0.0256\sin(5t + 3.01)$

5.14 $V(s) = \dfrac{37700(1 + e^{-s\pi/377})}{(s^2 + 377^2)(1 - e^{-2s\pi/377})}$

5.15 $V(s) = \dfrac{\dfrac{10}{s^2} - \left(\dfrac{10}{s} + \dfrac{10}{s^2}\right)e^{-s}}{1 - e^{-s}}$

5.16 $\dfrac{20}{9} + \dfrac{20}{3}t - 0.1537e^{-1.5t}$

5.17 $50\sin 377t + 0.1326\cos 377t - 1.1674e^{-1.5t}$

5.18 The phase shift will be 180° for $\omega = \sqrt{6}$.

5.19 $10t - 60 + 67.921e^{-0.198t} - 3.551e^{-1.555t} + 0.621e^{-3.247t}$

5.20 $\Phi(s) = \dfrac{16}{-s^2 + 4}$

5.21 (a) $e^{-4|t|}$ (b) $2e^{-2|t|} + 5e^{-3|t|}$

5.22 $\dfrac{\dfrac{1}{2}(1 - e^{-s\tau})}{1 - e^{sT}}$

5.23 $\left[\dfrac{2}{3} + \dfrac{1}{3}e^{-1.5t}\right]\gamma(t) + \left[\dfrac{2}{3} + \dfrac{1}{3}e^{-1.5(t-\tau)}\right]\gamma(t - \tau)$

5.24 (a) $5.9077 - 1.4536e^{-25t} - e^{-t}(4.4541\cos 5t - 7.8413\sin 5t)$

(b) $5.9077t + 1.27849 - 0.05814e^{-25t} - e^{-t}(1.3366\cos 5t$
$\quad + 1.15814\sin 5t)$

(c) $5.9077 - 2.6934e^{-25t} - e^{-t}(6.688\cos 5t - 7.1242\sin 5t)$,   during the first half cycle. That for the second half cycle follows from symmetry.

5.25 (a) $h(t) = \delta(t) - 4e^{-2t}$

(b) $G(j0) = e^{j\pi},\ G(j1) = e^{j2.2143},\ G(j2) = e^{j\pi/2},\ G(j5) = e^{j0.761},$
$\quad G(j10) = e^{j0.3948}$

5.26 $-10 + 30\cos(t + 2.2143) + 20\sin(2t + 5\pi/6)$

5.27 (a) $h(t) = e^{-t} + e^{-0.5t}(0.577\sin 0.866t - \cos 0.866t)$

(b) $G(j0) = 1,\qquad G(j1) = 0.707e^{-j3\pi/4},\qquad G(j2) = 0.124e^{-j3.66},$
$\quad G(j5) = 0.008e^{-j4.31},\qquad G(j10) = 0.001e^{-j4.51}$

5.28 $1 - 1.9963e^{-t} + e^{-0.5t}(0.0442 \cos 0.866t - 0.302 \sin 0.866t)$, during the first half cycle. That for the second half cycle follows from symmetry.

5.29 $1 - 1.9175e^{-t} + e^{-0.5t}(0.2857 \cos 0.866t - 0.4522 \sin 0.866t)$, during the first half cycle. That for the second half cycle follows from symmetry.

5.30 $y(t) = \begin{cases} (4t + 6)e^{-t} - \dfrac{16}{3}e^{-0.5t} \cos 0.886t & \text{for } t > 0 \\ \dfrac{2}{3}e^{t} & \text{for } t < 0 \end{cases}$

5.31 (a) $h(t) = 2 + 6e^{-2t} - 8e^{-3t} \rightarrow$ not stable in the BIBO sense

(b) $2t + \dfrac{1}{3} - 3e^{-2t} + \dfrac{8}{3}e^{-3t}$

5.32 (a) $h(t) = 2e^{-2t} + 6 \sin 2t - 2 \cos 2t \rightarrow$ not stable in the BIBO sense

(b) $3.2e^{-2t} - (4t - 7.6) \sin 2t - (12t + 3.2) \cos 2t$

5.33 (a) $4 - 36e^{-2t} + 24te^{-2t} + 32e^{-3t}$ (b) 4

(c) The final value theorem cannot be applied to the solution in problem 5.31(b), since $Y(s)$ has two poles at the origin.

CHAPTER 6

6.1 (a) $\dfrac{0.5z^3 + 1.25z^2 + 0.125z}{(z - 0.5)^2}$

(b) $\dfrac{z(3z^2 - 10.04736z + 12.7108)}{(z - 0.6)(z^2 - 2.63275z + 2.25)}$

(c) $\dfrac{z(5\sqrt{2}\,z - 10)}{z^2 - 2\sqrt{2}\,z + 4}$ (d) $\dfrac{z(5\sqrt{2}\,z - 10)}{z^2 - 2\sqrt{2}\,z + 4}$

(e) $\dfrac{z(z^2 + z + 1)}{(z - 1)^3}$ (f) $\dfrac{2z}{(z - 1)^3}$

6.2 (a) $10 - 8(0.5)^n$ (b) $18\,(2)^n - 16 + 2(0/5)^n$

(c) $2(0.8)^{n/2}\left(\dfrac{4}{3} \cos 0.6708n + 5.4775 \sin 0.6708n\right) - \dfrac{5}{3}$

(d) $1.5 \cos \dfrac{n\pi}{2} + 6.5 \sin \dfrac{n\pi}{2} - 0.5$

(e) $2 \sin \dfrac{n\pi}{2} - 1 + (-1)^n$

(f) $\cos \dfrac{n\pi}{2} + 1 + (-1)^n$

6.3 (a) $\dfrac{8}{15} - 3.7(-4)^n + \dfrac{31}{6}(-2)^n$

(b) $0.48(2)^n + 0.72(3)^n + 1.8(n + 1)(3)^{n+1}$

(c) $2(13)^{n/2}(0.025989 \sin 0.588n - 0.241412 \cos 0.588n)$
$+ 2(0.191758 \cos 2n - 0.0425101 \sin 2n)$

(d) $(0.6686)^n(2.6264 \cos 1.4347n + 4.82646 \sin 1.4347n)$
$- (0.4)^n(0.5062 \cos 0.5n + 0.0202 \sin 0.5n)$
$- 1.12099(1.118526)^n$

6.4 (a) $(80)^{n/2}(0.98556 \cos 2.03444n \; \square \; 0.74493 \sin 2.0344n)$

(b) $0.02093e^{-2n} + (80)^{n/2}(0.97808 \cos 2.03444n$
$- 0.7492 \sin 2.03444n)$

(c) $(80)^{n/2}(0.99956 \cos 2.03444n + 0.74926 \sin 2.03444n)$
$+ (0.00186n + 0.000429)e^{-3n}$

6.5 (a) $0.147237e^{-2n} + 0.952763(-3)^n + 0.469185n(-3)^n$

(b) $0.147237e^{-2n} + 0.952763(-3)^n + 4.69185n(-3)^n$

(c) $(0.0016255n + 0.0342489)e^{-3n} + (6.897425n + 0.0965763)(-3)^n$

6.6 (a) $\dfrac{3}{4z^2 - 2z + 1}$ (b) $\dfrac{3e^2z}{4z^2 - 2e^2z + e^4}$

(c) $\dfrac{12z^3 - 3z}{(4z^2 - 2z + 1)^2}$ (d) $\dfrac{6z^2 - 19z + 12}{4z^3 - 2z^2 + z}$

(e) $\dfrac{(12z^3 + 3z)\cos 0.5 - 6z^2}{(16z^3 + 4z)(z - \cos 0.5) + 8z^2 \cos 1 + 1}$

(f) $\dfrac{48z^5 + 24z^3 + 72z + 32}{(4z^2 - 2z + 1)^3}$

6.7 (a) $\dfrac{2z(z - 0.6 \cos 0.4)}{z^2 - 1.2z \cos 0.4 + 0.36}$

(b) (i) $3.5126 - (0.6)^n(1.125 \cos 0.4n - 1.8345 \sin 0.4n)$

(ii) $(0.6)^n(7.4814 \cos 0.4n + 0.8295 \sin 0.4n) - 1.4184e^{-2n}$

6.8 (a) $H(z) = \dfrac{3z(z - 0.8 \cos 0.5)}{z^2 - 1.6z \cos 0.5 + 0.64} + \dfrac{0.6z}{(z - 0.3)^2}$

(b) (i) $5.0143 - (0.8)^n(0.7894 \cos 0.5n - 4.8782 \sin 0.5n)$
$- 1.2249(0.3)^n - 0.2572n(0.3)^n$

(ii) $7.5012e^{-2n} - (8.9843 - 3.2794n)(0.3)^n$
$+ (0.8)^n(10.4741 \cos 0.5n + 0.9976 \sin 0.5n)$

6.9 (a) The system is stable.

(b) $49.18 + 10.82 \cos(2n + 0.231) + 16.88 \sin(3n + 1.058)$

6.10 $49.18 + 59.3(0.7)^n - 115.385(0.5)^n + (0.4)^n(2.091 \cos 0.5n$
$- 62.716 \sin 0.5n)$

6.11 (a) 2 (b) 4 (c) 1 (d) 1 (e) 0 (f) 0

6.12 (a) $x(0) = 30, x(\infty) = 0$ (b) $x(0) = 2, x(\infty) = 7.5$

(c) $x(0) = 7.5, x(\infty) = \infty$

6.13 $\dfrac{50z^2(z + 0.208)(z^2 - 6.8581z + 3.0823)}{(z - 1)(z^2 - 1.7552z + 1)(z^2 + 0.416z + 0.25)}$

6.14 $\dfrac{40z^2(z^2 - 1.5z + 1)(z + 0.208)}{(z - 2)(z - 1)^2(z^2 + 0.416z + 0.25)}$

6.15 (a) $\dfrac{2z + 3}{z^2 - z + 0.5}$ (b) $10 - 2^{n/2}\left(10 \cos \dfrac{n\pi}{4} + 6 \sin \dfrac{n\pi}{4}\right)$

(c) $39.2128 \cos 0.2n - (0.707)^n(39.2128 \cos n\pi/4 + 26.957 \sin n\pi/4)$
$+ 13.3572 \sin 0.2n$

6.16 $1 - (0.9827)^n(\cos 0.3047n + 0.24 \sin 0.3047n)$

6.17 Ω 0   0.2   0.5   1.0
$H(e^{j\Omega})$ 0.999 $2.4905e^{-j0.6395}$ $0.2609e^{-j0.1376}$ $0.1609e^{-j0.0066}$

2.0
$0.3207e^{-j0.0006}$

6.18 $0.999 + 4.891 \cos(0.2n - 0.6395) - 0.5638 \sin(0.5n - 0.376)$

6.19 Since the input is unbounded, there will be no steady-state.

6.20 (a) causal (b) noncausal (c) noncausal (d) noncausal

6.21 (a) The system will be stable *if and only if* $-1 < a < 1$.

(b) $|H(e^{j\Omega})|^{-2} = a^{-2}$, for all Ω.

(c) For $a = 0.5$, $|H(e^{j\Omega})| = 2$.

6.22 (a) $1 - 0.84(0.6)^n + (0.4)^{n/2}(3.84 \cos 1.249n + 2.88 \sin 1.249n)$

(b) Ω 0   0.5 $\pi/3$ $\pi/2$
$H(e^{j\Omega})$ 1 $2.7629e^{-j1.0125}$ $7.5593e^{-j5.5695}$ $8.6144e^{-j0.1582}$

6.23 $X(z) = \dfrac{4z(z - 0.2 \cos 0.3)}{z^2 - 0.4z \cos 0.3 + 0.04} + \dfrac{4z(z - 5 \cos 0.3)}{z^2 - 10z \cos 0.3 + 25}$
for $0.2 < |z| < 5$

6.24 $x(n) = 0.3(0.5)^{|n|}$

6.25 (a) $x(n) = \dfrac{10}{3}(0.5)^n - \dfrac{4}{3}(0.2)^n$, for $n \geq 0$

(b) $x(n) = \begin{cases} -\dfrac{4}{3}(0.2)^n, & \text{for } n \geq 0 \\ -\dfrac{10}{3}(0.5)^n, & \text{for } n < 0 \end{cases}$

(c) $x(n) = -\dfrac{10}{3}(0.5)^n + \dfrac{4}{3}(0.2)^n$, for $n < 0$

6.26 (a) $H(z) = \dfrac{Y(z)}{X(z)} = \dfrac{T}{2}\dfrac{1+z^{-1}}{1-z^{-1}} = \dfrac{T}{2}\left[1 + \dfrac{2z^{-1}}{1-z^{-1}}\right]$

6.27 (a) The parameters a and b must satisfy the following conditions:
(i) $a + b + 1 > 0$,   (ii) $b - a + 1 > 0$,   and (iii) $b < 1$

   (b) The region of stability in the parameter plane is the triangle formed by the intersection of the three straight lines obtained from these equations.

6.28 (a) $y(n) = 30500\left(\dfrac{151}{150}\right)^n - 30000$ (b) 37,699.02

6.29 (a) $y(n) = 24700\left(\dfrac{121}{120}\right)^n - 24200$ (b) 42,663.92

6.30 (a) Model from impulse invariant transformation is
$$\dfrac{1.49153z}{(z - 0.90484)(z - 0.60653)}$$
Model with numerical solution is
$$H_2(z) = \dfrac{4z^2}{(2.2z - 2)(3z - 2)}$$

   (b) For the continuous-time model, the step response is
$g(t) = 25 - 31.25e^{-0.2t} + 6.25e^{-t}$.
For the impulse-invariant model,
$g_1(n) = 37.9216 - 45.24725(0.90484)^n + (0.60653)^n$.
For the model based on numerical solution of differential equations,
$g_2(n) = 20 - 22.72727(0.90909)^n + 3.33333(0.66667)^n$
For the model based on bilinear transformation,
$g_3(n) = 20 - 23.80952(0.904762)^n + 3.99999(0.6)^n$

6.31 (a) (i) Impulse-invariant transformation
$$H_1(z) = \dfrac{0.37681z}{(z - 0.9802)(z - 0.90484)}$$
   (ii) Model with numerical solution
$$H_2(z) = \dfrac{4z^2}{(10.2z - 10)(11z - 10)}$$
   (iii) Bilinear transformation model
$$H_3(z) = \dfrac{4(z + 1)^2}{(20.2z - 19)(21z - 19)}$$

   (b) $g_1(n) = 199.971 - 247.5125(0.9802)^n + 47.5415(0.90484)^n$
$g_2(n) = 20.00005 - 24.50995(0.98039)^n + 4.54551(0.90909)^n$
$g_3(n) = 19.99997 - 24.75245(0.9802)^n + 4.7619(0.90476)^n$

6.32   Model with impulse invariant transformation is

$$H_1(z) = \frac{1.89641z - 0.8145}{(z - 0.90484)(z^2 - 1.895329z - 0.90484)}$$

Model based on numerical solution of differential equations is

$$H_2(z) = \frac{z^2}{(11z - 10)(111z^2 - 210z + 100)}$$

Model based on bilinear transformation is

$$H_3(z) = \frac{(z + 1)^3}{(21z - 19)(421z^2 - 798z + 381)}$$

CHAPTER 7

7.7 $\dfrac{100}{s + 10}$

7.8 $\dfrac{10^{2.5}(s + 10)}{s(s + 100)}$

7.9 $\dfrac{10}{s + 1}$

7.12 $\dfrac{10}{s(s + 2)}$

7.13 $\dfrac{10}{s^2 + 4s + 10}$

7.19   (a)   Sampling frequency of 40 rad/s will be adequate.

(b) $\dfrac{0.0875z^2 + 0.0681z}{(z - 0.8607)(z^2 - 1.465z + 0.5488)}$

7.20 $\dfrac{54(z + 1)^3}{(43z - 37)(425z^2 - 622z + 233)}$

CHAPTER 8

8.1 $\begin{bmatrix} 20t - 99 + 100e^{-0.2t} \\ 20(1 - e^{-0.2t}) \end{bmatrix}$

8.2 $\begin{bmatrix} 2e^{-t} - e^{-2t} & 2e^{-t} - 2e^{-2t} \\ e^{-2t} - e^{-t} & 2e^{-2t} - e^{-t} \end{bmatrix}$

8.3   (a) $\dfrac{1}{3} \begin{bmatrix} 2(0.6)^k + 0.3^k & 2(0.6^k - 0.3^k) \\ 0.6^k - 0.3^k & 0.6^k + 2(0.3)^k \end{bmatrix}$

(b) $\begin{bmatrix} 3(-0.25)^k - 2(-0.5)^k & 2(-0.5)^k - 2(-0.25)^k \\ 3(-0.5)^k - 3(-0.25)^k & 3(-0.5)^k - 2(-0.25)^k \end{bmatrix}$

(c) $\begin{bmatrix} 0.5(2)^k & 0.1(2)^k \\ 2.5(2)^k & 0.5(2)^k \end{bmatrix}$

8.5   (a) $\begin{bmatrix} e^{-2t}(\cos 2t + \sin 2t) & e^{-2t} \sin 2t \\ -4e^{-2t} \sin 2t & e^{-2t}(\cos 2t - \sin 2t) \end{bmatrix}$

(b) $\begin{bmatrix} 1 & 2 & 0 \\ -1 & -4 & -4 \\ 1 & 0 & 16 \end{bmatrix}$

$\times \begin{bmatrix} e^{-t} & 0 & 0 \\ 0 & e^{-2t}\cos 2t & -e^{-2t}\sin 2t \\ 0 & 0 & e^{-2t}\sin 2t & e^{-2t}\cos 2t \end{bmatrix}$

$\begin{bmatrix} 1 & 2 & 0 \\ -1 & 4 & -4 \\ 1 & 0 & 16 \end{bmatrix}^{-1}$

8.6   (a) $\begin{bmatrix} e^{2t} & te^{-2t} \\ 0 & e^{2t} \end{bmatrix}$

(b) $\begin{bmatrix} e^{2t} & e^{2t} & \dfrac{1}{2}t^2 e^{2t} \\ 0 & e^{2t} & te^{2t} \\ 0 & 0 & e^{2t} \end{bmatrix}$

(c) $\begin{bmatrix} e^{2t} & te^{2t} & 0 \\ 0 & e^{2t} & 0 \\ 0 & 0 & e^{2t} \end{bmatrix}$

8.7   (a) $\begin{bmatrix} (1 + 2t)e^{-2t} & te^{-2t} \\ -4te^{-2t} & (1 - 2t)e^{-2t} \end{bmatrix}$

(b) $\begin{bmatrix} (1 + 2t + 2t^2)e^{-2t} & t(1 + 2t)e^{-2t} & 0.5^2 e^{-2t} \\ -4t^2 e^{-2t} & (1 + 2t - 4t^2)e^{-2t} & t(1 - t)e^{-2t} \\ 4t(3 + 2t)e^{-2t} & -4t(3 - 2t)e^{-2t} & (1 - 4t + 2t^2)e^{-2t} \end{bmatrix}$

8.8
$$\frac{0.0473263}{z^4 - 0.3z^3 + 0.0316z^2 - 0.00132z + 0.000016}$$

8.9
$$\frac{6.3s - 0.0854}{s^3 - 1.598s^2 - 0.8172s + 0.1244}$$

8.10
$$\frac{s^2 + 3}{s^4 + 4s^2 - 9}$$

8.11
$$\dot{x} = \begin{bmatrix} -27 & -75 & -625 \\ 1 & 0 & 0 \\ 0 & 1 & 0 \end{bmatrix} x + \begin{bmatrix} 1 \\ 0 \\ 0 \end{bmatrix} u$$

$$y = [20 \quad 120 \quad 160]x$$

8.12 $y_{ss} = -1.631$

8.14 (a) $F = \begin{bmatrix} 0.818731 & 0.20136 \\ 0 & 1.221403 \end{bmatrix}$, $G = \begin{bmatrix} 0.271904 \\ 0 \end{bmatrix}$

(b) $F = \begin{bmatrix} 0.628873 & 0.019162 & 1.084788 \\ 0.135848 & 0.473862 & 0.019162 \\ 0.193335 & 0.155011 & 0.003045 \end{bmatrix}$, $G = \begin{bmatrix} 0.223356 \\ 0.022782 \\ 0.249757 \end{bmatrix}$

8.15 $F = \begin{bmatrix} 0.9998522 & -0.085473 & 1.084788 \\ -0.00098 & 0.960481 & -0.000518 \\ -0.000053 & 0.108591 & 1.221385 \end{bmatrix}$, $G = \begin{bmatrix} 0.947124 \\ 0.617095 \\ 0.033255 \end{bmatrix}$

8.16 $x(k+1) = \begin{bmatrix} 1.2 & -0.45 & 0.05 \\ 1 & 0 & 0 \\ 0 & 1 & 0 \end{bmatrix} x(k) + \begin{bmatrix} 1 \\ 0 \\ 0 \end{bmatrix} u(k)$

$$y(k) = [2 \quad 5 \quad 0] \ x(k)$$

8.21 The system is unstable, with one eigenvalue in the right half of the s-plane and a conjugate pair of eigenvalues on the $j\omega$-axis.

$$F = \begin{bmatrix} 1.059803 & 0.198701 & -0.007936 & 0.039471 \\ 0.596104 & 0.980861 & -0.118413 & 0.398466 \\ -0.007936 & -0.039471 & 0.94139 & 0.190765 \\ -0.118413 & -0.389466 & -0.572294 & 0.862448 \end{bmatrix},$$

$$G = \begin{bmatrix} 0.019334 \\ 0.198701 \\ 0.002465 \\ -0.039471 \end{bmatrix}$$

8.22 (a) $\dot{x} = \begin{bmatrix} -10.2 & -9.5 & -7.5 \\ 1 & 0 & 0 \\ 0 & 1 & 1 \end{bmatrix} x + \begin{bmatrix} 1 \\ 0 \\ 0 \end{bmatrix} u$, $y = [0 \quad 60 \quad 4] \ x$

8.23 (a) $x(k + 1) = \begin{bmatrix} 0.8 & 0.21 & -0.01 \\ 1 & 0 & 0 \\ 0 & 1 & 0 \end{bmatrix} x(k) + \begin{bmatrix} 1 \\ 0 \\ 0 \end{bmatrix} u(k)$

$y(k) = [1 \quad 0.5 \quad 0]x(k)$

(b) $x(k + 1) = \begin{bmatrix} 1 & 0 & 0 \\ 0 & -0.24142 & 0 \\ 0 & 0 & 0.04142 \end{bmatrix} x(k) + \begin{bmatrix} 1 \\ 1 \\ 1 \end{bmatrix} u(k)$

$y(k) = [1.2605 \quad 0.73644 \quad -1.99694] \quad x(k)$

8.24 (a) $\dot{x} = \begin{bmatrix} -6 & -26 & -46 & -65 \\ 1 & 0 & 0 & 0 \\ 0 & 1 & 0 & 0 \\ 0 & 0 & 1 & 0 \end{bmatrix} x + \begin{bmatrix} 1 \\ 0 \\ 0 \\ 0 \end{bmatrix} u$

$y = [0 \quad 0 \quad 20 \quad 40]x$

CHAPTER 9

9.1 $\dfrac{V_2(s)}{V_1(s)} = \dfrac{s^3}{s^3 + 2000s^2 + 2 \times 10^6 s + 2 \times 10^9}$

9.4 (a) $H(z) = \dfrac{-1.75807z^2 + 0.8593}{(z - 0.95587)(z^2 - 1.94766z + 0.95568)}$

(b) $H(z) = \dfrac{-1.55696z^2 + 0.73334z}{(z - 0.798)(z^2 - 1.61556z + 0.79796)}$

9.5 (a) $H(z) = \dfrac{0.374226(z + 1)^3}{8382.1129z^3 - 24339.299z^2 + 23619.384z - 7659.2026}$

(b) $H(z) = \dfrac{0.374226(z + 1)^3}{82.922162z^3 - 201.188786z^2 + 174.547742z - 53.31431}$

9.6 $H(z) = \dfrac{0.374226(z - 1)}{3.30986z^3 + 1.747088z^2 + 2.187044z + 0.756008}$

9.7 $H(z) = \displaystyle\sum_{n=-4}^{4} \dfrac{1}{3} \operatorname{sinc}\left(\dfrac{n\pi}{3}\right) z^{-(n+4)}$

9.8 $H(z) = \displaystyle\sum_{n=-8}^{8} \dfrac{1}{3} \operatorname{sinc}\left(\dfrac{n\pi}{3}\right) z^{-(n+8)}$

9.9 $H(z) = \displaystyle\sum_{n=0}^{N-1/2} \dfrac{(-1)^n}{\dfrac{N-1}{2} - n} z^{-n} + \displaystyle\sum_{n=N+1/2}^{N-1} \dfrac{(-1)^n}{n - \dfrac{N+1}{2}} z^{-n}$

9.10 $H(z) = \displaystyle\sum_{i=-8}^{3} \frac{1}{4} \operatorname{sinc} \frac{(4-i)\pi}{4} z^{-i} + \frac{\pi - 1}{4} z^{-4}$

$$+ \sum_{i=5}^{8} \frac{1}{4} \operatorname{sinc} \frac{(i-4)\pi}{4} z^{-i}$$

9.21 $H(z) = \dfrac{-0.0779z^4 + 0.23604z^3 - 0.2382z^2 + 0.8009z}{(z - 0.9905)(z^2 - 1.8515z + 0.85061)(z^2 + 1.9304z + 0.9401)}$

9.22 $H(z) = \dfrac{(z+1)^3}{(21z - 9)(433.36z^2 - 798z + 368.64)(413.36z^3 - 798z + 388.64)}$

9.23 $H(z) = \dfrac{3.04277z^2 - 4.0523z}{(z - 0.95587)(z2 - 1.9478z + 0.95589)}$

9.24 $H(z) = \dfrac{(z+1)^3}{(20.4513z - 19.5497)(4190z^2 - 798.342z + 391.901)}$

Index

459

Printed by
Fong & Sons Printers Pte Ltd